Student Solutions Manual

General Chemistry

TENTH EDITION

Darrell D. Ebbing
Wayne State University

Steven D. Gammon
Western Washington University

Prepared by

David Shinn
US Merchant Marine Academy

BROOKS/COLE
CENGAGE Learning·

Australia · Brazil · Japan · Korea · Mexico · Singapore · Spain · United Kingdom · United States

BROOKS/COLE
CENGAGE Learning·

For product information and technology assistance, contact us at
**Cengage Learning Customer & Sales Support,
1-800-354-9706**

For permission to use material from this text or product, submit
all requests online at **www.cengage.com/permissions**
Further permissions questions can be emailed to
permissionrequest@cengage.com

ISBN-13: 978-1-111-98941-5
ISBN-10: 1-111-98941-9

Brooks/Cole
20 Davis Drive
Belmont, CA 94002-3098
USA

Cengage Learning is a leading provider of customized
learning solutions with office locations around the globe,
including Singapore, the United Kingdom, Australia,
Mexico, Brazil, and Japan. Locate your local office at:
www.cengage.com/global

Cengage Learning products are represented in
Canada by Nelson Education, Ltd.

To learn more about Brooks/Cole, visit
www.cengage.com/brookscole

Purchase any of our products at your local college
store or at our preferred online store
www.cengagebrain.com

Printed in the United States of America
1 2 3 4 5 6 7 16 15 14 13 12

Contents

CHAPTER 1

Chemistry and Measurement

■ SOLUTIONS TO EXERCISES

Note on significant figures: If the final answer to a solution needs to be rounded off, it is given first with one nonsignificant figure, and the last significant figure is underlined. The final answer is then rounded to the correct number of significant figures. In multistep problems, intermediate answers are given with at least one nonsignificant figure; however, only the final answer has been rounded off.

1.1.   From the law of conservation of mass,

   Mass of wood + mass of air = mass of ash + mass of gases

Substituting, you obtain

   1.85 grams + 9.45 grams = 0.28 grams + mass of gases

or,

   Mass of gases = (1.85 + 9.45 − 0.28) grams = 11.02 grams

Thus, the mass of gases in the vessel at the end of the experiment is 11.02 grams.

1.2.   Physical properties: soft, silvery-colored metal; melts at 64°C.
        Chemical properties: reacts vigorously with water, with oxygen, and with chlorine.

1.3.   a.   The factor 9.1 has the fewest significant figures, so the answer should be reported to two significant figures.

$$\frac{5.61 \times 7.891}{9.1} = 4.\underline{8}6 = 4.9$$

   b.   The number with the least number of decimal places is 8.91. Therefore, round the answer to two decimal places.

   $8.91 - 6.435 = 2.4\underline{7}5 = 2.48$

   c.   The number with the least number of decimal places is 6.81. Therefore, round the answer to two decimal places.

   $6.81 - 6.730 = 0.0\underline{8}0 = 0.08$

   d.   You first do the subtraction within parentheses. In this step, the number with the least number of decimal places is 6.81, so the result of the subtraction has two decimal places. The least significant figure for this step is underlined.

   $38.91 \times (6.81 - 6.730) = 38.91 \times 0.0\underline{8}0$

   Next, perform the multiplication. In this step, the factor 0.0$\underline{8}$0 has the fewest significant figures, so round the answer to one significant figure.

   $38.91 \times 0.0\underline{8}0 = \underline{3}.11 = 3$

1.4. a. 1.84×10^{-9} m = 1.84 nm

  b. 5.67×10^{-12} s = 5.67 ps

  c. 7.85×10^{-3} g = 7.85 mg

  d. 9.7×10^{3} m = 9.7 km

  e. 0.000732 s = 0.732 ms, or 732 μs

  f. 0.000000000154 m = 0.154 nm, or 154 pm

1.5. a. Substituting, we find that

$$t_C = \frac{5°C}{9°F} \times (t_F - 32°F) = \frac{5°C}{9°F} \times (102.5°F - 32°F) = 39.\underline{1}67°C$$

$$= 39.2°C$$

  b. Substituting, we find that

$$T_K = \left(t_c \times \frac{1\,K}{1°C} \right) + 273.15\,K = \left(-78°C \times \frac{1\,K}{1°C} \right) + 273.15\,K = 195.15\,K$$

$$= 195\,K$$

1.6. Recall that density equals mass divided by volume. You substitute 159 g for the mass and 20.2 g/cm^3 for the volume.

$$d = \frac{m}{V} = \frac{159\,g}{20.2\,cm^3} = 7.8\underline{7}1\,g/cm^3 = 7.87\,g/cm^3$$

The density of the metal equals that of iron.

1.7. Rearrange the formula defining the density to obtain the volume.

$$V = \frac{m}{d}$$

Substitute 30.3 g for the mass and 0.789 g/cm^3 for the density.

$$V = \frac{30.3\,g}{0.789\,g/cm^3} = 38.\underline{4}0\,cm^3 = 38.4\,cm^3$$

1.8. Since one pm = 10^{-12} m, and the prefix milli- means 10^{-3}, you can write

$$121\,pm \times \frac{10^{-12}\,m}{1\,pm} \times \frac{1\,mm}{10^{-3}\,m} = 1.21 \times 10^{-7}\,mm$$

1.9. $67.6\,\text{Å}^3 \times \left(\dfrac{10^{-10}\,m}{1\,\text{Å}} \right)^3 \times \left(\dfrac{1\,dm}{10^{-1}\,m} \right)^3 = 6.76 \times 10^{-26}\,dm^3$

1.10. From the definitions, you obtain the following conversion factors:

$$1 = \frac{36\,in}{1\,yd} \qquad 1 = \frac{2.54\,cm}{1\,in} \qquad 1 = \frac{10^{-2}\,m}{1\,cm}$$

The conversion factor for yards to meters is as follows:

$$1.000 \text{ yd} \times \frac{36 \text{ in}}{1 \text{ yd}} \times \frac{2.54 \text{ cm}}{1 \text{ in}} \times \frac{10^{-2} \text{ m}}{1 \text{ cm}} = 0.9144 \text{ m (exact)}$$

Finally,

$$3.5\underline{4} \text{ yd} \times \frac{0.9144 \text{ m}}{1 \text{ yd}} = 3.2\underline{3}7 \text{ m} = 3.24 \text{ m}$$

■ ANSWERS TO CONCEPT CHECKS

1.1. Box A contains a collection of identical units; therefore, it must represent an element. Box B contains a compound because a compound is the chemical combination of two or more elements (two elements in this case). Box C contains a mixture because it is made up of two different substances.

1.2. a. For a person who weighs less than 100 pounds, two significant figures are typically used, although one significant figure is possible (for example, 60 pounds). For a person who weighs 100 pounds or more, three significant figures are typically used to report the weight (given to the whole pound), although people often round to the nearest unit of 10, which may result in reporting the weight with two significant figures (for example, 170 pounds).

     b. Assuming a weight of 165 pounds, rounded to two significant figures this would be reported as 1.7×10^2 pounds.

     c. For example, 165 lb weighed on a scale that can measure in 100-lb increments would be 200 lb. Using the conversion factor 1 lb = 0.4536 kg, 165 lb is equivalent to 74.8 kg. Thus, on a scale that can measure in 50-kg increments, 165 lb would be 50 kg.

1.3. a. If your leg is approximately 32 inches long, this would be equivalent to 0.81 m, 8.1 dm, or 81 cm.

     b. One story is approximately 10 feet, so three stories is 30 feet. This would be equivalent to approximately 9 m.

     c. Normal body temperature is 98.6°F, or 37.0°C. Thus, if your body temperature were 39°C (102°F), you would feel as if you had a moderate fever.

     d. Room temperature is approximately 72°F, or 22°C. Thus, if you were sitting in a room at 23°C (73°F), you would be comfortable in a short-sleeve shirt.

1.4. Gold is a very unreactive substance, so comparing physical properties is probably your best option. However, color is a physical property you cannot rely on in this case to get your answer.

One experiment you could perform is to determine the densities of the metal and the chunk of gold. You could measure the mass of the nugget on a balance and the volume of the nugget by water displacement. Using this information, you could calculate the density of the nugget. Repeat the experiment and calculations for the sample of gold. If the nugget is gold, the two densities should be equal and be 19.3 g/cm³.

Also, you could determine the melting points of the metal and the chunk of pure gold. The two melting points should be the same (1338 K) if the metal is gold.

■ ANSWERS TO SELF-ASSESSMENT AND REVIEW QUESTIONS

1.1.   One area of technology that chemistry has changed is the characteristics of materials. The liquid-crystal displays (LCDs) in devices such as watches, cell phones, computer monitors, and televisions are materials made of molecules designed by chemists. Electronics and communications have been transformed by the development of optical fibers to replace copper wires. In biology, chemistry has changed the way scientists view life. Biochemists have found that all forms of life share many of the same molecules and molecular processes.

1.2.   An experiment is an observation of natural phenomena carried out in a controlled manner so that the results can be duplicated and rational conclusions obtained. A theory is a tested explanation of basic natural phenomena. They are related in that a theory is based on the results of many experiments and is fruitful in suggesting other, new experiments. Also, an experiment can disprove a theory but can never prove it absolutely. A hypothesis is a tentative explanation of some regularity of nature.

1.3.   Rosenberg conducted controlled experiments and noted a basic relationship that could be stated as a hypothesis—that is, that certain platinum compounds inhibit cell division. This led him to do new experiments on the anticancer activity of these compounds.

1.4.   Matter is the general term for the material things around us. It is whatever occupies space and can be perceived by our senses. Mass is the quantity of matter in a material. The difference between mass and weight is that mass remains the same wherever it is measured, but weight is proportional to the mass of the object divided by the square of the distance between the center of mass of the object and that of the earth.

1.5.   The law of conservation of mass states that the total mass remains constant during a chemical change (chemical reaction). To demonstrate this law, place a sample of wood in a sealed vessel with air, and weigh it. Heat the vessel to burn the wood, and weigh the vessel after the experiment. The weight before the experiment and that after it should be the same.

1.6.   Mercury metal, which is a liquid, reacts with oxygen gas to form solid mercury(II) oxide. The color changes from that of metallic mercury (silvery) to a color that varies from red to yellow depending on the particle size of the oxide.

1.7.   Gases are easily compressible and fluid. Liquids are relatively incompressible and fluid. Solids are relatively incompressible and rigid.

1.8.   An example of a substance is the element sodium. Among its physical properties: It is a solid, and it melts at 98°C. Among its chemical properties: It reacts vigorously with water, and it burns in chlorine gas to form sodium chloride.

1.9.   An example of an element: sodium; of a compound: sodium chloride, or table salt; of a heterogeneous mixture: salt and sugar; of a homogeneous mixture: sodium chloride dissolved in water to form a solution.

1.10.   A glass of bubbling carbonated beverage with ice cubes contains three phases: gas, liquid, and solid.

1.11.   A compound may be decomposed by chemical reactions into elements. An element cannot be decomposed by any chemical reaction. Thus, a compound cannot also be an element in any case.

1.12. The precision refers to the closeness of the set of values obtained from identical measurements of a quantity. The number of digits reported for the value of a measured or calculated quantity (significant figures) indicates the precision of the value.

1.13. Multiplication and division rule: In performing the calculation 100.0 x 0.0634 ÷ 25.31, the calculator display shows 0.2504938. We would report the answer as 0.250 because the factor 0.0634 has the least number of significant figures (three).

Addition and subtraction rule: In performing the calculation 184.2 + 2.324, the calculator display shows 186.524. Because the quantity 184.2 has the least number of decimal places (one), the answer is reported as 186.5.

1.14. An exact number is a number that arises when you count items or sometimes when you define a unit. For example, a foot is defined to be 12 inches. A measured number is the result of a comparison of a physical quantity with a fixed standard of measurement. For example, a steel rod measures 9.12 centimeters, or 9.12 times the standard centimeter unit of measurement.

1.15. For a given unit, the SI system uses prefixes to obtain units of different sizes. Units for all other possible quantities are obtained by deriving them from any of the seven base units. You do this by using the base units in equations that define other physical quantities.

1.16. An absolute temperature scale is a scale in which the lowest temperature that can be attained theoretically is zero. Degrees Celsius and kelvins have units of equal size and are related by the formula

$$t_C = (T_K - 273.15 \text{ K}) \times \frac{1°C}{1 \text{ K}}$$

1.17. The density of an object is its mass per unit volume. Because the density is characteristic of a substance, it can be helpful in identifying it. Density can also be useful in determining whether a substance is pure. It also provides a useful relationship between mass and volume.

1.18. Units should be carried along because (1) the units for the answers will come out in the calculations, and (2), if you make an error in arranging factors in the calculation, this will become apparent because the final units will be nonsense.

1.19. The answer is c, three significant figures.

1.20. The answer is a, 4.43×10^2 mm.

1.21. The answer is e, 75 mL.

1.22. The answer is c, 0.23 mg.

■ ANSWERS TO CONCEPTUAL PROBLEMS

1.25.   a.   Two phases: liquid and solid.

b.   Three phases: liquid water, solid quartz, and solid seashells.

1.27.   a.   You need to establish two points on the thermometer with known (defined) temperatures—for example, the freezing point (0°C) and boiling point (100°C) of water. You could first immerse the thermometer in an ice-water bath and mark the level at this point as 0°C. Then, immerse the thermometer in boiling water, and mark the level at this point as 100°C. As long as the two points are far enough apart to obtain readings of the desired accuracy, the thermometer can be used in experiments.

   b.   You could make 19 evenly spaced marks on the thermometer between the two original points, each representing a difference of 5°C. You may divide the space between the two original points into fewer spaces as long as you can read the thermometer to obtain the desired accuracy.

1.29.   a.   To answer this question, you need to develop an equation that converts between °F and °YS. To do so, you need to recognize that one degree on the Your Scale does not correspond to one degree on the Fahrenheit scale and that −100°F corresponds to 0° on Your Scale (different "zero" points). As stated in the problem, in the desired range of 100 Your Scale degrees, there are 120 Fahrenheit degrees. Therefore, the relationship can be expressed as 120°F = 100°YS, since it covers the same temperature range. Now you need to "scale" the two systems so that they correctly convert from one scale to the other. You could set up an equation with the known data points and then employ the information from the relationship above.

   For example, to construct the conversion between °YS and °F, you could perform the following steps:

   Step 1:   °F = °YS

   Not a true statement, but one you would like to make true.

   Step 2: $°F = °YS \times \dfrac{120°F}{100°YS}$

   This equation takes into account the difference in the size between the temperature unit on the two scales but will not give you the correct answer because it doesn't take into account the different zero points.

   Step 3: By subtracting 100°F from your equation from Step 2, you now have the complete equation that converts between °F and °YS.

   $$°F = \left(°YS \times \dfrac{120°F}{100°YS}\right) - 100°F$$

   b.   Using the relationship from part a, 66°YS is equivalent to

   $$\left(66°YS \times \dfrac{120°F}{100°YS}\right) - 100°F = -2\underline{0}.8°F = -21°F$$

1.31.   The empty boxes are identical, so they do not contribute to any mass or density difference. Since the edge of the cube and the diameter of the sphere are identical, they will occupy the same volume in each of the boxes; therefore, each box will contain the same number of cubes or spheres. If you view the spheres as cubes that have been rounded by removing wood, you can conclude that the box containing the cubes must have a greater mass of wood; hence, it must have a greater density.

1.33. a.   A paper clip has a mass of about 1 g.

b.   Answers will vary depending on your particular sample. Keeping in mind that the SI unit for mass is kg, the approximate weights for the items presented in the problem are as follows: a grain of sand, 1×10^{-5} kg; a paper clip, 1×10^{-3} kg; a nickel, 5×10^{-3} kg; a 5.0-gallon bucket of water, 2.0×10^{1} kg; a brick, 3 kg; a car, 1×10^{3} kg.

1.35. a.   The number of significant figures in this answer follows the rules for multiplication and division. Here, the measurement with the fewest significant figures is the reported volume 0.310 m^3, which has three. Therefore, the answer will have three significant figures. Since Volume = L x W x H, you can rearrange and solve for one of the measurements, say the length.

$$L = \frac{V}{W \times H} = \frac{0.310 \text{ m}^3}{(0.7120 \text{ m}) (0.52145 \text{ m})} = 0.83\underline{4}96 \text{ m} = 0.835 \text{ m}$$

b.   The number of significant figures in this answer follows the rules for addition and subtraction. The measurement with the least number of decimal places is the result 1.509 m, which has three. Therefore, the answer will have three decimal places. Since the result is the sum of the three measurements, the third length is obtained by subtracting the other two measurements from the total.

Length = 1.509 m $- 0.7120$ m $- 0.52145$ m $= 0.27\underline{5}55$ m $= 0.276$ m

■ SOLUTIONS TO PRACTICE PROBLEMS

Note on significant figures: If the final answer to a solution needs to be rounded off, it is given first with one nonsignificant figure, and the last significant figure is underlined. The final answer is then rounded to the correct number of significant figures. In multistep problems, intermediate answers are given with at least one nonsignificant figure; however, only the final answer has been rounded off.

1.37 .   By the law of conservation of mass:

Mass of sodium carbonate + mass of acetic acid solution = mass of contents of reaction vessel + mass of carbon dioxide

Plugging in gives

15.9 g $+ 20.0$ g $= 29.3$ g $+$ mass of carbon dioxide

Mass of carbon dioxide = 15.9 g $+ 20.0$ g $- 29.3$ g $= 6.6$ g

1.39.   By the law of conservation of mass:

Mass of zinc + mass of sulfur = mass of zinc sulfide

Rearranging and plugging in give

Mass of zinc sulfide = 65.4 g $+ 32.1$ g $= 97.5$ g

For the second part, let x = mass of zinc sulfide that could be produced. By the law of conservation of mass:

20.0 g $+$ mass of sulfur = x

Write a proportion that relates the mass of zinc reacted to the mass of zinc sulfide formed, which should be the same for both cases.

$$\frac{\text{mass zinc}}{\text{mass zinc sulfide}} = \frac{65.4 \text{ g}}{97.5 \text{ g}} = \frac{20.0 \text{ g}}{x}$$

Solving gives $x = 29.\underline{8}1$ g $= 29.8$ g

1.41.   a. Solid   b. Liquid   c. Gas   d. Solid

1.43.   a.   Physical change

        b.   Physical change

        c.   Chemical change

        d.   Physical change

1.45.   Physical change: Liquid mercury is cooled to solid mercury.

        Chemical changes: (1) Solid mercury oxide forms liquid mercury metal and gaseous oxygen; (2) glowing wood and oxygen form burning wood (form ash and gaseous products).

1.47.   a.   Physical property

        b.   Chemical property

        c.   Physical property

        d.   Physical property

        e.   Chemical property

1.49.   Physical properties: (1) Iodine is solid; (2) the solid has lustrous blue-black crystals; (3) the crystals vaporize readily to a violet-colored gas.

        Chemical properties: (1) Iodine combines with many metals, such as with aluminum to give aluminum iodide.

1.51.   a.   Physical process

        b.   Chemical reaction

        c.   Physical process

        d.   Chemical reaction

        e.   Physical process

1.53.   a.   Solution

        b.   Substance

        c.   Substance

        d.   Heterogeneous mixture

1.55. a.   A pure substance with two phases present, liquid and gas.

b.   A mixture with two phases present, solid and liquid.

c.   A pure substance with two phases present, solid and liquid.

d.   A mixture with two phases present, solid and solid.

1.57. a.   four

b.   three

c.   four

d.   five

e.   three

f.   four

1.59. $40{,}000$ km $= 4.0 \times 10^4$ km

1.61. a. $\dfrac{8.71 \times 0.0301}{0.031} = 8.\underline{4}57 = 8.5$

b. $0.71 + 89.3 = 90.\underline{0}1 = 90.0$

c. $934 \times 0.00435 + 107 = 4.0\underline{6}29 + 107 = 111.\underline{0}6 = 111$

d. $(847.89 - 847.73) \times 14673 = 0.1\underline{6} \times 14673 = 2\underline{3}47 = 2.3 \times 10^3$

1.63.   The volume of the first sphere is

$$V_1 = (4/3)\pi r^3 = (4/3)\pi \times (5.15 \text{ cm})^3 = 57\underline{2}.15 \text{ cm}^3$$

The volume of the second sphere is

$$V_2 = (4/3)\pi r^3 = (4/3)\pi \times (5.00 \text{ cm})^3 = 52\underline{3}.60 \text{ cm}^3$$

The difference in volume is

$$V_1 - V_2 = 57\underline{2}.15 \text{ cm}^3 - 52\underline{3}.60 \text{ cm}^3 = 4\underline{8}.55 \text{ cm}^3 = 49 \text{ cm}^3$$

1.65. a. 5.89×10^{-12} s $= 5.89$ ps

b. 0.2010 m $= 2.01$ dm

c. 2.560×10^{-9} g $= 2.560$ ng

d. 6.05×10^3 m $= 6.05$ km

1.67. a. 6.15 ps $= 6.15 \times 10^{-12}$ s

b. 3.781 μm $= 3.781 \times 10^{-6}$ m

c. 1.546 Å $= 1.546 \times 10^{-10}$ m

d. 9.7 mg $= 9.7 \times 10^{-3}$ g

1.69. a. $t_C = \dfrac{5°C}{9°F} \times (t_F - 32°F) = \dfrac{5°C}{9°F} \times (68°F - 32°F) = 2\underline{0}.0°C = 20.°C$

b. $t_C = \dfrac{5°C}{9°F} \times (t_F - 32°F) = \dfrac{5°C}{9°F} \times (-23°F - 32°F) = -3\underline{0}.56°C = -31°C$

c. $t_F = (t_C \times \dfrac{9°F}{5°C}) + 32°F = (26°C \times \dfrac{9°F}{5°C}) + 32°F = 7\underline{8}.8°F = 79°F$

d. $t_F = (t_C \times \dfrac{9°F}{5°C}) + 32°F = (-81°C \times \dfrac{9°F}{5°C}) + 32°F = -11\underline{3}.8°F = -114°F$

1.71. $t_F = (t_C \times \dfrac{9°F}{5°C}) + 32°F = (-20.0°C \times \dfrac{9°F}{5°C}) + 32°F = -4.\underline{0}°F = -4.0°F$

1.73. $d = \dfrac{m}{V} = \dfrac{12.4 \text{ g}}{1.64 \text{ cm}^3} = 7.5\underline{6}0 \text{ g/cm}^3 = 7.56 \text{ g/cm}^3$

1.75. First, determine the density of the liquid.

$$d = \dfrac{m}{V} = \dfrac{6.71 \text{ g}}{8.5 \text{ mL}} = 0.7\underline{8}94 = 0.79 \text{ g/mL}$$

The density is closest to ethanol (0.789 g/cm³).

1.77. The mass of platinum is obtained as follows.

Mass $= d \times V = 21.4 \text{ g/cm}^3 \times 5.9 \text{ cm}^3 = 1\underline{2}6 \text{ g} = 1.3 \times 10^2 \text{ g}$

1.79. The volume of ethanol is obtained as follows. Recall that 1 mL = 1 cm³.

Volume $= \dfrac{m}{d} = \dfrac{19.8 \text{ g}}{0.789 \text{ g/cm}^3} = 25.\underline{0}9 \text{ cm}^3 = 25.1 \text{ cm}^3 = 25.1 \text{ mL}$

1.81. Since 1 kg = 10³ g, and 1 mg = 10⁻³ g, you can write

$$0.480 \text{ kg} \times \dfrac{10^3 \text{ g}}{1 \text{ kg}} \times \dfrac{1 \text{ mg}}{10^{-3} \text{ g}} = 4.80 \times 10^5 \text{ mg}$$

1.83. Since 1 nm = 10⁻⁹ m, and 1 cm = 10⁻² m, you can write

$$555 \text{ nm} \times \dfrac{10^{-9} \text{ m}}{1 \text{ nm}} \times \dfrac{1 \text{ cm}}{10^{-2} \text{ m}} = 5.55 \times 10^{-5} \text{ cm}$$

1.85. Since 1 km = 10³ m, you can write

$$3.73 \times 10^8 \text{ km}^3 \times \left(\dfrac{10^3 \text{ m}}{1 \text{ km}}\right)^3 = 3.73 \times 10^{17} \text{ m}^3$$

Now, 1 dm = 10⁻¹ m. Also, note that 1 dm³ = 1 L. Therefore, you can write

$$3.73 \times 10^{17} \text{ m}^3 \times \left(\dfrac{1 \text{ dm}}{10^{-1} \text{ m}}\right)^3 = 3.73 \times 10^{20} \text{ dm}^3 = 3.73 \times 10^{20} \text{ L}$$

1.87. $3.58 \text{ short ton} \times \dfrac{2000 \text{ lb}}{1 \text{ short ton}} \times \dfrac{16 \text{ oz}}{1 \text{ lb}} \times \dfrac{1 \text{ g}}{0.03527 \text{ oz}} = 3.2\underline{4}8 \times 10^6 \text{ g} = 3.25 \times 10^6 \text{ g}$

1.89. $2425 \text{ fathoms} \times \dfrac{6 \text{ ft}}{1 \text{ fathom}} \times \dfrac{12 \text{ in.}}{1 \text{ ft}} \times \dfrac{2.54 \times 10^{-2} \text{ m}}{1 \text{ in.}} = 443\underline{4}.8 \text{ m} = 4.435 \times 10^3 \text{ m}$

1.91. $(20.0 \text{ in.}) \times (20.0 \text{ in.}) \times (10.0 \text{ in.}) \times \left(\dfrac{2.54 \text{ cm}}{1 \text{ in.}} \right)^3 \times \dfrac{1 \text{ L}}{1000 \text{ cm}^3} = 65.\underline{5}4 \text{ L} = 65.5 \text{ L}$

■ SOLUTIONS TO GENERAL PROBLEMS

1.93. From the law of conservation of mass,

Mass of sodium + mass of water = mass of hydrogen + mass of solution

Substituting, you obtain

$19.70 \text{ g} + 126.22 \text{ g} = \text{mass of hydrogen} + 145.06 \text{ g}$

or,

Mass of hydrogen $= 19.70 \text{ g} + 126.22 \text{ g} - 145.06 \text{ g} = 0.8\underline{6} \text{ g}$

Thus, the mass of hydrogen produced was 0.86 g.

1.95. From the law of conservation of mass,

Mass of aluminum + mass of iron(III) oxide = mass of iron +

mass of aluminum oxide + mass of unreacted iron(III) oxide

$5.40 \text{ g} + 18.50 \text{ g} = 11.17 \text{ g} + 10.20 \text{ g} + \text{mass of iron(III) oxide unreacted}$

Mass of iron(III) oxide unreacted $= 5.40 \text{ g} + 18.50 \text{ g} - 11.17 \text{ g} - 10.20 \text{ g} = 2.53 \text{ g}$

Thus, the mass of unreacted iron(III) oxide is 2.53 g.

1.97. $53.10 \text{ g} + 5.348 \text{ g} + 56.1 \text{ g} = 114.\underline{5}4 \text{ g} = 114.5 \text{ g total}$

1.99. a. Chemical   b. Physical   c. Physical   d. Chemical

1.101. Compounds always contain the same proportions of the elements by mass. Thus, if we let X be the proportion of iron in a sample, we can calculate the proportion of iron in each sample as follows.

Sample A: $X = \dfrac{\text{mass of iron}}{\text{mass of sample}} = \dfrac{1.094 \text{ g}}{1.518 \text{ g}} = 0.720\underline{6}8 = 0.7207$

Sample B: $X = \dfrac{\text{mass of iron}}{\text{mass of sample}} = \dfrac{1.449 \text{ g}}{2.056 \text{ g}} = 0.704\underline{7}6 = 0.7048$

Sample C: $X = \dfrac{\text{mass of iron}}{\text{mass of sample}} = \dfrac{1.335 \text{ g}}{1.873 \text{ g}} = 0.712\underline{7}6 = 0.7128$

Since each sample has a different proportion of iron by mass, the material is not a compound.

1.103. $V = (\text{edge})^3 = (39.3 \text{ cm})^3 = 6.0\underline{6}9 \times 10^4 \text{ cm}^3 = 6.07 \times 10^4 \text{ cm}^3$

1.105. $V = LWH = 47.8 \text{ in.} \times 12.5 \text{ in.} \times 19.5 \text{ in.} \times \dfrac{1 \text{ gal}}{231 \text{ in}^3} = 50.\underline{4}3 \text{ gal} = 50.4 \text{ gal}$

1.107. The volume of the first sphere is given by

$$V_1 = (4/3)\pi r^3 = (4/3)\pi \times (5.61 \text{ cm})^3 = 73\underline{9}.5 \text{ cm}^3$$

The volume of the second sphere is given by

$$V_2 = (4/3)\pi r^3 = (4/3)\pi \times (5.85 \text{ cm})^3 = 83\underline{8}.6 \text{ cm}^3$$

The difference in volume between the two spheres is given by

$$V = V_2 - V_1 = 83\underline{8}.6 \text{ cm}^3 - 73\underline{9}.5 \text{ cm}^3 = 9.\underline{9}1 \times 10^1 = 9.9 \times 10^1 \text{ cm}^3$$

1.109. a. $\dfrac{56.1 - 51.1}{6.58} = 7.59 \times 10^{-1} = 7.6 \times 10^{-1}$

b. $\dfrac{56.1 + 51.1}{6.58} = 1.6\underline{2}9 \times 10^1 = 1.63 \times 10^1$

c. $(9.1 + 8.6) \times 26.91 = 4.7\underline{6}3 \times 10^2 = 4.76 \times 10^2$

d. $0.0065 \times 3.21 + 0.0911 = 1.1\underline{1}9 \times 10^{-1} = 1.12 \times 10^{-1}$

1.111. a. 9.12 cg

b. 66 pm

c. 7.1 μm

d. 56 nm

1.113. a. $1.07 \times 10^{-12} \text{ s}$

b. $5.8 \times 10^{-6} \text{ m}$

c. $3.19 \times 10^{-7} \text{ m}$

d. $1.53 \times 10^{-2} \text{ s}$

1.115. $t_F = (t_C \times \dfrac{9°F}{5°C}) + 32°F = (3410°C \times \dfrac{9°F}{5°C}) + 32°F = 617\underline{0}°F = 6170°F$

1.117. $t_F = (t_C \times \dfrac{9°F}{5°C}) + 32°F = (825°C \times \dfrac{9°F}{5°C}) + 32°F = 151\underline{7}°F = 1.52 \times 10^3 °F$

1.119. The temperature in kelvins is

$$T_K = (t_C \times \dfrac{1 \text{ K}}{1°C}) + 273.15 \text{ K} = (29.8°C \times \dfrac{1 \text{ K}}{1°C}) + 273.15 \text{ K} = 302.\underline{9}5 \text{ K}$$
$$= 303.0 \text{ K}$$

The temperature in degrees Fahrenheit is

$$t_F = (t_C \times \frac{9°F}{5°C}) + 32°F = (29.8°C \times \frac{9°F}{5°C}) + 32°F = 85.\underline{6}4°F = 85.6°F$$

1.121.   The temperature in degrees Celsius is

$$t_C = \frac{5°C}{9°F} \times (t_F - 32°F) = \frac{5°C}{9°F} \times (1666°F - 32°F) = 907.\underline{7}7°C = 907.8°C$$

The temperature in kelvins is

$$T_K = (t_C \times \frac{1\ K}{1°C}) + 273.15\ K = (907.\underline{7}7°C \times \frac{1\ K}{1°C}) + 273.15\ K = 1180.\underline{9}2\ K$$
$$= 1180.9\ K$$

1.123.   Density $= \frac{2.70\ g}{1\ cm^3} \times \frac{1\ kg}{10^3\ g} \times \left(\frac{1\ cm}{10^{-2}\ m}\right)^3 = 2.70 \times 10^3\ kg/m^3$

1.125.   The volume of the quartz is 65.7 mL − 51.2 mL = 14.5 mL. Then, the density is

$$\text{Density} = \frac{\text{mass}}{\text{volume}} = \frac{38.4\ g}{14.5\ mL} = 2.6\underline{4}8\ g/mL = 2.65\ g/mL = 2.65\ g/cm^3$$

1.127.   First, determine the density of the liquid sample.

$$\text{Density} = \frac{\text{mass}}{\text{volume}} = \frac{22.3\ g}{15.0\ mL} = 1.4\underline{8}6\ g/mL = 1.49\ g/mL = 1.49\ g/cm^3$$

This density is closest to that of chloroform (1.489 g/cm^3), so the unknown liquid is chloroform.

1.129.   First, determine the volume of the cube of platinum.

$$V = (\text{edge})^3 = (4.40\ cm)^3 = 85.\underline{1}8\ cm^3$$

Now, use the density to determine the mass of the platinum.

$$\text{Mass} = d \times V = 21.4\ g/cm^3 \times 85.\underline{1}8\ cm^3 = 18\underline{2}2.9\ g = 1.82 \times 10^3\ g$$

1.131.   Volume $= \dfrac{\text{mass}}{\text{density}} = \dfrac{35.00\ g}{1.053\ g/mL} = 33.2\underline{3}8\ mL = 33.24\ mL$

1.133.   a. $8.45\ kg \times \dfrac{10^3\ g}{1\ kg} \times \dfrac{1\ \mu g}{10^{-6}\ g} = 8.45 \times 10^9\ \mu g$

b. $318\ \mu s \times \dfrac{10^{-6}\ s}{1\ \mu s} \times \dfrac{1\ ms}{10^{-3}\ s} = 3.18 \times 10^{-1}\ ms$

c. $93\ km \times \dfrac{10^3\ m}{1\ km} \times \dfrac{1\ nm}{10^{-9}\ m} = 9.3 \times 10^{13}\ nm$

d. $37.1\ mm \times \dfrac{10^{-3}\ m}{1\ mm} \times \dfrac{1\ cm}{10^{-2}\ m} = 3.71\ cm$

1.135. a. $5.91 \text{ kg} \times \dfrac{10^3 \text{ g}}{1 \text{ kg}} \times \dfrac{1 \text{ mg}}{10^{-3} \text{ g}} = 5.91 \times 10^6 \text{ mg}$

   b. $753 \text{ mg} \times \dfrac{10^{-3} \text{ g}}{1 \text{ mg}} \times \dfrac{1 \text{ } \mu\text{g}}{10^{-6} \text{ g}} = 7.53 \times 10^5 \text{ } \mu\text{g}$

   c. $90.1 \text{ MHz} \times \dfrac{10^6 \text{ Hz}}{1 \text{ MHz}} \times \dfrac{1 \text{ kHz}}{10^3 \text{ Hz}} = 9.01 \times 10^4 \text{ kHz}$

   d. $498 \text{ mJ} \times \dfrac{10^{-3} \text{ J}}{1 \text{ mJ}} \times \dfrac{1 \text{ kJ}}{10^3 \text{ J}} = 4.98 \times 10^{-4} \text{ kJ}$

1.137. $\text{Volume} = 12{,}230 \text{ km}^3 \times \left(\dfrac{10^3 \text{ m}}{1 \text{ km}}\right)^3 \times \left(\dfrac{1 \text{ dm}}{10^{-1} \text{ m}}\right)^3 \times \dfrac{1 \text{ L}}{1 \text{ dm}^3} = 1.2230 \times 10^{16} \text{ L}$

1.139. First, calculate the volume of the room in cubic feet.

   $\text{Volume} = LWH = 10.0 \text{ ft} \times 11.0 \text{ ft} \times 9.0 \text{ ft} = 9\underline{9}0 \text{ ft}^3$

   Next, convert the volume to liters.

   $V = 9\underline{9}0 \text{ ft}^3 \times \left(\dfrac{12 \text{ in}}{1 \text{ ft}}\right)^3 \times \left(\dfrac{2.54 \text{ cm}}{1 \text{ in}}\right)^3 \times \dfrac{1 \text{ L}}{10^3 \text{ cm}^3} = 2.8\underline{0} \times 10^4 \text{ L} = 2.8 \times 10^4 \text{ L}$

1.141. $\text{Mass} = 275 \text{ carats} \times \dfrac{200 \text{ mg}}{1 \text{ carat}} \times \dfrac{10^{-3} \text{ g}}{1 \text{ mg}} = 55.\underline{0}0 \text{ g} = 55.0 \text{ g}$

1.143. The adhesive is not permanent, is easily removable, and does no harm to the object.

1.145. Chromatography depends on how fast a substance moves in a stream of gas or liquid, past a stationary phase to which the substance is slightly attracted.

■ SOLUTIONS TO STRATEGY PROBLEMS

1.147. $5 \times 10^{-2} \text{ mg} = 0.05 \text{ mg}$. So $4.7 \text{ mg} - 0.05 \text{ mg} = 4.\underline{6}5 \text{ mg} = 4.7 \text{ mg}$

1.149. $V = V_A + V_B = \dfrac{m_A}{d_A} + 50.0 \text{ mL} = \dfrac{175 \text{ g}}{3.00 \text{ g/mL}} + 50.0 \text{ mL} = 58.\underline{3}3 \text{ mL} + 50.0 \text{ mL}$

   $= 108.\underline{3}3 = 108.3 \text{ mL}$

1.151. Here it is necessary to convert the data into comparable units, mL for example. Converting 0.100 qt to mL gives (0.100 qt = 0.106 L) 106 mL. Next, using the density relationship, and the fact that 1 mL = 1 cm^3, 50.0 g of Pb corresponds to 4.42 mL Pb. The last quantity is first converted to gram mass units, and then to mL using the density relationship. In this case 0.0250 lb = 11.3 g Pb = 1.00 cm^3 = 1.00 mL Pb. Thus, ranking from smallest volume to greatest:

   0.0250 lb Pb (or 1.00 mL) < 50.0 g Pb (or 4.42 mL) < 50.0 mL Pb < 0.100 qt Pb (or 106 mL)

1.153. $2 \text{ converters} \times \dfrac{5.0 \times 10^3 \text{ beads}}{\text{converter}} \times \dfrac{1.0 \times 10^6 \text{ cm}^2}{\text{bead}} \times \left(\dfrac{1 \text{ m}}{100 \text{ cm}}\right)^2 \times \left(\dfrac{1 \text{ km}}{10^3 \text{ m}}\right)^2 = 1.\underline{0}0 = 1.0 \text{ km}^2$

1.155 $55.0 \text{ cm}^3 \times \dfrac{1025 \text{ kg}}{\text{m}^3} \times \left(\dfrac{10^{-2} \text{ m}}{1 \text{ cm}}\right)^3 \times \dfrac{1000 \text{ g}}{1 \text{ kg}} = 56.\underline{3}8 = 56.4 \text{ g sample of ocean water originally}$

Assuming a density of 1.0 g/mL for the evaporated water, and recognizing the equivalency between cm^3 and mL units, when 5.0 mL of water evaporates, the sample loses 5.0 g in mass and 5.0 cm^3 in volume. The density of the partially evaporated ocean water sample is obtained by dividing the remaining mass (56.4 g – 5.0 g = 51.4 g) by the remaining volume (55.0 cm^3 - 5.0 cm^3 = 50.0 cm^3).

$$d = \frac{mass}{volume} = \frac{51.4 \text{ g}}{50.0 \text{ cm}^3} = 1.03 \text{ g/cm}^3 \left(= \frac{1030 \text{ kg}}{\text{m}^3}\right)$$

As one would expect, the remaining salt solution is now slightly more dense than the original ocean water sample.

1.157. a. Since there is the same number of atoms of the gas in each container, the mass is the same in each container.

   b. Since $d = m/V$, for the same mass, when the volume is smaller, the density is greater. Since the volume is less in container A, the density is greater.

   c. If the volume of container A was doubled, the density would decrease and become equal to the density in container B

1.159. $\dfrac{300 \text{ million people}}{1} \times \dfrac{1 \times 10^{10} \text{ miles}}{1 \text{ person}} \times \dfrac{1.609 \text{ km}}{1 \text{ mi}} \times \dfrac{1000 \text{ m}}{1 \text{ km}} \times \dfrac{1 \text{ lightyear}}{9.46 \times 10^{15} \text{ m}}$
   $= 5.\underline{1}02 \times 10^5 = 5 \times 10^5 \text{ lightyears}$

1.161. a. Since $d = m/V$, an increased mass for the same volume means a higher density for the solution.

   b. There would be less water for the same mass of salt. Since the salt is more dense than water, the density would be higher than in part a.

   c. Since there would be a greater volume of water for the same mass of salt, the density would be lower than in part a.

■ SOLUTIONS TO CUMULATIVE-SKILLS PROBLEMS

1.163. The mass of hydrochloric acid is obtained from the density and the volume.

Mass = density x volume = 1.096 g/mL × 50.0 mL = 54.$\underline{8}$0 g

Next, from the law of conservation of mass,

Mass of marble + mass of acid = mass of solution + mass of carbon dioxide gas

Plugging in gives

10.0 g + 54.$\underline{8}$0 g = 60.4 g + mass of carbon dioxide gas

Mass of carbon dioxide gas = 10.0 g + 54.$\underline{8}$0 g − 60.4 g = 4.$\underline{4}$0 g

Finally, use the density to convert the mass of carbon dioxide gas to volume.

$$\text{Volume} = \frac{\text{mass}}{\text{density}} = \frac{4.\underline{4}0 \text{ g}}{1.798 \text{ g/ L}} = 2.\underline{4}47 \text{ L} = 2.4 \text{ L}$$

1.165. First, calculate the volume of the steel sphere.

$$V = (4/3)\pi r^3 = (4/3)\pi \times (1.58 \text{ in})^3 \times \left(\frac{2.54 \text{ cm}}{1 \text{ in}}\right)^3 = 27\underline{0}.7 \text{ cm}^3$$

Next, determine the mass of the sphere using the density.

Mass = density x volume = 7.88 g/cm^3 × 27$\underline{0}$.7 cm^3 = 21$\underline{3}$3 g = 2.13 × 10^3 g

1.167. The area of the ice is 840,000 mi^2 − 132,000 mi^2 = 70$\underline{8}$,000 mi^2. Now, determine the volume of this ice.

Volume = area × thickness

$$= 70\underline{8},000 \text{ mi}^2 \times \underline{5}000 \text{ ft} \times \left(\frac{5280 \text{ ft}}{1 \text{ mi}}\right)^2 \times \left(\frac{12 \text{ in}}{1 \text{ ft}}\right)^3 \times \left(\frac{2.54 \text{ cm}}{1 \text{ in}}\right)^3$$

$$= \underline{2}.794 \times 10^{21} \text{ cm}^3$$

Now use the density to determine the mass of the ice.

Mass = density x volume = 0.917 g/cm^3 × $\underline{2}$.794 × 10^{21} cm^3 = $\underline{2}$.56 × 10^{21} g = 3 × 10^{21} g

1.169. Let x = mass of ethanol and y = mass of water. Then, use the total mass to write $x + y = 49.6$ g, or $y = 49.6$ g − x. Thus, the mass of water is 49.6 g − x. Next,

Total volume = volume of ethanol + volume of water

Since the volume is equal to the mass divided by density, you can write

$$\text{Total volume} = \frac{\text{mass of ethanol}}{\text{density of ethanol}} + \frac{\text{mass of water}}{\text{density of water}}$$

Substitute in the known and unknown values to get an equation for x.

$$54.2 \text{ cm}^3 = \frac{x}{0.789 \text{ g/cm}^3} + \frac{49.6 \text{ g} - x}{0.998 \text{ g/cm}^3}$$

Multiply both sides of this equation by (0.789)(0.998). Also, multiply both sides by g/cm^3 to simplify the units. This gives the following equation to solve for x.

$$(0.789)(0.998)(54.2) \text{ g} = (0.998)\, x + (0.789)(49.6 \text{ g} - x)$$

$$42.\underline{6}78 \text{ g} = 0.998\, x + 39.\underline{1}34 \text{ g} - 0.789\, x$$

$$0.209\, x = 3.\underline{5}44 \text{ g}$$

$$x = \text{mass of ethanol} = 1\underline{6}.95 \text{ g}$$

The percentage of ethanol (by mass) in the solution can now be calculated.

$$\text{Percent (mass)} = \frac{\text{mass of ethanol}}{\text{mass of solution}} \times 100\% = \frac{1\underline{6}.95 \text{ g}}{49.6 \text{ g}} \times 100\% = 3\underline{4}.1\% = 34\%$$

To determine the proof, you must first find the percentage by volume of ethanol in the solution. The volume of ethanol is obtained using the mass and the density.

$$\text{Volume} = \frac{\text{mass of ethanol}}{\text{density of ethanol}} = \frac{1\underline{6}.95 \text{ g}}{0.789 \text{ g/ cm}^3} = 2\underline{1}.48 \text{ cm}^3$$

The percentage of ethanol (by volume) in the solution can now be calculated.

$$\text{Percent (volume)} = \frac{\text{volume of ethanol}}{\text{volume of solution}} \times 100\% = \frac{2\underline{1}.48 \text{ cm}^3}{54.2 \text{ cm}^3} \times 100\% = 3\underline{9}.63\%$$

The proof can now be calculated.

$$\text{Proof} = 2 \times \text{Percent (volume)} = 2 \times 3\underline{9}.63 = 7\underline{9}.27 = 79 \text{ proof}$$

1.171.   The volume of the mineral can be obtained from the mass difference between the water displaced and the air displaced, and the densities of water and air.

Mass difference = 18.49 g − 16.21 g = 2.28 g

$$\text{Volume of mineral} = \frac{\text{mass difference}}{\text{density of water - density of air}}$$

$$= \frac{2.28 \text{ g}}{0.9982 \text{ g/cm}^3 - 1.205 \times 10^{-3} \text{ g/cm}^3} = 2.2\underline{8}6 \text{ cm}^3$$

The mass of the mineral is equal to its mass in air plus the weight of the displaced air. The weight of the displaced air is obtained from the volume of the mineral and the density of air.

Mass of displaced air = density x volume

$$= 1.205 \text{ g/L x } 2.2\underline{8}6 \text{ cm}^3 \times \frac{1 \text{ L}}{10^3 \text{ cm}^3} = 2.7\underline{5}5 \times 10^{-3} \text{ g}$$

Mass of mineral = 18.49 g + 2.7\underline{5}5 × 10^{-3} g = 18.4\underline{9}27 g

The density of the mineral can now be calculated.

$$\text{Density} = \frac{\text{mass}}{\text{volume}} = \frac{18.4\underline{9}27 \text{ g}}{2.2\underline{8}6 \text{ cm}^3} = 8.0\underline{8}9 \text{ g/cm}^3 = 8.09 \text{ g/cm}^3$$

1.173. The volume of the object can be obtained from the mass of the ethanol displaced and the density of ethanol.

Mass of ethanol displaced = 15.8 g − 10.5 g = 5.3 g

$$\text{Volume of object} = \frac{\text{mass of ethanol}}{\text{density of ethanol}} = \frac{5.3 \text{ g}}{0.789 \text{ g/ cm}^3} = 6.\underline{7}17 \text{ cm}^3$$

The density of the object can now be calculated.

$$\text{Density} = \frac{\text{mass}}{\text{volume}} = \frac{15.8 \text{ g}}{6.\underline{7}17 \text{ cm}^3} = 2.\underline{3}52 \text{ g/cm}^3 = 2.4 \text{ g/cm}^3$$

CHAPTER 2

Atoms, Molecules, and Ions

■ SOLUTIONS TO EXERCISES

Note on significant figures: If the final answer to a solution needs to be rounded off, it is given first with one nonsignificant figure, and the last significant figure is underlined. The final answer is then rounded to the correct number of significant figures. In multistep problems, intermediate answers are given with at least one nonsignificant figure; however, only the final answer has been rounded off.

2.1.　The element with atomic number 17 (the number of protons in the nucleus) is chlorine, symbol Cl. The mass number is $17 + 18 = 35$. The symbol is $^{35}_{17}Cl$.

2.2.　Multiply each isotopic mass by its fractional abundance; then sum:

　　34.96885 amu × 0.75771　　=　　26.496247

　　36.96590 amu × 0.24229　　=　　　8.956467

　　　　　　35.452714 = 35.453 amu

　　The atomic mass of chlorine is 35.453 amu.

2.3.　a.　Se: Group VIA, Period 4; nonmetal

　　b.　Cs: Group IA, Period 6; metal

　　c.　Fe: Group VIIIB, Period 4; metal

　　d.　Cu: Group IB, Period 4; metal

　　e.　Br: Group VIIA, Period 4; nonmetal

2.4.　Take as many cations as there are units of charge on the anion and as many anions as there are units of charge on the cation. Two K^+ ions have a total charge of 2+, and one CrO_4^{2-} ion has a charge of 2−, giving a net charge of zero. The simplest ratio of K^+ to CrO_4^{2-} is 2:1, and the formula is K_2CrO_4.

2.5.　a.　CaO: Calcium, a Group IIA metal, is expected to form only a 2+ ion (Ca^{2+}, the calcium ion). Oxygen (Group VIA) is expected to form an anion of charge equal to the group number minus 8 (O^{2-}, the oxide ion). The name of the compound is calcium oxide.

　　b.　$PbCrO_4$: Lead has more than one monatomic ion. You can find the charge on the Pb ion if you know the formula of the anion. From Table 2.5, the CrO_4 refers to the anion CrO_4^{2-} (the chromate ion). Therefore, the Pb cation must be Pb^{2+} to give electrical neutrality. The name of Pb^{2+} is lead(II) ion, so the name of the compound is lead(II) chromate.

2.6.　Thallium(III) nitrate contains the thallium(III) ion, Tl^{3+}, and the nitrate ion, NO_3^-. The formula is $Tl(NO_3)_3$.

2.7.   a.   Dichlorine hexoxide

b.   Phosphorus trichloride

c.   Phosphorus pentachloride

2.8.   a. CS_2 b. SO_3

2.9.   a. Boron trifluoride   b. Hydrogen selenide

2.10.   When you remove one H^+ ion from $HBrO_4$, you obtain the BrO_4^- ion. You name the ion from the acid by replacing *-ic* with *-ate*. The anion is called the perbromate ion.

2.11.   Sodium carbonate decahydrate

2.12.   Sodium thiosulfate is composed of sodium ions (Na^+) and thiosulfate ions ($S_2O_3^{2-}$), so the formula of the anhydrous compound is $Na_2S_2O_3$. Since the material is a pentahydrate, the formula of the compound is $Na_2S_2O_3 \bullet 5H_2O$.

2.13.   Balance O first in parts (a) and (b) because it occurs in only one product. Balance S first in part (c) because it appears in only one product. Balance H first in part (d) because it appears in just one reactant as well as in the product.

a.   Write a 2 in front of $POCl_3$ for O; this requires a 2 in front of PCl_3 for final balance:

$$O_2 + 2PCl_3 \rightarrow 2POCl_3$$

b.   Write a 6 in front of N_2O to balance O; this requires a 6 in front of N_2 for final balance:

$$P_4 + 6N_2O \rightarrow P_4O_6 + 6N_2$$

c.   Write $2As_2S_3$ and $6SO_2$ to achieve an even number of oxygens on the right to balance what will always be an even number of oxygens on the left. The $2As_2S_3$ then requires $2As_2O_3$. Finally, to balance (6 + 12) O's on the right, write $9O_2$.

$$2As_2S_3 + 9O_2 \rightarrow 2As_2O_3 + 6SO_2$$

d.   Write a 4 in front of H_3PO_4; this requires a 3 in front of $Ca(H_2PO_4)_2$ for twelve H's.

$$Ca_3(PO_4)_2 + 4H_3PO_4 \rightarrow 3Ca(H_2PO_4)_2$$

■ ANSWERS TO CONCEPT CHECKS

2.1. CO_2 is a compound that is a combination of 1 carbon atom and 2 oxygen atoms. Therefore, the chemical model must contain a chemical combination of 3 atoms stuck together with 2 of the atoms being the same (oxygen). Since each "ball" represents an individual atom, the three models on the left can be eliminated since they don't contain the correct number of atoms. Keeping in mind that balls of the same color represent the same element, only the model on the far right contains two elements with the correct ratio of atoms, 1:2; therefore, it must be CO_2.

2.2.   If 7999 out of 8000 alpha particles deflected back at the alpha-particle source, this would imply that the atom was a solid, impenetrable mass. Keep in mind that this is in direct contrast to what was observed in the actual experiments, where the majority of the alpha particles passed through without being deflected.

2.3.   Elements are listed together in groups because they have similar chemical and/or physical properties.

2.4.   Statement (a) is the best statement regarding molecular compounds. Although you may have wanted to classify Br_2 as a molecular compound, it is an element and not a compound. Regarding statement (b), quite a few molecular compounds exit that don't contain carbon. Water and the nitrogen oxides associated with smog are prime examples. Statement (c) is false; ionic compounds consist of anions and cations. Statement (d) is very close to the right selection but it is too restrictive. Some molecular compounds containing both metal and nonmetal atoms are known to exist, e.g., cisplatin, $Ni(CO)_4$, etc. Because numerous molecular compounds are either solids or liquids at room temperature, statement (e) is false.

2.5.   a.   This compound is an ether because it has a functional group of an oxygen atom between two carbon atoms (–O–).

   b.   This compound is an alcohol because it has an –OH functional group.

   c.   This compound is a carboxylic acid because it has the –COOH functional group.

   d.   This compound is a hydrocarbon because it contains only carbon and hydrogen atoms.

2.6.   The SO_4^{2-}, NO_2^-, and I_3^- are considered to be polyatomic ions. Statement (a) is true based on the prefix *poly*. By definition, any ion must have a negative or positive charge; thus, statement (b) is true. Bring that the triiodide ion has only iodine atoms bonded together, and no other elements present, statement (c) is false. There are numerous examples to show that statement (d) is true, e.g., chromate, dichromate, permanganate to name a few. Oxoanions are polyatomic ions containing a central characteristic element surrounded by a number of oxygen atoms, e.g., sulfate and nitrite given in this concept check's. Statement (e) is true.

2.7.   A bottle containing a compound with the formula Al_2Q_3 would have an anion, Q, with a charge of 2–. The total positive charge in the compound due to the Al^{3+} is 6+ (2 x 3+), so the total negative charge must be 6–; therefore, each Q ion must have a charge of 2–. Thus, Q would probably be an element from Group VIA on the periodic table.

■ ANSWERS TO SELF-ASSESSMENT AND REVIEW QUESTIONS

2.1.   Atomic theory is an explanation of the structure of matter in terms of different combinations of very small particles called atoms. Since compounds are composed of atoms of two or more elements, there is no limit to the number of ways in which the elements can be combined. Each compound has its own unique properties. A chemical reaction consists of the rearrangement of the atoms present in the reacting substances to give new chemical combinations present in the substances formed by the reaction.

2.2.   Divide each amount of chlorine, 1.270 g and 1.904 g, by the lower amount, 1.270 g. This gives 1.000 and 1.499, respectively. Convert these to whole numbers by multiplying by 2, giving 2.000 and 2.998. The ratio of these amounts of chlorine is essentially 2:3. This is consistent with the law of multiple proportions because, for a fixed mass of iron (1 gram), the masses of chlorine in the other two compounds are in a ratio of small whole numbers.

2.3.   A cathode-ray tube consists of a negative electrode, or cathode, and a positive electrode, or anode, in an evacuated tube. Cathode rays travel from the cathode to the anode when a high voltage is turned on. Some of the rays pass through the hole in the anode to form a beam, which is then bent toward positively charged electric plates in the tube. This implies that a cathode ray consists of a beam of negatively charged particles (or electrons) and that electrons are constituents of all matter.

2.4.   Millikan performed a series of experiments in which he obtained the charge on the electron by observing how a charged drop of oil falls in the presence and in the absence of an electric field. An atomizer introduces a fine mist of oil drops into the top chamber (Figure 2.6). Several drops happen to fall through a small hole into the lower chamber, where the experimenter follows the motion of one drop with a microscope. Some of these drops have picked up one or more electrons as a result of friction in the atomizer and have become negatively charged. A negatively charged drop will be attracted upward when the experimenter turns on a current to the electric plates. The drop's upward speed (obtained by timing its rise) is related to its mass-to-charge ratio, from which you can calculate the charge on the electron.

2.5.   The nuclear model of the atom is based on experiments of Geiger, Marsden, and Rutherford. Rutherford stated that most of the mass of an atom is concentrated in a positively charged center called the nucleus around which negatively charged electrons move. The nucleus, although it contains most of the mass, occupies only a very small portion of the space of the atom. Most of the alpha particles passed through the metal atoms of the foil undeflected by the lightweight electrons. When an alpha particle does happen to hit a metal-atom nucleus, it is scattered at a wide angle because it is deflected by the massive, positively charged nucleus (Figure 2.8).

2.6.   The atomic nucleus consists of two kinds of particles, protons and neutrons. The mass of each is about the same, on the order of 1.67×10^{-27} kg, and about 1800 times that of the electron. An electron has a much smaller mass, on the order of 9.11×10^{-31} kg. The neutron is electrically neutral, but the proton is positively charged. An electron is negatively charged. The charges on the proton and the electron are equal in magnitude.

2.7.   Protons (hydrogen nuclei) were discovered as products of experiments involving the collision of alpha particles with nitrogen atoms that resulted in a proton being knocked out of the nitrogen nucleus. Neutrons were discovered as the radiation product of collisions of alpha particles with beryllium atoms. The resulting radiation was discovered to consist of particles having a mass approximately equal to that of a proton and having no charge (neutral).

2.8.   Oxygen consists of three different isotopes, each having 8 protons but a different number of neutrons.

2.9.   The percentages of the different isotopes in most naturally occurring elements have remained essentially constant over time and in most cases are independent of the origin of the element. Thus, what Dalton actually calculated were average atomic masses (relative masses). He could not weigh individual atoms, but he could find the average mass of one atom relative to the average mass of another.

2.10.   A mass spectrometer measures the mass-to-charge ratio of positively charged atoms (and molecules). It produces a mass spectrum, which shows the relative numbers of atoms (fractional abundances) of various masses (isotopic masses). The mass spectrum gives us all the information needed to calculate the atomic weight.

2.11.   The atomic mass of an element is the average atomic mass for the naturally occurring element expressed in atomic mass units. The atomic mass would be different elsewhere in the universe if the percentages of isotopes in the element were different from those on earth. Recent research has shown that isotopic abundances actually do differ slightly depending on the location found on earth.

2.12.   The element in Group IVA and Period 5 is tin (atomic number 50).

2.13.   A metal is a substance or mixture that has characteristic luster, or shine, and is generally a good conductor of heat and electricity.

2.14.   The formula for ethane is C_2H_6.

2.15.   A molecular formula gives the exact number of different atoms of an element in a molecule. A structural formula is a chemical formula that shows how the atoms are bonded to one another in a molecule.

2.16.   Organic molecules contain carbon combined with other elements such as hydrogen, oxygen, and nitrogen. An inorganic molecule is composed of elements other than carbon. Some inorganic molecules that contain carbon are carbon monoxide (CO), carbon dioxide (CO_2), carbonates, and cyanides.

2.17.   An ionic binary compound: NaCl; a molecular binary compound: H_2O.

2.18.   a.   The elements are represented by B, F, and I.

   b.   The compounds are represented by A, E, and G.

   c.   The mixtures are represented by C, D, and H.

   d.   The ionic solid is represented by A.

   e.   The gas made up of an element and a compound is represented by C.

   f.   The mixtures of elements are represented by D and H.

   g.   The solid element is represented by F.

   h.   The solids are represented by A and F.

   i.   The liquids are represented by E, H, and I.

2.19.   In the Stock system, CuCl is called copper(I) chloride, and $CuCl_2$ is called copper(II) chloride. One of the advantages of the Stock system is that more than two different ions of the same metal can be named with this system. In the former (older) system, a new suffix other than -ic and -ous must be established and/or memorized.

2.20.   A balanced chemical equation has the numbers of atoms of each element equal on both sides of the arrow. The coefficients are the smallest possible whole numbers.

2.21.   The answer is a: 50 p, 69 n, and 48 e^-.

2.22.   The answer is d: 65%.

2.23.   The answer is c: magnesium hydroxide, $Mg(OH)_2$.

2.24.   The answer is b: Li.

■ ANSWERS TO CONCEPTUAL PROBLEMS

2.27.   If atoms were balls of positive charge with the electrons evenly distributed throughout, there would be no massive, positive nucleus to deflect the beam of alpha particles when it is shot at the gold foil.

2.29.   You could group elements by similar physical properties such as density, mass, color, conductivity, etc., or by chemical properties, such as reaction with air, reaction with water, etc.

2.31.   a.   In each case, the total positive charge and the total negative charge in the compounds must cancel. Therefore, the compounds with the cations X^+, X^{2+}, and X^{5+}, combined with the SO_4^{2-} anion, are X_2SO_4, XSO_4, and $X_2(SO_4)_5$, respectively.

    b.   You recognize the fact that whenever a cation can have multiple oxidation states (1+, 2+, and 5+ in this case), the name of the compound must indicate the charge. Therefore, the names of the compounds in part (a) would be exy(I) sulfate, exy(II) sulfate, and exy(V) sulfate, respectively.

2.33.   A potassium-39 atom in this case would contain 19 protons and 20 neutrons. If the charge of the proton were twice that of an electron, it would take twice as many electrons as protons, or 38 electrons, to maintain a charge of zero.

2.35.   a. $2Li + Cl_2 \rightarrow 2LiCl$

    b. $16Na + S_8 \rightarrow 8Na_2S$

    c. $2Al + 3I_2 \rightarrow 2AlI_3$

    d. $3Ba + N_2 \rightarrow Ba_3N_2$

    e. $12V + 5P_4 \rightarrow 4V_3P_5$

■ SOLUTIONS TO PRACTICE PROBLEMS

Note on significant figures: If the final answer to a solution needs to be rounded off, it is given first with one nonsignificant figure, and the last significant figure is underlined. The final answer is then rounded to the correct number of significant figures. In multistep problems, intermediate answers are given with at least one nonsignificant figure; however, only the final answer has been rounded off.

2.37.   a. Argon   b. Zinc   c. Silver   d. Magnesium

2.39.   a. K   b. S   c. Fe   d. Mn

2.41.   The mass of the electron is found by multiplying the two values:

$$1.602 \times 10^{-19}\ C \times \frac{5.64 \times 10^{-12}\ kg}{1\ C} = 9.0\underline{3}5 \times 10^{-31}\ kg = 9.04 \times 10^{-31}\ kg$$

2.43.   The isotope of atom A is the atom with 18 protons, atom C; the atom that has the same mass number as atom A (37) is atom D.

2.45.   Each isotope of chlorine (atomic number 17) has 17 protons. Each neutral atom will also have 17 electrons. The number of neutrons for Cl-35 is 35 – 17 = 18 neutrons. The number of neutrons for Cl-37 is 37 – 17 = 20 neutrons.

2.47.   The element with 14 protons in its nucleus is silicon (Si). The mass number = 14 + 14 = 28. The notation for the nucleus is $^{28}_{14}\text{Si}$.

2.49.   Since the atomic ratio of nitrogen to hydrogen is 1:3, divide the mass of N by one-third of the mass of hydrogen to find the relative mass of N.

$$\frac{\text{Atomic mass of N}}{\text{Atomic mass of H}} = \frac{7.933 \text{ g}}{1/3 \times 1.712 \text{ g}} = \frac{13.901 \text{ g N}}{1 \text{ g H}} = \frac{13.90}{1}$$

2.51.   Multiply each isotopic mass by its fractional abundance, and then sum:

X-63:	62.930 × 0.6909	=	43.4783
X-65:	64.928 × 0.3091	=	20.0692
			63.5475 = 63.55 amu

The element is copper, atomic mass 63.546 amu.

2.53.   Multiply each isotopic mass by its fractional abundance, and then sum:

38.964 × 0.9326	=	36.3378
39.964 × 1.00 × 10^{-4}	=	0.0039964
40.962 × 0.0673	=	2.75674
	=	39.09853 = 39.10 amu

The atomic mass of this element is 39.10 amu. The element is potassium (K).

2.55.   According to the picture, there are 20 atoms, 5 of which are brown and 15 of which are green. Using the isotopic masses in the problem, the atomic mass of element X is

$$\frac{5}{20}(23.02 \text{ amu}) + \frac{15}{20}(25.147 \text{ amu}) = 5.755 + 18.8602 = 24.6152 = 24.615 \text{ amu}$$

2.57.   a.   C: Group IVA, Period 2; nonmetal

b.   Po: Group VIA, Period 6; metal

c.   Cr: Group VIB, Period 4; metal

d.   Mg: Group IIA, Period 3; metal

e.   B: Group IIIA, Period 2; metalloid

2.59.   a. Tellurium   b. Aluminum

2.61.   Examples are:

a.   O (oxygen)

b.   F (fluorine)

c.   Fe (iron)

d.   Ce (cerium)

2.63.   They are different in that the solid sulfur consists of S_8 molecules, whereas the hot vapor consists of S_2 molecules. The S_8 molecules are four times as heavy as the S_2 molecules. Hot sulfur is a mixture of S_8 and S_2 molecules, but at high enough temperatures only S_2 molecules are formed. Both hot sulfur and solid sulfur consist of molecules with only sulfur atoms.

2.65.   The number of nitrogen atoms in the 1.50-g sample of N_2O is

$$2.05 \times 10^{22} \text{ N}_2\text{O molecules} \times \frac{2 \text{ N atoms}}{1 \text{ N}_2\text{O molecule}} = 4.10 \times 10^{22} \text{ N atoms}$$

The number of nitrogen atoms in 44.0 g of N_2O is

$$44.0 \text{ g N}_2\text{O} \times \frac{4.10 \times 10^{22} \text{ N atoms}}{1.50 \text{ g N}_2\text{O}} = 1.2\underline{0}3 \times 10^{24} \text{ N atoms} = 1.20 \times 10^{24} \text{ N atoms}$$

2.67. $3.3 \times 10^{21} \text{ H atoms} \times \dfrac{1 \text{ NH}_3 \text{ molecule}}{3 \text{ H atoms}} = 1.1 \times 10^{21} \text{ NH}_3 \text{ molecules}$

2.69.   a. N_2H_4

        b. H_2O_2

        c. C_3H_8O

        d. PCl_3

2.71.   a. PCl_5

        b. NO_2

        c. $C_3H_6O_2$

2.73. $\dfrac{1 \text{ Fe atom}}{1 \text{ Fe(NO}_3)_2 \text{ unit}} \times \dfrac{1 \text{ Fe(NO}_3)_2 \text{ unit}}{2 \text{ NO}_3^- \text{ ions}} \times \dfrac{1 \text{ NO}_3^- \text{ ion}}{3 \text{ O atoms}} = \dfrac{1 \text{ Fe atom}}{6 \text{ O atoms}} = \dfrac{1}{6}$

Thus, the ratio of iron atoms to oxygen atoms is one Fe atom to six O atoms.

2.75.   a. $Fe(CN)_3$

        b. K_2CO_3

        c. Li_3N

        d. Ca_3P_2

2.77.   a. Na_2SO_4: sodium sulfate (Group IA forms only 1+ cations.)

        b. Na_3N: sodium nitride (Group IIA forms only 1+ cations.)

        c. $CuCl$: copper(I) chloride (Group IB forms 1+ and 2+ cations.)

        d. Cr_2O_3: chromium(III) oxide (Group VIB forms numerous oxidation states.)

2.79.   a.   Lead(II) permanganate: $Pb(MnO_4)_2$ (Permanganate is in Table 2.6.)

      b.   Barium hydrogen carbonate: $Ba(HCO_3)_2$ (The HCO_3^- ion is in Table 2.6.)

      c.   Cesium sulfide: Cs_2S (Group 1A ions form 1+ cations.)

      d.   Iron(III) acetate: $Fe(C_2H_3O_2)_3$ (The acetate ion = 1– [from Table 2.6]; for the sum of charges to be zero, three must be used.)

2.81.   a.   Molecular

      b.   Ionic

      c.   Molecular

      d.   Ionic

2.83.   a.   Dinitrogen monoxide

      b.   Tetraphosphorus dec(a)oxide

      c.   Arsenic trichloride

      d.   Dichlorine hept(a)oxide

2.85.   a. NBr_3

      b. XeF_6

      c.   CO

      d. Cl_2O_5

2.87.   a.   Selenium trioxide

      b.   Disulfur dichloride

      c.   Carbon monoxide

2.89.   a.   Sulfurous acid: H_2SO_3

      b.   Hyponitrous acid: $H_2N_2O_2$

      c.   Disulfurous acid: $H_2S_2O_5$

      d.   Arsenic acid: H_3AsO_4

2.91. $Na_2SO_4 \bullet 10H_2O$ is sodium sulfate decahydrate.

2.93.   Iron(II) sulfate heptahydrate is $FeSO_4 \bullet 7H_2O$.

2.95. $1 \ PbCO_3 \times \dfrac{3 \ O \ atoms}{1 \ PbCO_3 \ unit} + 2 \ KNO_3 \times \dfrac{3 \ O \ atoms}{1 \ KNO_3 \ unit} = 9 \ O \ atoms$

2.97.   a.   Balance: $Sn + NaOH \rightarrow Na_2SnO_2 + H_2$

      If Na is balanced first by writing a 2 in front of NaOH, the entire equation is balanced.

          $Sn + 2NaOH \rightarrow Na_2SnO_2 + H_2$

b. Balance: $Al + Fe_3O_4 \rightarrow Al_2O_3 + Fe$

First balance O (it appears once on each side) by writing a 3 in front of Fe_3O_4 and a 4 in front of Al_2O_3:

$$Al + 3Fe_3O_4 \rightarrow 4Al_2O_3 + Fe$$

Now balance Al against the 8 Al's on the right and Fe against the 9 Fe's on the left:

$$8Al + 3Fe_3O_4 \rightarrow 4Al_2O_3 + 9Fe$$

c. Balance: $CH_3OH + O_2 \rightarrow CO_2 + H_2O$

First balance H (it appears once on each side) by writing a 2 in front of H_2O:

$$CH_3OH + O_2 \rightarrow CO_2 + 2H_2O$$

To avoid fractional coefficients for O, multiply the equation by 2:

$$2CH_3OH + 2O_2 \rightarrow 2CO_2 + 4H_2O$$

Finally, balance O by changing $2O_2$ to "$3O_2$"; this balances the entire equation:

$$2CH_3OH + 3O_2 \rightarrow 2CO_2 + 4H_2O$$

d. Balance: $P_4O_{10} + H_2O \rightarrow H_3PO_4$

First balance P (it appears once on each side) by writing a 4 in front of H_3PO_4:

$$P_4O_{10} + H_2O \rightarrow 4H_3PO_4$$

Finally, balance H by writing a 6 in front of H_2O; this balances the entire equation:

$$P_4O_{10} + 6H_2O \rightarrow 4H_3PO_4$$

e. Balance: $PCl_5 + H_2O \rightarrow H_3PO_4 + HCl$

First balance Cl (it appears once on each side) by writing a 5 in front of HCl:

$$PCl_5 + H_2O \rightarrow H_3PO_4 + 5HCl$$

Finally, balance H by writing a 4 in front of H_2O; this balances the entire equation:

$$PCl_5 + 4H_2O \rightarrow H_3PO_4 + 5HCl$$

2.99. Balance: $Ca_3(PO_4)_2(s) + H_2SO_4(aq) \rightarrow CaSO_4(s) + H_3PO_4(aq)$

Balance Ca first with a 3 in front of $CaSO_4$:

$$Ca_3(PO_4)_2(s) + H_2SO_4(aq) \rightarrow 3CaSO_4(s) + H_3PO_4(aq)$$

Next, balance the P with a 2 in front of H_3PO_4:

$$Ca_3(PO_4)_2(s) + H_2SO_4(aq) \rightarrow 3CaSO_4(s) + 2H_3PO_4(aq)$$

Finally, balance the S with a 3 in front of H_2SO_4; this balances the equation:

$$Ca_3(PO_4)_2(s) + 3H_2SO_4(aq) \rightarrow 3CaSO_4(s) + 2H_3PO_4(aq)$$

2.101. Balance: $NH_4Cl(aq) + Ba(OH)_2(aq) \rightarrow NH_3(g) + BaCl_2(aq) + H_2O(l)$

Balance O first with a 2 in front of H_2O:

$$NH_4Cl + Ba(OH)_2 \rightarrow NH_3 + BaCl_2 + 2H_2O$$

Balance H with a 2 in front of NH_4Cl and a 2 in front of NH_3; this balances the equation:

$$2NH_4Cl(aq) + Ba(OH)_2(aq) \xrightarrow{\Delta} 2NH_3(g) + BaCl_2(aq) + 2H_2O(l)$$

■ SOLUTIONS TO GENERAL PROBLEMS

2.103. Calculate the ratio of oxygen for 1 g (fixed amount) of nitrogen in both compounds:

A: $\dfrac{2.755 \text{ g O}}{1.206 \text{ g N}} = \dfrac{2.2844 \text{ g O}}{1 \text{ g N}}$ B: $\dfrac{4.714 \text{ g O}}{1.651 \text{ g N}} = \dfrac{2.8552 \text{ g O}}{1 \text{ g N}}$

Next, find the ratio of oxygen per gram of nitrogen for the two compounds.

$$\frac{\text{g O in B/1 g N}}{\text{g O in A/1 g N}} = \frac{2.8552 \text{ g O}}{2.2844 \text{ g O}} = \frac{1.2498 \text{ g O}}{1 \text{g O}}$$

B contains 1.25 times as many O atoms as A does (there are five O's in B for every four O's in A).

2.105. The smallest difference is between -1.12×10^{-18} C and 9.60×10^{-19} C and is equal to -1.6×10^{-19} C. If this charge is equivalent to one electron, the number of excess electrons on a drop may be found by dividing the negative charge by the charge of one electron.

Drop 1: $\dfrac{-3.20 \times 10^{-19} \text{ C}}{-1.6 \times 10^{-19} \text{ C}} = 2.\underline{0} \cong 2$ electrons

Drop 2: $\dfrac{-6.40 \times 10^{-19} \text{ C}}{-1.6 \times 10^{-19} \text{ C}} = 4.\underline{0} \cong 4$ electrons

Drop 3: $\dfrac{-9.60 \times 10^{-19} \text{ C}}{-1.6 \times 10^{-19} \text{ C}} = 6.\underline{0} \cong 6$ electrons

Drop 4: $\dfrac{-1.12 \times 10^{-18} \text{ C}}{-1.6 \times 10^{-19} \text{ C}} = 7.\underline{0} \cong 7$ electrons

2.107. For the Eu atom to be neutral, the number of electrons must equal the number of protons, so a neutral europium atom has 63 electrons. The 3+ charge on the Eu^{3+} indicates there are three more protons than electrons, so the number of electrons is $63 - 3 = 60$.

2.109. The number of protons = mass number − number of neutrons = $81 - 46 = 35$. The element with $Z = 35$ is bromine (Br).

The ionic charge = number of protons − number of electrons = $35 - 36 = -1$.

Symbol: $^{81}_{35}Br^-$.

2.111. The sum of the fractional abundances must equal 1. Let y equal the fractional abundance of ^{63}Cu. Then the fractional abundance of ^{65}Cu equals $(1 - y)$. We write one equation in one unknown:

Atomic mass = $63.546 = 62.9298y + 64.9278(1 - y)$

$63.546 = 64.9278 - 1.9980y$

$y = \dfrac{64.9278 - 63.546}{1.9980} = 0.691\underline{5}9$

The fractional abundance of ^{63}Cu = 0.691<u>59</u> = 0.6916.

The fractional abundance of ^{65}Cu = 1 − 0.69159 = 0.308<u>41</u> = 0.3084.

2.113. a. Bromine, Br

      b. Hydrogen, H

      c. Niobium, Nb

      d. Fluorine, F

2.115. a. Chromium(III) ion

      b. Lead(IV) ion

      c. Titanium(II) ion

      d. Copper(II) ion

2.117. All possible ionic compounds: Na_2SO_4, NaCl, $CoSO_4$, and $CoCl_2$.

2.119. a. Tin(II) phosphate

      b. Ammonium nitrite

      c. Magnesium hydroxide

      d. Nickel(II) sulfite

2.121. a. Hg_2S [Mercury(I) exists as the polyatomic Hg_2^{2+} ion (Table 2.6).]

      b. $Co_2(SO_3)_3$

      c. $(NH_4)_2Cr_2O_7$

      d. AlF_3

2.123. a. Arsenic tribromide

      b. Hydrogen telluride (dihydrogen telluride)

      c. Diphosphorus pent(a)oxide

      d. Silicon dioxide

2.125. a. Balance the C and H first:

$$C_2H_6 + O_2 \rightarrow 2CO_2 + 3H_2O$$

Avoid a fractional coefficient for O on the left by doubling all coefficients except O_2's, and then balance the O's:

$$2C_2H_6 + 7O_2 \rightarrow 4CO_2 + 6H_2O$$

      b. Balance the P first:

$$P_4O_6 + H_2O \rightarrow 4H_3PO_3$$

Then balance the O (or H), which also gives the H (or O) balance:

$$P_4O_6 + 6H_2O \rightarrow 4H_3PO_3$$

c. Balancing the O first is the simplest approach. (Starting with K and Cl and then proceeding to O will cause the initial coefficient for $KClO_3$ to be changed in balancing O last.)

$$4KClO_3 \rightarrow KCl + 3KClO_4$$

d. Balance the N first:

$$(NH_4)_2SO_4 + NaOH \rightarrow 2NH_3 + H_2O + Na_2SO_4$$

Then balance the Na, followed by O; this also balances the H:

$$(NH_4)_2SO_4 + 2NaOH \rightarrow 2NH_3 + 2H_2O + Na_2SO_4$$

e. Balance the N first:

$$2NBr_3 + NaOH \rightarrow N_2 + NaBr + HOBr$$

Note that NaOH and HOBr each have one O and that NaOH and NaBr each have one Na; thus the coefficients of all three are equal; from $2NBr_3$, this coefficient must be $6Br/2 = 3$:

$$2NBr_3 + 3NaOH \rightarrow N_2 + 3NaBr + 3HOBr$$

2.127. Let: x = number of protons. Then $1.21x$ is the number of neutrons. Since the mass number is 62, you get

$$62 = x + 1.21x = 2.21x$$

Thus, $x = 28.054$, or 28. The element is nickel (Ni). Since the ion has a +2 charge, there are 26 electrons.

2.129. The average atomic mass would be

Natural carbon: $12.011 \times 1/2$ =   6.005500

Carbon-13: $13.00335 \times 1/2$ =   6.501675

Average   =   12.507175

The average atomic mass of the sample is 12.507 amu.

2.131. The island of stability is a region of the periodic table where a relatively stable super-heavy nuclide is at the peak of stability and is surrounded by foothills consisting of less stable nuclides. It is centered around the most stable nuclide, which is predicted to have an atomic number of 114 and a mass number of 298.

■ SOLUTIONS TO STRATEGY PROBLEMS

2.133. SO_3, sulfur trioxide; NO_2, nitrogen dioxide; PO_4^{3-}, phosphate ion;

N_2, nitrogen; $Mg(OH)_2$, magnesium hydroxide

2.135. The name of the product is aluminum oxide. The reaction is

$$4Al(s) + 3O_2(g) \rightarrow 2Al_2O_3(s)$$

2.137. $(0.7721)(37.24 \text{ amu}) + (1 - 0.7721)(x) = 37.45 \text{ amu}$

$$x = \frac{37.45 - (0.7721)(37.24)}{(1 - 0.7721)} = 38.161 \text{ amu} = 38.2 \text{ amu}$$

2.139. 6.5×10^{20} formula units $CaCl_2 \times \dfrac{3 \text{ ions}}{1 \text{ formula unit}} = 1.95 \times 10^{21}$ ions

2.141. SO_3, sulfur trioxide

HNO_2, nitrous acid

Mg_3N_2, magnesium nitride

$HI(aq)$, hydroiodic acid

$Cu_3(PO_4)_2$, copper(II) phosphate

$CuSO_4 \bullet 5H_2O$, copper(II) sulfate pentahydrate

2.143. a.   An aqueous solution of lead(II) chloride is mixed with an aqueous solution of sodium sulfide to form an aqueous solution of sodium chloride and a lead(II) sulfide precipitate.

b.   When gaseous sulfur trioxide is passed into liquid water an aqueous solution of sulfuric acid is formed.

c.   Graphite is combusted in an oxygen atmosphere to form gaseous carbon dioxide.

d.   Gaseous hydrogen iodide forms when hydrogen gas and gaseous iodine are mixed.

2.145. Each $^1H_2{}^{16}O$ molecule contains 8 neutrons, 10 protons, and 10 electrons.

neutrons in 6.0×10^{23} molecules $= 8 \times (6.0 \times 10^{23}) = 4.8 \times 10^{24}$ neutrons

protons in 6.0×10^{23} molecules $= 10 \times (6.0 \times 10^{23}) = 6.0 \times 10^{24}$ protons

Because the water molecules are neutrally charged there must also be 6.0×10^{24} electrons.

2.147. We are told that a ^{238}U nucleus decays by emitting a ^4He atom while the remaining subatomic particles remain intact. In equation form, we can write this as follows:

$$^{238}_{92}U \rightarrow {}^4_2He + {}^y_zX$$

Such nuclear decay processes must follow conservation laws. In this regard, the total mass number of the reactants must equal that of the products. It follows that if $238 = 4 + y$, then $y = 234$. Likewise, the total atomic number of the reactants must equal that of the products. Again, if $92 = 2 + z$, then $z = 90$. The symbol for the other nuclide being produced in this decay process is $^{234}_{90}Th$. Thorium (Th) is produced.

■ SOLUTIONS TO CUMULATIVE-SKILLS PROBLEMS

2.149. The spheres occupy a diameter of 2×1.86 Å $= 3.72$ Å. The line of sodium atoms would stretch a length of

$$\text{Length} = \frac{3.72 \text{ Å}}{1 \text{ Na atom}} \times 2.619 \times 10^{22} \text{ Na atoms} = 9.7\underline{4}2 \times 10^{22} \text{ Å}$$

Now, convert this to miles.

$$9.7\underline{4}2 \times 10^{22} \text{ Å} \times \frac{10^{-10} \text{ m}}{1 \text{ Å}} \times \frac{1 \text{ mile}}{1.609 \times 10^3 \text{ m}} = 6.0\underline{5}5 \times 10^9 \text{ miles} = 6.06 \times 10^9 \text{ miles}$$

2.151. $NiSO_4 \cdot 7H_2O(s) \rightarrow NiSO_4 \cdot 6H_2O(s) + H_2O(g)$

[8.753 g] = [8.192 g + (8.753 − 8.192 = 0.561 g)]

The 8.192 g of $NiSO_4 \cdot 6H_2O$ must contain $6 \times 0.561 = 3.366$ g H_2O.

Mass of anhydrous $NiSO_4$ = 8.192 g $NiSO_4 \cdot 6H_2O$ − 3.366 g $6H_2O$ = 4.826 g $NiSO_4$

2.153.   Mass of O = $0.6015 \text{ L} \times \dfrac{1.330 \text{ g O}}{1 \text{ L}} = 0.799995 \text{ g} = 0.8000$ g oxygen

$15.9994 \text{ amu O} \times \dfrac{3.177 \text{ g X}}{0.799995 \text{ g O}} = 63.5\underline{3}8 \text{ amu X} = 63.54$ amu

The atomic mass of X is 63.54 amu; X is copper.

CHAPTER 3

Calculations with Chemical Formulas and Equations

■ SOLUTIONS TO EXERCISES

Note on significant figures: If the final answer to a solution needs to be rounded off, it is given first with one nonsignificant figure, and the last significant figure is underlined. The final answer is then rounded to the correct number of significant figures. In multistep problems, intermediate answers are given with at least one nonsignificant figure; however, only the final answer has been rounded off.

3.1. a. NO_2 1 × AM of N   =   14.0067 amu

                2 × AM of O   =   2 × 15.9994   =   31.9988 amu

                MM of NO_2 =   46.0055 = 46.0 amu (3 s.f.)

      b. $C_6H_{12}O_6$ 6 × AM of C   =   6 × 12.011   =   72.066 amu

                12 × AM of H   =   12 × 1.0079   =   12.0948 amu

                6 × AM of O   =   6 × 15.9994   =   95.9964 amu

            MM of $C_6H_{12}O_6$ =   180.1572 amu = 180. amu (3 s.f.)

      c. NaOH   1 × AM of Na   =   22.98977 amu

                1 × AM of O   =   15.9994 amu

                1 × AM of H   =   1.0079 amu

                MM of NaOH   =   39.9971   amu = 40.0 amu (3 s.f.)

      d. $Mg(OH)_2$ 1 × AM of Mg   =   24.305 amu

                2 × AM of O   =   2 × 15.9994   =   31.9988 amu

                2 × AM of H   =   2 × 1.0079   =   2.0158 amu

                MM of $Mg(OH)_2$ =   58.3196 amu = 58.3 amu (3 s.f.)

3.2. a. The molecular model represents a molecule made up of one S and three O. The chemical formula is SO_3. Calculating the formula mass by using the same approach as in Example 3.1 in the text yields 80.1 amu.

      b. The molecular model represents one S, four O, and two H. The chemical formula is then H_2SO_4. The formula mass is 98.1 amu.

3.3.   a.   The atomic mass of Ca = 40.08 amu; thus, the molar mass = 40.08 g/mol, and 1 mol Ca = 6.022×10^{23} Ca atoms.

$$\text{Mass of one Ca} = \frac{40.08 \text{ g}}{1 \text{ mol Ca}} \times \frac{1 \text{ mol}}{6.022 \times 10^{23} \text{ atoms}} = 6.65\underline{5}6 \times 10^{-23}$$

$$= 6.656 \times 10^{-23} \text{ g/atom}$$

   b.   The molecular mass of C_2H_5OH, or C_2H_6O, = $(2 \times 12.01) + (6 \times 1.008) + 16.00 = 46.0\underline{6}8$. Its molar mass = 46.07 g/mol, and 1 mol = 6.022×10^{23} molecules of C_2H_6O.

$$\text{Mass of one } C_2H_6O = \frac{46.07 \text{ g}}{1 \text{ mol } C_2H_6O} \times \frac{1 \text{ mol}}{6.022 \times 10^{23} \text{ molecules}}$$

$$= 7.65\underline{0}3 \times 10^{-23} = 7.650 \times 10^{-23} \text{ g/molecule}$$

3.4.   The molar mass of H_2O_2 is 34.02 g/mol. Therefore,

$$0.909 \text{ mol } H_2O_2 \times \frac{34.02 \text{ g } H_2O_2}{1 \text{ mol } H_2O_2} = 30.\underline{9}2 = 30.9 \text{ g } H_2O_2$$

3.5.   The molar mass of HNO_3 is 63.01 g/mol. Therefore,

$$28.5 \text{ g } HNO_3 \times \frac{1 \text{ mol } HNO_3}{63.01 \text{ g } HNO_3} = 0.45\underline{2}3 = 0.452 \text{ mol } HNO_3$$

3.6.   Convert the mass of HCN from milligrams to grams. Then convert grams of HCN to moles of HCN. Finally, convert moles of HCN to the number of HCN molecules.

$$56 \text{ mg HCN} \times \frac{1 \text{ g}}{1000 \text{ mg}} \times \frac{1 \text{ mol HCN}}{27.02 \text{ g HCN}} \times \frac{6.022 \times 10^{23} \text{ HCN molecules}}{1 \text{ mol HCN}}$$

$$= 1.\underline{2}48 \times 10^{21} = 1.2 \times 10^{21} \text{ HCN molecules}$$

3.7.   The molecular mass of NH_4NO_3 = 80.05; thus, its molar mass = 80.05 g/mol. Hence

$$\text{Percent N} = \frac{28.02 \text{ g}}{80.05 \text{ g}} \times 100\% = 35.\underline{0}0 = 35.0\%$$

$$\text{Percent H} = \frac{4.032 \text{ g}}{80.05 \text{ g}} \times 100\% = 5.0\underline{3}6 = 5.04\%$$

$$\text{Percent O} = \frac{48.00 \text{ g}}{80.05 \text{ g}} \times 100\% = 59.\underline{9}6 = 60.0\%$$

3.8.   From the previous exercise, NH_4NO_3 is 35.0% N (fraction N = 0.350), so the mass of N in 48.5 g of NH_4NO_3 is

$$48.5 \text{ g } NH_4NO_3 \times (0.350 \text{ g N}/1 \text{ g } NH_4NO_3) = 16.\underline{9}75 = 17.0 \text{ g N}$$

3.9.   First, convert the mass of CO_2 to moles of CO_2. Next, convert this to moles of C (1 mol CO_2 is equivalent to 1 mol C). Finally, convert to mass of carbon, changing milligrams to grams first:

$$5.80 \times 10^{-3} \text{ g } CO_2 \times \frac{1 \text{ mol } CO_2}{44.01 \text{ g}} \times \frac{1 \text{ mol C}}{1 \text{ mol } CO_2} \times \frac{12.01 \text{ g C}}{1 \text{ mol C}} = 1.5\underline{8}3 \times 10^{-3} \text{g C}$$

Do the same series of calculations for water, noting that 1 mol H_2O contains 2 mol H.

$$1.58 \times 10^{-3} \text{ g } H_2O \times \frac{1 \text{ mol } H_2O}{18.02 \text{ g}} \times \frac{2 \text{ mol H}}{1 \text{ mol } H_2O} \times \frac{1.008 \text{ g H}}{1 \text{ mol H}} = 1.7\underline{6}7 \times 10^{-4} \text{g H}$$

The mass percentages of C and H can be calculated using the masses from the previous calculations:

$$\text{Percent C} = \frac{1.583 \text{ mg}}{3.87 \text{ mg}} \times 100\% = 40.\underline{9}0 = 40.9\% \text{ C}$$

$$\text{Percent H} = \frac{0.1767 \text{ mg}}{3.87 \text{ mg}} \times 100\% = 4.5\underline{6}58 = 4.57\% \text{ H}$$

The mass percentage of O can be determined by subtracting the sum of the above percentages from 100%:

$$\text{Percent O} = 100.000\% - (40.90 + 4.5658) = 54.\underline{5}342 = 54.5\% \text{ O}$$

3.10. Convert the masses to moles that are proportional to the subscripts in the empirical formula:

$$33.4 \text{ g S} \times \frac{1 \text{ mol S}}{32.07 \text{ g S}} = 1.0\underline{4}14 \text{ mol S}$$

$$(83.5 - 33.4) \text{ g O} \times \frac{1 \text{ mol O}}{16.00 \text{ g O}} = 3.1\underline{3}12 \text{ mol O}$$

Next, obtain the smallest integers from the moles by dividing each by the smallest number of moles:

$$\text{For O: } \frac{3.1312 \text{ mol O}}{1.0414 \text{ mol S}} = 3.01 \qquad \text{For S: } \frac{1.0414 \text{ mol S}}{1.0414 \text{ mol S}} = 1.00$$

The empirical formula is SO_3.

3.11. For a 100.0-g sample of benzoic acid, 68.8 g are C, 5.0 g are H, and 26.2 g are O. Using the molar masses, convert these masses to moles:

$$68.8 \text{ g C} \times \frac{1 \text{ mol C}}{12.01 \text{ g C}} = 5.7\underline{2}9 \text{ mol C}$$

$$5.0 \text{ g H} \times \frac{1 \text{ mol H}}{1.008 \text{ g H}} = 4.\underline{9}6 \text{ mol H}$$

$$26.2 \text{ g O} \times \frac{1 \text{ mol O}}{16.00 \text{ g O}} = 1.6\underline{3}8 \text{ mol O}$$

These numbers are in the same ratio as the subscripts in the empirical formula. They must be changed to integers. First, divide each one by the smallest number of moles:

$$\text{For C: } \frac{5.729}{1.638} = 3.497 \quad \text{For H: } \frac{4.96}{1.638} = 3.03 \quad \text{For O: } \frac{1.638}{1.638} = 1.000$$

Rounding off, we obtain $C_{3.5}H_{3.0}O_{1.0}$. Multiplying the numbers by 2 gives whole numbers, for an empirical formula of $C_7H_6O_2$.

3.12. For a 100.0-g sample of acetaldehyde, 54.5 g are C, 9.2 g are H, and 36.3 g are O. Using the molar masses, convert these masses to moles:

$$54.5 \text{ g C} \times \frac{1 \text{ mol C}}{12.01 \text{ g C}} = 4.5\underline{3}7 \text{ mol C}$$

$$9.2 \text{ g H} \times \frac{1 \text{ mol H}}{1.008 \text{ g H}} = 9.\underline{1}2 \text{ mol H}$$

$$36.3 \text{ g O} \times \frac{1 \text{ mol O}}{16.00 \text{ g O}} = 2.2\underline{6}8 \text{ mol O}$$

These numbers are in the same ratio as the subscripts in the empirical formula. They must be changed to integers. First, divide each one by the smallest number of moles:

For C: $\dfrac{4.537}{2.268} = 2.000$ For H: $\dfrac{9.12}{2.268} = 4.02$ For O: $\dfrac{2.268}{2.268} = 1.000$

Rounding off, we obtain C_2H_4O, the empirical formula, which is also the molecular formula.

3.13.
H_2	$+$	Cl_2	$\rightarrow$	$2HCl$
1 molec. (mol) H_2	$+$	1 molec. (mol) Cl_2	$\rightarrow$	2 molec. (mol) HCl (molec., mole interp.)
2.016 g H_2	$+$	70.9 g Cl_2	$\rightarrow$	2×36.5 g HCl (mass interp.)

3.14. Equation: $Na + H_2O \rightarrow 1/2 H_2 + NaOH$, or $2Na + 2H_2O \rightarrow H_2 + 2NaOH$. From this equation, one mole of Na corresponds to one-half mole of H_2, or two moles of Na corresponds to one mole of H_2. Therefore,

$$7.81 \text{ g H}_2 \times \frac{1 \text{ mol H}_2}{2.016 \text{ g H}_2} \times \frac{2 \text{ mol Na}}{1 \text{ mol H}_2} \times \frac{22.99 \text{ g Na}}{1 \text{ mol Na}} = 17\underline{8}.1 = 178 \text{ g Na}$$

3.15. Balanced equation: $2ZnS + 3O_2 \rightarrow 2ZnO + 2SO_2$

Convert grams of ZnS to moles of ZnS. Then determine the relationship between ZnS and O_2 (2ZnS is equivalent to $3O_2$). Finally, convert to mass of O_2.

$$5.00 \times 10^3 \text{g ZnS} \times \frac{1 \text{ mol ZnS}}{97.45 \text{ g ZnS}} \times \frac{3 \text{ mol O}_2}{2 \text{ mol ZnS}} \times \frac{32.00 \text{ g O}_2}{1 \text{ mol O}_2} \times \frac{1 \text{ kg}}{1000 \text{ g}}$$

$$= 2.4\underline{6}3 = 2.46 \text{ kg O}_2$$

3.16. Balanced equation: $2HgO \rightarrow 2Hg + O_2$

Convert the mass of O_2 to moles of O_2. Using the fact that one mole of O_2 is equivalent to two moles of Hg, determine the number of moles of Hg, and convert to mass of Hg.

$$6.47 \text{ g O}_2 \times \frac{1 \text{ mol O}_2}{32.00 \text{ g O}_2} \times \frac{2 \text{ mol Hg}}{1 \text{ mol O}_2} \times \frac{200.59 \text{ g Hg}}{1 \text{ mol Hg}} = 81.\underline{1}1 = 81.1 \text{ g Hg}$$

3.17. First, determine the limiting reactant by calculating the moles of $AlCl_3$ that would be obtained if Al and HCl were totally consumed:

$$0.15 \text{ mol Al} \times \frac{2 \text{ mol AlCl}_3}{2 \text{ mol Al}} = 0.1\underline{5}0 \text{ mol AlCl}_3$$

$$0.35 \text{ mol HCl} \times \frac{2 \text{ mol AlCl}_3}{6 \text{ mol HCl}} = 0.1\underline{1}66 \text{ mol AlCl}_3$$

Because the HCl produces the smaller amount of $AlCl_3$, the reaction will stop when HCl is totally consumed but before the Al is consumed. The limiting reactant is therefore HCl. The amount of $AlCl_3$ produced must be 0.1$\underline{1}$66, or 0.12 mol.

3.18. First, determine the limiting reactant by calculating the moles of ZnS produced by totally consuming Zn and S_8:

$$7.36 \text{ g Zn} \times \frac{1 \text{ mol Zn}}{65.38 \text{ g Zn}} \times \frac{8 \text{ mol ZnS}}{8 \text{ mol Zn}} = 0.11\underline{2}57 \text{ mol ZnS}$$

$$6.45 \text{ g S}_8 \times \frac{1 \text{ mol S}_8}{256.52 \text{ g S}_8} \times \frac{8 \text{ mol ZnS}}{1 \text{ mol S}_8} = 0.20\underline{1}2 \text{ mol ZnS}$$

The reaction will stop when Zn is totally consumed; S_8 is in excess, and not all of it is converted to ZnS. The limiting reactant is therefore Zn. Now convert the moles of ZnS obtained from the Zn to grams of ZnS:

$$0.11\underline{2}57 \text{ mol ZnS} \times \frac{97.45 \text{ g ZnS}}{1 \text{ mol ZnS}} = 10.\underline{9}7 = 11.0 \text{ g ZnS}$$

3.19. First, write the balanced equation:

$$CH_3OH + CO \rightarrow HC_2H_3O_2$$

Convert grams of each reactant to moles of acetic acid:

$$15.0 \text{ g CH}_3\text{OH} \times \frac{1 \text{ mol CH}_3\text{OH}}{32.04 \text{ g CH}_3\text{OH}} \times \frac{1 \text{ mol HC}_2\text{H}_3\text{O}_2}{1 \text{ mol CH}_3\text{OH}} = 0.468\underline{1} \text{ mol HC}_2\text{H}_3\text{O}_2$$

$$10.0 \text{ g CO} \times \frac{1 \text{ mol CO}}{28.01 \text{ g CO}} \times \frac{1 \text{ mol HC}_2\text{H}_3\text{O}_2}{1 \text{ mol CO}} = 0.35\underline{7}0 \text{ mol HC}_2\text{H}_3\text{O}_2$$

Thus, CO is the limiting reactant, and 0.3570 mol $HC_2H_3O_2$ is obtained. The theoretical mass of product is

$$0.35\underline{7}0 \text{ mol HC}_2\text{H}_3\text{O}_2 \times \frac{60.05 \text{ g HC}_2\text{H}_3\text{O}_2}{1 \text{ mol HC}_2\text{H}_3\text{O}_2} = 21.\underline{4}4 = 21.4 \text{ g HC}_2\text{H}_3\text{O}_2$$

The percentage yield is

$$\frac{19.1 \text{ g actual yield}}{21.44 \text{ g theoretical yield}} \times 100\% = 89.\underline{0}9 = 89.1\%$$

■ ANSWERS TO CONCEPT CHECKS

3.1.   a.   Each tricycle has one seat, so you have a total of 1.5 mol of seats.

   b.   Each tricycle has three tires, so you have 1.5 mol × 3 = 4.5 mol of tires.

   c.   Each $Mg(OH)_2$ has two OH^- ions, so there are 1.5 mol × 2 = 3.0 mol OH^- ions.

3.2.   a.   When conducting this type of experiment, you are assuming that all of the carbon and hydrogen show up in the CO_2 and H_2O, respectively. In this experiment, where all of the carbon and hydrogen do not show up, when you analyze the CO_2 for carbon and H_2O for hydrogen, you find that the masses in the products are less than those in the carbon and hydrogen you started with.

   b.   Since you collected less carbon and hydrogen than were present in the original sample, the calculated mass percentage will be less than the expected (real) value. For example, say you have a 10.0-g sample that contains 7.5 g of carbon. You run the experiment on the 10.0-g sample and collect only 5.0 g of carbon. The calculated percent carbon based on your experimental results would be 50% instead of the correct amount of 75%.

3.3.   a. $C_2H_8O_2$ is not an empirical formula because each of the subscripts can be divided by 2 to obtain a possible empirical formula of CH_4O. (The empirical formula is not the <u>smallest</u> integer ratio of subscripts.)

   b. $C_{1.5}H_4$ is not a correct empirical formula because one of the subscripts is not an integer. Multiply each of the subscripts by 2 to obtain the possible empirical formula C_3H_8. (Since the subscript of carbon is the decimal number 1.5, the empirical formula is not the smallest <u>integer</u> ratio of subscripts.)

   c.   Yes, the empirical formula and the molecular formula can be the same, as is the case in this problem, where the formula is written with the smallest integer subscripts.

3.4.   a.   Correct. Coefficients in balanced equations can represent amounts in atoms and molecules.

   b.   Incorrect. The coefficients in a balanced chemical equation do not represent amounts in grams. One gram of carbon and one gram of oxygen represent different molar amounts.

   c.   Incorrect. The coefficients in a balanced chemical equation do not represent amounts in grams. Furthermore, the data do not support the law of mass conservation.

   d.   Correct. You might initially think this is an incorrect representation; however, 12 g of C, 32 g of O_2, and 44 g of CO_2 all represent one mole of the substance, so the relationship of the chemical equation is obeyed.

   e.   Correct. The coefficients in balanced equations can represent amounts in moles.

   f.   Incorrect. The amount of O_2 present is not enough to react completely with one mole of carbon. Only one-half of the carbon would react, and one-half mole of CO_2 would form.

   g.   Incorrect. In this representation, oxygen is being shown as individual atoms of O, not as molecules of O_2, so the drawings are not correctly depicting the chemical reaction.

   h.   Correct. The molecular models correctly depict a balanced chemical reaction since the same number of atoms of each element appears on both sides of the equation.

3.5.   a.   The balanced chemical equation stipulates that for 7 mol of ReO_3 to form, the molar ratio of Re to Re_2O_7 must be 1 to 3. Statement a is false.

        b.   Rhenium is in excess by 2 moles. The rhenium(VII) oxide is the limiting reagent. Statement b is false.

        c.   Statement c implies that 3 moles of rhenium(VII) oxide actually reacts with at least enough Re or even an excess of Re. According to the balanced equation, 7 mol of ReO_3 will then form. Statement c is true and is the best reason that 7 mol of ReO_3 are produced during the reaction.

        d.   This is equivalent to statement b and it also is false.

        e.   The excess Re undergoes no further reaction since it is limited by how much rhenium(VII) is present. Statement c is false.

3.6.   a. $X_2(g) + 2Y(g) \rightarrow 2XY(g)$

        b.   Since the product consists of a combination of X and Y in a 1:1 ratio, it must consist of two atoms hooked together. If you count the total number of X atoms (split apart the X_2 molecules) and Y atoms present prior to the reaction, you find that there are four X atoms and three Y atoms. From these starting quantities, you are limited to three XY molecules and left with an unreacted X. Option #1 represents this situation and is therefore the correct answer.

        c.   Since $Y(g)$ was completely used up during the course of the reaction, it is the limiting reactant.

■ ANSWERS TO SELF-ASSESSMENT AND REVIEW QUESTIONS

3.1.   The molecular mass is the sum of the atomic masses of all the atoms in a molecule of the substance whereas the formula mass is the sum of the atomic masses of all the atoms in one formula unit of the compound, whether the compound is molecular or not. A given substance could have both a molecular mass and a formula mass if it existed as discrete molecules.

3.2.   To obtain the formula mass of a substance, sum up the atomic masses of all atoms in the formula of the compound.

3.3.   A mole of N_2 contains Avogadro's number (6.02×10^{23}) of N_2 molecules and $2 \times 6.02 \times 10^{23}$ N atoms. One mole of $Fe_2(SO_4)_3$ contains three moles of SO_4^{2-} ions, and it contains twelve moles of O atoms.

3.4.   A sample of the compound of known mass is burned, and CO_2 and H_2O are obtained as products. Next, you relate the masses of CO_2 and H_2O to the masses of carbon and hydrogen. Then you calculate the mass percentages of C and H. You find the mass percentage of O by subtracting the mass percentages of C and H from 100.

3.5.   The empirical formula is obtained from the percentage composition by assuming for the purposes of the calculation a sample of 100 g of the substance. Then the mass of each element in the sample equals the numerical value of the percentage. Convert the masses of the elements to moles of the elements using the atomic mass of each element. Divide the moles of each by the smallest number to obtain the smallest ratio of each atom. If necessary, find a whole-number factor to multiply these results by to obtain integers for the subscripts in the empirical formula.

3.6. The empirical formula is the formula of a substance written with the smallest integer (whole-number) subscripts. Each of the subscripts in the formula $C_6H_{12}O_2$ can be divided by 2, so the empirical formula of the compound is C_3H_6O.

3.7. The number of empirical formula units in a compound, n, equals the molecular mass divided by the empirical formula mass.

$$n = \frac{34.0 \text{ amu}}{17.0 \text{ amu}} = 2.00$$

The molecular formula of hydrogen peroxide is therefore $(HO)_2$, or H_2O_2.

3.8. The coefficients in a chemical equation can be interpreted directly in terms of molecules or moles. For the mass interpretation, you will need the molar masses of CH_4, O_2, CO_2, and H_2O, which are 16.0, 32.0, 44.0, and 18.0 g/mol, respectively. A summary of the three interpretations is given below the balanced equation:

CH_4	+	$2O_2$	$\rightarrow$	CO_2	+	$2H_2O$
1 molecule	+	2 molecules	$\rightarrow$	1 molecule	+	2 molecules
1 mole	+	2 moles	$\rightarrow$	1 mole	+	2 moles
16.0 g	+	2×32.0 g	$\rightarrow$	44.0 g	+	2×18.0 g

3.9. A chemical equation yields the mole ratio of a reactant to a second reactant or product. Once the mass of a reactant is converted to moles, this can be multiplied by the appropriate mole ratio to give the moles of a second reactant or product. Multiplying this number of moles by the appropriate molar mass gives mass. Thus, the masses of two different substances are related by a chemical equation.

3.10. The limiting reactant is the reactant that is entirely consumed when the reaction is complete. Because the reaction stops when the limiting reactant is used up, the moles of product are always determined by the starting number of moles of the limiting reactant.

3.11. Two examples are given in the book. The first involves making cheese sandwiches. Each sandwich requires two slices of bread and one slice of cheese. The limiting reactant is the cheese because some bread is left unused. The second example is assembling automobiles. Each auto requires one steering wheel, four tires, and other components. The limiting reactant is the tires, since they will run out first.

3.12. Since the theoretical yield represents the maximum amount of product that can be obtained by a reaction from given amounts of reactants under any conditions, in an actual experiment you can never obtain more than this amount.

3.13. The answer is a, 3.27 g of NH_3.

3.14. The answer is b, 1 g of formaldehyde.

3.15. The answer is d, 4.85×10^{24} atoms.

3.16. The answer is a, $C_3H_4O_3$.

■ ANSWERS TO CONCEPTUAL PROBLEMS

3.19.   a. $3H_2(g) + N_2(g) \rightarrow 2NH_3(g)$

       b.   Since there is no H_2 present in the container, it was entirely consumed during the reaction, which makes it the limiting reactant.

       c.   According to the chemical reaction, three molecules of H_2 are required for every molecule of N_2. Since there are two molecules of unreacted N_2, you would need six additional molecules of H_2 to complete the reaction.

3.21.   a.   This answer is unreasonable because 1.0×10^{-3} g is too small a mass for 0.33 mol of an element. For example, 0.33 mol of hydrogen (as H_2), the lightest element, would have a mass of 0.67 g.

       b.   This answer is unreasonable because 1.80×10^{-10} g is too large for one water molecule. (The mass of one water molecule is 2.99×10^{-23} g.)

       c.   This answer is reasonable because 3.01×10^{23} is one-half of Avogadro's number.

       d.   This answer is unreasonable because the units for molar mass should be g/mol, so this quantity is 1000 times too large.

3.23.   a.   The limiting reactant would be the charcoal because the air would supply as much oxygen as is needed.

       b.   The limiting reactant would be the magnesium because the beaker would contain much more water than is needed for the reaction (approximately 18 mL of water is 1 mole).

       c.   The limiting reactant would be the H_2 because the air could supply as much nitrogen as is needed.

3.25.   a.   The problem is that Avogadro's number was inadvertently used for the molar mass of calcium, which should be 40.08 g/mol. The correct calculation is

$$27.0 \text{ g Ca} \times \frac{1 \text{ mol Ca}}{40.08 \text{ g Ca}} = 0.673\underline{6} = 0.674 \text{ mol Ca}$$

       b.   The problem here is an incorrect mole ratio. There are 2 mol K^+ ions per 1 mol K_2SO_4. The correct calculation is

$$2.5 \text{ mol } K_2SO_4 \times \frac{2 \text{ mol } K^+ \text{ ions}}{1 \text{ mol } K_2SO_4} \times \frac{6.022 \times 10^{23} \text{ } K^+ \text{ ions}}{1 \text{ mol } K^+ \text{ ions}}$$

$$= 3.0\underline{1} \times 10^{24} = 3.0 \times 10^{24} \text{ } K^+ \text{ ions}$$

       c.   The problem here is an incorrect mole ratio. The result should be

$$0.50 \text{ mol Na} \times \frac{2 \text{ mol } H_2O}{2 \text{ mol Na}} = 0.50 \text{ mol } H_2O$$

■ SOLUTIONS TO PRACTICE PROBLEMS

Note on significant figures: If the final answer to a solution needs to be rounded off, it is given first with one nonsignificant figure, and the last significant figure is underlined. The final answer is then rounded to the correct number of significant figures. In multistep problems, intermediate answers are given with at least one nonsignificant figure; however, only the final answer has been rounded off.

3.27.   a.   FM of CH_3OH = AM of C + 4(AM of H) + AM of O

= 12.01 amu + (4 × 1.008 amu) + 16.00 amu
= 32.0$\underline{4}$2 = 32.0 amu (3 s.f.)

b.   FM of NO_3 = AM of N + 3(AM of O)

= 14.01 amu + (3 × 16.00 amu) = 62.01 = 62.0 amu (3 s.f.)

c.   FM of K_2CO_3 = 2(AM of K) + AM of C + 3(AM of O)

= (2 × 39.10 amu) + 12.01 amu + (3 × 16.00 amu)
= 138.2$\underline{1}$0 = 138 amu (3 s.f.)

d.   FM of $Ni_3(PO_4)_2$ = 3(AM of Ni) + 2(AM of P) + 8(AM of O)

= (3 × 58.70 amu) + (2 × 30.97 amu) + (8 × 16.00 amu)
= 366.0$\underline{4}$0 = 366 amu (3 s.f.)

3.29.   a. SO_2 1 × AM of S   =   32.07 amu

2 × AM of O   =   2 × 16.00   = $\underline{32.00\ amu}$

MM of SO_2 =   64.$\underline{0}$7 amu = 64.1 amu (3 s.f.)

b. PCl_3 1 × AM of P   =   30.97 amu

3 × AM of Cl   =   3 × 35.45   = $\underline{106.35\ amu}$

MM of PCl_3 =   137.32 amu = 137 amu (3 s.f.)

3.31.   First, find the formula mass of NH_4NO_3 by adding the respective atomic masses. Then convert it to the molar mass:

FM of NH_4NO_3 = 2(AM of N) + 4(AM of H) + 3(AM of O)

= (2 × 14.01 amu) + (4 × 1.008 amu) + (3 × 16.00 amu)

= 80.0$\underline{5}$2 amu

The molar mass of NH_4NO_3 is 80.05 g/mol.

3.33.   a.   The atomic mass of Na equals 22.99 amu; thus, the molar mass equals 22.99 g/mol. Because 1 mol of Na atoms equals 6.022×10^{23} Na atoms, we calculate

$$\text{Mass of one Na atom} = \frac{22.99\ \text{g/mol}}{6.022 \times 10^{23}\ \text{atom/mol}} = 3.81\underline{7}7 \times 10^{-23}$$

$$= 3.818 \times 10^{-23}\ \text{g/atom}$$

b.   The atomic mass of N equals 14.01 amu; thus, the molar mass equals 14.01 g/mol. Because 1 mol of N atoms equals 6.022×10^{23} N atoms, we calculate

$$\text{Mass of one N atom} = \frac{14.01 \text{ g/mol}}{6.022 \times 10^{23} \text{ atom/mol}} = 2.32\underline{6}4 \times 10^{-23}$$

$$= 2.326 \times 10^{-23} \text{ g/atom}$$

c. The formula mass of $CH_3Cl = [12.01 + (3 \times 1.008) + 35.45] = 50.48$ amu; thus, the molar mass equals 50.48 g/mol. Because 1 mol of CH_3Cl molecules equals 6.022×10^{23} CH_3Cl molecules, we calculate

$$\text{Mass of one } CH_3Cl \text{ molecule} = \frac{50.48 \text{ g/mol}}{6.022 \times 10^{23} \text{ molecules/mol}} = 8.38\underline{2}6 \times 10^{-23}$$

$$= 8.383 \times 10^{-23} \text{ g/molecule}$$

d. The formula mass of $Hg(NO_3)_2 = 200.59 + (2 \times 14.01) + (6 \times 16.00)] = 324.61$ amu; thus, the molar mass equals 324.61 g/mol. Because 1 formula mass of $Hg(NO_3)_2$ equals 6.022×10^{23} $Hg(NO_3)_2$ formula units, we calculate

$$\text{Mass of one } Hg(NO_3)_2 = \frac{324.61 \text{ g/mol}}{6.022 \times 10^{23} \text{ units/mol}} = 5.39\underline{0}4 \times 10^{-22}$$

$$= 5.390 \times 10^{-22} \text{ g/unit}$$

3.35. First, find the formula mass (in amu) using the periodic table (inside front cover):

$$\text{FM of } (CH_3CH_2)_2O = (4 \times 12.01 \text{ amu}) + (10 \times 1.008 \text{ amu}) + 16.00 \text{ amu} = 74.12 \text{ amu}$$

$$\text{Mass of one } (CH_3CH_2)_2O \text{ molecule} = \frac{74.12 \text{ g/mol}}{6.022 \times 10^{23} \text{ molecules/mol}}$$

$$= 1.23\underline{0}8 \times 10^{-22} = 1.231 \times 10^{-22} \text{ g/molecule}$$

3.37. From the table of atomic masses, we obtain the following molar masses for parts a through d: Na = 22.99 g/mol; S = 32.07 g/mol; C = 12.01 g/mol; H = 1.008 g/mol; Cl = 35.45 g/mol; and N = 14.01 g/mol.

a. $0.15 \text{ mol Na} \times \dfrac{22.99 \text{ g}}{1 \text{ mol Na}} = 3.\underline{4}48 = 3.4 \text{ g Na}$

b. $0.594 \text{ mol S} \times \dfrac{32.07 \text{ g S}}{1 \text{ mol S}} = 19.\underline{0}4 = 19.0 \text{ g S}$

c. Using molar mass = 84.93 g/mol for CH_2Cl_2, we obtain

$$2.78 \text{ mol } CH_2Cl_2 \times \frac{84.93 \text{ g } CH_2Cl_2}{1 \text{ mol } CH_2Cl_2} = 23\underline{6}.1 = 236 \text{ g } CH_2Cl_2$$

d. Using molar mass = 68.14 g/mol for $(NH_4)_2S$, we obtain

$$38 \text{ mol } (NH_4)_2S \times \frac{68.14 \text{ g } (NH_4)_2S}{1 \text{ mol } (NH_4)_2S} = 2.\underline{5}8 \times 10^3 = 2.6 \times 10^3 \text{ g } (NH_4)_2S$$

3.39. First, find the molar mass of H_3BO_3: $(3 \times 1.008 \text{ amu}) + 10.81 \text{ amu} + (3 \times 16.00 \text{ amu}) = 61.83$. Therefore, the molar mass of $H_3BO_3 = 61.83$ g/mol. The mass of H_3BO_3 is calculated as follows:

$$0.543 \text{ mol } H_3BO_3 \times \frac{61.83 \text{ g } H_3BO_3}{1 \text{ mol } H_3BO_3} = 33.\underline{5}7 = 33.6 \text{ g } H_3BO_3$$

3.41.   From the table of atomic masses, we obtain the following rounded molar masses for parts a through d: C = 12.01 g/mol; Cl = 35.45 g/mol; H = 1.008 g/mol; Al = 26.98 g/mol; and O = 16.00 g/mol.

a. $2.86 \text{ g C} \times \dfrac{1 \text{ mol C}}{12.01 \text{ g C}} = 0.238\underline{1} = 0.238 \text{ mol C}$

b. $7.05 \text{ g Cl}_2 \times \dfrac{1 \text{ mol Cl}_2}{70.90 \text{ g Cl}_2} = 0.099\underline{4}3 = 0.0994 \text{ mol Cl}_2$

c.   The molar mass of C_4H_{10} = (4 × 12.01) + (10 × 1.008) = 58.12 g C_4H_{10}/mol C_4H_{10}. The mass of C_4H_{10} is calculated as follows:

$$76 \text{ g C}_4\text{H}_{10} \times \dfrac{1 \text{ mol C}_4\text{H}_{10}}{58.12 \text{ g C}_4\text{H}_{10}} = 1.\underline{3}07 = 1.3 \text{ mol C}_4\text{H}_{10}$$

d.   The molar mass of $Al_2(CO_3)_3$ = (2 × 26.98) + (3 × 12.01) + (9 × 16.00 g) = 233.99 g/mol $Al_2(CO_3)_3$. The mass of $Al_2(CO_3)_3$ is calculated as follows:

$$26.2 \text{ g Al}_2(\text{CO}_3)_3 \times \dfrac{1 \text{ mol Al}_2(\text{CO}_3)_3}{233.99 \text{ g Al}_2(\text{CO}_3)_3} = 0.111\underline{9} = 0.112 \text{ mol Al}_2(\text{CO}_3)_3$$

3.43.   Calculate the formula mass of calcium sulfate: 40.08 amu + 32.07 amu + (4 × 16.00 amu) = 136.15 amu. Therefore, the molar mass of $CaSO_4$ is 136.15 g/mol. Use this to convert the mass of $CaSO_4$ to moles:

$$0.791 \text{ g CaSO}_4 \times \dfrac{1 \text{ mol CaSO}_4}{136.15 \text{ g CaSO}_4} = 5.8\underline{0}9 \times 10^{-3} = 5.81 \times 10^{-3} \text{ mol CaSO}_4$$

Calculate the molecular mass of water: (2 × 1.008 amu) + 16.00 amu = 18.02 amu. Therefore, the molar mass of H_2O equals 18.02 g/mol. Use this to convert the rest of the sample to moles of water:

$$0.209 \text{ g H}_2\text{O} \times \dfrac{1 \text{ mol H}_2\text{O}}{18.02 \text{ g H}_2\text{O}} = 1.1\underline{5}9 \times 10^{-2} = 1.16 \times 10^{-2} \text{ mol H}_2\text{O}$$

Because 0.01159 mol is about twice 0.005811 mol, both numbers of moles are consistent with the formula, $CaSO_4 \bullet 2H_2O$.

3.45.   The following rounded atomic masses are used: Li = 6.94 g/mol; Br = 79.90 g/mol; N = 14.01 g/mol; H = 1.008 g/mol; Pb = 207.2 g/mol; Cr = 52.00 g/mol; O = 16.00 g/mol; and S = 32.07 g/mol. Also, Avogadro's number is 6.022×10^{23} atoms, so

a.   No. Li atoms = $8.21 \text{ g Li} \times \dfrac{6.022 \times 10^{23} \text{ atoms}}{6.941 \text{ g Li}} = 7.1\underline{2}2 \times 10^{23} = 7.12 \times 10^{23} \text{ atoms}$

b.   No. Br atoms = $32.0 \text{ g Br}_2 \times \dfrac{2 \times 6.022 \times 10^{23} \text{ atoms}}{(2 \times 79.90) \text{ g Br}_2} = 2.4\underline{1}2 \times 10^{23} = 2.41 \times 10^{23} \text{ atoms}$

c.   No. NH_3 molecules = $45 \text{ g NH}_3 \times \dfrac{6.022 \times 10^{23} \text{ molecules}}{17.03 \text{ g NH}_3} = 1.\underline{5}9 \times 10^{24}$

$= 1.6 \times 10^{24} \text{ molecules}$

d.   No. $PbCrO_4$ units $= 201$ g $PbCrO_4 \times \dfrac{6.022 \times 10^{23} \text{ units}}{323.2 \text{ g } PbCrO_4} = 3.7\underline{4}5 \times 10^{23}$

$\qquad = 3.75 \times 10^{23}$ units

e.   No. SO_4^{2-} ions $= 14.3$ g $Cr_2(SO_4)_3 \times \dfrac{3 \times 6.022 \times 10^{23} \text{ ions}}{392.21 \text{ g } Cr_2(SO_4)_3} = 6.5\underline{8}7 \times 10^{22}$

$\qquad = 6.59 \times 10^{22}$ ions

3.47.   Calculate the molecular mass of CCl_4: 12.01 amu $+ (4 \times 35.45 \text{ amu}) = 153.81$ amu. Use this and Avogadro's number to express it as 153.81 g/N_A in order to calculate the number of molecules:

$\qquad 7.58$ mg $CCl_4 \times \dfrac{1 \text{ g}}{1000 \text{ mg}} \times \dfrac{6.022 \times 10^{23} \text{ molecules}}{153.81 \text{ g } CCl_4} = 2.9\underline{6}8 \times 10^{19}$

$\qquad = 2.97 \times 10^{19}$ molecules

3.49.   Mass percentage carbon $= \dfrac{\text{mass of C in sample}}{\text{mass of sample}} \times 100\%$

Percent carbon $= \dfrac{1.584 \text{ g}}{1.836 \text{ g}} \times 100\% = 86.2\underline{7}4 = 86.27\%$

3.51.   Mass percentage phosphorus $= \dfrac{\text{mass of P in sample}}{\text{mass of sample}} \times 100\%$

Percent P $= \dfrac{1.72 \text{ mg}}{8.53 \text{ mg}} \times 100\% = 20.\underline{1}6 = 20.2\%$

3.53.   Start with the definition for percentage nitrogen, and rearrange this equation to find the mass of N in the fertilizer.

$\qquad$ Mass percentage nitrogen $= \dfrac{\text{mass of N in fertilizer}}{\text{mass of fertilizer}} \times 100\%$

$\qquad$ Mass N $= \dfrac{\text{mass \% N}}{100\%} \times \text{mass of fertilizer} = \dfrac{14.0\%}{100\%} \times 4.15 \text{ kg} = 0.58\underline{1}0 = 0.581$ kg N

3.55.   Convert moles to mass using the molar masses from the respective atomic masses. Then calculate the mass percentages from the respective masses.

$\qquad 0.0898$ mol Al $\times \dfrac{26.98 \text{ g Al}}{1 \text{ mol Al}} = 2.4\underline{2}2$ g Al

$\qquad 0.0381$ mol Mg $\times \dfrac{24.31 \text{ g Mg}}{1 \text{ mol Mg}} = 0.92\underline{6}2$ g Mg

$$\text{Percent Al} = \frac{\text{mass of Al}}{\text{mass of alloy}} = \frac{2.422 \text{ g Al}}{3.349 \text{ g alloy}} \times 100\% = 72.\underline{34} = 72.3\% \text{ Al}$$

$$\text{Percent Mg} = \frac{\text{mass of Mg}}{\text{mass of alloy}} = \frac{0.9262 \text{ g Mg}}{3.349 \text{ g alloy}} \times 100\% = 27.\underline{655} = 27.7\% \text{ Mg}$$

3.57. In each part, the numerator consists of the mass of the element in one mole of the compound; the denominator is the mass of one mole of the compound. Use the atomic weights of C = 12.01 g/mol; O = 16.00 g/mol; Na = 22.99 g/mol; H = 1.008 g/mol; P = 30.97 g/mol; Co = 58.93 g/mol; and N = 14.01 g/mol.

a. $$\text{Percent C} = \frac{\text{mass of C}}{\text{mass of CO}} = \frac{12.01 \text{ g C}}{28.01 \text{ g CO}} \times 100\% = 42.878 = 42.9\%$$

Percent O = 100.000% − 42.878%C = 57.122 = 57.1%

b. $$\text{Percent C} = \frac{\text{mass of C}}{\text{mass of CO}_2} = \frac{12.01 \text{ g C}}{44.01 \text{ g CO}_2} \times 100\% = 27.289 = 27.3\%$$

Percent O = 100.000% − 27.2$\underline{89}$% C = 72.711 = 72.7%

c. $$\text{Percent Na} = \frac{\text{mass of Na}}{\text{mass of NaH}_2\text{PO}_4} = \frac{22.99 \text{ g Na}}{119.98 \text{ g NaH}_2\text{PO}_4} \times 100\% = 19.161 = 19.2\%$$

$$\text{Percent H} = \frac{\text{mass of H}}{\text{mass of NaH}_2\text{PO}_4} = \frac{2.016 \text{ g H}}{119.98 \text{ g NaH}_2\text{PO}_4} \times 100\% = 1.6802 = 1.68\%$$

$$\text{Percent P} = \frac{\text{mass of P}}{\text{mass of NaH}_2\text{PO}_4} = \frac{30.97 \text{ g P}}{119.98 \text{ g NaH}_2\text{PO}_4} \times 100\% = 25.812 = 25.8\%$$

Percent O = 100.000% − (19.161 + 1.6802 + 25.812)% = 53.346 = 53.3%

d. $$\text{Percent Co} = \frac{\text{mass of Co}}{\text{mass of Co(NO}_3)_2} = \frac{58.93 \text{ g Co}}{182.95 \text{ g Co(NO}_3)_2} \times 100\% = 32.211 = 32.2\%$$

$$\text{Percent N} = \frac{\text{mass of N}}{\text{mass of Co(NO}_3)_2} = \frac{2 \times 14.01 \text{ g N}}{182.95 \text{ g Co(NO}_3)_2} \times 100\% = 15.316 = 15.3\%$$

Percent O = 100.000% − (32.211 + 15.316)% = 52.473 = 52.5%

3.59. The molecular model of toluene contains seven carbon atoms and eight hydrogen atoms, so the molecular formula of toluene is C_7H_8. The molar mass of toluene is 92.134 g/mol. The mass percentages are

$$\text{Percent C} = \frac{\text{mass of C}}{\text{mass of C}_7\text{H}_8} = \frac{7 \times 12.01 \text{ g}}{92.134 \text{ g}} \times 100\% = 91.247 = 91.2\%$$

Percent H = 100% − 91.247 = 8.753 = 8.75%

3.61. Find the moles of C in each amount in one-step operations. Calculate the moles of each compound using the molar mass; then multiply by the number of moles of C per mole of compound:

$$\text{Mol C (glucose)} = 6.01 \text{ g} \times \frac{1 \text{ mol}}{180.2 \text{ g}} \times \frac{6 \text{ mol C}}{1 \text{ mol glucose}} = 0.20\underline{0} \text{ mol}$$

$$\text{Mol C (ethanol)} = 5.85 \text{ g} \times \frac{1 \text{ mol}}{46.07 \text{ g}} \times \frac{2 \text{ mol C}}{1 \text{ mol ethanol}} = 0.25\underline{4} \text{ mol (more C)}$$

3.63. First, calculate the mass of C in the glycol by multiplying the mass of CO_2 by the molar mass of C and the reciprocal of the molar mass of CO_2. Next, calculate the mass of H in the glycol by multiplying the mass of H_2O by the molar mass of 2H and the reciprocal of the molar mass of H_2O. Then use the masses to calculate the mass percentages. Calculate O by difference.

$$9.06 \text{ mg CO}_2 \times \frac{1 \text{ mol CO}_2}{44.01 \text{ g CO}_2} \times \frac{12.01 \text{ g C}}{1 \text{ mol C}} = 2.4\underline{7}2 \text{ mg C}$$

$$5.58 \text{ mg H}_2\text{O} \times \frac{1 \text{ mol H}_2\text{O}}{18.02 \text{ g H}_2\text{O}} \times \frac{2 \text{ H}}{1 \text{ H}_2\text{O}} \times \frac{1.008 \text{ g H}}{1 \text{ mol H}} = 0.62\underline{4}3 \text{ mg H}$$

Mass O = 6.38 mg − (2.472 + 0.6243) = 3.2\underline{8}4 mg O

Percent C = (2.472 mg C/6.38 mg glycol) × 100% = 38.\underline{7}4 = 38.7%

Percent H = (0.6243 mg H/6.38 mg glycol) × 100% = 9.7\underline{8}5 = 9.79%

Percent O = (3.284 mg O/6.38 mg glycol) × 100% = 51.\underline{4}7 = 51.5%

3.65. Start by calculating the moles of Os and O; then divide each by the smaller number of moles to obtain integers for the empirical formula.

$$\text{Mol Os} = 2.16 \text{ g Os} \times \frac{1 \text{ mol Os}}{190.2 \text{ g Os}} = 0.011\underline{3}6 \text{ mol (smaller number)}$$

$$\text{Mol O} = (2.89 - 2.16) \text{ g O} \times \frac{1 \text{ mol O}}{16.00 \text{ g O}} = 0.04\underline{5}6 \text{ mol}$$

Integer for Os = 0.01136 ÷ 0.01136 = 1.0\underline{0}0

Integer for O = 0.0456 ÷ 0.01136 = 4.\underline{0}1

Within experimental error, the empirical formula is OsO_4.

3.67. Assume a sample of 100.0 g of potassium manganate. By multiplying this by the percentage composition, we obtain 39.6 g of K, 27.9 g of Mn, and 32.5 g of O. Convert each of these masses to moles by dividing by molar mass.

$$\text{Mol K} = 39.6 \text{ g K} \times \frac{1 \text{ mol K}}{39.10 \text{ g K}} = 1.0\underline{1}3 \text{ mol}$$

$$\text{Mol Mn} = 27.9 \text{ g Mn} \times \frac{1 \text{ mol Mn}}{54.94 \text{ g Mn}} = 0.50\underline{7}8 \text{ mol (smallest number)}$$

$$\text{Mol O} = 32.5 \text{ g O} \times \frac{1 \text{ mol O}}{16.00 \text{ g O}} = 2.0\underline{3}1 \text{ mol}$$

Now, divide each number of moles by the smallest number to obtain the smallest set of integers for the empirical formula.

Integer for K = 1.013 ÷ 0.5078 = 1.998, or 2

Integer for Mn = 0.5078 ÷ 0.5078 = 1.000, or 1

Integer for O = 2.031 ÷ 0.5078 = 3.999, or 4

The empirical formula is thus K_2MnO_4.

3.69. Assume a sample of 100.0 g of acrylic acid. By multiplying this by the percentage composition, we obtain 50.0 g C, 5.6 g H, and 44.4 g O. Convert each of these masses to moles by dividing by the molar mass.

$$\text{Mol C} = 50.0 \text{ g C} \times \frac{1 \text{ mol C}}{12.01 \text{ g C}} = 4.1\underline{6}3 \text{ mol}$$

$$\text{Mol H} = 5.6 \text{ g H} \times \frac{1 \text{ mol H}}{1.008 \text{ g H}} = 5.\underline{5}6 \text{ mol}$$

$$\text{Mol O} = 44.0 \text{ g O} \times \frac{1 \text{ mol O}}{16.00 \text{ g O}} = 2.7\underline{7}5 \text{ mol (smallest number)}$$

Now, divide each number of moles by the smallest number to obtain the smallest number of moles and the tentative integers for the empirical formula.

Tentative integer for C = 4.163 ÷ 2.775 = 1.50, or 1.5

Tentative integer for H = 5.56 ÷ 2.775 = 2.00, or 2

Tentative integer for O = 2.775 ÷ 2.775 = 1.00, or 1

Because 1.5 is not a whole number, multiply each tentative integer by 2 to obtain the final integer for the empirical formula:

C: 2 × 1.5 = 3

H: 2 × 2 = 4

O: 2 × 1 = 2

The empirical formula is thus $C_3H_4O_2$.

3.71. a. Assume for the calculation that you have 100.0 g; of this quantity, 92.25 g is C and 7.75 g is H. Now, convert these masses to moles:

$$92.25 \text{ g C} \times \frac{1 \text{ mol C}}{12.01 \text{ g C}} = 7.68\underline{1}09 \text{ mol C}$$

$$7.75 \text{ g H} \times \frac{1 \text{ mol H}}{1.008 \text{ g H}} = 7.6\underline{8}8 \text{ mol H}$$

Usually, you divide all the mole numbers by the smaller one, but in this case the mole numbers are equal, so the ratio of the number of C atoms to the number of H atoms is 1:1. Thus, the empirical formula for both compounds is CH.

b. Obtain *n*, the number of empirical formula units in the molecule, by dividing the molecular mass of 52.03 amu and 78.05 amu by the empirical formula mass of 13.018 amu:

$$\text{For 52.03: } n = \frac{52.03 \text{ amu}}{13.018 \text{ amu}} = 3.99\underline{68}, \text{ or } 4$$

$$\text{For 78.05: } n = \frac{78.05 \text{ amu}}{13.018 \text{ amu}} = 5.99\underline{55}, \text{ or } 6$$

The molecular formulas are as follows: for 52.03, $(CH)_4$ or C_4H_4; for 78.05, $(CH)_6$ or C_6H_6.

3.73. The formula mass corresponding to the empirical formula C_2H_6N may be found by adding the respective atomic masses.

Formula mass = $(2 \times 12.01 \text{ amu}) + (6 \times 1.008 \text{ amu}) + 14.01 \text{ amu} = 44.08 \text{ amu}$

Dividing the molecular mass by the formula mass gives the number of times the C_2H_6N unit occurs in the molecule. Because the molecular mass is an average of 88.5 ($[90 + 87] \div 2$), this quotient is

88.5 amu ÷ 44.1 amu = 2.$\underline{006}$, or 2

Therefore, the molecular formula is $(C_2H_6N)_2$, or $C_4H_{12}N_2$.

3.75. Assume a sample of 100.0 g of oxalic acid. By multiplying this by the percentage composition, we obtain 26.7 g C, 2.2 g H, and 71.1 g O. Convert each of these masses to moles by dividing by the molar mass.

$$\text{Mol C} = 26.7 \text{ g C} \times \frac{1 \text{ mol C}}{12.01 \text{ g C}} = 2.2\underline{23} \text{ mol}$$

$$\text{Mol H} = 2.2 \text{ g H} \times \frac{1 \text{ mol H}}{1.008 \text{ g H}} = 2.\underline{18} \text{ mol (smallest number)}$$

$$\text{Mol O} = 71.1 \text{ g O} \times \frac{1 \text{ mol O}}{16.00 \text{ g O}} = 4.4\underline{43} \text{ mol}$$

Now, divide each number of moles by the smallest number to obtain the smallest set of integers for the empirical formula.

Integer for C = 2.223 ÷ 2.18 = 1.02, or 1

Integer for H = 2.18 ÷ 2.18 = 1.00, or 1

Integer for O = 4.443 ÷ 2.18 = 2.0$\underline{38}$, or 2

The empirical formula is thus CHO_2. The formula mass corresponding to this formula may be found by adding the respective atomic masses:

Formula mass = 12.01 amu + 1.008 amu + $(2 \times 16.00 \text{ amu})$ = 45.02 amu

Dividing the molecular mass by the formula mass gives the number of times the CHO_2 unit occurs in the molecule. Because the molecular mass is 90 amu, this quotient is

90 amu ÷ 45.02 amu = 2.$\underline{00}$, or 2

The molecular formula is thus $(CHO_2)_2$, or $C_2H_2O_4$.

3.77.

C_2H_4	+	$3O_2$	$\rightarrow$	$2CO_2$	+	$2H_2O$
1 molecule C_2H_4	+	3 molecules O_2	$\rightarrow$	2 molecules CO_2	+	2 molecules H_2O
1 mole C_2H_4	+	3 moles O_2	$\rightarrow$	2 moles CO_2	+	2 moles H_2O
28.052 g C_2H_4	+	3×32.00 g O_2	$\rightarrow$	2×44.01 g CO_2	+	2×18.016 g H_2O

3.79. By inspecting the balanced equation, obtain a conversion factor of eight mol CO_2 to two mol C_4H_{10}. Multiply the given amount of 0.41 mol of C_4H_{10} by the conversion factor to obtain the moles of CO_2.

$$0.41 \text{ mol } C_4H_{10} \times \frac{8 \text{ mol } CO_2}{2 \text{ mol } C_4H_{10}} = 1.\underline{6}4 = 1.6 \text{ mol } CO_2$$

3.81. By inspecting the balanced equation, obtain a conversion factor of three mol O_2 to two mol Fe_2O_3. Multiply the given amount of 3.91 mol Fe_2O_3 by the conversion factor to obtain moles of O_2.

$$3.91 \text{ mol } Fe_2O_3 \times \frac{3 \text{ mol } O_2}{2 \text{ mol } Fe_2O_3} = 5.8\underline{6}5 = 5.87 \text{ mol } O_2$$

3.83. $3NO_2 + H_2O \rightarrow 2HNO_3 + NO$

Three moles of NO_2 are equivalent to two moles of HNO_3 (from equation).

One mole of NO_2 is equivalent to 46.01 g NO_2 (from molecular mass of NO_2).

One mole of HNO_3 is equivalent to 63.02 g HNO_3 (from molecular mass of HNO_3).

$$7.50 \text{ g } HNO_3 \times \frac{1 \text{ mol } HNO_3}{63.02 \text{ g } HNO_3} \times \frac{3 \text{ mol } NO_2}{2 \text{ mol } HNO_3} \times \frac{46.01 \text{ g } NO_2}{1 \text{ mol } NO_2} = 8.2\underline{1}3 = 8.21 \text{ g } NO_2$$

3.85. $WO_3 + 3H_2 \rightarrow W + 3H_2O$

One mole of W is equivalent to three moles of H_2 (from equation).

One mole of H_2 is equivalent to 2.016 g H_2 (from molecular mass of H_2).

One mole of W is equivalent to 183.8 g W (from atomic mass of W).

4.81 kg of H_2 is equivalent to 4.81×10^3 g of H_2.

$$4.81 \times 10^3 \text{ g } H_2 \times \frac{1 \text{ mol } H_2}{2.016 \text{ g } H_2} \times \frac{1 \text{ mol } W}{3 \text{ mol } H_2} \times \frac{183.85 \text{ g } W}{1 \text{ mol } W} = 1.4\underline{6}2 \times 10^5 = 1.46 \times 10^5 \text{ g } W$$

3.87. Write the equation, and set up the calculation below the equation (after calculating the two molecular masses):

$$CS_2 + 3Cl_2 \rightarrow CCl_4 + S_2Cl_2$$

$$62.7 \text{ g } Cl_2 \times \frac{1 \text{ mol } Cl_2}{70.90 \text{ g } Cl_2} \times \frac{1 \text{ mol } CS_2}{3 \text{ mol } Cl_2} \times \frac{76.15 \text{ g } CS_2}{1 \text{ mol } CS_2} 22.\underline{4}48 = 22.4 \text{ g } CS_2$$

3.89. Write the equation, and set up the calculation below the equation (after calculating the two molecular masses):

$$2N_2O_5 \rightarrow 4NO_2 + O_2$$

$$1.381 \text{ g O}_2 \times \frac{1 \text{ mol O}_2}{32.00 \text{ g O}_2} \times \frac{4 \text{ mol NO}_2}{1 \text{ mol O}_2} \times \frac{46.01 \text{ g NO}_2}{1 \text{ mol NO}_2} = 7.94\underline{2}48 = 7.942 \text{ g NO}_2$$

3.91. First determine whether KO_2 or H_2O is the limiting reactant by calculating the moles of O_2 that each would form if it were the limiting reactant. Identify the limiting reactant by the smaller number of moles of O_2 formed.

$$0.15 \text{ mol H}_2\text{O} \times \frac{3 \text{ mol O}_2}{2 \text{ mol H}_2\text{O}} = 0.2\underline{2}5 \text{ mol O}_2$$

$$0.25 \text{ mol KO}_2 \times \frac{3 \text{ mol O}_2}{4 \text{ mol KO}_2} = 0.1\underline{8}7 \text{ mol O}_2 \ (KO_2 \text{ is the limiting reactant.})$$

Moles of O_2 produced = 0.19 mol

3.93. First determine whether CO or H_2 is the limiting reactant by calculating the moles of CH_3OH that each would form if it were the limiting reactant. Identify the limiting reactant by the smaller number of moles of CH_3OH formed. Use the molar mass of CH_3OH to calculate the mass of CH_3OH formed. Then calculate the mass of the unconsumed reactant.

$$CO + 2H_2 \rightarrow CH_3OH$$

$$10.2 \text{ g H}_2 \times \frac{1 \text{ mol H}_2}{2.016 \text{ g H}_2} \times \frac{1 \text{ mol CH}_3\text{OH}}{2 \text{ mol H}_2} = 2.5\underline{2}9 \text{ mol CH}_3\text{OH}$$

$$35.4 \text{ g CO} \times \frac{1 \text{ mol CO}}{28.01 \text{ g CO}} \times \frac{1 \text{ mol CH}_3\text{OH}}{1 \text{ mol CO}} = 1.2\underline{6}3 \text{ mol CH}_3\text{OH}$$

CO is the limiting reactant.

$$\text{Mass CH}_3\text{OH formed} = 1.2\underline{6}3 \text{ mol CH}_3\text{OH} \times \frac{32.042 \text{ g CH}_3\text{OH}}{1 \text{ mol CH}_3\text{OH}} = 40.\underline{4}7 = 40.5 \text{ g CH}_3\text{OH}$$

Hydrogen is left unconsumed at the end of the reaction. The mass of H_2 that reacts can be calculated from the moles of product obtained:

$$1.2\underline{6}3 \text{ mol CH}_3\text{OH} \times \frac{2 \text{ mol H}_2}{1 \text{ mol CH}_3\text{OH}} \times \frac{2.016 \text{ g H}_2}{1 \text{ mol H}_2} = 5.0\underline{9}2 \text{ g H}_2$$

Unreacted H_2 = 10.2 g total H_2 − 5.092 g reacted H_2 = 5.$\underline{1}$08 = 5.1 g H_2

3.95. First, determine which of the three reactants is the limiting reactant by calculating the moles of $TiCl_4$ that each would form if it were the limiting reactant. Identify the limiting reactant by the smallest number of moles of $TiCl_4$ formed. Use the molar mass of $TiCl_4$ to calculate the mass of $TiCl_4$ formed.

$$3TiO_2 + 4C + 6Cl_2 \rightarrow 3TiCl_4 + 2CO_2 + 2CO$$

$$4.15 \text{ g TiO}_2 \times \frac{1 \text{ mol TiO}_2}{79.88 \text{ g TiO}_2} \times \frac{3 \text{ mol TiCl}_4}{3 \text{ mol TiO}_2} = 0.051\underline{9}5 \text{ mol TiCl}_4$$

$$5.67 \text{ g C} \times \frac{1 \text{ mol C}}{12.01 \text{ g C}} \times \frac{3 \text{ mol TiCl}_4}{4 \text{ mol C}} = 0.35\underline{4}07 \text{ mol TiCl}_4$$

$$6.78 \text{ g Cl}_2 \times \frac{1 \text{ mol Cl}_2}{70.90 \text{ g Cl}_2} \times \frac{3 \text{ mol TiCl}_4}{6 \text{ mol Cl}_2} = 0.047\underline{8}1 \text{ mol TiCl}_4$$

Cl_2 is the limiting reactant.

$$\text{Mass TiCl}_4 \text{ formed} = 0.047\underline{8}1 \text{ mol TiCl}_4 \times \frac{189.68 \text{ g TiCl}_4}{1 \text{ mol TiCl}_4} = 9.0\underline{6}8 = 9.07 \text{ g TiCl}_4$$

3.97. First, determine which of the two reactants is the limiting reactant by calculating the moles of aspirin that each would form if it were the limiting reactant. Identify the limiting reactant by the smallest number of moles of aspirin formed. Use the molar mass of aspirin to calculate the theoretical yield in grams of aspirin. Then calculate the percentage yield.

$$C_7H_6O_3 + C_4H_6O_3 \rightarrow C_9H_8O_4 + C_2H_4O_2$$

$$2.00 \text{ g C}_7H_6O_3 \times \frac{1 \text{ mol C}_7H_6O_3}{138.12 \text{ g C}_7H_6O_3} \times \frac{1 \text{ mol C}_9H_8O_4}{1 \text{ mol C}_7H_6O_3} = 0.014\underline{4}8 \text{ mol C}_9H_8O_4$$

$$4.00 \text{ g C}_4H_6O_3 \times \frac{1 \text{ mol C}_4H_6O_3}{102.09 \text{ g C}_4H_6O_3} \times \frac{1 \text{ mol C}_9H_8O_4}{1 \text{ mol C}_4H_6O_3} = 0.039\underline{1}8 \text{ mol C}_9H_8O_4$$

Thus, $C_7H_6O_3$ is the limiting reactant. The theoretical yield of $C_9H_8O_4$ is

$$0.014\underline{4}8 \text{ mol C}_9H_8O_4 \times \frac{180.15 \text{ g C}_9H_8O_4}{1 \text{ mol C}_9H_8O_4} = 2.6\underline{0}9 \text{ g C}_9H_8O_4$$

The percentage yield is

$$\text{Percentage yield} = \frac{\text{actual yield}}{\text{theoretical yield}} \times 100\% = \frac{1.86 \text{ g}}{2.609 \text{ g}} \times 100\% = 71.\underline{2}9 = 71.3\%$$

■ SOLUTIONS TO GENERAL PROBLEMS

3.99. For 1 mol of caffeine, there are eight mol of C, ten mol of H, four mol of N, and two mol of O. Convert these amounts to masses by multiplying them by their respective molar masses:

8 mol C × 12.01 g C/1 mol C	=	96.08 g C
10 mol H × 1.008 g H/1 mol H	=	10.08 g H
4 mol N × 14.01 g N/1 mol N	=	56.04 g N
2 mol O × 16.00 g O/1 mol O	=	32.00 g O
1 mol of caffeine (total)	=	194.20 g (molar mass)

Each mass percentage is calculated by dividing the mass of the element by the molar mass of caffeine and multiplying by 100 percent: Mass percentage = (mass element ÷ mass caffeine) × 100%.

Mass percentage C = (96.08 g ÷ 194.20 g) × 100% = 49.5% (3 s.f.)

Mass percentage H = (10.08 g ÷ 194.20 g) × 100% = 5.19% (3 s.f.)

Mass percentage N = (56.04 g ÷ 194.20 g) × 100% = 28.9% (3 s.f.)

Mass percentage O = (32.00 g ÷ 194.20 g) × 100% = 16.5% (3 s.f.)

3.101. Assume a sample of 100.0 g of *p*-dichlorobenzene. By multiplying this by the percentage composition, we obtain 49.1 g C, 2.7 g of H, and 48.2 g of Cl. Convert each mass to moles by dividing by the molar mass:

$$49.1 \text{ g C} \times \frac{1 \text{ mol C}}{12.01 \text{ g C}} = 4.0\underline{8}8 \text{ mol C}$$

$$2.7 \text{ g H} \times \frac{1 \text{ mol H}}{1.008 \text{ g H}} = 2.\underline{6}8 \text{ mol H}$$

$$48.2 \text{ g Cl} \times \frac{1 \text{ mol Cl}}{35.45 \text{ g Cl}} = 1.3\underline{6}0 \text{ mol Cl}$$

Divide each number of moles by the smallest number to obtain the smallest set of integers for the empirical formula.

Integer for C = 4.088 mol ÷ 1.360 mol = 3.00, or 3

Integer for H = 2.68 mol ÷ 1.360 mol = 1.97, or 2

Integer for Cl = 1.360 mol ÷ 1.360 mol = 1.00, or 1

The empirical formula is thus C_3H_2Cl. Find the formula mass by adding the atomic masses:

Formula mass = (3 × 12.01 amu) + (2 × 1.008 amu) + 35.45 amu = 73.4\underline{9}6 = 73.50 amu

Divide the molecular mass by the formula mass to find the number of times the C_3H_2Cl unit occurs in the molecule. Because the molecular mass is 147 amu, this quotient is

147 amu ÷ 73.50 amu = 2.00, or 2

The molecular formula is $(C_3H_2Cl)_2$, or $C_6H_4Cl_2$.

3.103. Find the percentage composition of C and S from the analysis:

$$0.01665 \text{ g CO}_2 \times \frac{1 \text{ mol CO}_2}{44.01 \text{ g CO}_2} \times \frac{1 \text{ mol C}}{1 \text{ mol CO}_2} \times \frac{12.01 \text{ g C}}{1 \text{ mol C}} = 0.00454\underline{4} \text{ g C}$$

Percent C = (0.004544 g C ÷ 0.00796 g comp.) × 100% = 57.\underline{0}9%

$$0.01196 \text{ g BaSO}_4 \times \frac{1 \text{ mol BaSO}_4}{233.39 \text{ g BaSO}_4} \times \frac{1 \text{ mol S}}{1 \text{ mol BaSO}_4} \times \frac{32.07 \text{ g S}}{1 \text{ mol S}} = 0.00164\underline{3} \text{ g S}$$

Percent S = (0.001643 g S ÷ 0.00431 g comp.) × 100% = 38.\underline{1}2%

Percent H = 100.00% − (57.09 + 38.12)% = 4.\underline{7}9%

We now obtain the empirical formula by calculating moles from the grams corresponding to each mass percentage of element:

$$57.09 \text{ g C} \times \frac{1 \text{ mol C}}{12.01 \text{ g C}} = 4.75\underline{4} \text{ mol C}$$

$$38.12 \text{ g S} \times \frac{1 \text{ mol S}}{32.07 \text{ g S}} = 1.18\underline{9} \text{ mol S}$$

$$4.79 \text{ g H} \times \frac{1 \text{ mol H}}{1.008 \text{ g H}} = 4.7\underline{52} \text{ mol H}$$

Dividing the moles of the elements by the smallest number (1.189), we obtain for C: 3.997, or 4; for S: 1.000, or 1; and for H: 3.996, or 4. Thus, the empirical formula is C_4H_4S (formula mass = 84). Because the formula mass was given as 84 amu, the molecular formula is also C_4H_4S.

3.105. For g $CaCO_3$, use this equation: $CaCO_3 + H_2C_2O_4 \rightarrow CaC_2O_4 + H_2O + CO_2$.

$$0.469 \text{ g CaC}_2O_4 \times \frac{1 \text{ mol CaC}_2O_4}{128.10 \text{ g CaC}_2O_4} \times \frac{1 \text{ mol CaCO}_3}{1 \text{ mol CaC}_2O_4} \times \frac{100.09 \text{ g CaCO}_3}{1 \text{ mol CaCO}_3}$$

$$= 0.36\underline{64} \text{ g CaCO}_3$$

$$\text{Mass percentage CaCO}_3 = \frac{\text{mass CaCO}_3}{\text{mass limestone}} \times 100\% = \frac{0.3664 \text{ g}}{0.438 \text{ g}} \times 100\%$$

$$= 83.\underline{66} = 83.7\%$$

3.107. Calculate the theoretical yield using this equation: $2C_2H_4 + O_2 \rightarrow 2C_2H_4O$.

$$10.6 \text{ g C}_2H_4 \times \frac{1 \text{ mol C}_2H_4}{28.05 \text{ g C}_2H_4} \times \frac{2 \text{ mol C}_2H_4O}{2 \text{ mol C}_2H_4} \times \frac{44.05 \text{ g C}_2H_4O}{1 \text{ mol C}_2H_4O} = 16.\underline{65} \text{ g C}_2H_4O$$

$$\text{Percentage yield} = \frac{\text{actual yield}}{\text{theoretical yield}} \times 100\% = \frac{9.91 \text{ g}}{16.65 \text{ g}} \times 100\% = 59.\underline{53} = 59.5\%$$

3.109. To find Zn, use these equations:

$$2C + O_2 \rightarrow 2CO \text{ and } ZnO + CO \rightarrow Zn + CO_2$$

Two moles of C produces 2 mol CO; because 1 mol ZnO reacts with 1 mol CO, 2 mol ZnO will react with 2 mol CO. Thus, 2 mol C is equivalent to 2 mol ZnO, or 1 mol C is equivalent to 1 mol ZnO.

Using this to calculate mass of C from mass of ZnO, we have

$$75.0 \text{ g ZnO} \times \frac{1 \text{ mol ZnO}}{81.39 \text{ g ZnO}} \times \frac{1 \text{ mol C}}{1 \text{ mol ZnO}} \times \frac{12.01 \text{ g C}}{1 \text{ mol C}} = 11.\underline{07} \text{ g C}$$

Thus, all of the ZnO is used up in reacting with just 11.07 g of C, making ZnO the limiting reactant. Use the mass of ZnO to calculate the mass of Zn formed:

$$75.0 \text{ g ZnO} \times \frac{1 \text{ mol ZnO}}{81.39 \text{ g ZnO}} \times \frac{1 \text{ mol Zn}}{1 \text{ mol ZnO}} \times \frac{65.39 \text{ g Zn}}{1 \text{ mol Zn}} = 60.\underline{256} = 60.3 \text{ g Zn}$$

3.111. For $CaO + 3C \rightarrow CaC_2 + CO$, find the limiting reactant in terms of moles of CaC_2 obtainable:

$$\text{Mol } CaC_2 = 2.60 \times 10^3 \text{ g C} \times \frac{1 \text{ mol C}}{12.01 \text{ g C}} \times \frac{1 \text{ mol } CaC_2}{3 \text{ mol C}} = 72.\underline{1}6 \text{ mol}$$

$$\text{Mol } CaC_2 = 2.60 \times 10^3 \text{ g CaO} \times \frac{1 \text{ mol CaO}}{56.08 \text{ g CaO}} \times \frac{1 \text{ mol } CaC_2}{1 \text{ mol CaO}} = 46.\underline{3}62 \text{ mol}$$

Because CaO is the limiting reactant, calculate the mass of CaC_2 from it:

$$\text{Mass } CaC_2 = 46.\underline{3}62 \text{ mol } CaC_2 \times \frac{64.10 \text{ g } CaC_2}{1 \text{ mol } CaC_2} = 2.9\underline{7}1 \times 10^3 = 2.97 \times 10^3 \text{ g } CaC_2$$

3.113. From the equation $2Na + H_2O \rightarrow 2NaOH + H_2$, convert mass of H_2 to mass of Na, and then use the mass to calculate the percentage:

$$0.108 \text{ g } H_2 \times \frac{1 \text{ mol } H_2}{2.016 \text{ g } H_2} \times \frac{2 \text{ mol Na}}{1 \text{ mol } H_2} \times \frac{22.99 \text{ g Na}}{1 \text{ mol Na}} = 2.4\underline{6}3 \text{ g Na}$$

$$\text{Percent Na} = \frac{\text{mass Na}}{\text{mass amalgam}} \times 100\% = \frac{2.463 \text{ g}}{15.23 \text{ g}} \times 100\% = 16.\underline{1}7 = 16.2\%$$

3.115. The mass spectrometer measures the masses of positive ions produced from a very small sample and displays the data as a mass spectrum. This mass spectrum can be used to identify a substance or to obtain the molecular formula of a compound. The mass spectrum contains a wealth of information about molecular structure.

■ SOLUTIONS TO STRATEGY PROBLEMS

3.117.   a. $48 \text{ } O_2 \text{ molecules} \times \dfrac{2 \text{ } H_2 \text{ molec}}{1 \text{ } O_2 \text{ molec}} = 96 \text{ } H_2 \text{ molecules}$

       b. $5 \text{ mol } H_2O \times \dfrac{1 \text{ mol } O_2}{2 \text{ mol } H_2O} = 2.5 \text{ mol } O_2$

            $5 \text{ mol } H_2O \times \dfrac{2 \text{ mol } H_2}{2 \text{ mol } H_2O} = 5.0 \text{ mol } H_2$

       c. $37.5 \text{ g } O_2 \times \dfrac{4.0 \text{ g } H_2}{32 \text{ g } O_2} = 4.\underline{6}8 = 4.7 \text{ g } H_2$

       d.   The mass of water formed is $4.0 \text{ g} + 32 \text{ g} = 3\underline{6}.0 \text{ g}$

            $30.0 \text{ g } H_2O \times \dfrac{32 \text{ g } O_2}{36 \text{ g } H_2O} = 2\underline{6}.6 = 27 \text{ g } O_2$

            $30.0 \text{ g } H_2O \times \dfrac{4.0 \text{ g } H_2}{36 \text{ g } H_2O} = 3.\underline{3}3 = 3.3 \text{ g } H_2$

3.119.   a.   First, determine the limiting reactant.

$$25 \text{ g H}_2\text{SO}_4 \times \frac{1 \text{ mol H}_2\text{SO}_4}{98.086 \text{ g}} \times \frac{1 \text{ mol K}_2\text{SO}_4}{1 \text{ mol H}_2\text{SO}_4} \times \frac{174.27 \text{ g}}{1 \text{ mol K}_2\text{SO}_4} = 4\underline{4}.4 = 44 \text{ g}$$

$$7.7 \text{ g KOH} \times \frac{1 \text{ mol KOH}}{56.108 \text{ g}} \times \frac{1 \text{ mol K}_2\text{SO}_4}{2 \text{ mol KOH}} \times \frac{174.27 \text{ g}}{1 \text{ mol K}_2\text{SO}_4} = 1\underline{1}.95 = 12 \text{ g}$$

KOH is the limiting reactant, and 12 g K_2SO_4 is produced.

b.   KOH is the limiting reactant. The mass of H_2SO_4 that reacts is

$$7.7 \text{ g KOH} \times \frac{1 \text{ mol KOH}}{56.108 \text{ g}} \times \frac{1 \text{ mol H}_2\text{SO}_4}{2 \text{ mol KOH}} \times \frac{98.086 \text{ g}}{1 \text{ mol H}_2\text{SO}_4} = 6.\underline{7}3 \text{ g reacted}$$

The mass remaining after reaction is 25 g − 6.73 g = 1$\underline{8}$.27 = 18 g.

c.   The theoretical yield was determined in part a to be 1$\underline{1}$.95 g. For an actual yield of 67.1%, the amount of K_2SO_4 formed is

$$1\underline{1}.95 \text{ g} \times 0.671 = 8.\underline{0}2 = 8.0 \text{ g}$$

3.121.   The balance chemical equation is $4NH_3 + 5O_2 \rightarrow 4NO + 6H_2O$. The theoretical yield of NO is

$$8.5 \text{ g NH}_3 \times \frac{1 \text{ mol NH}_3}{17.034 \text{ g NH}_3} \times \frac{4 \text{ mol NO}}{4 \text{ mol NH}_3} \times \frac{30.01 \text{ g NO}}{1 \text{ mol NO}} = 1\underline{4}.97 \text{ g NO}$$

The percentage yield is

$$\text{Percentage Yield} = \frac{12.0 \text{ g}}{14.97 \text{ g}} \times 100\% = 8\underline{0}.1\% = 80.\%$$

3.123.   The fraction of O in Na_2SO_3 is: $X_1 = \dfrac{48.00 \text{ g O}}{126.03 \text{ g Na}_2\text{SO}_3} = 0.380\underline{8}6$

The fraction of O in $MgSO_4$ is: $X_2 = \dfrac{64.00 \text{ g O}}{120.38 \text{ g MgSO}_4} = 0.531\underline{6}5$

The total mass of oxygen present is

Mass O = $(0.38086 \times 12.1 \text{ g}) + (0.53165 \times 14.6 \text{ g}) = 4.6\underline{0}8 \text{ g} + 7.7\underline{6}2 \text{ g} = 12.3\underline{7}0 = 12.37 \text{ g}$

3.125. $175 \text{ tablets} \times \dfrac{68.4 \times 10^{-3} \text{ g}}{1 \text{ tablet}} \times \dfrac{1 \text{ mol CaCO}_3}{100.09 \text{ g CaCO}_3} = 0.119\underline{6} = 0.120 \text{ mol CaCO}_3$

3.127.   First, using the successive reactions, calculate the mass of sulfur required to produce 87.0 g of H_2SO_4:

$$87.0 \text{ g H}_2\text{SO}_4 \times \frac{1 \text{ mol H}_2\text{SO}_4}{98.08 \text{ g H}_2\text{SO}_4} \times \frac{1 \text{ mol SO}_3}{1 \text{ mol H}_2\text{SO}_4} \times \frac{2 \text{ mol SO}_2}{2 \text{ mol SO}_3} \times \frac{1 \text{ mol S}_8}{8 \text{ mol SO}_2}$$

$$\times \frac{256.52 \text{ g S}_8}{1 \text{ mol S}_8} = 28.\underline{4}4 \text{ g S}_8 \text{ (sulfur)}$$

Finally, calculate the mass of the starting material required using the fact that every 100 g of the material contains only 65.0 g of sulfur (presumably as S_8):

$$28.\underline{4}4 \text{ g sulfur} \times \frac{100.0 \text{ g sulfur source}}{65.0 \text{ g sulfur}} = 43.\underline{7}6 \text{ g} = 43.8 \text{ g of starting material required.}$$

3.129. The balanced combustion reaction for this problem is

$$CH_4 + 2 O_2 \rightarrow CO_2 + 2 H_2O$$

Using the volumes of the reactants and the density relationship, the amount of CO_2 that can be produced by either reactant is calculated as follows:

$$20.\underline{0} \text{ L CH}_4 \times \frac{1 \text{ m}^3}{1000 \text{ L}} \times \frac{1.82 \text{ kg}}{1 \text{ m}^3} \times \frac{1 \text{ kmol CH}_4}{16.04 \text{ kg CH}_4} \times \frac{1 \text{ kmol CO}_2}{1 \text{ kmol CH}_4} \times \frac{44.01 \text{ kg CO}_2}{1 \text{ kmol CO}_2}$$

$$= 0.099\underline{8}7 = 0.0999 \text{ kg CO}_2$$

$$30.\underline{0} \text{ L O}_2 \times \frac{1 \text{ m}^3}{1000 \text{ L}} \times \frac{1.31 \text{ kg}}{1 \text{ m}^3} \times \frac{1 \text{ kmol O}_2}{32.00 \text{ kg O}_2} \times \frac{1 \text{ kmol CO}_2}{2 \text{ kmol O}_2} \times \frac{44.01 \text{ kg CO}_2}{1 \text{ kmol CO}_2}$$

$$= 0.027\underline{0}2 = 0.0270 \text{ kg CO}_2$$

Thus, the limiting reactant is O_2 which yields 2.70×10^{-2} kg of CO_2.

3.131. This problem is best approached by first combining the two steps given in the synthesis of NaN_3. In the process of doing this, the intermediate $NaNH_2(s)$ and one $NH_3(g)$ cancel giving the following result:

$$2Na(s) + NH_3(g) + N_2O(g) \rightarrow NaN_3(s) + H_2(g) + NaOH(s)$$

The problem clearly becomes a limiting reagent problem where we have the starting masses of each reactant. Determining which provides the least amount of NaN_3 product will yield the desired result:

$$1.\underline{0} \text{ kg Na} \times \frac{1 \text{ kmol Na}}{22.99 \text{ kg Na}} \times \frac{1 \text{ kmol NaN}_3}{2 \text{ kmol Na}} \times \frac{65.02 \text{ kg NaN}_3}{1 \text{ kmol NaN}_3} = 2.\underline{8}3 = 2.8 \text{ kg NaN}_3$$

$$6.\underline{0} \text{ kg NH}_3 \times \frac{1 \text{ kmol NH}_3}{17.03 \text{ kg NH}_3} \times \frac{1 \text{ kmol NaN}_3}{1 \text{ kmol NH}_3} \times \frac{65.02 \text{ kg NaN}_3}{1 \text{ kmol NaN}_3} = 22.\underline{9} = 23 \text{ kg NaN}_3$$

$$1.\underline{0} \text{ kg N}_2O \times \frac{1 \text{ kmol N}_2O}{44.02 \text{ kg N}_2O} \times \frac{1 \text{ kmol NaN}_3}{1 \text{ kmol N}_2O} \times \frac{65.02 \text{ kg NaN}_3}{1 \text{ kmol NaN}_3} = 1.\underline{4}8 = 1.5 \text{ kg NaN}_3$$

Thus, the limiting reactant is N_2O which yields 1.5 kg of NaN_3.

■ SOLUTIONS TO CUMULATIVE-SKILLS PROBLEMS

3.133. Let y equal the mass of CuO in the mixture. Then 0.500 g − y equals the mass of Cu_2O in the mixture. Multiplying the appropriate conversion factors for Cu times the mass of each oxide will give one equation in one unknown for the mass of 0.425 g Cu:

$$0.425 = y \left[\frac{63.55 \text{ g Cu}}{79.55 \text{ g CuO}} \right] + (0.500 - y) \left[\frac{127.10 \text{ g Cu}}{143.10 \text{ g Cu}_2\text{O}} \right]$$

Simplifying the equation by dividing the conversion factors and combining terms gives

$0.425 = 0.79887\, y + 0.888190\, (0.500 - y)$

$0.08932\, y = 0.019095$

$y = 0.2139 = 0.21$ g = mass of CuO

3.135. If one heme molecule contains one iron atom, then the number of moles of heme in 35.2 mg of heme must be the same as the number of moles of iron in 3.19 mg of iron. Start by calculating the moles of Fe (equals moles of heme):

$$3.19 \times 10^{-3} \text{ g Fe} \times \frac{1 \text{ mol Fe}}{55.85 \text{ g Fe}} = 5.712 \times 10^{-5} \text{ mol Fe or heme}$$

$$\text{Molar mass of heme} = \frac{35.2 \times 10^{-3} \text{ g}}{5.712 \times 10^{-5} \text{ mol}} = 616.2 = 616 \text{ g/mol}$$

The molecular mass of heme is 616 amu.

3.137. Use the data to find the molar mass of the metal and anion. Start with X_2.

Mass X_2 in MX = 4.52 g − 3.41 g = 1.11 g

$$\text{Molar mass } X_2 = \frac{1.11 \text{ g}}{0.0158 \text{ mol}} = 70.25 \text{ g/mol}$$

$$\text{Molar mass } X = \frac{70.25 \text{ g/mol } X_2}{2 \text{ mol X/mol } X_2} = 35.14 = 35.1 \text{ g/mol}$$

Thus X is Cl, chlorine.

Moles of M in 4.52 g MX = 0.0158 × 2 = 0.0316 mol

$$\text{Molar mass of M} = \frac{3.41 \text{ g}}{0.0316 \text{ mol}} = 107.9 = 108 \text{ g/mol}$$

Thus M is Ag, silver.

3.139. After finding the volume of the alloy, convert it to mass Fe using density and percent Fe. Then use Avogadro's number and the atomic mass for the number of atoms.

$$\text{Volume} = 10.0 \text{ cm} \times 20.0 \text{ cm} \times 15.0 \text{ cm} = 3.00 \times 10^3 \text{ cm}^3$$

$$\text{Mass Fe} = 3.00 \times 10^3 \text{ cm}^3 \times \frac{8.17 \text{ g alloy}}{1 \text{ cm}^3} \times \frac{54.7 \text{ g Fe}}{100.0 \text{ g alloy}} = 1.3\underline{4}07 \times 10^4 \text{ g}$$

$$\text{No. of Fe atoms} = 1.3\underline{4}07 \times 10^{-4} \text{ g Fe} \times \frac{1 \text{ mol Fe}}{55.85 \text{ g Fe}} \times \frac{6.022 \times 10^{23} \text{ Fe atoms}}{1 \text{ mol Fe}}$$

$$= 1.4\underline{4}56 \times 10^{26} = 1.45 \times 10^{26} \text{ Fe atoms}$$

CHAPTER 4

Chemical Reactions

■ SOLUTIONS TO EXERCISES

Note on significant figures: If the final answer to a solution needs to be rounded off, it is given first with one nonsignificant figure, and the last significant figure is underlined. The final answer is then rounded to the correct number of significant figures. In multistep problems, intermediate answers are given with at least one nonsignificant figure; however, only the final answer has been rounded off.

4.1. a. According to Table 4.1, all compounds that contain sodium, Na^+, are soluble. Thus, NaBr is soluble in water.

   b. According to Table 4.1, most compounds that contain hydroxides, OH^-, are insoluble in water. However, $Ba(OH)_2$ is listed as one of the exceptions to this rule, so it is soluble in water.

   c. Calcium carbonate is $CaCO_3$. According to Table 4.1, most compounds that contain carbonate, CO_3^{2-}, are insoluble. $CaCO_3$ is not one of the exceptions, so it is insoluble in water.

4.2. a. The problem states that HNO_3 is a strong electrolyte, but $Mg(OH)_2$ is a solid, so retain its formula. On the product side, $Mg(NO_3)_2$ is a soluble ionic compound, but water is a nonelectrolyte, so retain its formula. The resulting complete ionic equation is

$$2H^+(aq) + 2NO_3^-(aq) + Mg(OH)_2(s) \rightarrow 2H_2O(l) + Mg^{2+}(aq) + 2NO_3^-(aq)$$

   The corresponding net ionic equation is

$$2H^+(aq) + Mg(OH)_2(s) \rightarrow 2H_2O(l) + Mg^{2+}(aq)$$

   b. Both reactants are soluble ionic compounds, and on the product side, $NaNO_3$ is also a soluble ionic compound. $PbSO_4$ is a solid, so retain its formula. The resulting complete ionic equation is

$$Pb^{2+}(aq) + 2NO_3^-(aq) + 2Na^+(aq) + SO_4^{2-}(aq) \rightarrow PbSO_4(s) + 2Na^+(aq) + 2NO_3^-(aq)$$

   The corresponding net ionic equation is

$$Pb^{2+}(aq) + SO_4^{2-}(aq) \rightarrow PbSO_4(s)$$

4.3. The formulas of the compounds are NaI and $Pb(C_2H_3O_2)_2$. Exchanging anions, you get sodium acetate, $NaC_2H_3O_2$, and lead(II) iodide, PbI_2. The equation for the exchange reaction is

$$NaI + Pb(C_2H_3O_2)_2 \rightarrow NaC_2H_3O_2 + PbI_2$$

From Table 4.1, you see that NaI is soluble, $Pb(C_2H_3O_2)_2$ is soluble, $NaC_2H_3O_2$ is soluble, and PbI_2 is insoluble. Thus, lead(II) iodide precipitates. The balanced molecular equation with phase labels is

$$Pb(C_2H_3O_2)_2(aq) + 2NaI(aq) \rightarrow PbI_2(s) + 2NaC_2H_3O_2(aq)$$

To get the net ionic equation, you write the soluble ionic compounds as ions and cancel the spectator ions, $(C_2H_3O_2^-$ and $Na^+)$. The final result is

$$Pb^{2+}(aq) + 2I^-(aq) \rightarrow PbI_2(s)$$

4.4.   a. H_3PO_4 is not listed as a strong acid in Table 4.3, so it is a weak acid.

       b.   Hypochlorous acid, HClO, is not one of the strong acids listed in Table 4.3, so we assume that HClO is a weak acid.

       c.   As noted in Table 4.3, $HClO_4$ is a strong acid.

       d.   As noted in Table 4.3, $Sr(OH)_2$ is a strong base.

4.5.   The salt consists of the cation from the base (Li^+) and the anion from the acid (CN^-); its formula is LiCN. You will need to add H_2O as a product to complete and balance the molecular equation:

$$HCN(aq) + LiOH(aq) \rightarrow LiCN(aq) + H_2O(l)$$

Note that LiOH (a strong base) and LiCN (a soluble ionic substance) are strong electrolytes; HCN is a weak electrolyte (it is not one of the strong acids in Table 4.3). After eliminating the spectator ions $(Li^+$ and $CN^-)$, the net ionic equation is

$$HCN(aq) + OH^-(aq) \rightarrow H_2O(l) + CN^-(aq)$$

4.6.   The first step in the neutralization is described by the following molecular equation:

$$H_2SO_4(aq) + KOH(aq) \rightarrow KHSO_4(aq) + H_2O(l)$$

The corresponding net ionic equation is

$$H^+(aq) + OH^-(aq) \rightarrow H_2O(l)$$

The reaction of the acid salt $KHSO_4$ is given by the following molecular equation:

$$KHSO_4(aq) + KOH(aq) \rightarrow K_2SO_4(aq) + H_2O(l)$$

The corresponding net ionic equation is

$$HSO_4^-(aq) + OH^-(aq) \rightarrow H_2O(l) + SO_4^{2-}(aq)$$

4.7.   First, write the molecular equation for the exchange reaction, noting that the products of the reaction would be soluble $Ca(NO_3)_2$ and H_2CO_3. The carbonic acid decomposes to water and carbon dioxide gas. The molecular equation for the process is

$$CaCO_3(s) + 2HNO_3(aq) \rightarrow Ca(NO_3)_2(aq) + H_2O(l) + CO_2(g)$$

The corresponding net ionic equation is

$$CaCO_3(s) + 2H^+(aq) \rightarrow Ca^{2+}(aq) + H_2O(l) + CO_2(g)$$

4.8. a. For potassium dichromate, $K_2Cr_2O_7$,

$2 \times$ (oxidation number of K) $+ 2 \times$ (oxidation number of Cr) $+ 7 \times$ (oxidation number of O) $= 0$

For oxygen, the oxidation number is -2 (rule 3), and for potassium ion, the oxidation number is $+1$ (rule 2)

$[2 \times (+1)] + 2 \times$ (oxidation number of Cr) $+ [7 \times (-2)] = 0$

Therefore,

$2 \times$ oxidation number of Cr $= - [2 \times (+1)] - [7 \times (-2)] = +12$

or, oxidation number of Cr $= +6$.

b. For the permanganate ion, MnO_4^-,

(Oxidation number of Mn) $+ 4 \times$ (oxidation number of O) $= -1$

For oxygen, the oxidation number is -2 (rule 3).

(oxidation number of Mn) $+ [4 \times (-2)] = -1$

Therefore,

Oxidation number of Mn $= -1 - [4 \times (-2)] = +7$

4.9. Identify the oxidation states of the elements.

$$\overset{0}{Ca} + \overset{0}{Cl_2} \rightarrow \overset{+2\ -1}{CaCl_2}$$

Break the reaction into two half-reactions, making sure that both mass and charge are balanced.

$Ca \rightarrow Ca^{2+} + 2e^-$

$Cl_2 + 2e^- \rightarrow 2Cl^-$

Since each half-reaction has two electrons, it is not necessary to multiply the reactions by any factors to cancel them out. Adding the two half-reactions together and canceling out the electrons, you get

$Ca(s) + Cl_2(g) \rightarrow CaCl_2(s)$

4.10. Convert mass of NaCl (molar mass, 58.44 g) to moles of NaCl. Then divide moles of solute by liters of solution. Note that 25.0 mL = 0.0250 L.

$0.0678 \text{ g NaCl} \times \dfrac{1 \text{ mol NaCl}}{58.44 \text{ g NaCl}} = 1.1\underline{6}0 \times 10^{-3} \text{ mol NaCl}$

$\text{Molarity} = \dfrac{1.160 \times 10^{-3} \text{ mol NaCl}}{0.0250 \text{ L soln}} = 0.0464\underline{1} = 0.0464 \ M$

4.11. Convert grams of NaCl (molar mass, 58.44 g) to moles NaCl and then to volume of NaCl solution.

$0.0958 \text{ g NaCl} \times \dfrac{1 \text{ mol NaCl}}{58.44 \text{ g NaCl}} \times \dfrac{1 \text{ L solution}}{0.163 \text{ mol NaCl}} \times \dfrac{1000 \text{ mL}}{1 \text{ L}} = 10.\underline{0}6 = 10.1 \text{ mL NaCl}$

4.12. One (1) liter of solution is equivalent to 0.15 mol NaCl. The amount of NaCl in 50.0 mL of solution is

$$50.0 \text{ mL} \times \frac{1 \text{ L}}{1000 \text{ mL}} \times \frac{0.15 \text{ mol NaCl}}{1 \text{ L soln}} = 0.00750 \text{ mol NaCl}$$

Convert to grams using the molar mass of NaCl (58.44 g/mol).

$$0.00750 \text{ mol NaCl} \times \frac{58.4 \text{ g NaCl}}{1 \text{ mol NaCl}} = 0.438 = 0.44 \text{ g NaCl}$$

4.13. Use the rearranged version of the dilution formula from the text to calculate the initial volume of 1.5 M sulfuric acid required:

$$V_i = \frac{M_f V_f}{M_i} = \frac{0.18 \ M \times 100.0 \text{ mL}}{1.5 \ M} = 12.0 = 12 \text{ mL}$$

4.14. There are two different reactions taking place in forming the CaC_2O_4 (molar mass 128.10 g/mol) precipitate. These are

$$CaCO_3(s) + 2HCl(aq) \rightarrow CaCl_2(aq) + CO_2(g) + H_2O(l)$$

$$CaCl_2(aq) + Na_2C_2O_4(aq) \rightarrow CaC_2O_4(s) + 2NaCl(aq)$$

The overall stoichiometry of the reactions is one mol $CaCO_3$/one mol CaC_2O_4. Also note that each $CaCO_3$ contains one Ca atom, so this gives an overall conversion factor of one mol Ca/one mol CaC_2O_4.

The mass of Ca can now be calculated.

$$0.1402 \text{ g } CaC_2O_4 \times \frac{1 \text{ mol } CaC_2O_4}{128.10 \text{ g } CaC_2O_4} \times \frac{1 \text{ mol Ca}}{1 \text{ mol } CaC_2O_4} \times \frac{40.08 \text{ g Ca}}{1 \text{ mol Ca}} = 0.043866 \text{ g Ca}$$

Now, calculate the percentage of calcium in the 128.3 mg (0.1283 g) limestone:

$$\frac{0.043866 \text{ g Ca}}{0.1283 \text{ g limestone}} \times 100\% = 34.190 = 34.19\%$$

4.15. Convert the volume of Na_3PO_4 to moles using the molarity of Na_3PO_4. Note that 45.7 mL = 0.0457 L.

$$0.0457 \text{ L } Na_3PO_4 \times \frac{0.265 \text{ mol } Na_3PO_4}{1 \text{ L}} = 0.01211 \text{ mol } Na_3PO_4$$

Finally, calculate the amount of $NiSO_4$ required to react with this amount of Na_3PO_4:

$$0.1211 \text{ mol } Na_3PO_4 \times \frac{3 \text{ mol } NiSO_4}{2 \text{ mol } Na_3PO_4} \times \frac{1 \text{ L } NiSO_4}{0.375 \text{ mol } NiSO_4} = 0.04844 \text{ L (48.4 mL)}$$

4.16. Convert the volume of NaOH solution (0.0391 L) to moles NaOH (from the molarity of NaOH). Then convert moles NaOH to moles $HC_2H_3O_2$ (from the chemical equation). Finally, convert moles of $HC_2H_3O_2$ (molar mass 60.05 g/mol) to grams $HC_2H_3O_2$.

$$0.0391 \text{ L NaOH} \times \frac{0.108 \text{ mol NaOH}}{1 \text{ L}} \times \frac{1 \text{ mol } HC_2H_3O_2}{1 \text{ mol NaOH}} \times \frac{60.05 \text{ g } HC_2H_3O_2}{1 \text{ mol } HC_2H_3O_2} = 0.25359 \text{ g}$$

The mass percentage of acetic acid in the vinegar can now be calculated.

$$\text{Percentage mass} = \frac{0.25\underline{3}59 \text{ g } HC_2H_3O_2}{5.00 \text{ g vinegar}} \times 100\% = 5.0\underline{7}1 = 5.07\%$$

■ ANSWERS TO CONCEPT CHECKS

4.1.   Of the six compounds, only NH_4Cl, $MgBr_2$, and HCl are strong electrolytes. H_2O is nearly a nonelectrolyte, $Ca_3(PO_4)_2$ would be considered a weak electrolyte because of its low solubility in water, and the molecular compound methanol, CH_3OH, dissolves molecularly in water. Statements c and e are valid statements. Statement a is invalid in the context of insoluble ionic compounds. Statement b is invalid in the context of the highly ionizable behavior of molecular strong acids. Statement d is invalid because water by itself is not a strong conductor of electricity, i.e., it's nearly a nonconductor.

4.2.   The left beaker contains two types of individual atoms (ions) and no solid; therefore, it must represent the soluble, LiI. Because LiI is a soluble ionic compound, it is an electrolyte. The beaker on the right represents a molecular compound that is soluble but not dissociated in solution. Therefore, it must be the CH_3OH. Because the CH_3OH is not dissociated in solution, and no ions are present, it is a nonelectrolyte.

4.3.   a.   In order to solve this part of the problem, keep in mind that this is an exchange (metathesis) reaction. Since you are given the products in the picture, you need to work backward to determine the reactants. Starting with the solid $SrSO_4(s)$, you know that the SO_4^{2-} anion started the reaction with a different cation (not Sr^{2+}). Since Na^+ is the only option, you can conclude that one of the reactants must be Na_2SO_4. Based on solubility rules, you know that Na_2SO_4 is soluble, so you represent it as $Na_2SO_4(aq)$. The remaining cation and anion indicate that the other reactant is the soluble $Sr(C_2H_3O_2)_2$. Observing the soluble and insoluble species in the picture, you can conclude that the molecular equation is

$$Na_2SO_4(aq) + Sr(C_2H_3O_2)_2(aq) \rightarrow SrSO_4(s) + 2NaC_2H_3O_2(aq)$$

b.   Writing the strong electrolytes in the form of ions and the solid with its molecular formula, the complete ionic equation for the reaction is

$$2Na^+(aq) + SO_4^{2-}(aq) + Sr^{2+}(aq) + 2C_2H_3O_2^-(aq)$$
$$\rightarrow SrSO_4(s) + 2Na^+(aq) + 2C_2H_3O_2^-(aq)$$

c.   After canceling the spectator ions, the net ionic equation for the reaction is

$$Sr^{2+}(aq) + SO_4^{2-}(aq) \rightarrow SrSO_4(s)$$

4.4. $HClO_4(aq) + H_2O(l) \rightarrow H_3O^+(aq) + ClO_4^-(aq)$

$HBr(aq) + H_2O(l) \rightarrow H_3O^+(aq) + Br^-(aq)$

a.   HBr is a strong acid and completely ionizes in aqueous solution. Statement a is false.

b. $HClO_4$ is a strong acid and completely ionizes in aqueous solution. Statement b is true.

c.   Since $HClO_4$ is a strong acid and completely ionizes, very few of the unionized molecules are expected to be found. On the other hand, there should be as many ClO_4^- ions present as the number of $HClO_4$ molecules originally placed in solution. Statement c is true

    d.   Since HBr is a strong acid, very few unionized HBr molecules will be present in solution. Statement d is false.

    e.   With statements b and c being true, statement e is false.

4.5.   e.   MOH must be a base since OH^- is being produced in solution. It must be a strong base because the reaction indicates that MOH is completely soluble (strong electrolyte). In order to maintain charge balance in the formula, the element M must be a 1+ cation, probably a metal from Group IA of the periodic table. Examples of bases that fall into this category include NaOH and KOH.

    f.   This must be an acid since H^+ is being produced in solution. It is a weak acid because the double arrow is used, indicating only a partial ionization in solution. From the chemical reaction, A^- represents an anion with a 1– charge. Acetic acid, $HC_2H_3O_2$, is a weak acid of this type.

    g.   This must be an acid since H^+ is being produced in solution. $H_2A(aq)$ is a weak acid because the equation indicates only partial ionization in solution. A^{2-} represents an anion with a 2– charge. Carbonic acid, H_2CO_3, is a weak acid of this type.

    h.   Examples of M include Na^+, K^+, and Li^+. Examples of A for reaction b include F^-, $C_2H_3O_2^-$, and CN^-. Examples of A for reaction c. include S^{2-}, CO_3^{2-}, and $C_4H_4O_6^{2-}$.

4.6.   a.   In order to answer this question, you need to compare the number of atoms of X per unit of volume. In order to compare volumes, use the lines on the sides of the beakers. Beaker A has concentration of five atoms per two volume units, 5/2 or 2.5/1. Beaker B has a concentration of ten atoms per one volume unit, 10/1. Beaker C has a concentration of ten atoms per two volume units, 10/2 or 5/1. Beaker D has a concentration of five atoms per volume unit, 5/1. Comparing the concentrations reveals that the ranking from lowest to highest concentration is Beaker A < Beaker C = Beaker D < Beaker B.

    b.   To make the concentrations of X equal in each beaker, they all have to be made to match the beaker with the lowest concentration. This is Beaker A, which has five atoms of X in one-half a beaker of solution. To make the concentrations equal, do the following: double the volume of Beakers C and D, and quadruple the volume of Beaker B by adding the solvent. Overall, Beakers A and B will contain a full beaker of solution, and Beakers C and D will contain a half-beaker of solution.

4.7.   a.   Since flask C required three times the amount of titrant (NaOH) as of acid A, you have learned that acid C has three times as many acidic protons as acid A. Since flask B required two times the amount of titrant as of acid A, you have also learned that acid B has two times as many acidic protons as acid A.

    b.   If you assume that acid A contains a monoprotic acid, then you know the number of moles of A in the flask. After performing the titration, you know that the moles of NaOH must equal the moles of acid in flask A. You take the number of moles of NaOH and divide it by the volume of NaOH added during the titration to determine the concentration of the NaOH solution.

■ ANSWERS TO SELF-ASSESSMENT AND REVIEW QUESTIONS

4.1.   Some electrolyte solutions are strongly conducting because they are almost completely ionized, and others are weakly conducting because they are weakly ionized. The former solutions will have many more ions to conduct electricity than will the latter solutions if both are present at the same concentrations.

4.2.   A strong electrolyte is an electrolyte that exists in solution almost entirely as ions. An example is NaCl. When NaCl dissolves in water, it dissolves almost completely to give Na^+ and Cl^- ions. A weak electrolyte is an electrolyte that dissolves in water to give a relatively small percentage of ions. An example is NH_3. When NH_3 dissolves in water, it reacts very little with the water, so the level of NH_3 is relatively high, and the level of the NH_4^+ and OH^- ions is relatively low.

4.3.   Soluble means the ability of a substance to dissolve in water. A compound is insoluble if it does not dissolve appreciably in water. An example of a soluble ionic compound is sodium chloride, NaCl, and an example of an insoluble ionic compound is calcium carbonate, $CaCO_3$.

4.4.   The advantage of using a molecular equation to represent an ionic equation is that it states explicitly what chemical species have been added and what chemical species are obtained as products. It also makes stoichiometric calculations easy to perform. The disadvantages are (1) the molecular equation does not represent the fact that the reaction actually involves ions, and (2) the molecular equation does not indicate which species exist as ions and which exist as molecular solids or molecular gases.

4.5.   A spectator ion is an ion that does not take part in the reaction. In the following ionic reaction, the Na^+ and Cl^- are spectator ions:

$$Na^+(aq) + OH^-(aq) + H^+(aq) + Cl^-(aq) \rightarrow Na^+(aq) + Cl^-(aq) + H_2O(l)$$

4.6.   A net ionic equation is an ionic equation from which spectator ions have been canceled. The value of such an equation is that it shows the reaction that actually occurs at the ionic level. An example is the ionic equation representing the reaction of calcium chloride ($CaCl_2$) with potassium carbonate(K_2CO_3).

$$CaCl_2(aq) + K_2CO_3(aq) \rightarrow CaCO_3(s) + 2\ KCl(aq):$$

$$Ca^{2+}(aq) + CO_3^{2-}(aq) \rightarrow CaCO_3(s) \qquad \text{(net ionic equation)}$$

4.7.   The three major types of chemical reactions are precipitation reactions, acid–base reactions, and oxidation–reduction reactions. Oxidation–reduction reactions can be further classified as combination reactions, decomposition reactions, displacement reactions, and combustion reactions. Brief descriptions and examples of each are given below.

   A precipitation reaction is a reaction that involves the formation of an insoluble solid compound. An example is $2KCl\ (aq) + Pb(NO_3)_2(aq) \rightarrow 2KNO_3(aq) + PbI_2(s)$.

   An acid–base reaction, or neutralization reaction, results in an ionic compound and possibly water. An example is $HCl(aq) + NaOH(aq) \rightarrow NaCl(aq) + H_2O(l)$.

   A combination reaction is a reaction in which two substances combine to form a third substance. An example is $2Na(s) + Cl_2(g) \rightarrow 2NaCl(s)$.

A decomposition reaction is a reaction in which a single compound reacts to give two or more substances. An example is $2HgO(s) \xrightarrow{\Delta} 2Hg(l) + O_2(g)$.

A displacement reaction, or single replacement reaction, is a reaction in which an element reacts with a compound displacing an element from it. An example is $Cu(s) + 2AgNO_3(aq) \rightarrow 2Ag(s) + Cu(NO_3)_2(aq)$.

A combustion reaction is a reaction of a substance with oxygen, usually with rapid release of heat to produce a flame. The products include one or more oxides. An example is $CH_4(g) + 2O_2(g) \rightarrow CO_2(g) + 2H_2O(l)$.

4.8.   To prepare crystalline AgCl and $NaNO_3$, first make solutions of $AgNO_3$ and NaCl by weighing equivalent molar amounts of both solid compounds. Then mix the two solutions together, forming a precipitate of silver chloride and a solution of soluble sodium nitrate. Filter off the silver chloride, and wash it with water to remove the sodium nitrate solution. Then allow it to dry to obtain pure crystalline silver chloride. Finally, take the filtrate containing the sodium nitrate and evaporate it, leaving pure crystalline sodium nitrate.

4.9.   An example of a neutralization reaction is

$$HBr \; + \; KOH \; \rightarrow \; KBr \; + \; H_2O(l)$$
$$\text{acid} \qquad \text{base} \qquad\quad \text{salt}$$

4.10.   An example of a polyprotic acid is carbonic acid, H_2CO_3. The successive neutralization is given by the following molecular equations:

$$H_2CO_3(aq) + NaOH(aq) \rightarrow NaHCO_3(aq) + H_2O(l)$$
$$NaHCO_3(aq) + NaOH(aq) \rightarrow Na_2CO_3(aq) + H_2O(l)$$

4.11.   Since an oxidation–reduction reaction is an electron transfer reaction, one substance must lose the electrons and be oxidized while another substance must gain electrons and be reduced.

4.12.   A displacement reaction is an oxidation–reduction reaction in which a free element reacts with a compound, displacing an element from it.

$$Cu(s) + 2AgNO_3(aq) \rightarrow 2Ag(s) + Cu(NO_3)_2(aq)$$

Ag^+ is the oxidizing agent, and Cu is the reducing agent.

4.13.   The number of moles present does not change when the solution is diluted.

4.14.   The reaction is

$$HCl + NaOH \rightarrow NaCl + H_2O$$

After titration, the volume of hydrochloric acid is converted to moles of HCl using the molarity. Since the stoichiometry of the reaction is 1 mol HCl to 1 mol NaOH, these quantities are equal.

Moles HCl = moles NaOH = molarity × volume

You could then multiply by the molar mass of NaOH to obtain the amount in the mixture.

4.15.   The answer is e, $HF(aq) + OH^-(aq) \rightarrow F^-(aq) + H_2O(l)$.

4.16. The answer is c, magnesium hydroxide(*s*).

4.17. The answer is d, $MgCl_2$.

4.18. The answer is d, HNO_2.

■ ANSWERS TO CONCEPTUAL PROBLEMS

4.21.   a.   Any soluble salt that will form a precipitate when reacted with Ag^+ ions in solution will work, for example: $CaCl_2$, Na_2S, $(NH_4)_2CO_3$.

      b.   No, no precipitate will form.

      c.   You would underestimate the amount of silver present in the solution.

4.23.   a. $3Ca(C_2H_3O_2)_2(aq) + 2(NH_4)_3PO_4(aq) \rightarrow Ca_3(PO_4)_2(s) + 6NH_4C_2H_3O_2(aq)$

      b. $3Ca^{2+}(aq) + 6C_2H_3O_2^{-}(aq) + 6NH_4^{+}(aq) + 2PO_4^{3-}(aq)$

$$\rightarrow Ca_3(PO_4)_2(s) + 6NH_4^{+}(aq) + 6C_2H_3O_2^{-}(aq)$$

      c. $3Ca^{2+}(aq) + 2PO_4^{3-}(aq) \rightarrow Ca_3(PO_4)_2(s)$

4.25.   Probably not, since the ionic compound that is a nonelectrolyte is not soluble.

4.27.   a.   Since both solutions are made with compounds that contain chloride ions, the total chloride ion concentration is highest.

      b.   First, determine the concentrations of the compounds after mixing them together. Use the dilution relationship, $M_1V_1 = M_2V_2$. Since equal volumes of equal molar solutions are mixed, the resulting concentrations are 0.50 *M* KBr and 0.50 *M* K_3PO_4. There is one Br^- ion per KBr, so the concentration of Br^- is 0.50 *M*. There is also one PO_4^{3-} ion per K_3PO_4, so its concentration is also 0.50 *M*. Potassium ion can be determined as follows:

$$0.50 \, M \, \text{KBr} \times \frac{1 \, \text{mol K}^+}{1 \, \text{mol KBr}} + 0.50 \, M \, \text{K}_3\text{PO}_4 \times \frac{3 \, \text{mol K}^+}{1 \, \text{mol K}_3\text{PO}_4} = 2.0 \, \text{M K}^+$$

■ SOLUTIONS TO PRACTICE PROBLEMS

Note on significant figures: If the final answer to a solution needs to be rounded off, it is given first with one nonsignificant figure, and the last significant figure is underlined. The final answer is then rounded to the correct number of significant figures. In multistep problems, intermediate answers are given with at least one nonsignificant figure; however, only the final answer has been rounded off.

4.29.   a.   Insoluble

      b.   Soluble

      c.   Soluble

      d.   Soluble

4.31.   a.   Insoluble

   b.   Soluble; the ions present would be Li^+ and SO_4^{2-}.

$$Li_2SO_4(s) \rightarrow 2Li^+(aq) + SO_4^{2-}(aq)$$

   c.   Insoluble

   d.   Soluble; the ions present would be Na^+ and CO_3^{2-}.

$$Na_2CO_3(s) \rightarrow 2Na^+(aq) + CO_3^{2-}(aq)$$

4.33.   a. $H^+(aq) + OH^-(aq) \rightarrow H_2O(l)$

   b. $Ag^+(aq) + Br^-(aq) \rightarrow AgBr(s)$

   c. $S^{2-}(aq) + 2H^+(aq) \rightarrow H_2S(g)$

   d. $OH^-(aq) + NH_4^+(aq) \rightarrow NH_3(g) + H_2O(l)$

4.35.   Molecular equation: $Pb(NO_3)_2(aq) + Na_2SO_4(aq) \rightarrow PbSO_4(s) + 2NaNO_3(aq)$

   Net ionic equation: $Pb^{2+}(aq) + SO_4^{2-}(aq) \rightarrow PbSO_4(s)$

4.37.   a. $FeSO_4(aq) + NaCl(aq) \rightarrow NR$

   b. $Na_2CO_3(aq) + MgBr_2(aq) \rightarrow MgCO_3(s) + 2NaBr(aq)$

   $CO_3^{2-}(aq) + Mg^{2+}(aq) \rightarrow MgCO_3(s)$

   c. $MgSO_4(aq) + 2NaOH(aq) \rightarrow Mg(OH)_2(s) + Na_2SO_4(aq)$

   $Mg^{2+}(aq) + 2OH^-(aq) \rightarrow Mg(OH)_2(s)$

   d. $NiCl_2(aq) + NaBr(aq) \rightarrow NR$

4.39.   a. $Ba(NO_3)_2(aq) + Li_2SO_4(aq) \rightarrow BaSO_4(s) + 2LiNO_3(aq)$

   $Ba^{2+}(aq) + SO_4^{2-}(aq) \rightarrow BaSO_4(s)$

   b. $Ca(NO_3)_2(aq) + NaBr(aq) \rightarrow NR$

   c. $Al_2(SO_4)_3(aq) + 6NaOH(aq) \rightarrow 2Al(OH)_3(s) + 3Na_2SO_4(aq)$

   $Al^{3+}(aq) + 3OH^-(aq) \rightarrow Al(OH)_3(s)$

   d. $3CaBr_2(aq) + 2Na_3PO_4(aq) \rightarrow Ca_3(PO_4)_2(s) + 6NaBr(aq)$

   $3Ca^{2+}(aq) + 2PO_4^{3-}(aq) \rightarrow Ca_3(PO_4)_2(s)$

4.41.   a. Weak acid   b. Strong base

   c. Strong acid   d. Weak acid

4.43.   a. $NaOH(aq) + HNO_3(aq) \rightarrow H_2O(l) + NaNO_3(aq)$

   $H^+(aq) + OH^-(aq) \rightarrow H_2O(l)$

   b. $2HCl(aq) + Ba(OH)_2(aq) \rightarrow 2H_2O(l) + BaCl_2(aq)$

   $H^+(aq) + OH^-(aq) \rightarrow H_2O(l)$

    c. $2HC_2H_3O_2(aq) + Ca(OH)_2(aq) \rightarrow 2H_2O(l) + Ca(C_2H_3O_2)_2(aq)$

           $HC_2H_3O_2(aq) + OH^-(aq) \rightarrow H_2O(l) + C_2H_3O_2^-(aq)$

    d. $NH_3(aq) + HNO_3(aq) \rightarrow NH_4NO_3(aq)$

           $NH_3(aq) + H^+(aq) \rightarrow NH_4^+(aq)$

4.45.   a. $2HBr(aq) + Ca(OH)_2(aq) \rightarrow 2H_2O(l) + CaBr_2(aq)$

           $H^+(aq) + OH^-(aq) \rightarrow H_2O(l)$

    b. $3HNO_3(aq) + Al(OH)_3(s) \rightarrow 3H_2O(l) + Al(NO_3)_3(aq)$

           $3H^+(aq) + Al(OH)_3(s) \rightarrow 3H_2O(l) + Al^{3+}(aq)$

    c. $2HCN(aq) + Ca(OH)_2(aq) \rightarrow 2H_2O(l) + Ca(CN)_2(aq)$

           $HCN(aq) + OH^-(aq) \rightarrow H_2O(l) + CN^-(aq)$

    d. $HCN(aq) + LiOH(aq) \rightarrow H_2O(l) + LiCN(aq)$

           $HCN(aq) + OH^-(aq) \rightarrow H_2O(l) + CN^-(aq)$

4.47.   a. $2KOH(aq) + H_3PO_4(aq) \rightarrow K_2HPO_4(aq) + 2H_2O(l)$

           $2OH^-(aq) + H_3PO_4(aq) \rightarrow HPO_4^{2-}(aq) + 2H_2O(l)$

    b. $3H_2SO_4(aq) + 2Al(OH)_3(s) \rightarrow 6H_2O(l) + Al_2(SO_4)_3(aq)$

           $3H^+(aq) + Al(OH)_3(s) \rightarrow 3H_2O(l) + Al^{3+}(aq)$

    c. $2HC_2H_3O_2(aq) + Ca(OH)_2(aq) \rightarrow 2H_2O(l) + Ca(C_2H_3O_2)_2(aq)$

           $HC_2H_3O_2(aq) + OH^-(aq) \rightarrow H_2O(l) + C_2H_3O_2^-(aq)$

    d. $H_2SO_3(aq) + NaOH(aq) \rightarrow H_2O(l) + NaHSO_3(aq)$

           $H_2SO_3(aq) + OH^-(aq) \rightarrow HSO_3^-(aq) + H_2O(l)$

4.49.   Molecular equations: $2H_2SO_3(aq) + Ca(OH)_2(aq) \rightarrow 2H_2O(l) + Ca(HSO_3)_2(aq)$

                           $Ca(HSO_3)_2(aq) + Ca(OH)_2(aq) \rightarrow 2H_2O(l) + 2CaSO_3(s)$

      Ionic equations: $H_2SO_3(aq) + OH^-(aq) \rightarrow H_2O(l) + HSO_3^-(aq)$

                           $Ca^{2+}(aq) + HSO_3^-(aq) + OH^-(aq) \rightarrow CaSO_3(s) + H_2O(l)$

4.51.   a.   Molecular equation: $CaS(s) + 2HBr(aq) \rightarrow CaBr_2(aq) + H_2S(g)$

           Ionic equation: $CaS(s) + 2H^+(aq) \rightarrow Ca^{2+}(aq) + H_2S(g)$

    b.   Molecular equation: $MgCO_3(s) + 2HNO_3(aq) \rightarrow CO_2(g) + H_2O(l) + Mg(NO_3)_2(aq)$

           Ionic equation: $MgCO_3(s) + 2H^+(aq) \rightarrow CO_2(g) + H_2O(l) + Mg^{2+}(aq)$

    c.   Molecular equation: $K_2SO_3(aq) + H_2SO_4(aq) \rightarrow K_2SO_4(aq) + SO_2(g) + H_2O(l)$

           Ionic equation: $SO_3^{2-}(aq) + 2H^+(aq) \rightarrow SO_2(g) + H_2O(l)$

4.53.   Molecular equation: $FeS(s) + 2HCl(aq) \rightarrow H_2S(g) + FeCl_2(aq)$

Ionic equation: $FeS(s) + 2H^+(aq) \rightarrow H_2S(g) + Fe^{2+}(aq)$

4.55.   a.   Because all three O's = a total of −6, both Ga's = +6; thus, the oxidation number of Ga = +3.

b.   Because both O's = a total of −4, the oxidation number of Nb = +4.

c.   Because the four O's = a total of −8 and K = +1, the oxidation number of Br = +7.

d.   Because the four O's = a total of −8 and the 2 K's = +2, the oxidation number of Mn = +6.

4.57.   a.   Because the charge of −1 = $[x_N + 2$ (from 2 H's)], x_N must equal −3.

b.   Because the charge of −1 = $[x_I - 6$ (from 3 O's)], x_I must equal +5.

c.   Because this is a neutral element, the oxidation number is 0.

d.   Because the charge of 0 = $[x_{Cl} - 8$ (4 O's) + 1 (1 H's)], x_{Cl} must equal +7.

4.59.   a.   From the list of common polyatomic anions in Table 2.6, the formula of the ClO_2 anion must be ClO_2^-. Thus, the formula of Mn is Mn^{2+} (see also Tables 2.5 and 4.5). Since the oxidation state of O is −2 and the net ionic charge is −1, the oxidation state of chlorine is determined by $x_{Cl} - 4 = -1$, so x_{Cl} must equal +3.

b.   From the list of common polyatomic anions in Table 2.6, the formula of the CrO_4 anion must be CrO_4^{2-}. Thus, the formula of Fe is Fe^{3+}. Since the oxidation state of O is −2 and the net ionic charge is −2, the oxidation state of Cr is determined by $x_{Cr} - 8 = -2$, so x_{Cr} must equal +6.

c.   From the list of common polyatomic anions in Table 2.6, the formula of the Cr_2O_7 anion must be $Cr_2O_7^{2-}$. Thus, the formula of Hg is Hg^{2+}. Since the oxidation state of O is −2 and the net ionic charge is −2, the oxidation state of Cr is determined by $2x_{Cr} - 14 = -2$, so x_{Cr} must equal +6.

d.   From the list of common polyatomic anions in Table 2.6, the formula of the PO_4 anion must be PO_4^{3-}. Thus, the formula of Co is Co^{2+}. Since the oxidation state of O is −2 and the net ionic charge is −3, the oxidation state of P is determined by $x_P - 8 = -3$, so x_P must equal +5.

4.61.   a.   Phosphorus changes from an oxidation number of zero in P_4 to +5 in P_4O_{10}, losing electrons and acting as a reducing agent. Oxygen changes from an oxidation number of zero in O_2 to −2 in P_4O_{10}, gaining electrons and acting as an oxidizing agent.

b.   Cobalt changes from an oxidation number of zero in Co(s) to +2 in $CoCl_2$, losing electrons and acting as a reducing agent. Chlorine changes from an oxidation number of zero in Cl_2 to −1 in $CoCl_2$, gaining electrons and acting as an oxidizing agent.

4.63.   a.   Al changes from oxidation number zero to +3; Al is the reducing agent.

F changes from oxidation number zero to −1; F_2 is the oxidizing agent.

b.   Hg changes from oxidation state +2 to 0; Hg^{2+} is the oxidizing agent.

N changes from oxidation state +3 to +5; NO_2^- is the reducing agent.

4.65.   a.   First, identify the species being oxidized and reduced, and assign the appropriate oxidation states. Since $CuCl_2$ and $AlCl_3$ are both soluble ionic compounds, Cl^- is a spectator ion and can be removed from the equation. The resulting net ionic equation is

$$\overset{+2}{Cu^{2+}}(aq) \; + \; \overset{0}{Al}(s) \; \rightarrow \; \overset{+3}{Al^{3+}}(aq) \; + \; \overset{0}{Cu}(s)$$

Next, write the half-reactions in an unbalanced form.

$Al \rightarrow Al^{3+}$ (oxidation)

$Cu^{2+} \rightarrow Cu$ (reduction)

Next, balance the charge in each equation by adding electrons to the more positive side to create balanced half-reactions.

$Al \rightarrow Al^{3+} + 3e^-$ (oxidation half-reaction)

$Cu^{2+} + 2e^- \rightarrow Cu$ (reduction half-reaction)

Multiply each half-reaction by a factor that will cancel out the electrons.

$2 \times (Al \rightarrow Al^{3+} + 3e^-)$

$\underline{3 \times (Cu^{2+} + 2e^- \rightarrow Cu)}$

$3Cu^{2+} + 2Al + \cancel{6e^-} \rightarrow 2Al^{3+} + 3Cu + \cancel{6e^-}$

Therefore, the balanced oxidation-reduction reaction is

$3Cu^{2+} + 2Al \rightarrow 2Al^{3+} + 3Cu$

Finally, add six Cl^- ions to each side, and add phase labels. The resulting balanced equation is

$3CuCl_2(aq) + 2Al(s) \rightarrow 2AlCl_3(aq) + 3Cu(s)$

    b.   First, identify the species being oxidized and reduced, and assign the appropriate oxidation states.

$$\overset{+3}{Cr^{3+}}(aq) \; + \; \overset{0}{Zn}(s) \; \rightarrow \; \overset{0}{Cr}(s) \; + \; \overset{+2}{Zn^{2+}}(aq)$$

Next, write the half-reactions in an unbalanced form.

$Zn \rightarrow Zn^{2+}$ (oxidation)

$Cr^{3+} \rightarrow Cr$ (reduction)

Next, balance the charge in each equation by adding electrons to the more positive side to create balanced half-reactions.

$Zn \rightarrow Zn^{2+} + 2e^-$ (oxidation half-reaction)

$Cr^{3+} + 3e^- \rightarrow Cr$ (reduction half-reaction)

Multiply each half-reaction by a factor that will cancel out the electrons.

$3 \times (Zn \rightarrow Zn^{2+} + 2e^-)$

$\underline{2 \times (Cr^{3+} + 3e^- \rightarrow Cr)}$

$2Cr^{3+} + 3Zn + \cancel{6e^-} \rightarrow 2Cr + 3Zn^{2+} + \cancel{6e^-}$

Therefore, the balanced oxidation-reduction reaction, including phase labels, is

$$2Cr^{3+}(aq) + 3Zn(s) \rightarrow 2Cr(s) + 3Zn^{2+}(aq)$$

4.67. $Molarity = \dfrac{moles\ solute}{liters\ solution} = \dfrac{0.0512\ mol}{0.0250\ L} = 2.0\underline{4}8 = 2.05\ M$

4.69.   Find the number of moles of solute ($KMnO_4$) using the molar mass of 158.03 g $KMnO_4$ per 1 mol $KMnO_4$:

$$0.798\ g\ KMnO_4 \times \dfrac{1\ mol\ KMnO_4}{158.03\ g\ KMnO_4} = 5.0\underline{4}97 \times 10^{-3}\ mol\ KMnO_4$$

$$Molarity = \dfrac{moles\ solute}{liters\ of\ solution} = \dfrac{5.0497 \times 10^{-3}\ mol}{0.0500\ L} = 0.10\underline{0}99 = 0.101\ M$$

4.71. $0.150\ mol\ CuSO_4 \times \dfrac{1\ L\ solution}{0.120\ mol\ CuSO_4} = 1.2\underline{5}0 = 1.25\ L\ solution$

4.73. $0.0353\ g\ KOH \times \dfrac{1\ mol\ KOH}{56.10\ g\ KOH} \times \dfrac{1\ L\ solution}{0.0176\ mol\ KOH} = 0.035\underline{7}51\ L = 35.8\ mL$

4.75.   From the molarity, one L of heme solution is equivalent to 0.0019 mol of heme solute. Before starting the calculation, note that 150 mL of solution is equivalent to 150×10^{-3} L of solution:

$$150 \times 10^{-3}\ L\ soln \times \dfrac{0.0019\ mol\ heme}{1\ L\ solution} = 2.\underline{8}50 \times 10^{-4} = 2.9 \times 10^{-4}\ mol\ heme$$

4.77.   Multiply the volume of solution by molarity to convert it to moles; then convert to mass of solute by multiplying by the molar mass:

$$100.0 \times 10^{-3}\ L\ soln \times \dfrac{0.025\ mol\ Na_2Cr_2O_7}{1\ L\ solution} \times \dfrac{262.0\ g\ Na_2Cr_2O_7}{1\ mol\ Na_2Cr_2O_7} = 0.6\underline{5}50$$

$$= 0.66\ g\ Na_2Cr_2O_7$$

4.79.   Use the rearranged version of the dilution formula to calculate the initial volume of 15.8 M HNO_3 required:

$$V_i = \dfrac{M_f V_f}{M_i} = \dfrac{0.12\ M\ \times\ 1000\ mL}{15.8\ M} = 7.\underline{5}9 = 7.6\ mL$$

4.81.   The initial concentration of KCl (molar mass, 74.55 g/mol) is

$$4.00\ g\ KCl \times \dfrac{1\ mol\ KCl}{74.55\ g\ KCl} \times \dfrac{1}{0.0100\ L} = 5.3\underline{66}\ M$$

Using the dilution factor, $M_1V_1 = M_2V_2$, with $V_2 = 10.0$ mL $+ 60.0$ mL $= 70.0$ mL, after the solutions are mixed, the concentration of KCl is

$$M_2 = \frac{M_1V_1}{V_2} = \frac{5.366\ M\ \times\ 10.0\ \text{mL}}{70.0\ \text{mL}} = 0.76\underline{6}5\ M\ \text{KCl}$$

For $CaCl_2$, the concentration is

$$M_2 = \frac{M_1V_1}{V_2} = \frac{0.500\ M\ \times\ 60.0\ \text{mL}}{70.0\ \text{mL}} = 0.42\underline{8}57\ M\ CaCl_2$$

Therefore, the concentrations of the ions are 0.767 M K$^+$ and 0.429 M Ca^{2+}. For Cl$^-$, it is 0. 76$\underline{6}$5 M + 2 V 0.42$\underline{8}$57 M = 1.62$\underline{3}$6 M = 1.624 M

4.83. Use the appropriate conversion factors to convert the mass of BaSO$_4$ to the mass of Ba^{2+} ions:

$$0.513\ \text{g}\ BaSO_4\ \times\ \frac{1\ \text{mol}\ BaSO_4}{233.40\ \text{g}\ BaSO_4}\ \times\ \frac{1\ \text{mol}\ Ba^{2+}}{1\ \text{mol}\ BaSO_4}\ \times\ \frac{137.33\ \text{g}\ Ba^{2+}}{1\ \text{mol}\ Ba^{2+}}$$

$$= 0.30\underline{1}84\ \text{g}\ Ba^{2+}$$

Then calculate the percentage of barium in the 458 mg (0.458 g) compound:

$$\frac{0.30184\ \text{g}\ Ba^{2+}}{0.458\ \text{g}}\ \times\ 100\% = 65.\underline{9}039 = 65.9\%\ Ba^{2+}$$

4.85. a. The mass of chloride ion in the AgCl from the copper chloride compound is

$$86.00\ \text{mg}\ AgCl\ \times\ \frac{35.45\ \text{mg}\ Cl^-}{143.32\ \text{mg}\ AgCl} = 21.2\underline{7}1\ \text{mg}\ Cl^-$$

The percentage of chlorine in the 59.40 mg sample is

$$\frac{21.2\underline{7}1\ \text{mg}\ Cl^-}{59.40\ \text{mg sample}}\ \times\ 100\% = 35.8\underline{0}9 = 35.81\%\ Cl^-$$

b. Of the various approaches, it is as easy to calculate the theoretical percentage of Cl$^-$ in both CuCl and CuCl$_2$ as it is to use another approach:

$$CuCl:\ \frac{35.45\ \text{mg}\ Cl^-}{99.00\ \text{mg}\ CuCl}\ \times\ 100\% = 35.8\underline{0}8\%$$

$$CuCl_2:\ \frac{70.90\ \text{mg}\ Cl^-}{134.45\ \text{mg}\ CuCl_2}\ \times\ 100\% = 52.7\underline{3}3\%$$

The compound must be CuCl.

4.87. First, calculate the moles of chlorine in the compound:

$$0.3048\ \text{g}\ AgCl \times \frac{1\ \text{mol}\ AgCl}{143.32\ \text{g}\ AgCl}\ \times\ \frac{1\ \text{mol}\ Cl^-}{1\ \text{mol}\ AgCl} = 0.00212\underline{6}7\ \text{mol}\ Cl^-$$

Then, calculate the g Fe^{x+} from the g Cl^-:

$$g\ Fe^{x+} = 0.1348\ g\ comp - \left(0.0021267\ mol\ Cl^- \times \frac{35.45\ g\ Cl^-}{1\ mol\ Cl^-} \right) = 0.059408\ g\ Fe^{x+}$$

Now, calculate the moles of Fe^{x+} using the molar mass:

$$0.059408\ g\ Fe^{x+} \times \frac{1\ mol\ Fe^{x+}}{55.85\ g\ Fe^{x+}} = 0.0010637\ mol\ Fe^{x+}$$

Finally, divide the mole numbers by the smallest mole number:

For Cl: $\dfrac{0.002127\ mol\ Cl^-}{0.0010637\ mol} = 2.00$; for Fe^{x+}: $\dfrac{0.0010637\ mol\ Fe^{x+}}{0.0010637\ mol} = 1.00$

Thus, the formula is $FeCl_2$.

4.89.   Using molarity, convert the volume of Na_2CO_3 to moles of Na_2CO_3; then use the equation to convert to moles of HNO_3 and finally to volume:

$$2HNO_3 + Na_2CO_3 \rightarrow 2NaNO_3 + H_2O + CO_2$$

$$44.8 \times 10^{-3}\ L\ Na_2CO_3 \times \frac{0.150\ mol\ Na_2CO_3}{1\ L\ soln} \times \frac{2\ mol\ HNO_3}{1\ mol\ Na_2CO_3} \times \frac{1\ L\ HNO_3}{0.250\ mol\ HNO_3}$$

$$= 0.05376\ L = 0.0538\ L = 53.8\ mL$$

4.91.   The reaction is $H_2SO_4 + 2NaHCO_3 \rightarrow Na_2SO_4 + 2H_2O + CO_2$.

$$8.20\ g\ NaHCO_3 \times \frac{1\ mol\ NaHCO_3}{84.01\ g\ NaHCO_3} \times \frac{1\ mol\ H_2SO_4}{2\ mol\ NaHCO_3} \times \frac{1\ L\ soln}{0.150\ mol\ H_2SO_4}$$

$$= 0.3253\ L\ (325\ mL)\ soln$$

4.93.   First, find the mass of H_2O_2 required to react with $KMnO_4$.

$$5H_2O_2 + 2KMnO_4 + 3H_2SO_4 \rightarrow 5O_2 + 2MnSO_4 + K_2SO_4 + 8H_2O$$

$$51.7 \times 10^{-3}\ L\ soln \times \frac{0.145\ mol\ KMnO_4}{1\ L\ soln} \times \frac{5\ mol\ H_2O_2}{2\ mol\ KMnO_4} \times \frac{34.02\ g\ H_2O_2}{1\ mol\ H_2O_2}$$

$$= 0.6375\ g\ H_2O_2$$

Percent H_2O_2 = (mass H_2O_2 ÷ mass sample) × 100% = (0.6375 g ÷ 20.0 g) × 100% = 3.187

$$= 3.19\%$$

■ SOLUTIONS TO GENERAL PROBLEMS

4.95.   For the reaction of magnesium metal and hydrobromic acid, the equations are as follows.

Molecular equation: $Mg(s) + 2HBr(aq) \rightarrow H_2(g) + MgBr_2(aq)$

Ionic equation: $Mg(s) + 2H^+(aq) \rightarrow H_2(g) + Mg^{2+}(aq)$

4.97. For the reaction of nickel(II) sulfate and sodium hydroxide, the equations are as follows.

Molecular equation: $NiSO_4(aq) + 2NaOH(aq) \rightarrow Ni(OH)_2(s) + Na_2SO_4(aq)$

Ionic equation: $Ni^{2+}(aq) + 2OH^-(aq) \rightarrow Ni(OH)_2(s)$

4.99. a. Molecular equation: $LiOH(aq) + HCN(aq) \rightarrow LiCN(aq) + H_2O(l)$

Ionic equation: $OH^-(aq) + HCN(aq) \rightarrow CN^-(aq) + H_2O(l)$

b. Molecular equation: $Li_2CO_3(aq) + 2HNO_3(aq) \rightarrow 2LiNO_3(aq) + CO_2(g) + H_2O(l)$

Ionic equation: $CO_3^{2-}(aq) + 2H^+(aq) \rightarrow CO_2(g) + H_2O(l)$

c. Molecular equation: $LiCl(aq) + AgNO_3(aq) \rightarrow LiNO_3(aq) + AgCl(s)$

Ionic equation: $Cl^-(aq) + Ag^+(aq) \rightarrow AgCl(s)$

d. Molecular equation: $MgSO_4(aq) + NaCl(aq) \rightarrow NR$

(Na_2SO_4 and $MgCl_2$ are soluble.)

4.101. a. Molecular equation: $Sr(OH)_2(aq) + 2HC_2H_3O_2(aq) \rightarrow Sr(C_2H_3O_2)_2(aq) + 2H_2O(l)$

Ionic equation: $HC_2H_3O_2(aq) + OH^-(aq) \rightarrow C_2H_3O_2^-(aq) + H_2O(l)$

b. Molecular equation: $NH_4I(aq) + CsCl(aq) \rightarrow NR$

(NH_4Cl and CsI are soluble.)

c. Molecular equation: $NaNO_3(aq) + CsCl(aq) \rightarrow NR$

($NaCl$ and $CsNO_3$ are soluble.)

d. Molecular equation: $NH_4I(aq) + AgNO_3(aq) \rightarrow NH_4NO_3(aq) + AgI(s)$

Ionic equation: $I^-(aq) + Ag^+(aq) \rightarrow AgI(s)$

4.103. For each preparation, the compound to be prepared is given first, followed by the compound from which it is to be prepared. Then the method of preparation is given, followed by the molecular equation for the preparation reaction. Steps such as evaporation are not given in the molecular equation.

a. To prepare $CuCl_2$ from $CuSO_4$, add a solution of $BaCl_2$ to a solution of the $CuSO_4$, precipitating $BaSO_4$. The $BaSO_4$ can be filtered off, leaving aqueous $CuCl_2$, which can be obtained in solid form by evaporation. Molecular equation:

$$CuSO_4(aq) + BaCl_2(aq) \rightarrow BaSO_4(s) + CuCl_2(aq)$$

b. To prepare $Ca(C_2H_3O_2)_2$ from $CaCO_3$, add a solution of acetic acid, $HC_2H_3O_2$, to the solid $CaCO_3$, forming CO_2, H_2O, and aqueous $Ca(C_2H_3O_2)_2$. The aqueous $Ca(C_2H_3O_2)_2$ can be converted to the solid form by evaporation, which also removes the CO_2 and H_2O products. Molecular equation:

$$CaCO_3(s) + 2HC_2H_3O_2(aq) \rightarrow Ca(C_2H_3O_2)_2(aq) + CO_2(g) + H_2O(l)$$

c. To prepare $NaNO_3$ from Na_2SO_3, add a solution of nitric acid, HNO_3, to the solid Na_2SO_3, forming SO_2, H_2O, and aqueous $NaNO_3$. The aqueous $NaNO_3$ can be converted to the solid by evaporation, which also removes the SO_2 and H_2O products. Molecular equation:

$$Na_2SO_3(s) + 2HNO_3(aq) \rightarrow 2NaNO_3(aq) + SO_2(g) + H_2O(l)$$

d.   To prepare $MgCl_2$ from $Mg(OH)_2$, add a solution of hydrochloric acid (HCl) to the solid $Mg(OH)_2$, forming H_2O and aqueous $MgCl_2$. The aqueous $MgCl_2$ can be converted to the solid form by evaporation. Molecular equation:

$$Mg(OH)_2(s) + 2HCl(aq) \rightarrow MgCl_2(aq) + 2H_2O(l)$$

4.105. a.   Decomposition

b.   Decomposition

c.   Combination

d.   Displacement

4.107. a. $Pb(NO_3)_2 + H_2SO_4$ $[\rightarrow PbSO_4(s) + HNO_3(aq)]$

$Pb(NO_3)_2 + MgSO_4$ $[\rightarrow PbSO_4(s) + Mg(NO_3)_2(aq)]$

$Pb(NO_3)_2 + Ba(OH)_2$ $[\rightarrow Pb(OH)_2(s) + Ba(NO_3)_2(aq)]$

b. $Ba(OH)_2 + MgSO_4$ $[\rightarrow BaSO_4(s) + Mg(OH)_2(s)]$

c. $Ba(OH)_2 + H_2SO_4$ $[\rightarrow BaSO_4(s) + H_2O(l)]$

4.109. Divide the mass of $CaCl_2$ by its molar mass and volume to find molarity:

$$5.00 \text{ g } CaCl_2 \times \frac{1 \text{ mol } CaCl_2}{110.98 \text{ g } CaCl_2} \times \frac{1}{1.000 \text{ L soln}} = 0.045\underline{0}53 = 0.0451 \text{ } M \text{ } CaCl_2$$

The $CaCl_2$ dissolves to form Ca^{2+} and $2Cl^-$ ions. Therefore, the molarities of the ions are 0.0451 M Ca^{2+} and $2 \times 0.045\underline{0}53$, or 0.0901, M Cl^- ions.

4.111. Divide the mass of $K_2Cr_2O_7$ by its molar mass and volume to find molarity. Then calculate the volume needed to prepare 1.00 L of a 0.100 M solution.

$$89.3 \text{ g } K_2Cr_2O_7 \times \frac{1 \text{ mol } K_2Cr_2O_7}{294.20 \text{ g } K_2Cr_2O_7} = 0.30\underline{3}5 \text{ mol } K_2Cr_2O_7$$

$$\text{Molarity} = \frac{0.3035 \text{ mol } K_2Cr_2O_7}{1.00 \text{ L}} = 0.30\underline{3}5 \text{ } M$$

$$V_i = \frac{M_f \text{ x } V_f}{M_i} = \frac{0.100 \text{ } M \text{ } \times \text{ } 1.00 \text{ L}}{0.3035 \text{ } M} = 0.32\underline{9}4 \text{ L (329 mL)}$$

4.113. Assume a volume of 1.000 L (1000 cm^3) for the 6.00% NaBr solution, and convert to moles and then to molarity.

$$1000 \text{ } cm^3 \times \frac{1.046 \text{ g soln}}{1 \text{ } cm^3} \times \frac{6.00 \text{ g NaBr}}{100 \text{ g soln}} \times \frac{1 \text{ mol NaBr}}{102.89 \text{ g NaBr}} = 0.60\underline{9}9 \text{ mol}$$

$$\text{Molarity NaBr} = \frac{0.6099 \text{ mol NaBr}}{1.000 \text{ L}} = 0.60\underline{9}9 = 0.610 \text{ } M$$

4.115. First, calculate the moles of $BaCl_2$:

$$1.128 \text{ g BaSO}_4 \times \frac{1 \text{ mol BaSO}_4}{233.40 \text{ g BaSO}_4} \times \frac{1 \text{ mol BaCl}_2}{1 \text{ mol BaSO}_4} = 0.0048329 \text{ mol BaCl}_2$$

Then calculate the molarity from the moles and volume (0.0500 L):

$$\text{Molarity} = \frac{0.0048329 \text{ mol BaCl}_2}{0.0500 \text{ L}} = 0.096\underline{6}58 = 0.0967 \text{ } M$$

4.117. First, calculate the grams of thallium(I) sulfate:

$$0.2122 \text{ g TlI} \times \frac{1 \text{ mol TlI}}{331.28 \text{ g TlI}} \times \frac{1 \text{ mol Tl}_2\text{SO}_4}{2 \text{ mol TlI}} \times \frac{504.83 \text{ g Tl}_2\text{SO}_4}{1 \text{ mol Tl}_2\text{SO}_4} = 0.161\underline{6}8 \text{ g Tl}_2\text{SO}_4$$

Then calculate the percent Tl_2SO_4 in the rat poison:

$$\text{Percent Ti}_2\text{SO}_4 = \frac{0.16168 \text{ g}}{0.7590 \text{ g}} \times 100\% = 21.3\underline{0}1 = 21.30\%$$

4.119. The mass of copper(II) ion and the mass of sulfate ion in the 98.77-mg sample are

$$0.09877 \text{ g} \times 0.3250 = 0.0321\underline{0}0 \text{ g Cu}^{2+} \text{ ion}$$

$$0.11666 \text{ g BaSO}_4 \times \frac{96.07 \text{ g SO}_4^{2-}}{233.40 \text{ g BaSO}_4} = 0.0480\underline{1}9 = 0.04802 \text{ g SO}_4^{2-}$$

Mass of water left = $0.09877 \text{ g} - (0.03210 \text{ g Cu}^{2+} + 0.04802 \text{ g SO}_4^{2-}) = 0.01865 \text{ g H}_2\text{O}$

Moles of water left = $0.01865 \text{ g} \div 18.02 \text{ g/mol} = 1.035 \times 10^{-3} \text{ mol}$

Moles of Cu^{2+} = $0.03210 \text{ g} \div 63.55 \text{ g/mol} = 5.05\underline{1}1 \times 10^{-4} \text{ mol}$

Ratio of water to Cu^{2+}, or $CuSO_4$ = $1.035 \times 10^{-3} \div 5.0511 \times 10^{-4} = 2.05$, or 2

The formula is thus $CuSO_4 \bullet 2H_2O$.

4.121. For these calculations, the relative numbers of moles of gold and chlorine must be determined. These can be found from the masses of the two elements in the sample:

Total mass = mass of Au + mass of Cl = 328 mg

The mass of chlorine in the precipitated AgCl is equal to the mass of chlorine in the compound of gold and chlorine. The mass of Cl in the 0.464 g of AgCl is

$$0.464 \text{ g AgCl} \times \frac{1 \text{ mol AgCl}}{143.32 \text{ g AgCl}} \times \frac{1 \text{ mol Cl}}{1 \text{ mol AgCl}} \times \frac{35.45 \text{ g Cl}}{1 \text{ mol Cl}}$$

$$= 0.11\underline{4}76 \text{ g Cl} (114.76 \text{ mg Cl})$$

$$\text{Mass percentage Cl} = \frac{\text{mass Cl}}{\text{mass comp}} \times 100\% = \frac{114.76 \text{ mg}}{328 \text{ mg}} \times 100\% = 35.0\% \text{ Cl}$$

To find the empirical formula, convert each mass to moles:

Mass percentage Au = 328 mg − 11$\underline{4}$.76 mg Cl = 21$\underline{3}$.23 mg Au

$$0.11476 \text{ g Cl} \times \frac{1 \text{ mol Cl}}{35.45 \text{ g Cl}} = 0.0032\underline{38} \text{ mol Cl}$$

$$0.21323 \text{ g Au} \times \frac{1 \text{ mol Au}}{196.97 \text{ g Au}} = 0.0010\underline{82} \text{ mol Au}$$

Divide both numbers of moles by the smaller number (0.001082) to find the integers.

Integer for Cl: 0.003238 mol ÷ 0.001082 mol = 2.99, or 3

Integer for Au: 0.001082 mol ÷ 0.001082 mol = 1.00, or 1

The empirical formula is $AuCl_3$.

4.123.   From the equations $NH_3 + HCl \rightarrow NH_4Cl$ and $NaOH + HCl \rightarrow NaCl + H_2O$, we write

Mol NH_3 = mol HCl(NH_3)

Mol NaOH = mol HCl(NaOH)

We can calculate the mol NaOH and the sum [mol HCl(NH_3) + mol HCl(NaOH)] from the titration data. Because the sum equals mol NH_3 plus mol NaOH, we can calculate the unknown mol NH_3 from the difference: Mol NH_3 = sum − mol NaOH.

$$\text{Mol HCl (NaOH)} + \text{ mol HCl (NH}_3) = 0.0463 \text{ L} \times \frac{0.213 \text{ mol HCl}}{1.000 \text{ L}} = 0.0098\underline{62} \text{ mol HCl}$$

$$\text{Mol NaOH} = 0.0443 \text{ L} \times \frac{0.128 \text{ mol NaOH}}{1.000 \text{ L}} = 0.0056\underline{70} \text{ mol NaOH}$$

Mol HCl(NH_3) = 0.009862 mol − 0.005670 mol = 0.004192 mol

Mol NH_3 = mol HCl(NH_3) = 0.004192 mol NH_3

Because all the N in the $(NH_4)_2SO_4$ was liberated as and titrated as NH_3, the amount of N in the fertilizer is equal to the amount of N in the NH_3. Thus, the moles of NH_3 can be used to calculate the mass percentage of N in the fertilizer:

$$0.004192 \text{ mol NH}_3 \times \frac{1 \text{ mol N}}{1 \text{ mol NH}_3} \times \frac{14.01 \text{ g N}}{1 \text{ mol N}} = 0.058\underline{73} \text{ g N}$$

$$\text{Mass percentage N} = \frac{\text{mass N}}{\text{mass fert.}} \times 100\% = \frac{0.05873 \text{ g N}}{0.608 \text{ g}} \times 100\% = 9.6\underline{59} = 9.66\%$$

■ SOLUTIONS TO STRATEGY PROBLEMS

4.125. The final volume to which the solution must be diluted is

$$V_2 = \frac{M_1 V_1}{M_2} = \frac{(3.47\ M)\,(100\ \text{mL})}{1.78\ M} = 19\underline{4}.94\ \text{mL}$$

The amount of water that must be added is $19\underline{4}.94\ \text{mL} - 100\ \text{mL} = 9\underline{4}.94\ \text{mL}$. Since the density of water is 1.00 g/mL, this is equivalent to 94.94 g of water, so the amount of ice is

$$9\underline{4}.94\ \text{g water} \times \frac{3\ \text{g ice}}{1\ \text{g water}} = 28\underline{4}.83 = 285\ \text{g ice}$$

($\sim 3 \times 10^2$ g is more appropriate considering the precision of some the data given in the problem)

4.127. $0.248\ M \times 38.2 \times 10^{-3}\ \text{L} \times \dfrac{2\ \text{mol Al}^{3+}}{1\ \text{mol Al}_2(\text{SO}_4)_3} \times \dfrac{26.98\ \text{g}}{1\ \text{mol Al}^{3+}} = 0.51\underline{1}19 = 0.511\ \text{g}$

4.129. $3.33 \times 10^{23}\ \text{ions} \times \dfrac{1\ \text{mol}}{6.022 \times 10^{23}\ \text{ions}} \times \dfrac{1\ \text{mol Zn(C}_2\text{H}_3\text{O}_2)_2}{2\ \text{mol C}_2\text{H}_3\text{O}_2^-} \times \dfrac{183.478\ \text{g}}{1\ \text{mol}} = 50.7\underline{2}$

$$= 50.7\ \text{g Zn(C}_2\text{H}_3\text{O}_2)_2$$

4.131. The reactions are

$$6 \times (\text{K} \rightarrow \text{K}^+ + \text{e}^-)$$

$$\underline{1 \times (\text{N}_2 + 6\text{e}^- \rightarrow 2\text{N}^{3-}\,)}$$

$$6\text{K}(s) + \text{N}_2(g) + \cancel{6\text{e}^-} \rightarrow 2\text{K}_3\text{N}(s) + \cancel{6\text{e}^-}$$

Thus six electrons are canceled.

4.133. Since the solution is homogeneous, the concentration of the solution in the beaker is the same as the original solution, 0.196 M. The concentration of the solution in the large flask is also the same.

4.135. Because portions of solutions of identical concentration are being added together, the resulting mixture will have the same concentration as the original solutions, i.e., 0.50 M NaOH. It's instructive to show this using the molarity concept. The total volume of solution prepared is 0.100 L. From the 25-mL sample of 0.50 M NaOH, 0.0125 mol NaOH is provided; the 75-mL portion of 0.50 M NaOH provides another 0.0375 mol NaOH. Thus, a total of 0.0500 mol of NaOH is present in the 0.100 L mixture. The molarity is thus calculated:

$$[\text{NaOH}] = \frac{\text{total mol NaOH}}{\text{total volume of solution}} = \frac{0.050\ \text{mol}}{0.100\ \text{L}} = 0.500 M \text{ (as expected)}$$

4.137. This is a limiting reagent problem. Using the balanced chemical equation we first calculate the amounts of product possible from the given amounts of both reagents:

$$3.75\ \text{g Zn} \times \frac{1\ \text{mol Zn}}{65.38\ \text{g Zn}} \times \frac{2\ \text{mol NO}_2}{1\ \text{mol Zn}} \times \frac{46.01\ \text{g NO}_2}{1\ \text{mol NO}_2} = 5.2\underline{7}8\ \text{g NO}_2$$

$$0.175 \text{ L} \times \frac{0.500 \text{ mol HNO}_3}{1 \text{ L}} \times \frac{2 \text{ mol NO}_2}{4 \text{ mol HNO}_3} \times \frac{46.01 \text{ g NO}_2}{1 \text{ mol NO}_2} = 2.0\underline{1}3 \text{ g NO}_2$$

Thus, the nitric acid is the limiting reagent yielding 2.01 g of NO_2.

4.139. The key to solving this problem is a sound foundation in chemical nomenclature. The 0.250-L solution you are to prepare is to have 0.500 mol of NO_3^- ions per liter of solution. The source of the nitrate ions is a solution of 1.00 M $Ca(NO_3)_2$. Since there are two nitrate ions for every formula unit of calcium nitrate, the source solution must have 2.00 mol of NO_3^- ions present per liter of solution. With this information you can use the dilution equation:

$$M_1V_1 = M_2V_2$$

$$\frac{0.500 \text{ mol NO}_3^-}{1 \text{ L}} \times 0.250 \text{ L} = \frac{2.00 \text{ mol NO}_3^-}{1 \text{ L}} \times V_2$$

Solving for V_2 yields 0.0625 L, or 62.5 mL. To make the desired solution, you would take 62.5-mL of the source solution and dilute it with water to a total volume 250 mL with mixing.

■ SOLUTIONS TO CUMULATIVE-SKILLS PROBLEMS

4.141. For this reaction, the formulas are listed first, followed by the molecular and net ionic equations, the names of the products, and the molecular equation for another reaction giving the same precipitate.

Lead(II) nitrate is $Pb(NO_3)_2$, and cesium sulfate is Cs_2SO_4.

Molecular equation: $Pb(NO_3)_2(aq) + Cs_2SO_4(aq) \rightarrow PbSO_4(s) + 2CsNO_3(aq)$

Net ionic equation: $Pb^{2+}(aq) + SO_4^{2-}(aq) \rightarrow PbSO_4(s)$

$PbSO_4$ is lead(II) sulfate, and $CsNO_3$ is cesium nitrate.

Molecular equation: $Pb(NO_3)_2(aq) + Na_2SO_4(aq) \rightarrow PbSO_4(s) + 2NaNO_3(aq)$

4.143. Net ionic equation: $2Br^-(aq) + Cl_2(g) \rightarrow 2Cl^-(aq) + Br_2(l)$

Molecular equation: $CaBr_2(aq) + Cl_2(g) \rightarrow CaCl_2(aq) + Br_2(l)$

Mass Br_2 = 40.0 g + 14.2 g − 22.2 g = 32.0 g

Combining the three known masses gives the unknown mass of Br_2. Now, use a ratio of the known masses of $CaBr_2$ to Br_2 to convert pounds of Br_2 to grams of $CaBr_2$:

$$10.0 \text{ lb Br}_2 \times \frac{40.0 \text{ g CaBr}_2}{32.0 \text{ g Br}_2} \times \frac{453.6 \text{ g}}{1 \text{ lb}} = 56\underline{7}0 = 5.67 \times 10^3 \text{ g CaBr}_2$$

4.145. Molecular equation: $Hg(NO_3)_2 + H_2S(g) \rightarrow HgS(s) + 2HNO_3(aq)$

Net ionic equation: $Hg^{2+} + H_2S(g) \rightarrow HgS(s) + 2H^+(aq)$

The acid formed is nitric acid, a strong acid. The other product is mercury(II) sulfide.

Mass HNO_3 = (81.15 g + 8.52 g) − 58.16 g = 31.5$\underline{1}$ g

Mass of solution = 550.$\underline{0}$ g H_2O + 31.5$\underline{1}$ g HNO_3 = 581.$\underline{51}$ = 581.5 g

4.147. Let the number of Fe^{3+} ions equal y; then the number of Fe^{2+} ions equals $(7 - y)$. Since Fe_7S_8 is neutral, the number of positive charges must equal the number of negative charges. If the signs are omitted, then

Total charge on both Fe^{2+} and Fe^{3+} = total charge on all eight sulfide ions

$$3y + 2(7 - y) = 8 \times 2$$

$$y + 14 = 16$$

$$y = 2$$

Thus, the ratio of Fe^{2+} to Fe^{3+} is 5/2.

4.149. Use the density, formula mass,, and percentage to convert to molarity. Then combine the 0.200 mol with mol/L to obtain the volume in liters.

$$\frac{0.807 \text{ g soln}}{1 \text{ mL}} \times \frac{0.940 \text{ g ethanol}}{1.00 \text{ g soln}} \times \frac{1 \text{ mol ethanol}}{46.07 \text{ g ethanol}} \times \frac{1000 \text{ mL}}{1 \text{ L}} = \frac{16.\underline{4}65 \text{ mol ethanol}}{1 \text{ L ethanol}}$$

$$\text{L ethanol} = 0.200 \text{ mol ethanol} \times \frac{1 \text{ L ethanol}}{16.465 \text{ mol ethanol}} = 0.012\underline{1}46 = 0.0121 \text{ L}$$

4.151. Convert the 2.183 g of AgI to mol AgI, which is chemically equivalent to mol KI. Use that to calculate the molarity of the KI.

$$2.183 \text{ g AgI} \times \frac{1 \text{ mol AgI}}{234.77 \text{ g AgI}} = 9.29\underline{8}4 \times 10^{-3} \text{ mol AgI (equivalent to mol KI)}$$

$$\text{Molarity} = \frac{9.29\underline{8}4 \times 10^{-3} \text{ mol KI}}{0.0100 \text{ L}} = 0.929\underline{8} = 0.930 \ M$$

4.153. Convert the 6.026 g of $BaSO_4$ to moles of $BaSO_4$; then, from the equation, deduce that 3 mol of $BaSO_4$ is equivalent to 1 mol of $M_2(SO_4)_3$ and is equivalent to 2 mol of M. Use that with 1.200 g of the metal M to calculate the atomic mass of M.

$$6.026 \text{ g BaSO}_4 \times \frac{1 \text{ mol BaSO}_4}{233.40 \text{ g BaSO}_4} \times \frac{2 \text{ mol M}}{3 \text{ mol BaSO}_4} = 0.01721\underline{2} \text{ mol M}$$

$$\text{Atomic mass of M in g/mol} = \frac{1.200 \text{ g M}}{0.01721\underline{2} \text{ mol M}} = 69.7\underline{1}9 \text{ g/mol (gallium)}$$

4.155. Use the density, formula mass, percentage, and volume to convert to moles of H_3PO_4. Then, from the equation $P_4O_{10} + 6H_2O \rightarrow 4H_3PO_4$, deduce that 4 mol H_3PO_4 is equivalent to 1 mol of P_4O_{10}, and use that to convert to moles of P_4O_{10}.

$$15\underline{0}0 \text{ mL} \times \frac{1.025 \text{ g soln}}{1 \text{ mL}} \times \frac{0.0500 \text{ g H}_3\text{PO}_4}{1 \text{ g soln}} \times \frac{1 \text{ mol H}_3\text{PO}_4}{98.00 \text{ g H}_3\text{PO}_4} = 0.78\underline{4}4 \text{ mol H}_3\text{PO}_4$$

$$0.78\underline{4}4 \text{ mol H}_3\text{PO}_4 \times \frac{1 \text{ mol P}_4\text{O}_{10}}{4 \text{ mol H}_3\text{PO}_4} = 0.19\underline{6}1 \text{ mol P}_4\text{O}_{10}$$

$$\text{Mass P}_4\text{O}_{10} = 0.19\underline{6}1 \text{ mol P}_4\text{O}_{10} \times \frac{283.92 \text{ g P}_4\text{O}_{10}}{1 \text{ mol P}_4\text{O}_{10}} = 55.\underline{6}77 = 55.7 \text{ g P}_4\text{O}_{10}$$

4.157.   Convert the 0.1068 g of hydrogen to moles of H_2; then deduce from the equation that 3 moles of H_2 is equivalent to 2 mol of Al. Use the moles of Al to calculate mass of Al and the percentage Al.

$$0.1068 \text{ g } H_2 \times \frac{1 \text{ mol } H_2}{2.016 \text{ g } H_2} \times \frac{2 \text{ mol Al}}{3 \text{ mol } H_2} = 0.035317 \text{ mol Al}$$

$$\text{Percentage Al} = \frac{0.035317 \text{ mol Al} \times \dfrac{26.98 \text{ g Al}}{1 \text{ mol Al}}}{1.118 \text{ g alloy}} \times 100\% = 85.229 = 85.23\%$$

4.159.   Use the formula mass of $Al_2(SO_4)_3$ to convert to moles of $Al_2(SO_4)_3$. Then deduce from the equation that 1 mol of $Al_2(SO_4)_3$ is equivalent to 3 mol of H_2SO_4, and calculate the moles of H_2SO_4 needed. Combine density, percentage, and formula mass to obtain molarity of H_2SO_4. Then combine molarity and moles to obtain volume.

$$37.4 \text{ g } Al_2(SO_4)_3 \times \frac{1 \text{ mol } Al_2(SO_4)_3}{342.17 \text{ g } Al_2(SO_4)_3} \times \frac{3 \text{ mol } H_2SO_4}{1 \text{ mol } Al_2(SO_4)_3} = 0.3279 \text{ mol } H_2SO_4$$

$$\frac{1.104 \text{ g soln}}{1 \text{ mL}} \times \frac{15.0 \text{ g } H_2SO_4}{100 \text{ g soln}} \times \frac{1 \text{ mol } H_2SO_4}{98.09 \text{ g } H_2SO_4} \times \frac{1000 \text{ mL}}{1 \text{ L}} = 1.688 \text{ mol } H_2SO_4 \text{ /L}$$

$$0.3279 \text{ mol } H_2SO_4 \times \frac{1 \text{ L } H_2SO_4}{1.688 \text{ mol } H_2SO_4} = 0.1942 = 0.194 \text{ L (194 mL)}$$

4.161.   The equations for the neutralization are $2HCl + Mg(OH)_2 \rightarrow MgCl_2 + 2H_2O$ and $3HCl + Al(OH)_3 \rightarrow AlCl_3 + 3H_2O$. Calculate the moles of HCl, and set it equal to the total moles of hydroxide ion, OH^-.

$$0.0485 \text{ L HCl} \times \frac{0.187 \text{ mol HCl}}{1 \text{ L HCl}} = 0.0090695 \text{ mol HCl}$$

$$0.0090695 \text{ mol HCl} = 2 \text{ [mol } Mg(OH)_2] + 3 \text{ [mol } Al(OH)_3]$$

Rearrange the last equation, and solve for the moles of $Al(OH)_3$.

(Eq 1) mol $Al(OH)_3$ = 0.0030231 mol HCl − 2/3 [mol $Mg(OH)_2$]

The total mass of chloride salts is equal to the sum of the masses of $MgCl_2$ (molar mass = 95.21 g/mol) and $AlCl_3$ (molar mass = 133.33 g/mol).

[95.21 g/mol × mol $MgCl_2$] + [133.33 g/mol × mol $AlCl_3$] = 0.4200 g

Since the moles of $Mg(OH)_2$ equals the moles of $MgCl_2$, and the moles of $Al(OH)_3$ equals the moles of $AlCl_3$, you can substitute these quantities into the last equation and get

[95.21 g/mol × mol $Mg(OH)_2$] + [133.33 g/mol × mol $Al(OH)_3$] = 0.4200 g

Substitute Equation 1 into this equation for the moles of $Al(OH)_3$:

[95.21 g/mol × mol $Mg(OH)_2$] + [133.33 g/mol × (0.0030231 mol − 2/3 mol $Mg(OH)_2$)]

= 0.4200 g

Rearrange the equation, and solve for the moles of $Mg(OH)_2$.

$$6.323 \text{ mol } Mg(OH)_2 + 0.403070 = 0.4200$$

$$\text{mol } Mg(OH)_2 = 0.01693 \div 6.323 = 0.0026728 \text{ mol}$$

Calculate the mass of $Mg(OH)_2$ in the antacid tablet (molar mass = 58.33 g/mol).

$$0.0026728 \text{ mol } Mg(OH)_2 \times \frac{58.33 \text{ g } Mg(OH)_2}{1 \text{ mol } Mg(OH)_2} = 0.15590 \text{ g } Mg(OH)_2$$

Use Eq 1 to find the moles and mass of $Al(OH)_3$ (molar mass 78.00 g/mol) in a similar fashion.

$$\text{mol } Al(OH)_3 = 0.0030231 - 2/3[0.0026728 \text{ mol } Mg(OH)_2] = 0.0012412 \text{ mol}$$

$$0.0012412 \text{ mol } Al(OH)_3 \times \frac{78.00 \text{ g } Al(OH)_3}{1 \text{ mol } Al(OH)_3} = 0.096681 \text{ g } Al(OH)_3$$

The mass percentage $Mg(OH)_2$ in the antacid is

$$\text{Mass percentage of } Mg(OH)_2 = [0.15590 \text{ g} \div (0.15590 + 0.096681) \text{ g}] \times 100\%$$

$$= 61.72 = 61.7\%$$

CHAPTER 5

The Gaseous State

■ SOLUTIONS TO EXERCISES

Note on significant figures: If the final answer to a solution needs to be rounded off, it is given first with one nonsignificant figure, and the last significant figure is underlined. The final answer is then rounded to the correct number of significant figures. In multistep problems, intermediate answers are given with at least one nonsignificant figure; however, only the final answer has been rounded off.

5.1.   First, convert to atm (57 kPa = 57×10^3 Pa).

$$57 \times 10^3 \text{ Pa} \times \frac{1 \text{ atm}}{1.01325 \times 10^5 \text{ Pa}} = 0.5\underline{6}2 = 0.56 \text{ atm}$$

Next, convert to mmHg.

$$57 \times 10^3 \text{ Pa} \times \frac{760 \text{ mmHg}}{1.01325 \times 10^5 \text{ Pa}} = 42\underline{7}.5 = 4.3 \times 10^2 \text{ mmHg}$$

5.2.   Application of Boyle's law gives

$$V_f = V_i \times \frac{P_i}{P_f} = 20.0 \text{ L} \times \frac{1.00 \text{ atm}}{0.830 \text{ atm}} = 24.\underline{0}96 = 24.1 \text{ L}$$

5.3.   First, convert the temperatures to the Kelvin scale.

$T_i = (19 + 273) = 292$ K

$T_f = (25 + 273) = 298$ K

Following is the data table.

$V_i = 4.38 \text{ dm}^3$ $P_i = 101$ kPa $T_i = 292$ K

$V_f = ?$ $P_f = 101$ kPa $T_f = 298$ K

Apply Charles's law to obtain

$$V_f = V_i \times \frac{T_f}{T_i} = 4.38 \text{ dm}^3 \times \frac{298 \text{ K}}{292 \text{ K}} = 4.4\underline{7}0 = 4.47 \text{ dm}^3$$

5.4.   First, convert the temperatures to kelvins.

$T_i = (24 + 273) = 297$ K

$T_f = (35 + 273) = 308$ K

Following is the data table.

$$V_i = 5.41 \text{ dm}^3 \qquad P_i = 101.5 \text{ kPa} \qquad T_i = 297 \text{ K}$$

$$V_f = ? \qquad P_f = 102.8 \text{ kPa} \qquad T_f = 308 \text{ K}$$

Apply both Boyle's law and Charles's law combined to get

$$V_f = V_i \times \frac{P_i}{P_f} \times \frac{T_f}{T_i} = 5.41 \text{ dm}^3 \times \frac{101.5 \text{ kPa}}{102.8 \text{ kPa}} \times \frac{308 \text{ K}}{297 \text{ K}} = 5.5\underline{3}9 = 5.54 \text{ dm}^3$$

5.5. Use the ideal gas law, $PV = nRT$, and solve for n:

$$n = \frac{PV}{RT} = \left(\frac{V}{RT}\right)P$$

Note that everything in parentheses is constant. Therefore, you can write

$$n = \text{constant} \times P$$

Or, expressing this as a proportion,

$$n \propto P$$

5.6. First, convert the mass of O_2 to moles of O_2 (molar mass 32.00 g/mol) and convert temperature to kelvins.

$$T = 23 + 273 = 296 \text{ K}$$

$$3.03 \text{ kg } O_2 \times \frac{1000 \text{ g}}{1 \text{ kg}} \times \frac{1 \text{ mol } O_2}{32.00 \text{ g } O_2} = 94.\underline{6}88 \text{ mol } O_2$$

Summarize the data in a table.

Variable	Value
P	?
V	50.0 L
T	296 K
n	94.$\underline{6}$88 mol

Solve the ideal gas equation for P, and substitute the data to get

$$P = \frac{nRT}{V} = \frac{(94.6\underline{8}8)(0.08206 \text{ L} \cdot \text{atm/K} \cdot \text{mol})(296 \text{ K})}{50.0 \text{ L}} = 46.\underline{0}0 = 46.0 \text{ atm}$$

5.7.   The data given are

Variable	Value
P	$752 \text{ mmHg} \times \dfrac{1 \text{ atm}}{760 \text{ mmHg}} = 0.98\underline{9}47 \text{ atm}$
V	1 L (exact number)
T	$(21 + 273) = 294 \text{ K}$
n	?

Using the ideal gas law, solve for n, the moles of helium.

$$n = \frac{PV}{RT} = \frac{(0.98\underline{9}47 \text{ atm})(1 \text{ L})}{(0.08206 \text{ L} \cdot \text{atm/K} \cdot \text{mol})(294 \text{ K})} = 0.041\underline{0}1 \text{ mol}$$

Now convert mol He to grams.

$$0.041\underline{0}1 \text{ mol He} \times \frac{4.00 \text{ g He}}{1 \text{ mol He}} = 0.16\underline{4}04 \text{ g He}$$

Therefore, the density of He at 21°C and 752 mmHg is 0.164 g/L.

The difference in mass between one liter of air and one liter of helium is

Mass air − mass He = 1.188 g − 0.16\underline{4}04 g = 1.02\underline{3}96 = 1.024 g difference

5.8.   Tabulate the values of the variables.

Variable	Value
P	0.862 atm
V	1 L (exact number)
T	$(25 + 273) = 298 \text{ K}$
n	?

From the ideal gas law, $PV = nRT$, you obtain

$$n = \frac{PV}{RT} = \frac{(0.862 \text{ atm})(1 \text{ L})}{(0.08206 \text{ L} \cdot \text{atm/K} \cdot \text{mol})(298 \text{ K})} = 0.03\underline{5}25 \text{ mol}$$

Dividing the mass of the vapor by moles gives you the mass per mole (the molar mass).

$$\text{Molar mass} = \frac{\text{grams vapor}}{\text{moles vapor}} = \frac{2.26 \text{ g}}{0.03525 \text{ mol}} = 64.\underline{1}14 \text{ g/mol}$$

Therefore, the molecular mass is 64.1 amu.

5.9. First, determine the number of moles of Cl_2 from the mass of HCl (molar mass 36.46 g/mol) and from the stoichiometry of the chemical equation:

$$9.41 \text{ g HCl} \times \frac{1 \text{ mol HCl}}{36.46 \text{ g HCl}} \times \frac{5 \text{ mol Cl}_2}{16 \text{ mol HCl}} = 0.080\underline{6}53 \text{ mol Cl}_2$$

Tabulate the values of the variables:

Variable	Value
P	$787 \text{ mmHg} \times \dfrac{1 \text{ atm}}{760 \text{ mmHg}} = 1.0355 \text{ atm}$
T	$(40 + 273) \text{ K} = 313 \text{ K}$
n	$0.080\underline{6}53 \text{ mol}$
V	?

Rearrange the ideal gas law to obtain V:

$$V = \frac{nRT}{P} = \frac{(0.080653 \text{ mol})(0.08206 \text{ L} \cdot \text{atm/K} \cdot \text{mol})(313 \text{ K})}{1.0355 \text{ atm}} = 2.0\underline{0}1 = 2.00 \text{ L}$$

5.10. Each gas obeys the ideal gas law. In each case, convert grams to moles and substitute into the ideal gas law to determine the partial pressure of each.

$$1.031 \text{ g O}_2 \times \frac{1 \text{ mol O}_2}{32.00 \text{ g O}_2} = 0.0322\underline{1}88 \text{ mol O}_2$$

$$P = \frac{nRT}{V} = \frac{(0.0322188)(0.08206 \text{ L} \cdot \text{atm/K} \cdot \text{mol})(291 \text{ K})}{10.0 \text{ L}} = 0.076\underline{9}36 \text{ atm}$$

$$0.572 \text{ g CO}_2 \times \frac{1 \text{ mol CO}_2}{44.01 \text{ g CO}_2} = 0.012\underline{9}97 \text{ mol CO}_2$$

$$P = \frac{nRT}{V} = \frac{(0.012997)(0.08206 \text{ L} \cdot \text{atm/K} \cdot \text{mol})(291 \text{ K})}{10.0 \text{ L}} = 0.031\underline{0}36 \text{ atm}$$

The total pressure is equal to the sum of the partial pressures:

$$P = P_{O_2} + P_{CO_2} = 0.076\underline{9}36 + 0.031\underline{0}36 = 0.107\underline{9}7 = 0.1080 \text{ atm}$$

The mole fraction of oxygen in the mixture is

$$\text{Mole fraction O}_2 = \frac{P_{O_2}}{P} = \frac{0.07694 \text{ atm}}{0.10802 \text{ atm}} = 0.71\underline{2}2 = 0.712$$

5.11. Determine the number of moles of O_2 from the mass of $KClO_3$ and from the stoichiometry of the chemical reaction.

$$1.300 \text{ g KClO}_3 \times \frac{1 \text{ mol KClO}_3}{122.5 \text{ g KClO}_3} \times \frac{3 \text{ mol O}_2}{2 \text{ mol KClO}_3} = 0.0159\underline{1}84 \text{ mol O}_2$$

The vapor pressure of water at 23°C is 21.1 mmHg (Table 5.6). Find the partial pressure of O_2 using Dalton's law:

$$P = P_{O_2} + P_{H_2O}$$

$$P_{O_2} = P - P_{H_2O} = (745 - 21.1) \text{ mmHg} = 72\underline{3}.9 \text{ mmHg}$$

Solve for the volume using the ideal gas law.

Variable	Value
P	$723.9 \text{ mmHg} \times \dfrac{1 \text{ atm}}{760 \text{ mmHg}} = 0.95\underline{2}5 \text{ atm}$
V	?
T	$(23 + 273) = 296 \text{ K}$
n	0.0159184

From the ideal gas law, $PV = nRT$, you have

$$V = \frac{nRT}{P} = \frac{(0.0159184 \text{ mol})(0.08206 \text{ L} \cdot \text{atm/K} \cdot \text{mol})(296 \text{ K})}{0.9525 \text{ atm}} = 0.40\underline{5}9 = 0.406 \text{ L}$$

5.12.   The absolute temperature is $(22 + 273) = 295$ K. In SI units, the molar mass of carbon tetrachloride, CCl_4, is 153.8×10^{-3} kg/mol. Therefore,

$$u = \left(\frac{3RT}{M}\right)^{\frac{1}{2}} = \left(\frac{3 \times 8.31 \text{ kg} \cdot \text{m}^2/(\text{s}^2 \cdot \text{K} \cdot \text{mol}) \times 295 \text{ K}}{153.8 \times 10^{-3} \text{ kg/mol}}\right)^{\frac{1}{2}} = 21\underline{8}.7 = 219 \text{ m/s}$$

5.13.   Determine the rms molecular speed for N_2 at 455°C (728 K):

$$u = \left(\frac{3RT}{M}\right)^{\frac{1}{2}} = \left(\frac{3 \times 8.31 \text{ kg} \cdot \text{m}^2/(\text{s}^2 \cdot \text{K} \cdot \text{mol}) \times 728 \text{ K}}{28.02 \times 10^{-3} \text{ kg/mol}}\right)^{\frac{1}{2}} = 80\underline{4}.81 \text{ m/s}$$

After writing this equation with the same speed for H_2, square both sides and solve for T. The molar mass of H_2 in SI units is 2.016×10^{-3} kg/mol. Therefore,

$$T = \frac{u^2 M}{3R} = \frac{(804.81 \text{ m/s})^2 (2.016 \times 10^{-3} \text{ kg/mol})}{(3)(8.31 \text{ kg} \cdot \text{m}^2/\text{s}^2 \cdot \text{K} \cdot \text{mol})} = 52.\underline{3}79 = 52.4 \text{ K}$$

Because the average kinetic energy of a molecule is proportional to only T, the temperature at which an H_2 molecule has the same average kinetic energy as an N_2 molecule at 455°C is exactly the same temperature, 455°C.

5.14.   The two rates of effusion are inversely proportional to the square roots of their molar masses, so you can write

$$\frac{\text{Rate of effusion of } O_2}{\text{Rate of effusion of He}} = \sqrt{\frac{M_m(\text{He})}{M_m(O_2)}}$$

where $M_m(\text{He})$ is the molar mass of He (4.00 g/mol) and $M_m(O_2)$ is the molar mass of O_2 (32.00 g/mol). Substituting these values into the formula gives

$$\frac{\text{Rate of effusion of O}_2}{\text{Rate of effusion of He}} = \sqrt{\frac{4.00 \text{ g/mol}}{32.00 \text{ g/mol}}} = 0.35\underline{3}55$$

Rearranging gives

Rate of effusion of $O_2 = 0.35\underline{3}55 \times$ rate of effusion of He.

Now, the problem states that the rate of effusion can be given in terms of volume of gas effused per second, so

$$\frac{\text{Volume of O}_2}{\text{Time for O}_2} = 0.35\underline{3}55 \times \frac{\text{Volume of He}}{\text{Time for He}}$$

Substituting in the values gives

$$\frac{10.0 \text{ mL}}{\text{Time for O}_2} = 0.35\underline{3}55 \times \frac{10.0 \text{ mL}}{3.52 \text{ s}}$$

Rearranging gives

$$\text{Time for O}_2 = \frac{3.52 \text{ s}}{0.35\underline{3}55} = 9.9\underline{5}6 = 9.96 \text{ s}$$

5.15.   The problem states that the rate of effusion is inversely proportional to the time it takes for a gas to effuse, so you can write

$$\frac{\text{Rate of effusion of H}_2}{\text{Rate of effusion of gas}} = \frac{\text{time for gas}}{\text{time for H}_2} = \sqrt{\frac{M_m(\text{gas})}{M_m(\text{H}_2)}} = 4.67$$

Rearranging and solving for $M_m(\text{H}_2)$ gives

$$M_m(\text{gas}) = (4.67)^2 \times M_m(\text{H}_2) = (4.67)^2 \times 2.016 \text{ g/mol} = 43.\underline{9}6 = 44.0 \text{ g/mol}$$

Thus, the molecular mass of the gas is 44.0 amu.

5.16.   From Table 5.7, $a = 5.570 \text{ L}^2 \bullet \text{atm/mol}^2$ and $b = 0.06499 \text{ L/mol}$. Substitute these values into the van der Waals equation, along with $R = 0.08206 \text{ L} \bullet \text{atm/K} \bullet \text{mol}$, $T = 273.2 \text{ K}$, $n = 1.000 \text{ mol}$, and $V = 22.41 \text{ L}$.

$$P = \frac{nRT}{(V - nb)} - \frac{n^2 a}{V^2}$$

$$P = \frac{(1.00 \text{ mol})(0.08206 \text{ L} \bullet \text{atm/K} \bullet \text{mol})(273.2 \text{ K})}{22.41 \text{ L} - (1.00 \text{ mol})(0.06499 \text{ L/mol})} - \frac{(1.00 \text{ mol})^2 (5.570 \text{ L}^2 \bullet \text{atm/mol}^2)}{(22.41 \text{ L})^2}$$

$$= 1.00\underline{3}3 - 0.011091 = 0.99\underline{2}21 = 0.992 \text{ atm}$$

Using the ideal gas law, $P = 1.00\underline{0}4$ atm (larger).

■ ANSWERS TO CONCEPT CHECKS

5.1.   The general relationship between pressure (P) and the height (h) of a liquid column in a barometer is $P = gdh$, where g is the constant acceleration of gravity and d is the density. Examination of the relationship indicates that, for a given pressure, as the density of the liquid in the barometer decreases, the height of the liquid must increase. In order to make this relationship more apparent, you can rearrange the equation to

$$gh = \frac{P}{d}$$

Because you are conducting the experiment at constant pressure and gravity is a constant, this mathematical relationship demonstrates that the height of the liquid in the barometer is inversely proportional to the density of the liquid in the barometer.

$$(h \propto \frac{1}{d})$$

This inverse relationship means that as the height of the liquid decreases, the density of the liquid must increase. Since the density of mercury is greater than the density of water, the barometer with the water will have the higher column.

5.2.   a.   In the first step, when the temperature decreases, the pressure will also decrease. This is because, according to the combined gas law, the pressure is directly proportional to the temperature ($P \propto T$). In the second step, when the volume increases, the pressure will decrease, since, according to Boyle's law, pressure and volume are inversely related ($P \propto 1/V$). Both changes result in the pressure decreasing, so the final pressure will be less than the starting pressure.

b.   In the first step, when the temperature increases, the pressure will also increase. This is because, according to the combined gas law, pressure is directly proportional to the temperature ($P \propto T$). In the second step, when the volume decreases, the pressure will increase, since, according to the ideal gas law, pressure and volume are inversely related ($P \propto 1/V$). Both changes result in the pressure increasing, so the final pressure will be greater than the starting pressure.

5.3.   a.   According to Avogadro's law, equal volumes of any two (or more) gases at the same temperature and pressure contain the same number of molecules (or atoms in this case). Therefore, all three flasks contain the same number of atoms.

b.   Since density is mass divided by volume, and all three flasks have the same volume (3.0 L), the gas with the largest molar mass, xenon (Xe), will have the greatest density.

c.   According to the ideal gas law, $PV = nRT$, pressure is directly proportional to the temperature. Since the helium flask is being heated, it will have the highest pressure.

d.   Since the three flasks started with the same number of atoms, and hence the same number of moles, they would all still have the same number of moles no matter how the temperatures of the flasks were changed.

5.4.   a.   In a mixture of gases, each gas exerts the pressure it would exert if it were the only gas in the flask. The pressure of H_2 is the same whether it is in the flask by itself or with the Ar. Therefore, the pressure of H_2 does not change.

b.   According to the ideal gas law, $PV = nRT$, pressure (P) is directly proportional to the number of moles (n). Since the number of moles of H_2 and the number of moles of Ar are equal, their pressures are also equal.

c.   The total pressure is equal to the sum of the pressures of the H_2 gas and the Ar gas in the container. The total pressure will also be equal to twice the pressure of the H_2 gas when it was in the flask by itself. It is also equal to twice the pressure that the Ar gas would exert if it were in the flask by itself.

5.5.   As the temperature of the gas is lowered, the average kinetic energy and velocity of the gaseous atoms decrease. Therefore, the pressure of the gas would decrease because (c) the frequency and force of the collisions of the helium atoms with the container walls decrease with decreasing temperature.

5.6.   a.   The rate of effusion is inversely proportional to the square root of the molecular mass of the gas at constant temperature and pressure. Thus, He (molecular mass 4.00 amu) will diffuse faster than Ar (molecular weight 39.95 amu) and reach the end of the tube first.

b.   The speed of an atom is directly proportional to the absolute temperature. If you raise the temperature of the Ar, you can make it reach the end of the tube at the same time as the He.

5.7.   a.   If the real gas molecules occupy a relatively small volume, then the volume of the gas is essentially equal to the volume of the container, the same as for an ideal gas. However, if there were large intermolecular attractions, the pressure would be less than for an ideal gas. Therefore, the pressure would be greater for the ideal gas.

b.   If the real gas molecules occupy a relatively large volume, then the volume available for the gas is less than for an ideal gas, and the pressure will be greater. If there are negligible intermolecular attractions, then the pressure is essentially the same as for an ideal gas. Overall, the pressure would be less for the ideal gas.

c.   Since the effect of molecular volume and intermolecular attractions on the pressure of a real gas are opposite, you cannot determine how the pressure of the two gases compare.

■ ANSWERS TO SELF-ASSESSMENT AND REVIEW QUESTIONS

5.1.   Pressure is the force exerted per unit area of surface. Force is further defined as mass multiplied by acceleration. The SI unit of mass is kg, of acceleration is m/s^2, and of area is m^2. Therefore, the SI unit of pressure (Pascal) is given by

$$\text{Pressure} = \frac{\text{force}}{\text{area}} = \frac{\text{mass} \times \text{acceleration}}{\text{area}} = \frac{\text{kg} \times \text{m/s}^2}{\text{m}^2} = \frac{\text{kg}}{\text{m} \cdot \text{s}^2} = \text{Pa}$$

5.2.   A manometer is a device that measures the pressure of a gas in a vessel. The gas pressure in the flask is proportional to the difference in height between the liquid levels in the manometer (Figure 5.4).

5.3.   The general relationship between the pressure (P) and the height (h) of the liquid in a manometer is $P = gdh$. Therefore, the variables that determine the height of the liquid in a manometer are the density (d) of the liquid and the pressure of the gas being measured. The acceleration of gravity (g) is a constant, 9.81 m/s^2.

5.4. From Boyle's law, PV = constant. Because this is true for conditions P_i and V_i as well as conditions P_f and V_f, we can write

$$P_f V_f = P_i V_i = \text{constant}$$

Dividing both sides of this equation by P_f gives

$$V_f = V_i \times \frac{P_i}{P_f}$$

5.5. A linear relationship between variables such as x and y is given by the mathematical relation

$$y = a + bx$$

The variable y is directly proportional to x only if $a = 0$.

5.6. First, find the equivalent of absolute zero on the Fahrenheit scale. Converting $-273.15°C$ to degrees Fahrenheit, you obtain $-459.67°F$. Since the volume of a gas varies linearly with the temperature, you get the following linear relationship:

$$V = a + bt_F$$

where t_F is the temperature on the Fahrenheit scale. Since the volume of an ideal gas is zero at absolute zero, you get

$$0 = a + b(-459.67), \text{ or } a = 459.67b$$

The equation can now be rewritten as

$$V = 459.67b + bt_F = b(459.67 + t_F) = bT_F$$

where T_F is the temperature in the new absolute scale based on the Fahrenheit scale. The relationship is

$$T_F = t_F + 459.67$$

5.7. From Charles's law, V = constant $\times T$. Because this is true for conditions T_i and V_i as well as conditions T_f and V_f, we can write

$$\frac{V_f}{T_f} = \frac{V_i}{T_i} = \text{constant}$$

Multiplying both sides of the equation by T_f gives

$$V_f = V_i \times \frac{T_f}{T_i}$$

5.8. Avogadro's law states that equal volumes of any two gases at the same temperature and pressure contain the same number of molecules. The law of combining volumes states that the volumes of reactant gases at a given pressure and temperature are in ratios of small whole numbers. The combining-volume law may be explained from Avogadro's law using the reaction $N_2 + 3H_2 \rightarrow 2NH_3$ as follows. In this equation, the molecules are in a ratio of small whole numbers, 1 to 3 to 2. In Avogadro's law, these numbers represent volumes. But since equal volumes contain the same number of molecules, the ratios for volumes are the same as the ratios for molecules.

5.9. The standard conditions are $0°C$ and 1 atm pressure (STP).

5.10. The molar gas volume, V_m, is the volume of one mole of gas at any given temperature and pressure. At standard conditions (STP), the molar gas volume equals 22.4 L.

5.11. Boyle's law ($V \propto 1/P$) and Charles's law ($V \propto T$) can be combined and expressed in a single statement: the volume occupied by a given amount of gas is proportional to the absolute temperature divided by the pressure. In equation form, this is

$$V = \text{constant} \times \frac{T}{P}$$

The constant is independent of temperature and pressure but does depend on the amount of gas. For one mole, the constant will have a specific value, denoted as R. The molar volume, V_m, is

$$V_m = R \times \frac{T}{P}$$

Because V_m has the same value for all gases, we can write this equation for n moles of gas if we multiply both sides by n. This yields the equation

$$nV_m = \frac{nRT}{P}$$

Because V_m is the volume per mole, nV_m is the total volume V. Substituting gives

$$V = \frac{nRT}{P} \quad \text{or} \quad PV = nRT$$

5.12. The variables in the ideal gas law are P, V, n, and T. The SI units of these variables are pascals (P), cubic meters (V), moles (n), and kelvins (T).

5.13. Use the value of R from Table 5.5 and the conversion factor 1 atm = 760 mmHg. This gives

$$0.082058 \, \frac{\text{L} \cdot \text{atm}}{\text{K} \cdot \text{mol}} \times \frac{760 \text{ mmHg}}{1 \text{ atm}} = 62.3640 = 62.364 \, \frac{\text{L} \cdot \text{mmHg}}{\text{K} \cdot \text{mol}}$$

5.14. Six empirical gas laws can be obtained. They can be stated as follows:

$$P \times V = \text{constant} \quad (T \text{ and } n \text{ constant})$$

$$\frac{P}{T} = \text{constant} \quad (V \text{ and } n \text{ constant})$$

$$\frac{P}{n} = \text{constant} \quad (T \text{ and } V \text{ constant})$$

$$\frac{V}{T} = \text{constant} \quad (P \text{ and } n \text{ constant})$$

$$\frac{V}{n} = \text{constant} \quad (P \text{ and } T \text{ constant})$$

$$n \times T = \text{constant} \quad (P \text{ and } V \text{ constant})$$

5.15.   The postulates and supporting evidence are the following:

(1)   Gases are composed of molecules whose sizes are negligible compared with the distance between them.

(2)   Molecules move randomly in straight lines in all directions and at various speeds.

(3)   The forces of attraction or repulsion between two molecules (intermolecular forces) in a gas are very weak or negligible, except when they collide.

(4)   When molecules collide with one another, the collisions are elastic.

(5)   The average kinetic energy of a molecule is proportional to the absolute temperature.

One example of evidence that supports the kinetic theory of gases is Boyle's law. Constant temperature means that the average molecular force from collision remains constant. If you increase the volume, you decrease the number of collisions per unit wall area, thus lowering the pressure in accordance with Boyle's law. Another example is Charles's law. If you raise the temperature, you increase the average molecular force from a collision with the wall, thus increasing the pressure. For the pressure to remain constant, it is necessary for the volume to increase so that the frequency of collisions with the wall decreases. Thus, when you raise the temperature of a gas while keeping the pressure constant, the volume increases in accordance with Charles's law.

5.16.   Boyle's law requires the temperature to be constant. Postulate 5 of the kinetic theory holds that the average kinetic energy of a molecule is constant at constant temperature. Therefore, the average molecular force from collisions is constant. If we increase the volume of a gas, this decreases the number of molecules per unit volume and so decreases the frequency of collisions per unit wall area, causing the pressure to decrease in accordance with Boyle's law.

5.17.   According to kinetic theory, the pressure of a gas results from the bombardment of container walls by molecules.

5.18.   The rms speed of a molecule equals $(3RT/M_m)^{\frac{1}{2}}$. Therefore, it varies directly with the square root of the absolute temperature. The rms speed does not depend on the molar volume.

5.19.   A gas appears to diffuse more slowly because it never travels very far in one direction before it collides with another molecule and moves in another direction. Thus, it must travel a very long, crooked path as the result of collisions.

5.20.   Effusion is the process in which a gas flows through a small hole in a container. It results from the gas molecules encountering the hole by chance, rather than by colliding with the walls of the container. The faster the molecules move, the more likely they are to encounter the hole. Thus, the rate of effusion depends on the average molecular speed, which depends inversely on molecular mass.

5.21.   The behavior of a gas begins to deviate significantly from that predicted by the ideal gas law at high pressures and at relatively low temperatures.

5.22.   The constant a is the proportionality constant in the van der Waals equation related to intermolecular forces The term nb represents the volume occupied by n moles of molecules.

5.23.   The answer is a; "the greater the volume occupied by a given amount of gas, the higher the intermolecular force" is not part of the kinetic-molecular theory.

5.24.   The answer is c, the container volume didn't change.

5.25.   The answer is b, to occupy the entire 22.4 L volume of the box.

5.26.   The answer is d; it is *not* true that the Ar atoms hit the walls of the flask with the greatest force of the three gases.

■ ANSWERS TO CONCEPTUAL PROBLEMS

5.29.   a.   The volume of the tire and the amount of air in the tire remain constant. From the ideal gas law, $PV = nRT$, under these conditions the pressure will vary directly with the temperature ($P \propto T$). Thus, on a cold day, you would expect the pressure in the tires to decrease, and they would appear flatter.

   b.   Aerosol cans are filled with a fixed amount of gas in a constant volume. From the ideal gas law, under these conditions the pressure will vary directly with the temperature ($P \propto T$). If you put an aerosol can in a fire, you will increase the temperature and thus the pressure. If the pressure gets high enough, the can will explode.

   c.   As the water bottle sits in the sun, the liquid water warms up. As the temperature of the water increases, so does its vapor pressure (Table 5.6). If the pressure gets high enough, it will pop the lid off the bottle.

   d.   The amount of air in the balloon and the temperature remain constant. From the ideal gas law, under these conditions the pressure is inversely proportional to the volume ($P \propto 1/V$). Thus, as you squeeze the balloon, you decrease the volume, resulting in an increase in pressure. If you squeeze hard enough and make the volume small enough, the balloon will pop.

5.31.   a.   The pressure and volume of a gas are inversely proportional; therefore, an increase by a factor of 2 in pressure would decrease the volume by ½ (C to D).

   b.   The pressure and volume of a gas are inversely proportional; therefore, a decrease by a factor of 2 in pressure would double the volume (C to A).

   c.   The volume and temperature of a gas are directly proportional; therefore an increase in kelvin temperature by a factor of 1.5 would result in an increase in volume by a factor of 1.5 (C to B).

   d.   Since the piston can move, the pressure would not change (it would be equal to the starting pressure). The volume of gas is directly proportional to the number of moles; therefore, an increase in the number of moles by a factor of 2 would cause the volume increase by a factor of 2 (C to A).

5.33.   a.   The container with the O_2 has the greater density, since the molar mass of O_2 (32.00 g/mol) is greater than that of H_2 (2.016 g/mol).

   b.   Since the H_2 molecules are lighter, they will be moving faster.

   c.   Both containers have the same number of molecules (Avogadro's law).

d. The pressure in each of the containers will not change when the valve is opened. Each container starts with the same pressure. Since the total volume remains constant, the pressure will not change.

e. The fraction of the total pressure due to the H_2 would now be ¼.

5.35. In order to double the volume, you could reduce the pressure by ½. You could also double the temperature in Kelvin scale, but you cannot determine the final temperature without knowing the initial temperature.

■ SOLUTIONS TO PRACTICE PROBLEMS

Note on significant figures: If the final answer to a solution needs to be rounded off, it is given first with one nonsignificant figure, and the last significant figure is underlined. The final answer is then rounded to the correct number of significant figures. In multistep problems, intermediate answers are given with at least one nonsignificant figure; however, only the final answer has been rounded off.

5.37. Use the conversion factor 1 atm = 760 mmHg.

$$0.047 \text{ atm} \times \frac{760 \text{ mmHg}}{1 \text{ atm}} = 3\underline{5}.7 = 36 \text{ mmHg}$$

5.39. Using Boyle's law, solve for V_f of the neon gas at 1.292 atm pressure.

$$V_f = V_i \times \frac{P_i}{P_f} = 3.15 \text{ L} \times \frac{0.951 \text{ atm}}{1.292 \text{ atm}} = 2.3\underline{1}8 = 2.32 \text{ L}$$

5.41. Using Boyle's law, let V_f = volume at 0.974 atm (P_f), V_i = 50.0 L, and P_i = 19.8 atm.

$$V_f = V_i \times \frac{P_i}{P_f} = 50.0 \text{ L} \times \frac{19.8 \text{ atm}}{0.974 \text{ atm}} = 101\underline{6}.4 = 1.02 \times 10^3 \text{ L}$$

5.43. Using Boyle's law, let P_i = pressure of 315 cm³ of gas, and solve for it.

$$P_i = P_f \times \frac{V_f}{V_i} = 2.51 \text{ kPa} \times \frac{0.0457 \text{ cm}^3}{315 \text{ cm}^3} = 3.6\underline{4}1 \times 10^{-4} = 3.64 \times 10^{-4} \text{ kPa}$$

5.45. Use Charles's law: T_i = 18°C + 273 = 291 K, and T_f = 0°C + 273 = 273 K.

$$V_f = V_i \times \frac{T_f}{T_i} = 3.92 \text{ mL} \times \frac{273 \text{ K}}{291 \text{ K}} = 3.6\underline{7}7 = 3.68 \text{ mL}$$

5.47. Use Charles's law: T_i = 22°C + 273 = 295 K, and T_f = −197°C + 273 = 76 K.

$$V_f = V_i \times \frac{T_f}{T_i} = 2.54 \text{ L} \times \frac{76 \text{ K}}{295 \text{ K}} = 0.6\underline{5}4 = 0.65 \text{ L}$$

5.49. Use Charles's law: $T_i = 25°C + 273 = 298$ K, and V_f is the difference between the vessel's volume of 39.5 cm^3 and the 7.5 cm^3 of ethanol that is forced into the vessel.

$$T_f = T_i \times \frac{V_f}{V_i} = 298 \text{ K} \times \frac{(39.5 - 7.5) \text{ cm}^3}{39.5 \text{ cm}^3} = 241.4 \text{ K} \ (-31.7 \text{ or } -32°C)$$

5.51. Use the combined law: $T_i = 31°C + 273 = 304$ K, and $T_f = 0°C + 273 = 273$ K.

$$V_f = V_i \times \frac{P_i}{P_f} \times \frac{T_f}{T_i} = 35.5 \text{ mL} \times \frac{753 \text{ mmHg}}{760 \text{ mmHg}} \times \frac{273 \text{ K}}{304 \text{ K}} = 31.58 = 31.6 \text{ mL}$$

5.53. The balanced equation is

$4NH_3 + 5O_2 \rightarrow 4NO + 6H_2O$

The ratio of moles of NH_3 to moles of NO is 4 to 4, or 1 to 1, so one volume of NH_3 will produce one volume of NO at the same temperature and pressure.

5.55. Solve the ideal gas law for V:

$$V = \frac{nRT}{P} = nRT\left(\frac{1}{P}\right)$$

If the temperature and number of moles are held constant, then the product nRT is constant, and volume is inversely proportional to pressure:

$$V = \text{constant} \times \frac{1}{P}$$

5.57. Calculate the moles of oxygen, and then solve the ideal gas law for P:

$$n = 91.3 \text{ g} \times \frac{1 \text{ mol O}_2}{32.00 \text{ g O}_2} = 2.853 \text{ mol O}_2$$

$$P = \frac{nRT}{V} = \frac{(2.853 \text{ mol})(0.08206 \text{ L} \cdot \text{atm/K} \cdot \text{mol})(294 \text{ K})}{8.58 \text{ L}} = 8.022 = 8.02 \text{ atm}$$

5.59. Using the moles of chlorine, solve the ideal gas law for V:

$$V = \frac{nRT}{P} = \frac{(3.50 \text{ mol})(0.08206 \text{ L} \cdot \text{atm/K} \cdot \text{mol})(307 \text{ K})}{4.00 \text{ atm}} = 22.04 = 22.0 \text{ L}$$

5.61. Solve the ideal gas law for temperature in K, and convert to °C:

$$T = \frac{PV}{nR} = \frac{(3.50 \text{ atm})(4.00 \text{ L})}{(0.410 \text{ mol})(0.08206 \text{ L} \cdot \text{atm/K} \cdot \text{mol})} = 416.1 = 416 \text{ K}$$

$°C = 416 - 273 = 143°C$

5.63. Because density equals mass per unit volume, calculating the mass of 1 L (exact number) of gas will give the density of the gas. Start from the ideal gas law, and calculate n; then convert the moles of gas to grams using the molar mass.

$$n = \frac{PV}{RT} = \frac{(751/760 \text{ atm})(1 \text{ L})}{(0.08206 \text{ L} \cdot \text{atm/K} \cdot \text{mol})(304 \text{ K})} = 0.03961 \text{ mol}$$

$$0.03961 \text{ mol} \times \frac{17.03 \text{ g}}{1 \text{ mol}} = 0.67458 = 0.675 \text{ g}$$

Therefore, the density of NH_3 at 31°C is 0.675 g/L.

5.65. Calculate the mass of 1 L (exact number) using the ideal gas law; convert to mass.

$$n = \frac{PV}{RT} = \frac{(0.897 \text{ atm})(1 \text{ L})}{(0.08206 \text{ L} \cdot \text{atm/K} \cdot \text{mol})(297 \text{ K})} = 0.036804 \text{ mol}$$

$$0.036804 \text{ mol} \times \frac{58.12 \text{ g}}{1 \text{ mol}} = 2.139 = 2.14 \text{ g}$$

Therefore, the density of C_4H_{10} is 2.14 g/L.

5.67. The ideal gas law gives n moles, which then are divided into the mass of 1.585 g for molar mass.

$$n = \frac{PV}{RT} = \frac{(753/760 \text{ atm})(1 \text{ L})}{(0.08206 \text{ L} \cdot \text{atm/K} \cdot \text{mol})(363 \text{ K})} = 0.033262 \text{ mol}$$

$$\text{Molar mass} = \frac{1.585 \text{ g}}{0.033262 \text{ mol}} = 47.651 \text{ g/mol}$$

The molecular weight is 47.7 amu.

5.69. The moles in 250 mL (0.250 L) of the compound are obtained from the ideal gas law. The 2.56-g mass of the gas then is divided by the moles to obtain the molar mass and molecular mass.

$$n = \frac{PV}{RT} = \frac{(786/760 \text{ atm})(0.250 \text{ L})}{(0.08206 \text{ L} \cdot \text{atm/K} \cdot \text{mol})(394 \text{ K})} = 0.007996 \text{ mol}$$

$$\text{Molar mass} = \frac{2.56 \text{ g}}{0.007996 \text{ mol}} = 3.201 \times 10^2 = 3.20 \times 10^2 \text{ g/mol}$$

The molecular mass is 3.20×10^2 amu.

5.71. For a gas at a given temperature and pressure, the density depends on molecular mass (or, for a mixture, on average molecular mass). Thus, at the same temperature and pressure, the density of NH_4Cl gas would be greater than that of a mixture of NH_3 and HCl, because the average molecular mass of NH_3 and HCl would be lower than that of NH_4Cl.

5.73. The 0.075 mol CaC_2 will form 0.075 mol C_2H_2. The volume is found from the ideal gas law:

$$V = \frac{(0.075 \text{ mol})(0.08206 \text{ L} \cdot \text{atm/K} \cdot \text{mol})(299 \text{ K})}{684/760 \text{ atm}} = 2.04 = 2.0 \text{ L}$$

5.75. Use the equation to obtain the moles of CO_2 and then the ideal gas law to obtain the volume.

$$2LiOH(s) + CO_2(g) \rightarrow Li_2CO_3(aq) + H_2O(l)$$

$$327 \text{ g LiOH} \times \frac{1 \text{ mol LiOH}}{23.95 \text{ g LiOH}} \times \frac{1 \text{ mol } CO_2}{2 \text{ mol LiOH}} = 6.8\underline{2}7 \text{ mol } CO_2$$

$$V = \frac{(6.8\underline{2}7 \text{ mol})(0.08206 \text{ L} \cdot \text{atm/K} \cdot \text{mol})(294 \text{ K})}{781/760 \text{ atm}} = 16\underline{0}.3 = 160. \text{ L}$$

5.77. Use the equation to obtain the moles of ammonia and then the ideal gas law to obtain the volume.

$$2NH_3(g) + CO_2(g) \rightarrow NH_2CONH_2(aq) + H_2O(l)$$

$$908 \text{ g urea} \times \frac{1 \text{ mol urea}}{60.06 \text{ g urea}} \times \frac{2 \text{ mol } NH_3}{1 \text{ mol urea}} = 30.\underline{2}3 \text{ mol } NH_3$$

$$V = \frac{(30.\underline{2}3 \text{ mol})(0.08206 \text{ L} \cdot \text{atm/K} \cdot \text{mol})(298 \text{ K})}{3.00 \text{ atm}} = 24\underline{6}.4 = 246 \text{ L}$$

5.79. Use the equation to obtain the moles of ammonia and then the ideal gas law to obtain the volume.

$$2NH_3(g) + H_2SO_4(aq) \rightarrow (NH_4)_2SO_4(aq)$$

$$150.0 \text{ g } (NH_4)_2SO_4 \times \frac{1 \text{ mol } (NH_4)_2SO_4}{132.1 \text{ g } (NH_4)_2SO_4} \times \frac{2 \text{ mol } NH_3}{1 \text{ mol } (NH_4)_2SO_4} = 2.2\underline{7}10 \text{ mol } NH_3$$

$$V = \frac{nRT}{P} = \frac{(2.2710 \text{ mol})(0.08206 \text{ L} \cdot \text{atm/K} \cdot \text{mol})(288 \text{ K})}{1.15 \text{ atm}} = 46.\underline{6}7 = 46.7 \text{ L}$$

5.81. Calculate the partial pressure of each gas; then add the pressures since the total pressure is equal to the sum of the partial pressures:

$$P(\text{He}) = \frac{(0.0200 \text{ mol})(0.08206 \text{ L} \cdot \text{atm/K} \cdot \text{mol})(283 \text{ K})}{2.50 \text{ L}} = 0.18\underline{5}78 \text{ atm}$$

$$P(H_2) = \frac{(0.0100 \text{ mol})(0.08206 \text{ L} \cdot \text{atm/K} \cdot \text{mol})(283 \text{ K})}{2.50 \text{ L}} = 0.092\underline{8}9 \text{ atm}$$

Total pressure = 0.18587 + 0.092\underline{8}9 = 0.27\underline{8}67 = 0.279

5.83. Convert mass of O_2 and mass of He to moles. Use the ideal gas law to calculate the partial pressures, and then add to obtain the total pressures.

$$0.00103 \text{ g } O_2 \times \frac{1 \text{ mol } O_2}{32.00 \text{ g } O_2} = 3.2\underline{1}9 \times 10^{-5} \text{ mol } O_2$$

$$0.00056 \text{ g He} \times \frac{1 \text{ mol He}}{4.00 \text{ g He}} = 1.\underline{4}0 \times 10^{-4} \text{ mol}$$

$$P = \frac{nRT}{V} = \frac{(3.219 \times 10^{-5} \text{ mol})(0.08206 \text{ L} \cdot \text{atm/K} \cdot \text{mol})(288 \text{ K})}{0.2000 \text{ L}} = 0.003804 \text{ atm } O_2$$

$$P = \frac{nRT}{V} = \frac{(1.40 \times 10^{-4} \text{ mol})(0.08206 \text{ L} \cdot \text{atm/K} \cdot \text{mol})(288 \text{ K})}{0.2000 \text{ L}} = 0.01654 \text{ atm He}$$

$$P = P_{O_2} + P_{He} = 0.003804 \text{ atm} + 0.01654 \text{ atm} = 0.0203 = 0.020 \text{ atm}$$

5.85.   For each gas, $P(\text{gas}) = P \times (\text{mole fraction of gas})$.

$P(H_2)$	$= 760 \text{ mmHg} \times 0.250$	$= 190.0$	$= 190 \text{ mmHg}$
$P(CO_2)$	$= 760 \text{ mmHg} \times 0.650$	$= 494.0$	$= 494 \text{ mmHg}$
$P(HCl)$	$= 760 \text{ mmHg} \times 0.054$	$= 41.04$	$= 41 \text{ mmHg}$
$P(HF)$	$= 760 \text{ mmHg} \times 0.028$	$= 21.28$	$= 21 \text{ mmHg}$
$P(SO_2)$	$= 760 \text{ mmHg} \times 0.017$	$= 12.92$	$= 13 \text{ mmHg}$
$P(H_2S)$	$= 760 \text{ mmHg} \times 0.001$	$= 0.76$	$= 0.8 \text{ mmHg}$

5.87.   The total pressure is the sum of the partial pressures of CO and H_2O, so

$$P_{CO} = P - P_{water} = 689 \text{ mmHg} - 23.8 \text{ mmHg} = 665.2 \text{ mmHg}$$

$$n_{CO} = \frac{P_{CO}V}{RT} = \frac{(665/760 \text{ atm})(3.85 \text{ L})}{(0.08206 \text{ L} \cdot \text{atm/K} \cdot \text{mol})(298 \text{ K})} = 0.1378 \text{ mol CO}$$

$$0.1378 \text{ mol CO} \times \frac{1 \text{ mol HCOOH}}{1 \text{ mol CO}} \times \frac{46.03 \text{ g HCOOH}}{1 \text{ mol HCOOH}} = 6.342 = 6.34 \text{ g HCOOH}$$

5.89.   Substitute 298 K (25°C) and 398 K (125°C) into Maxwell's distribution:

$$u_{25} = \left(\frac{3RT}{M}\right)^{\frac{1}{2}} = \left(\frac{3 \times 8.31 \text{ kg} \cdot \text{m}^2/(\text{s}^2 \cdot \text{K} \cdot \text{mol}) \times 298 \text{ K}}{28.02 \times 10^{-3} \text{ kg/mol}}\right)^{\frac{1}{2}} = 5.149 \times 10^2$$

$$= 5.15 \times 10^2 \text{ m/s}$$

$$u_{125} = \left(\frac{3RT}{M}\right)^{\frac{1}{2}} = \left(\frac{3 \times 8.31 \text{ kg} \cdot \text{m}^2/(\text{s}^2 \cdot \text{K} \cdot \text{mol}) \times 398 \text{ K}}{28.02 \times 10^{-3} \text{ kg/mol}}\right)^{\frac{1}{2}} = 5.9507 \times 10^2$$

$$= 5.95 \times 10^2 \text{ m/s}$$

Graph as in Figure 5.25.

5.91.   Substitute 330 K (57°C) into Maxwell's distribution:

$$u_{330 \text{ K}} = \left(\frac{3RT}{M}\right)^{\frac{1}{2}} = \left(\frac{3 \times 8.31 \text{ kg} \cdot \text{m}^2/(\text{s}^2 \cdot \text{K} \cdot \text{mol}) \times 330 \text{ K}}{352 \times 10^{-3} \text{ kg/mol}}\right)^{\frac{1}{2}} = 1.528 \times 10^2$$

$$= 1.53 \times 10^2 \text{ m/s}$$

5.93. Because $u(CO_2) = u(H_2)$, we can equate the two right-hand sides of the Maxwell distributions:

$$\left(\frac{3RT(CO_2)}{M_m(CO_2)} \right)^{\frac{1}{2}} = \left(\frac{3RT(H_2)}{M_m(H_2)} \right)^{\frac{1}{2}}$$

Squaring both sides, rearranging to solve for $T(CO_2)$, and substituting numerical values, we have

$$T(CO_2) = T(H_2) \times \frac{M_m(CO_2)}{M_m(H_2)} = 298 \text{ K} \times \frac{44.01 \text{ g/mol}}{2.016 \text{ g/mol}} = 6505.4 \text{ K}$$

Thus the temperature is

$$T = 6505.4 - 273 = 6232 = 6.23 \times 10^3 \text{ °C}$$

5.95. The rates of effusion are directly related to the rms speed. Assume the temperature is the same for both, and write a ratio of two Maxwell distributions.

$$\frac{u_{N_2}}{u_{O_2}} = \frac{\left(\frac{3RT}{M_m(N_2)} \right)^{\frac{1}{2}}}{\left(\frac{3RT}{M_m(O_2)} \right)^{\frac{1}{2}}} = \left(\frac{M_m(O_2)}{M_m(N_2)} \right)^{\frac{1}{2}} = \left(\frac{32.00 \text{ g/mol}}{28.02 \text{ g/mol}} \right)^{\frac{1}{2}} = 1.0686 = 1.069$$

Thus the ratio of the rates of effusion of N_2 and O_2 is 1.069 to 1.

5.97. The rates of effusion are directly related to the rms speed. Assume the temperature is the same for both, and write a ratio of two Maxwell distributions.

$$\frac{u_{H_2}}{u_{I_2}} = \left(\frac{M_m(I_2)}{M_m(H_2)} \right)^{\frac{1}{2}} = \left(\frac{253.8 \text{ g/mol}}{2.016 \text{ g/mol}} \right)^{\frac{1}{2}} = 11.220 = 11.22$$

Because hydrogen diffuses 11.22 times as fast as iodine, the time it would take would be 1/11.22 of the time required for iodine:

$$t(H_2) = 39 \text{ s} \times (1/11.22) = 3.47 = 3.5 \text{ s}$$

5.99. Since the volume of gas produced is directly related to the rate of effusion, the ratio of the volumes of gas can be written in terms of the ratio of the rms speeds. This in turn can be written in terms of the masses of the particles.

$$\frac{4.83 \text{ mL gas}}{9.23 \text{ m L Ar}} = \frac{u_{gas}}{u_{Ar}} = \left(\frac{M_m(Ar)}{M_m(gas)} \right)^{\frac{1}{2}} = \left(\frac{39.95 \text{ g/mol}}{M_m(gas)} \right)^{\frac{1}{2}}$$

Squaring both sides gives

$$0.27383 = \frac{39.95 \text{ g/mol}}{M_m(gas)}$$

Solving for the molar mass gives

$$M_m(\text{gas}) = \frac{39.95 \text{ g/mol}}{0.27383} = 145\underline{.}8 \text{ g/mol}; \text{ molecular mass} = 146 \text{ amu}$$

5.101. Solving the van der Waals equation for $n = 1$ and $T = 355.2$ K for P gives

$$P = \frac{RT}{(V - b)} - \frac{a}{V^2} = \frac{(0.08206 \text{ L} \cdot \text{atm/K} \cdot \text{mol})(355.2 \text{ K})}{(30.00 \text{ L/mol} - 0.08710 \text{ L/mol})} - \frac{12.56 \text{ L}^2 \cdot \text{atm/mol}^2}{(30.00 \text{ L/mol})^2}$$

$$P = 0.974\underline{4}19 - 0.0139\underline{5}55 = 0.960\underline{4}6 = 0.9605 \text{ atm}$$

$$P(\text{ideal gas law}) = 0.971\underline{5}9 = 0.9716 \text{ atm}$$

5.103. To calculate a/V^2 in the van der Waals equation, we obtain V from the ideal gas law at 1.00 atm:

$$V = \frac{RT}{P} = \frac{(0.08206 \text{ L} \cdot \text{atm/K} \cdot \text{mol})(273 \text{ K})}{1.00 \text{ atm}} = 22.40 \text{ L}$$

$$\frac{a}{V^2} = \frac{5.570}{(22.4 \text{ L})^2} = 1.1\underline{1}0 \times 10^{-2}$$

At 1.00 atm, $V = 22.4$ L, and $a/V^2 = 1.110 \times 10^{-2}$. Substituting into the van der Waals equation:

$$V = \frac{RT}{P + \dfrac{a}{V^2}} + b = \frac{(0.08206 \text{ L} \cdot \text{atm/K} \cdot \text{mol})(273 \text{ K})}{(1.00 + 1.110 \times 10^{-2}) \text{atm}} + 0.06499 = 22.\underline{2}2 = 22.2 \text{ L}$$

At 10.0 atm, the van der Waals equation gives 2.08 L. The ideal gas law gives 2.24 L for 10.0 atm.

■ SOLUTIONS TO GENERAL PROBLEMS

5.105. Calculate the mass of 1 cm² of the 20.5 m of water above the air in the glass. The volume is the product of the area of 1 cm² and the height of 20.5×10^2 cm (20.5 m) of water. The density of 1.00 g/cm³ must be used to convert volume to mass:

$$m = d \times V$$

$$m = 1.00 \text{ g/cm}^3 \times (1.00 \text{ cm}^2 \times 20.5 \times 10^2 \text{ cm}) = 2.05 \times 10^3 \text{ g, or } 2.05 \text{ kg}$$

The pressure exerted on an object at the bottom of the column of water is

$$P = \frac{\text{force}}{\text{area}} = \frac{(m)(g)}{\text{area}} = \frac{(2.05 \text{ kg})(9.807 \text{ m/s}^2)}{(1.00 \text{ cm}^2)\left(\dfrac{10^{-2} \text{ m}}{1 \text{ cm}}\right)^2} = 2.01 \times 10^5 \text{ kg/ms}^2 = 2.01 \times 10^5 \text{ Pa}$$

The total pressure on the air in the tumbler equals the sum of the barometric pressure and the water pressure:

$$P = 1.00 \times 10^2 \text{ kPa} + 2.01 \times 10^2 \text{ kPa} = 3.01 \times 10^2 \text{ kPa}$$

Multiply the initial volume by a factor accounting for the change in pressure to find V_f:

$$V_f = V_i \times \frac{P_i}{P_f} = 243 \text{ cm}^3 \times \left(\frac{1.00 \times 10^2 \text{ kPa}}{3.01 \times 10^2 \text{ kPa}} \right) = 80.\underline{7}3 = 80.7 \text{ cm}^3$$

5.107. Use the combined gas law and solve for V_f:

$$V_f = V_i \times \frac{P_i}{P_f} \times \frac{T_f}{T_i} = 201 \text{ mL} \times \frac{738 \text{ mmHg}}{760 \text{ mmHg}} \times \frac{273 \text{ K}}{294 \text{ K}} = 181.\underline{2}4 = 181 \text{ mL}$$

5.109. Use the combined gas law and solve for V_f:

$$V_f = V_i \times \frac{P_i}{P_f} \times \frac{T_f}{T_i} = 5.0 \text{ dm}^3 \times \frac{100.0 \text{ kPa}}{79.0 \text{ kPa}} \times \frac{293 \text{ K}}{287 \text{ K}} = 6.\underline{4}6 = 6.5 \text{ dm}^3$$

5.111. Use the ideal gas law to calculate the moles of helium, and combine this with Avogadro's number to obtain the number of helium atoms:

$$n = \frac{PV}{RT} = \frac{(765/760 \text{ atm})(0.01205 \text{ L})}{(0.08206 \text{ L} \cdot \text{atm/K} \cdot \text{mol})(296 \text{ K})} = 4.9\underline{9}3 \times 10^{-4} \text{ mol}$$

$$4.9\underline{9}3 \times 10^{-4} \text{ mol He} \times \frac{6.022 \times 10^{23} \text{ He}^{2+} \text{ ions}}{1 \text{ mol He}} \times \frac{1 \text{ atom}}{1 \text{ He}^{2+} \text{ ion}} = 3.0\underline{0}67 \times 10^{20}$$

$$= 3.01 \times 10^{20} \text{ atoms}$$

5.113. Calculate the molar mass, M_m, by dividing the mass of 1 liter of air by the moles of the gas from the ideal gas equation:

$$M_m = \frac{\text{mass}}{n} = 1.2929 \text{ g air} \times \frac{(0.082058 \text{ L} \cdot \text{atm/K} \cdot \text{mol})(273.15 \text{ K})}{(1 \text{ atm})(1 \text{ L})} = 28.97\underline{9}2 \text{ g/mol}$$

$$= 28.979 \text{ g/ mol (amu)}$$

5.115. Use the ideal gas law to calculate the moles of CO_2. Then convert to mass of LiOH.

$$n = \frac{PV}{RT} = \frac{(1.00 \text{ atm})(5.8 \times 10^2 \text{ L})}{(0.08206 \text{ L} \cdot \text{atm/K} \cdot \text{mol})(273 \text{ K})} = 2\underline{5}.89 \text{ mol } CO_2$$

$$2\underline{5}.89 \text{ mol } CO_2 \times \frac{2 \text{ mol LiOH}}{1 \text{ mol } CO_2} \times \frac{23.95 \text{ g LiOH}}{1 \text{ mol LiOH}} = 1\underline{2}40 = 1.2 \times 10^3 \text{ g LiOH}$$

Thus, each astronaut requires 1.2×10^3 g LiOH per day.

5.117. Convert mass to moles of $KClO_3$, and then use the equation below to convert to moles of O_2. Use the ideal gas law to convert moles of O_2 to pressure at 25°C (298 K).

$$2KClO_3(s) \rightarrow 2KCl(s) + 3O_2(g)$$

$$170.0 \text{ g KClO}_3 \times \frac{1 \text{ mol KClO}_3}{122.55 \text{ g KClO}_3} \times \frac{3 \text{ mol O}_2}{2 \text{ mol KClO}_3} = 2.0\underline{8}1 \text{ mol O}_2$$

$$P = \frac{nRT}{V} = \frac{(2.081 \text{ mol})\,(0.08206 \text{ L} \cdot \text{atm/ K} \cdot \text{mol})\,(298 \text{ K})}{2.50 \text{ L}} = 20.\underline{3}53 = 20.4 \text{ atm O}_2$$

5.119. Find the number of moles of CO_2 first. Then convert this to moles of HCl and molarity of HCl.

$$n = \frac{(727\,/\,760 \text{ atm}) \times 0.141 \text{ L}}{0.08206 \text{ L} \cdot \text{atm/K} \cdot \text{mol} \times 300 \text{ K}} = 0.00547\underline{8}8 \text{ mol}$$

$$\text{mol HCl} = 0.00547\underline{8}8 \text{ mol CO}_2 \times (2 \text{ mol HCl} /1 \text{ mol CO}_2) = 0.0109\underline{5}7 \text{ mol}$$

$$M \text{ HCl} = 0.0109\underline{5}7 \text{ mol HCl} \div 0.0249 \text{ L HCl} = 0.44\underline{0}0 = 0.440 \text{ mol/L HCl}$$

5.121. The number of moles of carbon dioxide is

$$n = \frac{646\,/\,760 \text{ atm} \times 0.1500 \text{ L}}{0.08206 \text{ L} \cdot \text{atm/ K} \cdot \text{mol} \times 300 \text{ K}} = 0.0051\underline{7}9 \text{ mol}$$

The number of moles of molecular acid used is

$$0.1250 \text{ mol/L} \times 0.04141 \text{ L} = 0.005176 \text{ mol acid}$$

Thus, the acid is H_2SO_4 since 1 mole of H_2SO_4 reacts to form 1 mole of CO_2

5.123. Use Maxwell's distribution to calculate the temperature in kelvins; then convert to °C.

$$T = \frac{u^2 M_m}{3R} = \frac{(0.600 \times 10^3 \text{ m/s})^2\,(17.03 \times 10^{-3} \text{ kg/mol})}{3\,(8.31 \text{ kg} \cdot \text{m}^2/\text{s}^2 \cdot \text{K} \cdot \text{mol})} = 24\underline{5}.9 = 246. \text{ K } (-27°\text{C})$$

5.125. Calculate the ratio of the root-mean-square (rms) molecular speeds, which is the same as the ratio of the rates of effusion:

$$\frac{u\,[U(235)F_6]}{u\,[U(238)F_6]} = \left(\frac{M_m\,[U(238)F_6]}{M_m\,[U(235)F_6]} \right)^{\frac{1}{2}} = \left(\frac{352.04 \text{ g/ mol}}{349.03 \text{ g/ mol}} \right)^{\frac{1}{2}} = 1.004\underline{3}02 = 1.0043$$

5.127. First, calculate the apparent molar masses at each pressure using the ideal gas law. Only the calculation of the apparent molar mass for 0.2500 atm will be shown; the other values will be summarized in a table.

$$n = \frac{PV}{RT} = \frac{(0.2500 \text{ atm})\,(3.1908 \text{ L})}{(0.082057 \text{ L} \cdot \text{atm/K} \cdot \text{mol})\,(273.15 \text{ K})} = 3.55\underline{8}96 \times 10^{-2} \text{ mol}$$

$$\text{Apparent molar mass} = \frac{1.000 \text{ g}}{3.55896 \times 10^{-2} \text{ mol}} = 28.0\underline{9}8 = 28.10 \text{ g/mol}$$

The following table summarizes the apparent molar masses calculated as above for all P's; these data are plotted in the graph below the table.

P (atm)	App. Molar Mass (g/mol)
0.2500	28.10
0.5000	28.14
0.7500	28.19
1.0000	28.26

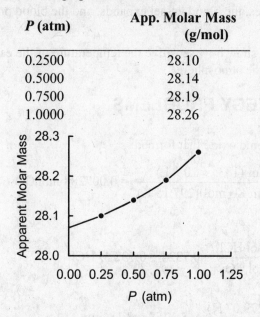

Extrapolation back to $P = 0$ gives 28.07 g/mol for the molar mass of the unknown gas.

5.129. Use $CO + \frac{1}{2}O_2 \rightarrow CO_2$, instead of 2CO. First, find the moles of CO and O_2 by using the ideal gas law.

$$n_{CO} = \frac{PV}{RT} = \frac{(0.500 \text{ atm})(2.00 \text{ L})}{(0.08206 \text{ L} \cdot \text{atm/K} \cdot \text{mol})(300 \text{ K})} = 0.040\underline{6}2 \text{ mol}$$

$$n_{O_2} = \frac{PV}{RT} = \frac{(1.00 \text{ atm})(1.00 \text{ L})}{(0.08206 \text{ L} \cdot \text{atm/K} \cdot \text{mol})(300 \text{ K})} = 0.040\underline{6}2 \text{ mol}$$

There are equal amounts of CO and O_2, but (from the equation) only half as many moles of O_2 as CO are required for the reaction. Therefore, when 0.04062 mol CO has been consumed, only 0.04062/2 mol O_2 will have been used up. Then 0.04062/2 mol O_2 will remain, and 0.04062 mol CO_2 will have been produced. At the end,

$$n_{CO} = 0 \text{ mol}; \ n_{O_2} = 0.0202 \text{ mol}; \text{ and } n_{CO_2} = 0.04062 \text{ mol}$$

However, the total volume with the valve open is 3.00 L, so the partial pressures of O_2 and CO_2 must be calculated from the ideal gas law for each:

$$\frac{nRT}{V} = \frac{(0.0203 \text{ mol O}_2)(0.08206 \text{ L} \cdot \text{atm/K} \cdot \text{mol})(300 \text{ K})}{3.00 \text{ L}} = 0.166\underline{5}8 = 0.167 \text{ atm O}_2$$

$$\frac{nRT}{V} = \frac{(0.04062 \text{ mol CO}_2)(0.08206 \text{ L} \cdot \text{atm/K} \cdot \text{mol})(300 \text{ K})}{3.00 \text{ L}} = 0.333\underline{3}2 = 0.333 \text{ atm CO}_2$$

5.131. Cells in the lining of arteries detect increased blood pressure and respond by producing nitric oxide. NO rapidly diffuses through the artery wall to cells in the surrounding muscle tissue. In response, the muscle tissue relaxes, the blood vessel expands, and the blood pressure drops.

5.133. Svante Arrhenius was the first to show how sensitive the temperature of the earth might be to the percentage of carbon dioxide in the atmosphere.

■ SOLUTIONS TO STRATEGY PROBLEMS

5.135. First calculate the moles of carbon dioxide that formed.

$$n = \frac{PV}{RT} = \frac{(738/760 \text{ atm})(183 \times 10^{-3} \text{ L})}{(0.08206 \text{ L} \cdot \text{atm/K} \cdot \text{mol})(297.15 \text{ K})} = 0.007288 \text{ mol CO}_2$$

Now, find the molarity.

$$\frac{0.007288 \text{ mol CO}_2}{19.9 \times 10^{-3} \text{ L}} \times \frac{2 \text{ mol HCl}}{1 \text{ mol CO}_2} = 0.7324 = 0.732 \ M \text{ HCl}$$

5.137. $P_f = \dfrac{P_i V_i T_f}{V_f T_i} = \dfrac{(1 \text{ atm})(162 \text{ L})(279.07 \text{ K})}{(18.8 \text{ L})(294.15 \text{ K})} = 8.1753 = 8.18 \text{ atm}$

5.139. First note that 16.0 g O_2 represents 0.500 mol O_2 and that 14.0 g N_2 represents 0.500 mol N_2. Altogether, then, there is 1.00 mol of gas present in the container.

a.   At STP 1.00 mol of gas occupies 22.4 L.

b. $P_{O_2} = X_{O_2} \times P_{tot} = \dfrac{0.500 \text{ mol O}_2}{0.500 \text{ mol O}_2 \ + \ 0.500 \text{ mol N}_2} \times 1.00 \text{ atm} = 0.500 \text{ atm}$

c. $X_{N_2} = \dfrac{0.500 \text{ mol N}_2}{0.500 \text{ mol O}_2 \ + \ 0.500 \text{ mol N}_2} = 0.500 \text{ mol fraction (50.0\% mole percent)}$

5.141. The density of a gas can be calculated by using $d = PM_m/RT$. For two different gases under the same conditions of temperature and pressure, this reduces to

$$\frac{d_2}{d_1} = \frac{M_2}{M_1} = \frac{146.07 \text{ g/mol}}{29.0 \text{ g/mol}} = 5.036 = 5.04$$

Thus, the density of gaseous SF_6 is 5.04 times the density of air.

5.143. The moles of H_2S gas formed is

$$n = \frac{(12.0 \text{ atm})(0.500 \text{ L})}{(0.08206 \text{ L} \cdot \text{atm/K} \cdot \text{mol})(398 \text{ K})} = 0.1837 \text{ mol H}_2\text{S}$$

The mass can now be calculated.

$$0.1837 \text{ mol H}_2\text{S} \times \frac{1 \text{ mol S}_8}{8 \text{ mol H}_2\text{S}} \times \frac{256.52 \text{ g}}{1 \text{ mol S}_8} = 5.891 = 5.89 \text{ g S}_8$$

5.145. First we will need the vapor pressure of water at 31°C and 39°C. Table 5.6 gives values for 30°C (31.8 mmHg) and 40°C (55.3 mmHg). Although vapor pressure does not vary linearly with temperature, these temperatures are close enough such that linear interpolation is reasonable. Doing so gives 34.2 mmHg at 31°C and 53.0 mmHg at 39°C. Using the ideal gas law (n = PV/RT), we next calculate how many moles of CO are present:

$$n_{CO} = \frac{((755-34.2)/760 \text{ atm})(0.275 \text{ L}))}{(0.08206 \text{ L} \cdot \text{atm/K} \cdot \text{mol})(304 \text{ K})} = 0.010\underline{4}5 \text{ mol CO}$$

The same number of moles of CO will be present at the higher temperature. Adjusting for the higher temperature and the corresponding rise in the vapor pressure of water, the desired volume is calculated via the ideal gas law (V = nRT/P).

$$V_{CO,312K} = \frac{(0.010\underline{4}5 \text{ mol CO})(0.08206 \text{ L} \cdot \text{atm/K} \cdot \text{mol})(312 \text{ K})}{((755-53.0)/760 \text{ atm})} = 0.28\underline{9}7 \text{ L (or 290. mL)}$$

5.147. The volume of the film to be deposited is its area times its thickness. Using this information and the density of Si_3N_4, the mass of Si_3N_4 is calculated:

$$mass_{Si_3N_4} = 9.0 \text{ mm}^2 \times 4.0 \times 10^{-5} \text{ mm} \times \left(\frac{1 \text{ cm}}{10 \text{ mm}}\right)^3 \times \left(\frac{3.29 \text{ g}}{1 \text{ cm}^3}\right) = 1.\underline{1}8 \times 10^{-6} \text{ g Si}_3N_4$$

Next, convert this film mass to moles and relate it to the moles of SiH_4 needed by way of the reaction stoichiometry:

$$mol_{SiH_4} = 1.\underline{1}8 \times 10^{-6} \text{ g Si}_3N_4 \times \frac{1 \text{ mol Si}_3N_4}{140.3 \text{ g Si}_3N_4} \times \frac{3 \text{ mol SiH}_4}{1 \text{ mol Si}_3N_4} = 2.\underline{5}3 \times 10^{-8} \text{ mol SiH}_4$$

Finally, apply the ideal gas law to determine the volume of SiH_4 needed to accomplish the task.

$$V_{SiH_4} = \frac{nRT}{P} = \frac{(2.\underline{5}3 \times 10^{-8} \text{ mol})(0.08206 \text{ L} \cdot \text{atm/K} \cdot \text{mol})(775 \text{ K})}{1.\underline{0} \times 10^{-5}/760 \text{ atm}} = 1\underline{2}2 = 1.2 \times 10^2 \text{ L}$$

5.149. $n_{Cl_2} = 1\underline{5}0 \text{ L} \times \frac{2.8 \text{ g}}{\text{L}} \times \frac{1 \text{ mol Cl}_2}{70.90 \text{ g}} = 5.\underline{9}2 = 5.9 \text{ mol Cl}_2$

Since the volume of the cylinder is fixed and the mass of chlorine is fixed (i.e., assuming no reaction is caused by the increased temperature), the density of the chlorine gas will remain the same. The one variable which must change with the temperature increase is the pressure which doubles as well.

■ SOLUTIONS TO CUMULATIVE-SKILLS PROBLEMS

5.151. Assume a 100.0-g sample, giving 85.2 g CH_4 and 14.8 g C_2H_6. Convert each to moles and then calculate the volumes of each gas:

$$85.2 \text{ g CH}_4 \times \frac{1 \text{ mol CH}_4}{16.04 \text{ g CH}_4} = 5.3\underline{1}2 \text{ mol CH}_4$$

$$14.8 \text{ g C}_2H_6 \times \frac{1 \text{ mol CH}_4}{30.07 \text{ g CH}_4} = 0.49\underline{2}2 \text{ mol C}_2H_6$$

$$V_{CH_4} = \frac{(5.3\underline{1}2 \text{ mol})(0.08206 \text{ L} \cdot \text{atm/K} \cdot \text{mol})(291 \text{ K})}{(771/760) \text{ atm}} = 12\underline{5}.0 \text{ L}$$

$$V_{C_2H_6} = \frac{(0.49\underline{2}2 \text{ mol})(0.08206 \text{ L} \cdot \text{atm/K} \cdot \text{mol})(291 \text{ K})}{(771/760) \text{ atm}} = 11.\underline{5}9 \text{ L}$$

The density is calculated as follows:

$$d = \frac{85.2 \text{ g CH}_4 + 14.8 \text{ g C}_2\text{H}_6}{(12\underline{5}.0 + 11.\underline{5}9) \text{ L}} = 0.73\underline{2}0 = 0.732 \text{ g/L}$$

5.153. First, subtract the height of mercury equivalent to the 25.0 cm (250. mm) of water inside the tube from 771 mmHg to get P_{gas}. Then subtract the vapor pressure of water, 18.7 mmHg, from P_{gas} to get P_{O_2}

$$h_{Hg} = \frac{(h_W)(d_W)}{d_{Hg}} = \frac{250. \text{ mm} \times 0.99987 \text{ g/cm}^3}{13.596 \text{ g/cm}^3} = 18.\underline{3}9 \text{ mmHg}$$

$$P_{gas} = P - P_{25 \text{ cm water}} = 771 \text{ mmHg} - 18.\underline{3}9 \text{ mmHg} = 75\underline{2}.61 \text{ mmHg}$$

$$P_{O_2} = 75\underline{2}.61 \text{ mmHg} - 18.7 \text{ mmHg} = 73\underline{3}.91 \text{ mmHg}$$

$$n = \frac{PV}{RT} = \frac{(73\underline{3}.91/760 \text{ atm})(0.0310 \text{ L})}{(0.08206 \text{ L} \cdot \text{atm/K} \cdot \text{mol})(294 \text{ K})} = 0.00124\underline{1} \text{ mol O}_2$$

$$\text{Mass} = 0.00124\underline{1} \text{ mol O}_2 \times \frac{2 \text{ mol Na}_2\text{O}_2}{1 \text{ mol O}_2} \times \frac{77.98 \text{ g Na}_2\text{O}_2}{1 \text{ mol Na}_2\text{O}_2} = 0.19\underline{3}5 = 0.194 \text{ g Na}_2\text{O}_2$$

5.155. First find the moles of CO_2 (note vapor pressure of water = 23.8 torr at 25 °C) :

$$n = \frac{PV}{RT} = \frac{((785-23.8)/760 \text{ atm})(1.94 \text{ L})}{(0.08206 \text{ L} \cdot \text{atm/K} \cdot \text{mol})(298 \text{ K})} = 0.0794\underline{6} \text{ mol CO}_2$$

Set up one equation in one unknown: $x = $ mol $CaCO_3$; $(0.0794\underline{6} - x) = $ mol $MgCO_3$.

7.85 g = (100.1 g/mol)x + (84.31 g/mol)($0.0794\underline{6} - x$)

$$x = \frac{(7.85 - 6.6\underline{9}9)}{(100.1 - 84.31)} = 0.072\underline{8}9 \text{ mol CaCO}_3$$

$(0.0794\underline{6} - x) = 0.006\underline{5}7$ mol $MgCO_3$

$$\text{Percent CaCO}_3 = \frac{0.072\underline{8}9 \text{ mol CaCO}_3 \times 100.1 \text{ g/mol}}{7.85 \text{ g}} \times 100\% = 92.\underline{9}4 = 92.9\% \text{ CaCO}_3$$

Percent $MgCO_3$ = 100.00% − 92.\underline{9}4 % = 7.\underline{0}6 = 7.1% $MgCO_3$

5.157. Write a mass-balance equation to solve for the moles of each gas, using 28.01 g/mol for the molar mass of N_2 and 20.18 g/mol for the molar mass of Ne. Let y equal moles of each gas:

28.01 y + 20.18 y = 10.0 g , y = (10.0 ÷ 48.19) = 0.207\underline{5}1 mol

Total moles (n) = 2y = 0.415\underline{0}2 mol (use below)

Use the ideal gas law to calculate the volume, which can then be used to calculate density.

$$\frac{(0.41\underline{5}02 \text{ mol})(0.08206 \text{ L} \bullet \text{atm/K} \bullet \text{mol})(500 \text{ K})}{15.00 \text{ atm}} = 1.1\underline{3}52 \text{ L}$$

$$d = 10.0 \text{ g} \div 1.1\underline{3}52 \text{ L} = 8.8\underline{0}9 = 8.81 \text{ g/L}$$

5.159. Rearrange the equation $PM_m = dRT$ to find the quantity RT/M_m. After converting to appropriate SI units, use the result in the equation for the root-mean-square speed.

$$\frac{RT}{M_m} = \frac{P}{d} = \frac{675 \text{ mmHg}}{3.00 \text{ g/L}} \times \frac{1000 \text{ g}}{1 \text{ kg}} \times \frac{1000 \text{ cm}^3}{1 \text{ L}} \times \frac{1 \text{ m}^3}{10^6 \text{ cm}^3} \times \frac{1.013 \times 10^5 \text{ kg/(ms}^2)}{760 \text{ mmHg}}$$

$$\frac{P}{d} = \frac{29\underline{9}90 \text{ m}^2}{\text{s}^2}$$

$$u = \left(\frac{3RT}{M_m}\right)^{\frac{1}{2}} = \left(\frac{3P}{d}\right)^{\frac{1}{2}} = \left(3 \times \frac{29\underline{9}90 \text{ m}^2}{\text{s}^2}\right)^{\frac{1}{2}} = 2.9\underline{9}95 \times 10^2 = 3.00 \times 10^2 \text{ m/s}$$

CHAPTER 6

Thermochemistry

■ SOLUTIONS TO EXERCISES

Note on significant figures: If the final answer to a solution needs to be rounded off, it is given first with one nonsignificant figure, and the last significant figure is underlined. The final answer is then rounded to the correct number of significant figures. In multistep problems, intermediate answers are given with at least one nonsignificant figure; however, only the final answer has been rounded off.

6.1.   Substitute into the formula $E_k = \frac{1}{2}mv^2$ using SI units:

$$E_k = \frac{1}{2} \times 9.11 \times 10^{-31} \text{ kg} \times (5.0 \times 10^6 \text{ m/s})^2 = 1.\underline{1}3 \times 10^{-17} = 1.1 \times 10^{-17} \text{ J}$$

$$1.13 \times 10^{-17} \text{ J} \times \frac{1 \text{ cal}}{4.184 \text{ J}} = 2.\underline{7}2 \times 10^{-18} = 2.7 \times 10^{-18} \text{ cal}$$

6.2.   The change in the internal energy of the system, ΔU, equals $q + w$. Relative to the system, q is negative because the system gives off heat and w is positive because the weights do work on the system by compressing the gas. The value of q is straightforward, i.e., -1.50 J. The value of w is equal to the change in the gravitational potential energy of the weights, *mgh*. Thus,

$$\Delta U = q + w = (-1.50 \text{ J}) + (2.20 \text{ kg} \times \frac{9.81 \text{ m}}{\text{s}^2} \times 0.250 \text{ m}) = -1.5\underline{0} \text{ J} + 5.3\underline{9}6 \text{ J} = +3.90 \text{ J}$$

6.3.   Heat is evolved; therefore, the reaction is exothermic. The value of q is -1170 kJ.

6.4   The change in volume, ΔV, can be calculated by taking the difference in the volume of gas before and after the reaction, using the ideal gas equation in each case:

$$\Delta V = V_{final} - V_{initial} = \frac{n_{final}RT}{P} - \frac{n_{initial}RT}{P} = \frac{(n_{final} - n_{initial})RT}{P}$$

$$\Delta V = \frac{(1 \text{ mol} - 3 \text{ mol})(0.08206 \frac{\text{L} \cdot \text{atm}}{\text{mol} \cdot \text{K}})(35\underline{0} \text{ K})}{1.0\underline{0} \text{ atm}} = -57.\underline{4}4 \text{ L}$$

Because the change is from two moles of gas to one mole of gas, this represents a compression being performed on the system. In other words, work is done on the system so should be positive. This pressure-volume work is calculated as follows:

$$w = -P \times \Delta V = -(1.0\underline{0} \text{ atm}) \times (-57.\underline{4}4 \text{ L}) = -(1.01 \times 10^5 \text{ Pa}) \times (-57.\underline{4}4 \times 10^{-3} \text{ m}^3)$$

$$w = +58\underline{0}1 \text{ J} = +5.80 \text{ kJ}$$

By the first law of thermodynamics, $\Delta U = q + w$. We are given q directly in the problem statement, i.e., $q = -885.5$ kJ. Combining q and w, ΔU can now be calculated.

$$\Delta U = q + w = -885.\underline{5} \text{ kJ} + 5.8\underline{0} \text{ kJ} = -879.\underline{7}0 = -879.7 \text{ kJ}$$

6.5.   The balanced thermochemical equation is

$$2N_2H_4(l) + N_2O_4(l) \rightarrow 3N_2(g) + 4H_2O(g); \Delta H = -1049 \text{ kJ}$$

6.6.   a. $N_2H_4(l) + 1/2N_2O_4(l) \rightarrow 3/2N_2(g) + 2H_2O(g); \Delta H = -524.5 \text{ kJ}$

   b. $4H_2O(g) + 3N_2(g) \rightarrow 2N_2H_4(l) + N_2O_4(l); \Delta H = 1049 \text{ kJ}$

6.7.   The reaction is

$$2N_2H_4(l) + N_2O_4(l) \rightarrow 3N_2(g) + 4H_2O(g); \Delta H = -1049 \text{ kJ}$$

$$10.0 \text{ g } N_2H_4 \times \frac{1 \text{ mol } N_2H_4}{32.02 \text{ g}} \times \frac{1 \text{ mol } N_2O_4}{2 \text{ mol } N_2H_4} \times \frac{-1049 \text{ kJ}}{1 \text{ mol } N_2O_4} = -16\underline{3}.80 = -164 \text{ kJ}$$

6.8.   Substitute into the equation $q = s \times m \times \Delta t$ to obtain the heat transferred. The temperature change is

$$\Delta t = t_f - t_i = 100.0°C - 20.0°C = 80.0°C$$

Therefore,

$$q = s \times m \, \Delta t = 0.449 \text{ J/(g•°C)} \times 5.00 \text{ g} \times 80.0°C = 1.7\underline{9}6 \times 10^2 = 1.80 \times 10^2 \text{ J}$$

6.9.   The total mass of the solution is obtained by adding the volumes together and by using the density of water (1.000 g/mL). This gives $33 + 42 = 75$ mL, or 75 g. The heat absorbed by the solution is

$$q = s \times m \times \Delta t = 4.184 \text{ J/(g•°C)} \times 75 \text{ g} \times (31.8°C - 25.0°C) = 2\underline{1}33.8 \text{ J}$$

The heat released by the reaction, q_{rxn}, is equal to the negative of this value, or $-2\underline{1}33.8$ J. To obtain the enthalpy change for the reaction, you need to calculate the moles of HCl that reacted. This is

   Mol HCl = 1.20 mol/L $\times$ 0.033 L = 0.039\underline{6} mol

The enthalpy change for the reaction can now be calculated.

$$\Delta H = \frac{-2\underline{1}33.8 \text{ J}}{0.039\underline{6} \text{ mol}} = -5\underline{3}884 \text{ J/mol} = -54 \text{ kJ/mol}$$

Expressing this result as a thermochemical equation, you have

$$HCl(aq) + NaOH(aq) \rightarrow NaCl(aq) + H_2O(l); \Delta H = -54 \text{ kJ}$$

6.10.   Use Hess's law to find ΔH for $4Al(s) + 3MnO_2(s) \rightarrow 2Al_2O_3(s) + 3Mn(s)$ from the following data for equations 1 and 2:

$$2Al(s) + 3/2O_2(g) \rightarrow Al_2O_3(s); \Delta H = -1676 \text{ kJ} \quad (1)$$

$$Mn(s) + O_2(g) \rightarrow MnO_2(s); \Delta H = -520 \text{ kJ} \quad (2)$$

If you take equation 1 and multiply it by 2, you obtain

$$4Al(s) + 3O_2(g) \rightarrow 2Al_2O_3(s); \Delta H = 2 \times (-1676 \text{ kJ}) = -3352 \text{ kJ}$$

Since the desired reaction has three MnO_2 on the left side, reverse equation 2 and multiply it by 3. The result is

$$3MnO_2(s) \rightarrow 3Mn(s) + 3O_2(g) \quad \Delta H = -3 \times (-520 \text{ kJ}) = 1560 \text{ kJ}$$

If you add the two equations and corresponding enthalpy changes, you obtain the enthalpy change of the desired equation.

$4Al(s) + 3O_2(g)$	$2Al_2O_3(s)$	$\Delta H = -3352 \text{ kJ}$
$3MnO_2(s)$	$3Mn(s) + 3O_2(g)$	$\Delta H = 1560 \text{ kJ}$
$4Al(s) + 3MnO_2(s)$	$2Al_2O_3(s) + 3Mn(s)$	$\Delta H = -1792 \text{ kJ}$

6.11.   The vaporization process, with the $\Delta H°_f$ values given below the substances, is

$$H_2O(l) \quad \rightarrow \quad H_2O(g)$$
$$-285.8 \qquad \quad -241.8 \qquad (kJ)$$

The calculation is

$$\Delta H°_{vap} = \Sigma n \, \Delta H°_f \text{ (products)} - \Sigma m \, \Delta H°_f \text{ (reactants)}$$

$$= (1 \text{ mol}) \Delta H°_f \, [H_2O(g)] - (1 \text{mol}) \Delta H°_f \, [H_2O(l)]$$

$$= (-241.8 \text{ kJ}) - (-285.8 \text{ kJ}) = 44.0 \text{ kJ}$$

6.12.   The reaction, with the $\Delta H°_f$ values given below the substances, is

$$3NO_2(g) \quad + \quad H_2O(l) \quad \rightarrow \quad 2HNO_3(aq) \quad + \quad NO(g)$$
$$33.10 \qquad \qquad -285.8 \qquad \qquad -207.4 \qquad \qquad 90.29 \qquad (kJ)$$

The calculation is

$$\Delta H°_{rxn} = \Sigma n \, \Delta H°_f \text{ (products)} - \Sigma m \, \Delta H°_f \text{ (reactants)}$$

$$\Delta H°_{rxn} = [(2 \text{ mol}) \Delta H°_f \, (HNO_3) + (1 \text{ mol}) \Delta H°_f \, (NO)] - [(3 \text{ mol}) \Delta H°_f \, (NO_2) + (1 \text{ mol}) \Delta H°_f \, (H_2O)]$$

$$\Delta H°_{rxn} = [2(-207.4) + (90.29)] \text{ kJ} - [3(33.10) + (-285.8)] \text{ kJ} = -138.\underline{01} = -138.0 \text{ kJ}$$

6.13.   The net chemical reaction, with the $\Delta H°_f$ values given below the substances, is

$$2 NH_4^+(aq) \quad + \quad 2OH^-(aq) \quad \rightarrow \quad 2NH_3(g) \quad + \quad 2H_2O(l)$$
$$2(-132.5) \qquad \quad 2(-230.0) \qquad \qquad \quad 2(-45.90) \qquad \quad 2(-285.8) \qquad (kJ)$$

The calculation is

$$\Delta H°_{rxn} = [2 \, \Delta H°_f \, (NH_3) + 2 \, \Delta H°_f \, (H_2O)] - [2 \, \Delta H°_f \, (NH_4^+) + 2 \, \Delta H°_f \, (OH^-)]$$

$$= [2(-45.90) + 2(-285.8)] - [2(-132.5) + 2(-230.0)] = 61.\underline{60} = 61.6 \text{ kJ}$$

■ ANSWERS TO CONCEPT CHECKS

6.1.   The photovoltaic cells collect the sun's energy, converting it to electrical energy. This electrical energy is stored in the battery as chemical energy, which is later changed back to electrical energy that runs a motor. As the motor rotates, it changes the electrical energy to kinetic energy (energy of motion) of the motor, then of water, which in turn is changed to potential energy (energy of position) of water as the water moves upward in the gravitational field of earth.

6.2.   The change in the internal energy of the system, ΔU, equals $q + w$. Relative to the system, q is negative because the system evolves (gives off) heat . The value of q is -89.1 kJ. Because the weights do work on the system by compressing the gas, w is positive relative to the system. The value of w is $+2.5$ kJ Thus,

$$\Delta U = q + w = (-89.1 \text{ kJ}) + (+2.5 \text{ kJ}) = -86.6 \text{ kJ (Selection d is the correct answer.)}$$

6.3.   a.   This reaction is the one shown in the problem, and it has a positive ΔH, so the reaction is endothermic.

   b.   This reaction is simply twice reaction a, so it is also endothermic.

   c.   This reaction is the reverse of reaction a, so it is exothermic.

   d.   This reaction is twice reaction c, so it is more exothermic than reaction c. Thus, reaction d is the most exothermic reaction.

6.4.   You can think of the sublimation of ice as taking place in two stages. First, the solid melts to liquid; then the liquid vaporizes. The first process has an enthalpy ΔH_{fus}. The second process has an enthalpy ΔH_{vap}. Therefore, the total enthalpy, which is the enthalpy of sublimation, is the sum of these two enthalpies:

$$\Delta H_{sub} = \Delta H_{fus} + \Delta H_{vap}$$

■ ANSWERS TO SELF-ASSESSMENT AND REVIEW QUESTIONS

6.1.   Energy is the potential or capacity to move matter. Kinetic energy is the energy associated with an object by virtue of its motion. Potential energy is the energy an object has by virtue of its position in a field of force. Internal energy is the sum of the kinetic and potential energies of the particles making up a substance.

6.2.   In terms of SI base units, a joule is $kg \bullet m^2/s^2$.

6.3.   Originally, a calorie was defined as the amount of energy required to raise the temperature of one gram of water by one degree Celsius. At present, the calorie is defined as 4.184 J.

6.4.   At either of the two highest points above the earth in a pendulum's cycle, the energy of the pendulum is all potential energy and is equal to the product mgh (m = mass of pendulum, g = constant acceleration of gravity, and h = height of pendulum). As the pendulum moves downward, its potential energy decreases from mgh to near zero, depending on how close it comes to the earth's surface. During the downward motion, its potential energy is converted to kinetic energy. When it reaches the lowest point (middle) of its cycle, the pendulum has its maximum kinetic energy and minimum potential energy. As it rises above the lowest point, its kinetic energy begins to be converted to potential energy. When it reaches the other high point in its cycle, the energy of the pendulum is again all potential energy. By the law of conservation of energy, this energy cannot be lost, only converted to other forms. At rest, the energy of the pendulum has been transferred to the surroundings in the form of heat.

6.5. As the heat flows into the gas, the gas molecules gain energy and move at a greater average speed. The internal energy of the gas increases.

6.6. An exothermic reaction is a chemical reaction or a physical change in which heat is evolved (q is negative). For example, burning one mole of methane, $CH_4(g)$, yields carbon dioxide, water, and 890 kJ of heat. An endothermic reaction is a chemical reaction or physical change in which heat is absorbed (q is positive). For example, the reaction of one mole of barium hydroxide with ammonium nitrate absorbs 170.8 kJ of heat in order to form ammonia, water, and barium nitrate.

6.7. Changes in internal energy depend only on the initial and final states of the system, which are determined by variables such as temperature and pressure. Such changes do not depend on any previous history of the system.

6.8. The enthalpy change equals the heat of reaction at constant pressure.

6.9. At constant pressure, the enthalpy change is positive (the enthalpy increases) for an endothermic reaction.

6.10. It is important to give the states when writing an equation for ΔH because ΔH depends on the states of all reactants and products. If any state changes, ΔH changes.

6.11. When the equation for the reaction is doubled, the enthalpy is also doubled. When the equation is reversed, the sign of ΔH is also reversed.

6.12. First, convert the 10.0 g of water to moles of water, using its molar mass (18.02 g/mol). Next, using the equation, multiply the moles of water by the appropriate mole ratio (1 mol CH_4 / 2 mol H_2O). Finally, multiply the moles of CH_4 by the heat of the reaction (-890.3 kJ/mol CH_4).

6.13. The heat capacity (C) of a substance is the quantity of heat needed to raise the temperature of the sample of substance one degree Celsius (or one kelvin). The specific heat of a substance is the quantity of heat required to raise the temperature of one gram of a substance by one degree Celsius (or one kelvin) at constant pressure.

6.14. A simple calorimeter consists of an insulated container (for example, a pair of styrene coffee cups as in Figure 6.15) with a thermometer. The heat of the reaction is obtained by conducting the reaction in the calorimeter. The temperature of the mixture is measured before and after the reaction, and since this is a constant-pressure process, the heat is directly related to the enthalpy change, ΔH.

6.15. Hess's law states that for a chemical equation that can be written as the sum of two or more steps, the enthalpy change for the overall equation is the sum of the enthalpy changes for the individual steps. In other words, no matter how you go from reactants to products, the enthalpy change for the overall chemical change is the same. This is because enthalpy is a state function.

6.16.   No, you can still obtain the enthalpy for the desired reaction. You will need to come up with a system of reactions that can be combined to give the desired reaction and will need to know the enthalpy changes for each of the steps. Then, using Hess's law, you can obtain the enthalpy change for the reaction under study.

6.17.   The thermodynamic standard state consists of the standard thermodynamic conditions chosen for substances when listing or comparing thermodynamic data: one atm pressure and the specified temperature (usually 25°C).

6.18.   The reference form of an element is the most stable form (physical state and allotrope) of the element under standard thermodynamic conditions. The standard enthalpy of formation of an element in its reference form is zero.

6.19.   The standard enthalpy of formation of a substance, ΔH°_f, is the enthalpy change for the formation of one mole of the substance in its standard state from its elements in their reference form and in their standard states.

6.20.   The equation for the formation of $H_2S(g)$ is

$$H_2(g) + 1/8 S_8(\text{rhombic}) \rightarrow H_2S(g)$$

6.21.   The reaction of $C(g) + 4H(g) \rightarrow CH_4(g)$ is not an appropriate equation for calculating the ΔH°_f of methane because the most stable form of each element is not used. Both $H_2(g)$ and $C(\text{graphite})$ should be used instead of $H(g)$ and $C(g)$, respectively.

6.22.   A fuel is any substance that is burned or similarly reacted to provide heat and other forms of energy. The fossil fuels are petroleum (oil), gas, and coal. They were formed millions of years ago when aquatic plants and animals were buried and compressed by layers of sediment at the bottoms of swamps and seas. Over time, this organic matter was converted by bacterial decay and pressure to fossil fuels.

6.23.   One of the ways of converting coal to methane involves the water-gas reaction.

$$C(s) + H_2O(g) \rightarrow CO(g) + H_2(g)$$

In this reaction, steam is passed over hot coal. This mixture is then reacted over a catalyst to give methane.

$$CO(g) + 3H_2(g) \rightarrow CH_4(g) + H_2O(g)$$

6.24.   Some possible rocket fuel/oxidizer combinations are H_2/O_2 and hydrazine/dinitrogen tetroxide. The chemical equations for their reactions are

$$H_2(g) + 1/2 O_2(g) \rightarrow H_2O(g); \Delta H^\circ = -242 \text{ kJ}$$

$$2N_2H_4(l) + N_2O_4(l) \rightarrow 3N_2(g) + 4H_2O(g); \Delta H^\circ = -1049 \text{ kJ}$$

6.24.   The answer is d, burning enough butane to produce one mole of water.

6.26.   The answer is b, 40.°C.

6.27.   The answer is c, endothermic, and the temperature of the resulting solution falls.

6.28.   The answer is c, the water with the mercury will be the hottest.

■ ANSWERS TO CONCEPTUAL PROBLEMS

6.31.

	Beaker A	Beaker B	Beaker C
(a) Endo- or Exothermic?	Exothermic – more energy is leaving the system as work than heat is entering it	Exothermic – energy is leaving the system as both work and heat	Endothermic – energy is entering the system as both work and heat
(b) Sign of w? (relative to system)	negative	negative	positive
(c) Sign of ΔH (= q) ?	positive	negative	Positive
	Beaker A	Beaker B	Beaker C
(d) Increase or decrease in U? $\Delta U = q + w$	Decrease; $q + w < 0$ $\|q\| < \|w\|$	Decrease; $q + w < 0$	Increase; $Q + w > 0$
(e) Hotter or colder than room temperature?	Hotter	Hotter	Colder

6.33.   Kinetic energy is proportional to mass and to speed squared. Compare the kinetic energy of the smaller car with that of the larger car (twice the mass), assuming both are traveling at the same speed. The larger car would have twice the kinetic energy of the smaller car. Or we could say that the smaller car has only half the kinetic energy of the larger car. Now suppose the speed of the smaller is increased by a factor of 2 (so it is now moving at twice its original speed). Its kinetic energy is increased by a factor of 4. Therefore, the smaller car now has one-half times four times, or twice, the kinetic energy of the larger car. The smaller car has the greater kinetic energy.

6.35.   a.   After the water is placed into the freezer, it will lose heat to the freezer, so q_{sys} is negative.

b.   The water will have turned to ice.

c.   The initial enthalpy (of the water) is higher than the final enthalpy (of the ice).

d.   After several hours, the temperature of the water will be −20°C.

6.37.   You can imagine this process taking place in two steps: first, the preparation of water vapor from the elements, and second, the change of the vapor to liquid. Here are the equations:

$$H_2(g) + \tfrac{1}{2}O_2(g) \rightarrow H_2O(g); \Delta H_f$$

$$H_2O(g) \rightarrow H_2O(l); -\Delta H_{vap}$$

The last equation is the reverse of the vaporization of water, so the enthalpy of the step is the negative of the enthalpy of vaporization. The enthalpy change for the preparation of one mole of liquid water, ΔH, is the sum of the enthalpy changes for these two steps:

$$\Delta H = \Delta H_f + (-\Delta H_{vap}) = \Delta H_f - \Delta H_{vap}$$

6.39. a. The heat lost by the metal is equal to the heat gained by the water. Since $q = s \times m \times \Delta t$, the heat gained by the water is directly proportional to Δt. Since Δt is larger for water with metal A, metal A lost more heat. Now, each metal has the same mass and Δt, so the specific heat is directly proportional to q. Since q is larger for A, the specific heat is larger for A.

  b. The metal with the higher specific heat will have absorbed more heat to reach the starting temperature of 95°C; therefore, it will release more heat to the water, causing the water to reach a higher temperature. The beaker with metal A will rise to the higher temperature.

6.41. Let us write ΔH_{rxn} for the enthalpy change when one mole of P_4S_3 burns in O_2 to give P_4O_{10} and SO_2. In principle, you could calculate ΔH_{rxn} from enthalpies of formation for the reactants and products of this reaction. You would require the values for P_4S_3, O_2 (which equals zero), P_4O_{10}, and SO_2. Enthalpies of formation for the products, P_4O_{10} and SO_2, are given in Table 6.2 in the text. This means that if you have measured ΔH_{rxn}, you can use the enthalpies of formation of P_4O_{10} and SO_2 to calculate the enthalpy of formation for P_4S_3. What you have done is this: you have used enthalpies of combustion to calculate enthalpies of formation. This is the idea most often used to obtain enthalpies of formation.

■ SOLUTIONS TO PRACTICE PROBLEMS

Note on significant figures: If the final answer to a solution needs to be rounded off, it is given first with one nonsignificant figure, and the last significant figure is underlined. The final answer is then rounded to the correct number of significant figures. In multistep problems, intermediate answers are given with at least one nonsignificant figure; however, only the final answer has been rounded off.

6.43. The heat released, in kilocalories, is

$$-445.1 \text{ kJ} \times \frac{1000 \text{ J}}{1 \text{ kJ}} \times \frac{1 \text{ cal}}{4.184 \text{ J}} \times \frac{1 \text{ kcal}}{1000 \text{ cal}} = -106.\underline{3}8 = -106.4 \text{ kcal}$$

6.45. The kinetic energy, in joules, is

$$E_k = \frac{1}{2} \times 4.85 \times 10^3 \text{ lb} \times \frac{0.4536 \text{ kg}}{1 \text{ lb}} \times \left[\frac{57 \text{ mi}}{1 \text{ h}} \right]^2 \times \left[\frac{1609 \text{ m}}{1 \text{ mi}} \right]^2 \times \left[\frac{1 \text{ h}}{3600 \text{ s}} \right]^2$$

$$= 7.\underline{1}3 \times 10^5 = 7.1 \times 10^5 \text{ J}$$

The kinetic energy, in calories, is

$$E_k = 7.\underline{1}3 \times 10^5 \text{ J} \times \frac{1 \text{ cal}}{4.184 \text{ J}} = 1.\underline{7}0 \times 10^5 = 1.7 \times 10^5 \text{ cal}$$

6.47.   To insert the mass of one molecule of ClO_2 in the formula, multiply the molar mass by the reciprocal of Avogadro's number. The kinetic energy in joules is

$$E_k = \frac{1}{2} \times \frac{67.45 \text{ g}}{1 \text{ mol}} \times \frac{1 \text{ mol}}{6.022 \times 10^{23} \text{ molec.}} \times \frac{1 \text{ kg}}{1000 \text{ g}} \times \left[\frac{306 \text{ m}}{1 \text{ s}} \right]^2$$

$$= 5.2\underline{4}3 \times 10^{-21} = 5.24 \times 10^{-21} \text{ J/molecule}$$

6.49.   The system contracts so $w = +29$ J. The system loses heat so $q = -82$ J. Thus, ΔU is readily calculated by the first law:

$$\Delta U = q + w = -82 \text{ J} + 29 \text{ J} = -53 \text{ J}$$

6.51.   Endothermic reactions absorb heat, so the sign of q will be positive because energy must be gained by the system from the surroundings. The flask will feel cold to the touch.

6.53.   The gain of 66.2 kJ of heat per 2 mol NO_2 means the reaction is endothermic. Because energy is gained by the system from the surroundings, q is positive and is +66.2 kJ for 2 mol NO_2 reacting.

6.55.   The vaporization of water is an endothermic process. Its thermochemical equation is:

$$H_2O(l) \rightarrow H_2O(g); \qquad \Delta H = +40.66 \text{ kJ}$$

The vaporization involves an expansion whereby work is performed on the surroundings as the liquid is converted into a gas. The change in internal energy, ΔU, is:

$$\Delta U = \Delta H - P\Delta V = \Delta H - \Delta n_{gar}RT$$

For the physical vaporization process described, the change in the number of moles of gas, Δn_{gar}, is +1 mol. Thus,

$$\Delta U = \Delta H - \Delta n_{gar}RT = +40.66 \text{ kJ} - (+1 \text{ mol}) \times \frac{8.3145 \times 10^{-3} \text{ kJ}}{\text{mol} \bullet \text{K}} \times 373 \text{ K}$$

$$\Delta U = +40.66 \text{ kJ} - 3.1\underline{0} \text{ kJ} = +37.56 \text{ kJ}$$

6.57.   The reaction of $Fe(s)$ with HCl must yield H_2 and $FeCl_2$. To balance the hydrogen, 2HCl must be written as a reactant:

$$Fe(s) + 2HCl(aq) \rightarrow FeCl_2(aq) + H_2(g)$$

To write a thermochemical equation, the sign of ΔH must be negative because heat is evolved:

$$Fe(s) + 2HCl(aq) \rightarrow FeCl_2(aq) + H_2(g); \Delta H = -89.1 \text{ kJ}$$

6.59.   The first equation is

$$P_4(s) + 5O_2(g) \rightarrow P_4O_{10}(s); \Delta H = -3010 \text{ kJ}$$

The second equation is

$$P_4O_{10}(s) \rightarrow P_4(s) + 5O_2(g); \Delta H = ?$$

The second equation has been obtained by reversing the first equation. Therefore, to obtain ΔH for the second equation, ΔH for the first equation must be reversed in sign: $-(-3010) = +3010$ kJ.

6.61. The first equation is

$$\tfrac{1}{4}P_4O_{10}(s) + 3/2H_2O(l) \rightarrow H_3PO_4(aq); \Delta H = -96.2 \text{ kJ}$$

The second equation is

$$P_4O_{10}(s) + 6H_2O(l) \rightarrow 4H_3PO_4(aq); \Delta H = ?$$

The second equation has been obtained from the first by multiplying each coefficient by 4. Therefore, to obtain the ΔH for the second equation, the ΔH for the first equation must be multiplied by 4; that is, $-96.2 \times 4 = -384.8 = -385$ kJ

6.63. Because nitric oxide is written as NO in the equation, the molar mass of NO equals 30.01 g per mol NO. From the equation, 2 mol NO evolve 114 kJ heat. Divide the 114 kJ by the 2 mol NO and by the 30.01 g/mol NO to obtain the amount of heat evolved per gram of NO:

$$\frac{-114 \text{ kJ}}{2 \text{ mol NO}} \times \frac{1 \text{ mol NO}}{30.01 \text{ g NO}} = -1.8\underline{9}9 = \frac{-1.90 \text{ kJ}}{\text{g NO}}$$

6.65. The molar mass of ammonia is 17.03 g/mol. From the equation, 4 mol NH_3 evolve 1267 kJ of heat. Divide 35.8 g NH_3 by its molar mass and the 4 mol NH_3 in the equation to obtain the amount of heat evolved:

$$35.8 \text{ g NH}_3 \times \frac{1 \text{ mol NH}_3}{17.03 \text{ g NH}_3} \times \frac{-1267 \text{ kJ}}{4 \text{ mol NH}_3} = -6.6\underline{5}9 \times 10^2 = -6.66 \times 10^2 \text{ kJ}$$

6.67. The molar mass of C_3H_8 is 44.06 g/mol. From the equation, 1 mol C_3H_8 evolves 2043 kJ heat. This gives

$$-369 \text{ kJ} \times \frac{1 \text{ mol C}_3\text{H}_8}{-2043 \text{ kJ}} \times \frac{44.06 \text{ g C}_3\text{H}_8}{1 \text{ mol C}_3\text{H}_8} = 7.9\underline{5}8 = 7.96 \text{ g C}_3\text{H}_8$$

6.69. Multiply the 180 g (0.180 kg) of water by the specific heat of 4.18 J/(g•°C) and by Δt to obtain heat in joules:

$$180. \text{ g} \times (96°C - 19°C) \times \frac{4.18 \text{ J}}{1 \text{ g} \bullet °C} = 5\underline{7}934 = 5.8 \times 10^4 \text{ J}$$

6.71. Use the 2.26×10^3 J/g (2.26 kJ/g) heat of vaporization to calculate the heat of condensation. Then use it to calculate Δt, the temperature change.

$$\text{Heat of condensation} = \frac{2.26 \times 10^3 \text{ J}}{1 \text{ g}} \times 168 \text{ g} = 3.7\underline{9}68 \times 10^5 \text{ J}$$

$$\text{Temperature change} = \Delta t = \frac{3.7\underline{9}68 \times 10^5 \text{ J}}{6.44 \times 10^4 \text{ g}} \times \frac{1 \text{ g} \bullet °C}{1.015 \text{ J}} = 5.8\underline{0}85 = 5.81°C$$

6.73. The enthalpy change for the reaction is equal in magnitude and opposite in sign to the heat-energy change occurring from the cooling of the solution and calorimeter.

$$q_{calorimeter} = (1071 \text{ J/°C})(21.56°C - 25.00°C) = -36\underline{8}4.2 \text{ J}$$

Thus, 15.3 g NaNO₃ is equivalent to −3684.2 J heat energy. The amount of heat absorbed by 1.000 mol NaNO₃ is calculated from +3684.2 J (opposite sign):

$$1.000 \text{ mol NaNO}_3 \times \frac{85.00 \text{ g NaNO}_3}{1 \text{ mol NaNO}_3} \times \frac{3684.2 \text{ J}}{15.3 \text{ g NaNO}_3} = 2.0\underline{4}7 \times 10^4 \text{ J}$$

Thus, the enthalpy change, ΔH, for the reaction is 2.05×10^4 J, or 20.5 kJ, per mol NaNO₃.

6.75. The energy change for the reaction is equal in magnitude and opposite in sign to the heat energy produced from the warming of the solution and the calorimeter.

$$q_{calorimeter} = (9.63 \text{ kJ/°C})(33.73 − 25.00°C) = +84.\underline{0}70 \text{ kJ}$$

Thus, 2.84 g C₂H₅OH is equivalent to 84.070 kJ heat energy. The amount of heat released by 1.000 mol C₂H₅OH is calculated from −84.070 kJ (opposite sign):

$$1.00 \text{ mol C}_2\text{H}_5\text{OH} \times \frac{46.07 \text{ g C}_2\text{H}_5\text{OH}}{1 \text{ mol C}_2\text{H}_5\text{OH}} \times \frac{-84.070 \text{ kJ}}{2.84 \text{ g C}_2\text{H}_5\text{OH}} = -13\underline{6}3.8 \text{ kJ}$$

Thus, q_{rxn} for the reaction is -1.36×10^3 kJ/mol ethanol. In bomb calorimeter experiments, the volume is fixed so no pressure-volume work is performed so the change in internal energy is directly measured. That is, $q = q_v = \Delta U$. This result also equals ΔH.

6.77. Using the equations in the data, reverse the direction of the first reaction, and reverse the sign of its ΔH. Then multiply the second equation by 2, multiply its ΔH by 2, and add. Setup:

$N_2(g)$ + $2H_2O(l)$ → $N_2H_4(l) + O_2(g)$; $\Delta H = (−622.2 \text{ kJ}) \times (−1)$

$2H_2(g)$ + $O_2(g)$ → $2H_2O(l)$; $\Delta H = (−285.8 \text{ kJ}) \times (2)$
_____
$N_2(g)$ + $2H_2(g)$ → $N_2H_4(l)$; $\Delta H = 50.6 \text{ kJ}$

6.79. Using the equations in the data, multiply the second equation by 2, and reverse its direction; do the same to its ΔH. Then multiply the first equation by 2 and its ΔH by 2. Finally, multiply the third equation by 3 and its ΔH by 3. Then add. Setup:

$4NH_3(g)$ → $2N_2(g) + 6H_2(g)$; $\Delta H = (−91.8 \text{ kJ}) \times (−2)$

$2N_2(g) + 2O_2(g)$ → $4NO(g)$; $\Delta H = (180.6 \text{ kJ}) \times (2)$

$6H_2(g) + 3O_2(g)$ → $6H_2O(g)$; $\Delta H = (−483.7 \text{ kJ}) \times (3)$
_____
$4NH_3(g) + 5O_2(g)$ → $4NO(g) + 6H_2O(g)$; $\Delta H = −906.3 \text{ kJ}$

6.81. After reversing the second equation in the data, add all the equations. Setup:

$C_2H_4(g) + 3O_2(g)$ → $2CO_2(g) + 2H_2O(l)$; $\Delta H = (−1411 \text{ kJ})$

$2CO_2(g) + 3H_2O(l)$ → $C_2H_6(g) + 7/2O_2(g)$; $\Delta H = (−1560) \times (−1)$

$H_2(g) + 1/2O_2(g)$ → $H_2O(l)$; $\Delta H = (−286 \text{ kJ})$
_____
$C_2H_4(g) + H_2(g)$ → $C_2H_6(g)$; $\Delta H = −137 \text{ kJ}$

6.83. Write the given $\Delta H°$ values underneath each compound in the balanced equation:

$$C_2H_5OH(l) \rightarrow C_2H_5OH(g)$$

$\Delta H°$ -277.7   -235.1 kJ/mol

$\Delta H°_{vap} = [\Delta H°_f(C_2H_5OH(g))] - [\Delta H°_f(C_2H_5OH(l))] = [-235.1] - [-277.7] = +42.6$ kJ

6.85. Write the $\Delta H°$ values (Table 6.2) underneath each compound in the balanced equation:

$$2H_2S(g) \quad + \quad 3O_2(g) \quad \rightarrow \quad 2H_2O(l) \quad + \quad 2SO_2(g)$$
    2(-20.50)   3(0)   2(-285.8)   2(-296.8)   (kJ)

$\Delta H°\ = \Sigma n\Delta H°_f(\text{products}) - \Sigma m\Delta H°_f(\text{reactants})$

$\quad\quad = [2(-285.8) + 2(-296.8)] - [2(-20.50) + 3(0)]$ kJ $= -1124.\underline{2}0 = -1124.2$ kJ

6.87. Write the $\Delta H°$ values (Appendix C) underneath each compound in the balanced equation:

$$Fe_2O_3(s) \quad + \quad 3CO(g) \quad \rightarrow \quad 2Fe(s) \quad + \quad 3CO_2(g)$$
    -825.5   3(-110.5)   2(0)   3(-393.5)   (kJ)

$\Delta H°\ = \Sigma n\Delta H°_f(\text{products}) - \Sigma m\Delta H°_f(\text{reactants})$

$\Delta H°\ = [2(0) + 3(-393.5)] - [(-825.5) + 3(-110.5)] = -23.5$ kJ

6.89. Write the $\Delta H°$ values (Table 6.2) underneath each compound in the balanced equation:

$$HCl(g) \quad \rightarrow \quad H^+(aq) \quad\quad Cl^-(aq)$$
    -92.31   0   -167.2 (kJ)

$\Delta H°\ = \Sigma n\Delta H°_f(\text{products}) - \Sigma m\Delta H°_f(\text{reactants}) = [(0) + (-167.2)] - [-92.31] = -74.9$ kJ

6.91. Calculate the molar heat of formation from the equation with the $\Delta H°$ values below each substance; then convert to the heat for 10.0 g of $MgCO_3$ using the molar mass of 84.3.

$$MgCO_3(s) \quad \rightarrow \quad MgO(s) \quad + \quad CO_2(g)$$
    -1111.7   -601.2   -393.5   (kJ)

$\Delta H°\ = \Sigma n\Delta H°_f(\text{products}) - \Sigma m\Delta H°_f(\text{reactants})$

$\Delta H°\ = -601.2$ kJ $+ (-393.5$ kJ$) - (-1111.7$ kJ$) = 117.\underline{0}$ kJ

$\text{Heat} = 10.0 \text{ g} \times \dfrac{1 \text{ mol}}{84.31 \text{ g}} \times \dfrac{117.0 \text{ kJ}}{\text{mol}} = 13.\underline{8}8 = 13.9$ kJ

■ SOLUTIONS TO GENERAL PROBLEMS

6.93. The SI units of force must be kg•m/s^2 (= newton, N) to be consistent with the joule, the SI unit of energy:

$$\frac{\text{kg} \cdot \text{m}}{\text{s}^2} \times \text{m} = \frac{\text{kg} \cdot \text{m}^2}{\text{s}^2} = \text{joule, J}$$

6.95. Using Table 1.4 and 4.184 J/cal, convert the 686 Btu/lb to J/g:

$$\frac{686 \text{ Btu}}{1 \text{ lb}} \times \frac{252 \text{ cal}}{1 \text{ Btu}} \times \frac{4.184 \text{ J}}{1 \text{ cal}} \times \frac{1 \text{ lb}}{0.4536 \text{ kg}} \times \frac{1 \text{ kg}}{10^3 \text{ g}} = 1.59\underline{4} \times 10^3 = 1.59 \times 10^3 \text{ J/g}$$

6.97. Substitute into the equation $E_p = mgh$, and convert to SI units.

$$E_p = 1.00 \text{ lb} \times \frac{9.807 \text{ m}}{\text{s}^2} \times 167 \text{ ft} \times \frac{0.4536 \text{ kg}}{1 \text{ lb}} \times \frac{0.9144 \text{ m}}{3 \text{ ft}} = \frac{22\underline{6}.433 \text{ kg} \cdot \text{m}^2}{\text{s}^2} = 226 \text{ J}$$

At the bottom, all the potential energy is converted to kinetic energy, so $E_k = 22\underline{6}.433$ kg•m^2/s^2. Because $E_k = 1/2mv^2$, solve for v, the speed (velocity):

$$v = \sqrt{\frac{E_k}{\frac{1}{2} \times m}} = \sqrt{\frac{226.433 \text{ kg} \cdot \text{m}^2/\text{s}^2}{\frac{1}{2} \times 1.00 \text{ lb} \times 0.4536 \text{ kg/lb}}} = 31.\underline{6}0 = 31.6 \text{ m/s}$$

6.99. The equation is $\qquad CaCO_3(s) \rightarrow CaO(s) + CO_2(g);\ \Delta H = 177.9$ kJ

Use the molar mass of 100.08 g/mol to convert the heat per mole to heat per 21.3 g.

$$21.3 \text{ g CaCO}_3 \times \frac{1 \text{ mol CaCO}_3}{100.08 \text{ g CaCO}_3} \times \frac{177.9 \text{ kJ}}{1 \text{ mol CaCO}_3} = 37.\underline{8}6 = 37.9 \text{ kJ}$$

6.101. The equation is $\qquad 2HCHO_2(l) + O_2(g) \rightarrow 2CO_2(g) + 2H_2O(l)$

Use the molar mass of 46.03 g/mol to convert −30.3 kJ/5.48 g to ΔH per mole of acid.

$$\frac{-30.3 \text{ kJ}}{5.48 \text{ g HCHO}_2} \times \frac{46.03 \text{ g HCHO}_2}{1 \text{ mol HCHO}_2} = -25\underline{4}.509 = -255 \text{ kJ/mol}$$

6.103. The heat gained by the water at the lower temperature equals the heat lost by the water at the higher temperature. Each heat term is $s \times m \times \Delta t$. This gives

$$(4.184 \text{ J/g} \cdot {}^\circ\text{C})(54.9 \text{ g})(t_f - 31.5^\circ\text{C}) = (4.184 \text{ J/g} \cdot {}^\circ\text{C})(21.0 \text{ g})(52.7^\circ\text{C} - t_f)$$

The specific heat and the units can be canceled from both sides to give

$$(54.9)(t_f - 31.5^\circ\text{C}) = (21.0)(52.7^\circ\text{C} - t_f)$$

After rearranging, you get 75.9 t_f = 2836.05. This gives $t_f = 37.\underline{3}6 = 37.4^\circ$C.

6.105. Divide the 235 J heat by the mass of lead and the Δt to obtain the specific heat.

$$\text{Specific heat} = \frac{235 \text{ J}}{121.6 \text{ g } (35.5^\circ\text{C} - 20.4^\circ\text{C})} = 0.12\underline{7}98 = \frac{0.128 \text{ J}}{\text{g} \cdot {}^\circ C}$$

6.107. The energy used to heat the Zn comes from cooling the water. Calculate q for water:

$$q_{wat} = \text{specific heat} \times \text{mass} \times \Delta t$$

$$q_{wat} = \frac{4.18 \text{ J}}{\text{g} \cdot {}^\circ\text{C}} \times 50.0 \text{ g} \times (96.68{}^\circ\text{C} - 100.00{}^\circ\text{C}) = -69\underline{3}.88 \text{ J}$$

The sign of q for the Zn is the reverse of the sign of q for water because the Zn absorbs heat:

$$q_{met} = -(q_{wat}) = -(-693.88) = 69\underline{3}.88 \text{ J}$$

$$\text{Specific heat} = \frac{693.88 \text{ J}}{25.3 \text{ g} (96.68{}^\circ\text{C} - 25.00{}^\circ\text{C})} = 0.382\underline{6} = \frac{0.383 \text{ J}}{\text{g} \cdot {}^\circ\text{C}}$$

6.109. First, multiply the molarities by the volumes, in liters, to get the moles of NaOH and the moles of HCl, and thus determine the limiting reactant.

$$\text{Mol NaOH} = M \times V = 0.996 \, M \times 0.0141 \text{ L} = 0.0140\underline{4} \text{ mol}$$

$$\text{Mol HCl} = M \times V = 0.905 \, M \times 0.0323 \text{ L} = 0.0292\underline{3} \text{ mol}$$

Therefore, NaOH is the limiting reactant. The total volume of the system is 14.1 mL + 32.3 mL = 46.4 mL. Since the density of water is 1.00 g/mL, the total mass of the system is 46.4 g. Next, set the heat released by the reaction (mol × molar enthalpy of reaction) equal to the heat absorbed by the water ($s \times m \times \Delta t$). This gives

$$(0.0140\underline{4} \text{ mol})(55.8 \times 10^3 \text{ J/mol}) = (4.184 \text{ J/g} \bullet {}^\circ\text{C})(46.4 \text{ g})(t_f - 21.6{}^\circ\text{C})$$

After dividing, this gives $t_f - 21.6{}^\circ\text{C} = 4.0\underline{3}5{}^\circ\text{C}$, or $t_f = 25.\underline{6}3 = 25.6{}^\circ\text{C}$.

6.111. Use Δt and the heat capacity of 547 J/°C to calculate q:

$$q = C\Delta t = (547 \text{ J/}{}^\circ\text{C})(36.66 - 25.00){}^\circ\text{C} = 6.3\underline{7}8 \times 10^3 \text{ J} \, (6.3\underline{7}8 \text{ kJ})$$

Energy is released in the solution process in raising the temperature, so ΔH is negative:

$$\Delta H = \frac{-6.378 \text{ kJ}}{6.48 \text{ g LiOH}} \times \frac{23.95 \text{ g LiOH}}{1 \text{ mol LiOH}} = -23.\underline{5}7 = -23.6 \text{ kJ/mol}$$

6.113. Use Δt and the heat capacity of 13.43 kJ/°C to calculate q:

$$q = C\Delta t = (13.43 \text{ kJ/}{}^\circ\text{C})(35.84 - 25.00){}^\circ\text{C} = 145.\underline{5}81 \text{ kJ}$$

As in the previous two problems, the sign of ΔH must be reversed, making the heat negative:

$$\Delta H = \frac{-145.581 \text{ kJ}}{10.00 \text{ g HC}_2\text{H}_3\text{O}_2} \times \frac{60.05 \text{ g HC}_2\text{H}_3\text{O}_2}{1 \text{ mol HC}_2\text{H}_3\text{O}_2} = -874.\underline{2}1 = -874.2 \text{ kJ/mol}$$

6.115. Using the equations in the data, reverse the direction of the first reaction, and reverse the sign of its ΔH. Then add the second and third equations and their ΔH's.

$\text{H}_2\text{O}(g) + \text{SO}_2(g)$	$\rightarrow$	$\text{H}_2\text{S}(g) + 3/2\text{O}_2(g)$;	$\Delta H = (-518 \text{ kJ}) \times (-1)$
$\text{H}_2(g) + 1/2\text{O}_2(g)$	$\rightarrow$	$\text{H}_2\text{O}(g)$;	$\Delta H = (-242 \text{ kJ})$
$1/8\text{S}_8(\text{rh.}) + \text{O}_2(g)$	$\rightarrow$	$\text{SO}_2(g)$;	$\Delta H = (-297 \text{ kJ})$
$\text{H}_2(g) + 1/8\text{S}_8(rh.)$	$\rightarrow$	$\text{H}_2\text{S}(g)$;	$\Delta H = -21 \text{ kJ}$

6.117. Write the $\Delta H°$ values (Table 6.2) underneath each compound in the balanced equation.

$$CH_4(g) \quad + \quad H_2O(g) \quad \rightarrow \quad CO(g) \quad + \quad 3H_2(g)$$

$$-74.87 \qquad\qquad -241.8 \qquad\qquad -110.5 \qquad 3(0) \quad (kJ)$$

$$\Delta H° = [-110.5 + 3(0)] - [(-74.87) + (-241.8)] = 206.\underline{1}7 = 206.2 \text{ kJ}$$

6.119. Write the $\Delta H°$ values (Table 6.2) underneath each compound in the balanced equation. The $\Delta H_f°$ of -635 kJ/mol CaO is given in the problem.

$$CaCO_3(s) \quad \rightarrow \quad CaO(s) \quad + \quad CO_2(g)$$

$$-1206.9 \qquad\qquad -635 \qquad -393.5 \qquad (kJ)$$

$$\Delta H° = [(-635) + (-393.5)] - [-1206.9] = 17\underline{8}.4 = 178 \text{ kJ}$$

6.121. Calculate the molar heat of reaction from the equation with the $\Delta H°$ values below each substance; then convert to the heat for the reaction at 25°C.

$$2H_2(g) \quad + \quad O_2(g) \quad \rightarrow \quad 2H_2O(l)$$

$$0.0 \text{ kJ} \qquad 0.0 \text{ kJ} \qquad -285.8 \text{ kJ}$$

$$\Delta H° = 2 \times (-285.8 \text{ kJ}) - 0 - 0 = -57\underline{1}.6 \text{ kJ}$$

The moles of oxygen in 2.000 L with a density of 1.11 g/L is

$$2.000 \text{ L O}_2 \times \frac{1.11 \text{ g O}_2}{1 \text{ L O}_2} \times \frac{1 \text{ mol O}_2}{32.00 \text{ g O}_2} = 0.069\underline{3}7 \text{ mol O}_2$$

The heat of reaction from 0.06937 mol O$_2$ is

$$0.069\underline{3}7 \text{ mol O}_2 \times \frac{-571.6 \text{ kJ}}{\text{mol O}_2} = -39.\underline{6}54 = -39.7 \text{ kJ}$$

6.123. Let $\Delta H_f° =$ the unknown standard enthalpy of formation for sucrose. Then write this symbol and the other $\Delta H_f°$ values underneath each compound in the balanced equation, and solve for $\Delta H_f°$ using the $\Delta H°$ of -5641 kJ for the reaction.

$$C_{12}H_{22}O_{11}(s) \quad + \quad 12O_2(g) \quad \rightarrow \quad 12CO_2(g) \quad + \quad 11H_2O(l)$$

$$\Delta H_f° \qquad\qquad 12(0) \qquad 12(-393.5) \qquad 11(-285.8) \qquad (kJ)$$

$$\Delta H° = -5641 = [12(-393.5) + 11(-285.8)] - [\Delta H_f° + 12(0)]$$

$$\Delta H_f° = -2225 \text{ kJ/mol sucrose}$$

6.125. First, calculate the heat evolved from the molar amounts represented by the balanced equation. From Appendix C, obtain the individual heats of formation, and write those below the reactants and products in the balanced equation. Then multiply the molar heats of formation by the number of moles in the balanced equation, and write those products below the molar heats of formation.

$$2Al(s) \quad + \quad 3NH_4NO_3(s) \quad \rightarrow \quad 3N_2(g) \quad + \quad 6H_2O(g) \quad + \quad Al_2O_3(s)$$

0.0 kJ	-365.6 kJ	0.0 kJ	-241.8	-1675.7 kJ (kJ/mol)
0.0 kJ	-1096.8 kJ	0.0 kJ	-1450.8	-1675.7 kJ (kJ/eqn.)

The total heat of reaction of 2 mol Al and 3 mol NH_4NO_3 is

$\Delta H = -1450.8 - 1675.7 - (-1096.8 \text{ kJ}) = -2029.7 \text{ kJ}$

Now, 245 kJ represents the following fraction of the total heat of reaction:

$$\frac{245 \text{ kJ}}{2029.7 \text{ kJ}} = 0.120\underline{7}$$

Thus, 245 kJ requires the fraction 0.1207 of the moles of each reactant: 0.1207×2, or $0.24\underline{1}4$, mol of Al and 0.1207×3, or $0.36\underline{2}1$, mol of NH_4NO_3. The mass of each reactant and the mass of the mixture are as follows:

0.2414 mol Al $\times$ 26.98 g/mol Al = 6.5$\underline{1}$3 g of Al

0.3621 mol NH_4NO_3 $\times$ 80.05 g/mol NH_4NO_3 = 28.$\underline{9}$9 g NH_4NO_3

6.513 g Al + 28.99 g NH_4NO_3 = 35.$\underline{5}$0 = 35.5 g of the mixture

6.127. White phosphorus is a yellowish-white, waxy substance often sold in the form of sticks looking something like fat crayons. It is not found in modern matches. It was outlawed in the early 1900s because workers began to show symptoms of white phosphorus poisoning, in which the jawbone disintegrated.

■ SOLUTIONS TO STRATEGY PROBLEMS

6.129. First determine the volume of the steel ball using the volume formula for a sphere:

$$V = \frac{4}{3}\pi r^3 = \frac{4}{3}\pi\left(\frac{D}{2}\right)^3 = \frac{4}{3\times 8}\pi(D)^3 = \frac{1}{6}\pi(4.00 \text{ cm})^3 = 33.\underline{5}1 \text{ cm}^3$$

Next determine the mass of the ball using the density relationship:

$$m = \text{density} \times \text{volume} = \frac{7.87 \text{ g}}{\text{cm}^3} \times 33.\underline{5}1 \text{ cm}^3 = 26\underline{3}.7 \text{ g} = 0.263\underline{7} \text{ kg}$$

Finally use the kinetic energy relationship to find the requested speed of the ball:

$$KE = 94.7 \text{ J} = 94.7 \frac{\text{kg m}^2}{\text{s}^2} = \frac{1}{2}mv^2$$

$$v = \sqrt{\frac{2KE}{m}} = \sqrt{\frac{2(94.7 \frac{\text{kg m}^2}{\text{s}^2})}{0.263\underline{7} \text{ kg}}} = 26.\underline{8}0 = 26.8 \text{ m/s}$$

6.131. The balanced thermochemical equation is

$$2H_2(g) + O_2(g) \rightarrow 2H_2O(l);\ \Delta H = 2 \times (-285.8\ kJ)$$

From the starting amounts of 3 mol H_2 and 1 mol O_2, it should be recognized that O_2 is the limiting reagent and H_2 is in excess by 1 mol. Thus, 2 mol $H_2O(l)$ will form and 571.6 kJ of heat ($q = \Delta H$) will evolve. The work done on the system by the external atmosphere is pressure-volume work ($w = -P\Delta V$) done while compressing the 4 mol of gas initially to 1 mol of gas in the final condition.

$$w = -P\Delta V = -P\frac{\Delta n_g RT}{P} = -\Delta n_g RT = -(n_{g,final} - n_{g,initial})RT$$

$$w = -(1.00\ mol\ -\ 4.00\ mol) \times \frac{0.08206\ L \bullet atm}{mol \bullet K} \times 298\ K = +73.\underline{3}6\ L \bullet atm$$

Converting to kJ,

$$w = +73.\underline{3}6\ L \bullet atm \times \frac{0.1013\ kJ}{1\ L \bullet atm} = +7.4\underline{3}2\ kJ$$

Work is positive relative to the system because it is work done by the surroundings. By the first law, the change in internal energy, ΔU, equals $q + w$:

$$\Delta U = q + w = -571.6\ kJ + 7.4\underline{3}\ kJ = -56\underline{4}.1 = -564\ kJ$$

6.133. The work done by the gas in expanding against the atmosphere is pressure-volume work ($w = -P\Delta V$) done when the $CO_2(s)$ expands to $CO_2(g)$:

$$CO_2(s) \rightarrow CO_2(g)$$

$$w = -P\Delta V = -P\frac{\Delta n_g RT}{P} = -\Delta n_g RT =$$

$$w = -21.5\ g\ CO_2 \times \frac{1\ mol\ CO_2}{44.01\ g\ CO_2} \times \frac{0.08206\ L \bullet atm}{mol \bullet K} \times 297\ K = -11.\underline{9}1\ L \bullet atm$$

Converting to kJ,

$$w = -11.\underline{9}1\ L \bullet atm \times \frac{0.1013\ kJ}{1\ L \bullet atm} = -1.2\underline{0}6 = -1.21\ kJ$$

Here, work is negative relative to the system because the system expends energy in pushing out against the surrounding atmosphere.

6.135. The described processes can be depicted with the following thermochemical equations:

Step 1: $S_{rhombic}(s, 25°C) \rightarrow S(l, 113°C)$; $\Delta H = \Delta H_1$

Step 2: $S(l, 113°C) \rightarrow S_{monoclinic}(s, 25°C)$; $\Delta H = \Delta H_2$

Step 3: $S_{monoclinic}(s, 25°C) \rightarrow S_{rhombic}(s, 25°C)$; $\Delta H = \Delta H_3$

Hess's law allows one to sum thermochemical equations. Doing so here gives the following result:

$$S_{rhombic}(s, 25°C) \rightarrow S_{rhombic}(s, 25°C);\ \Delta H_{total} = \Delta H_1 + \Delta H_2 + \Delta H_2$$

The goal is to determine ΔH_{total}. Because the final state of the sulfur is the same as its initial state, and because enthalpy is a state function, $\Delta H_{total} = 0$ by definition.

6.137. The reaction is

$$4Fe(s) + 3O_2(g) \rightarrow 2Fe_2O_3(s); \Delta H = -1651 \text{ kJ}$$

The heat released is

$$10.3 \text{ g Fe}_2O_3 \times \left(\frac{1 \text{ mol Fe}_2O_3}{159.69 \text{ g}}\right) \times \left(\frac{-651 \text{ kJ}}{2 \text{ mol Fe}_2O_3}\right) = 53.\underline{2}4 = -53.2 \text{ kJ}$$

If ozone gas was burned instead, you would need to know the heat of the following reaction:

$$2O_3(g) \rightarrow 3O_2(g)$$

6.139. We calculate the heat needed to raise the temperature of 50.0 g of iron from 21 °C to 225 °C.

$$q = ms\Delta T = 50.0 \text{ g} \times 0.449\frac{0.449 \text{ J}}{\text{g}°\text{C}} \times (225°\text{C} - 21°\text{C})$$

$$q = 458\underline{0} \text{ J} = 4.5\underline{8}0 \text{ kJ}$$

The heat absorbed by the iron (4.58 kJ) required heat released in burning hydrogen (−4.58 kJ). So, we need to now relate the stoichiometry of the thermochemical combustion reaction to this energy requirement:

$$\text{kJ of heat} \rightarrow \text{moles of H}_2 \rightarrow \text{grams of H}_2$$

$$-4.5\underline{8}0 \text{ kJ} \times \left(\frac{2 \text{ mol H}_2}{-484 \text{ kJ}}\right) \times \left(\frac{2.016 \text{ g H}_2}{1 \text{ mol H}_2}\right) = 0.038\underline{1}54 = 0.0382 \text{ g H}_2$$

6.141. Let $\times$ = mass of H_2 and y = mass of O_2. Then, 2.500 g = x + y. The balanced thermochemical equation for the process is :

$$2H_2(g) + O_2(g) \rightarrow 2H_2O(l); \quad \Delta H° = -571.6 \text{ kJ}$$

Given that 28.6 kJ of heat are liberated, the amount of H_2O produced can be calculated:

$$-28.6 \text{ kJ}\left(\frac{2 \text{ mol H}_2O}{-571.6 \text{ kJ}}\right) = 0.100 \text{ mol H}_2O \text{ formed}$$

This means that either 0.0500 mol of limiting O_2 reacted and H_2 was in excess, or 0.100 mol of limiting H_2 reacted and O_2 was in excess. Evaluating both cases should provide information in relation to the initial mixture's composition.

In the first case, if O_2 was the limiting reagent,

$$0.0500 \text{ mol O}_2\left(\frac{32.00 \text{ g O}_2}{1.00 \text{ mol O}_2}\right) = 1.600 \text{ g O}_2 \text{ reacted}$$

If this were true, this would mean 0.900 g H_2 was initially present in the mixture. Furthermore, if 0.100 mol H_2 reacted (i.e., 0.202 g), the mass of H_2 present in excess would be 0.698 g. Although these are feasible quantities, evaluation of the second case with H_2 limiting is warranted. In this case, i.e., with 0.100 mol H_2 limiting the reaction,

$$0.100 \text{ mol } H_2 \left(\frac{2.016 \text{ g } H_2}{1.00 \text{ mol } H_2} \right) = 0.202 \text{ g } H_2 \text{ reacted}$$

If true, this would mean 2.298 g O_2 was initially present in the mixture. Furthermore, if 0.0500 mol O_2 reacted (i.e., 1.600 g), the mass of O_2 present in excess would be 0.698 g. Again, feasible quantities result.

Although it is one or the other, considering the above, it is currently a 50-50 guess at best as to which is correct. Had the volume of the initial mixture also been measured, a second independent equation relating the masses of H_2 and O_2 would have been available to use:

$$n_{gas,\ total} = \frac{PV}{RT} = n_{O_2} + n_{H_2} = \frac{x}{32.00} + \frac{y}{2.02}$$

If the first case were true, its volume would have been V_1; if the second case were true, its volume would have been V_2. These volumes can readily be calculated from the masses shown above and the ideal gas law:

$$V_{\text{case i}} = \frac{n_{gas,total}RT}{P} = \frac{(n_{\text{case i},O_2} + n_{\text{case i}, H_2})RT}{P} = \frac{(\frac{x_i}{32.00 \text{ g/mol}} + \frac{y_i}{2.016 \text{ g/mol}})RT}{P}$$

$$V_{\text{case 1}} = \frac{(\frac{1.600 \text{ g}}{32.00 \text{ g/mol}} + \frac{0.900 \text{ g}}{2.016 \text{ g/mol}})(0.08206 \frac{L \bullet atm}{mol \bullet K})298 \text{ K}}{1.00 \text{ atm}} = 12.1 \text{ L if case 1 were true}$$

$$V_{\text{case 2}} = \frac{(\frac{2.298 \text{ g}}{32.00 \text{ g/mol}} + \frac{0.202 \text{ g}}{2.016 \text{ g/mol}})(0.08206 \frac{L \bullet atm}{mol \bullet K})298 \text{ K}}{1.00 \text{ atm}} = 4.21 \text{ L if case 2 were true}$$

In summary, a critical piece of information on the initial gas mixture was omitted.

6.143. First determine the amount of heat ($q = s \times m \times \Delta T$) required to heat the given amount of water from 25°C to 100°C (i.e., water's normal boiling point). To do this we need to convert the 1.000 qt of water into an equivalent mass of water beforehand:

$$1.000 \text{ qt} \times \frac{0.94635 \text{ L}}{1.000 \text{ qt}} \times \frac{10^3 \text{ mL}}{1 \text{ L}} \times \frac{1.000 \text{ g } H_2O}{1 \text{ mL}} = 946.\underline{3}5 \text{ g}$$

$$q = ms\Delta T = (946.\underline{3}5 \text{ g})\left(4.1\underline{8}4 \ \frac{J}{g \ °C} \right)(100.\underline{0}°C - 25.\underline{0}°C)(\frac{1 \text{ kJ}}{10^3 \text{ J}}) = 29\underline{6}.8 \text{ kJ}$$

Here we have assumed the density of water and the specific heat of water do not vary over the temperature range of this experiment. The density of water is actually known to vary by about 5% over this temperature range while the specific heat varies by no more than 1%. These approximations imply the result is more likely only good to 2 significant figures instead of 3.

The energy for this heating process is provided by the combustion of methane as depicted in the following thermochemical equation:

$$CH_4(g) \quad + 2O_2(g) \rightarrow CO_2(g) \quad + 2H_2O(l); \qquad \Delta H° = -890.2 \text{ kJ}$$

It is instructive for the student to confirm the value of −890.2 kJ by applying Hess's law to the combustion reaction and using the standard enthalpies of formation found in Table 6.2. In short, we are asked how much methane will provide us with the necessary 29<u>6</u>.8 kJ of heat. This is calculated by using the information in the thermochemical equation:

$$296.8 \text{ kJ} \times \left(\frac{1 \text{ mol CH}_4}{890.2 \text{ kJ}} \right) = 0.33\underline{3}3 \text{ mol CH}_4$$

Measured at 23.0°C and 745 mmHg, we conclude the problem by calculating the volume of the 0.3333 mol methane gas by using the ideal gas equation:

$$V_{\text{CH}_4} = \frac{nRT}{P} = \frac{(0.33\underline{3}3 \text{ mol})0\left(.08206 \dfrac{\text{L} \bullet \text{atm}}{\text{mol} \bullet \text{K}}\right)(29\underline{6} \text{ K})}{745/760 \text{ atm}} = 8.2\underline{6}0 = 8.26 \text{ L}$$

6.145. The heat released in the reaction is equal to the heat gained by the calorimeter.

$$m \times \left(\frac{1 \text{ mol C}_6\text{H}_5\text{COOH}}{122.12 \text{ g}} \right) \times (3226 \text{ kJ/mol}) = (12.41 \text{ kJ/°C})(27.65°C - 23.44°C)$$

Solve for the mass of benzoic acid.

$$m = \frac{(12.41 \text{ kJ/°C})(27.65°C - 23.44°C)(122.12 \text{ g/mol})}{3226 \text{ kJ/mol}} = 1.9\underline{7}7 = 1.98 \text{ g}$$

6.147. $\Delta H°_{comb} = \Sigma n \, \Delta H^\circ_f \text{ (products)} - \Sigma m \, \Delta H^\circ_f \text{ (reactants)}$

$$= [\, \Delta H^\circ_f (\text{P}_4\text{O}_{10}) + 3 \, \Delta H^\circ_f (\text{SO}_2)\,] - [\, \Delta H^\circ_f (\text{P}_4\text{S}_3) + 8 \, \Delta H^\circ_f (\text{O}_2)\,]$$

$$-3651 \text{ kJ} = [(-3009.9 \text{ kJ}) + 3(-296.8 \text{ kJ})] - [(1 \text{ mol}) \Delta H^\circ_f (\text{P}_4\text{S}_3) + 8(0 \text{ kJ})]$$

Solve for the enthalpy of formation of P_4S_3.

$$\Delta H^\circ_f (\text{P}_4\text{S}_3) = \frac{(-3009.9 \text{ kJ}) + (3)(-296.8 \text{ kJ}) - (-3651 \text{ kJ})}{1 \text{ mol}} = -24\underline{9}.3 = -249 \text{ kJ/mol}$$

The value from Appendix C is −224.6 kJ/mol, which is a difference of 10.9%.

■ SOLUTIONS TO CUMULATIVE-SKILLS PROBLEMS

6.149. The heat lost, q, by the water(s) with a temperature higher than the final temperature must be equal to the heat gained, q, by the water(s) with a temperature lower than the final temperature.

  q(lost by water at higher temp) = q(gained by water at lower temp)

  $\Sigma (s \times m \times \Delta t) = \Sigma (s \times m \times \Delta t)$

Divide both sides of the equation by the specific heat, s, to eliminate this term, and substitute the other values. Since the mass of the water at 50.0°C is greater than the sum of the masses of the other two waters, assume the final temperature will be greater than 37°C and greater than 15°C. Use this to set up the three Δt expressions, and write one equation in one unknown, letting t equal the final temperature. Simplify by omitting the "grams" from 45.0 g, 25.0 g, and 15.0 g.

$$\Sigma (m \times \Delta t) = \Sigma (m \times \Delta t)$$

$$45.0 \times (50.0°C - t) = 25.0 \times (t - 15.0°C) + 15.0 \times (t - 37°C)$$

$$2250°C - 45.0\,t = 25.0\,t - 375°C + 15.0\,t - 555.0°C$$

$$-85.0\,t = -3180°C$$

$$t = 37.\underline{4}1 = 37.4°C \text{ (the final temperature)}$$

6.151. First, calculate the mole fraction of each gas in the product, assuming 100 g product:

Mol CO = 33 g CO × 1 mol CO/28.01 g CO = 1.$\underline{1}$78 mol CO

Mol CO_2 = 67 g CO_2 × 1 mol CO_2/44.01 g CO_2 = 1.$\underline{5}$22 mol CO_2

$$\text{Mol frac. CO} = \frac{1.178 \text{ mol CO}}{(1.178 \,+\, 1.522) \text{ mol}} = 0.4\underline{3}63$$

$$\text{Mol frac. } CO_2 = \frac{1.522 \text{ mol } CO_2}{(1.178 \,+\, 1.522) \text{ mol}} = 0.5\underline{6}37$$

Now, calculate the starting moles of C, which equal the total moles of CO and CO_2:

Starting mol C(s) = 1.00 g C × 1 mol C/12.01 g C = 0.083$\underline{2}$6 mol C = mol CO + CO_2

Use the mole fractions to convert mol CO + CO_2 to mol CO and mol CO_2:

$$\text{Mol CO} = \frac{0.4363 \text{ mol CO}}{1 \text{ mol total}} \times 0.08326 \text{ mol total} = 0.03\underline{6}33 \text{ mol CO}$$

$$\text{Mol } CO_2 = \frac{0.5637 \text{ mol } CO_2}{1 \text{ mol total}} \times 0.08326 \text{ mol total} = 0.04\underline{6}93 \text{ mol } CO_2$$

Now, use enthalpies of formation (Table 6.2) to calculate the heat of combustion for both:

C(s)	+	1/2O_2(g)	→	CO(g)	
0.03633		excess		0.03633 (mol)	
0		0		-110.5 (kJ/mol)	
0		0		-110.5 (kJ/mol)	

C(s)	+	O_2(g)	→	CO_2(g)	
0.04693		excess		0.04693 (mol)	
0		0		-393.5 (kJ/mol)	
0		0		-18.47 (kJ/0.04693 mol)	

Total ΔH = −4.014 + (−18.47) = −2$\underline{2}$.48 = −22 kJ

Heat released = 22 kJ

6.153. The ΔH° for the reactions to produce CO and CO_2 in each case is equal to the ΔH_f° of the respective gases. Thus ΔH° to produce CO is -110.5 kJ/mol, and ΔH° to produce CO_2 is -393.5 kJ/mol. Since 1 mol graphite is needed to produce 1 mol either CO or CO_2, one equation in one unknown can be written for the heat produced, using m for the moles of CO and $(2.00 - m)$ for moles of CO_2.

-481 kJ $= m \times (-110.5$ kJ$) + (2.00 - m) \times (-393.5$ kJ$)$

$-481 = -110.5\, m - 787 + 393.5\, m$

mol CO $= m = 1.0\underline{8}1$; mass CO $= 1.081 \times 28.0$ g/mol $= 30.\underline{2}6 = 30.3$ g CO

mol $CO_2 = (2.00 - m) = 0.9\underline{1}9$; mass $CO_2 = 0.919$ mol $\times 44.0$ g/mol $= 4\underline{0}.4 = 40.$ g CO_2

6.155. The equation is

$$4NH_3(g) + 5O_2(g) \rightarrow 4NO(g) + 6H_2O(g); \quad \Delta H^\circ = -906 \text{ kJ}$$

First, determine the limiting reactant by calculating the moles of NH_3 and of O_2; then, assuming one of the reactants is totally consumed, calculate the moles of the other reactant needed for the reaction.

$$10.0 \text{ g } NH_3 \times \frac{1 \text{ mol } NH_3}{17.03 \text{ g } NH_3} = 0.58\underline{7}2 \text{ mol } NH_3$$

$$20.0 \text{ g } O_2 \times \frac{1 \text{ mol } O_2}{32.00 \text{ g } O_2} = 0.62\underline{5}0 \text{ mol } O_2$$

$$0.62\underline{5}0 \text{ mol } O_2 \times \frac{4 \text{ mol } NH_3}{5 \text{ mol } O_2} = 0.500 \text{ mol } NH_3 \text{ needed}$$

Because NH_3 is present in excess of what is needed, O_2 must be the limiting reactant. Now calculate the heat released on the basis of the complete reaction of $0.62\underline{5}0$ mol O_2:

$$\Delta H = \frac{-906 \text{ kJ}}{5 \text{ mol } O_2} \times 0.62\underline{5}0 \text{ mol } O_2 = -11\underline{3}.25 = -113 \text{ kJ}$$

The heat released by the complete reaction of the 20.0 g (0.6250 mol) of $O_2(g)$ is 113 kJ.

6.157. The equation is: $\quad N_2(g) + 3H_2(g) \rightarrow 2NH_3(g); \quad \Delta H^\circ = -91.8$ kJ

a. To find the heat evolved from the production of 1.00 L of NH_3, convert the 1.00 L to mol NH_3 using the density and molar mass (17.03 g/mol). Then convert the moles to heat (ΔH) using ΔH°.

$$\text{Mol } NH_3 = \frac{d \times V}{M_M} = \frac{0.696 \text{ g/L} \times 1 \text{ L}}{17.03 \text{ g/mol}} = 0.040\underline{8}7 \text{ mol } NH_3$$

$$\Delta H = \frac{-91.8 \text{ kJ}}{2 \text{ mol } NH_3} \times 0.040\underline{8}7 \text{ mol } NH_3 = -1.8\underline{7}6 \text{ (1.88 kJ heat evolved)}$$

b.   First, find the moles of N_2 using the density and molar mass (28.02 g/mol). Then convert to the heat needed to raise the N_2 from 25°C to 400°C.

$$\text{Mol } N_2 = \frac{d \times V}{M_M} = \frac{1.145 \text{ g/L} \times 0.500 \text{ L}}{28.02 \text{ g/mol}} = 0.020\underline{4}3 \text{ mol } N_2$$

$$0.020\underline{4}3 \text{ mol } N_2 \times \frac{29.12 \text{ J}}{\text{mol} \cdot {}°\text{C}} \times (400 - 25)°\text{C} = 22\underline{3}.2 \text{ J} (0.22\underline{3}2 \text{ kJ})$$

$$\text{Percent heat for } N_2 = \frac{0.2232 \text{ kJ}}{1.876 \text{ kJ}} \times 100\% = 11.\underline{8}9 = 11.9\%$$

6.159.   The glucose equation is

$$C_6H_{12}O_6 + 6O_2 \rightarrow 6CO_2(g) + 6H_2O(l) \; ; \; \Delta H° = -280\underline{2}.8 \text{ kJ}$$

Convert the 2.50×10^3 kcal to mol of glucose using the $\Delta H°$ of -2802.8 kJ for the reaction and the conversion factor of 4.184 kJ/kcal:

$$2.50 \times 10^3 \text{ kcal} \times \frac{4.184 \text{ kJ}}{1.000 \text{ kcal}} \times \frac{1 \text{ mol glucose}}{2802.8 \text{ kJ}} = 3.7\underline{3}19 \text{ mol glucose}$$

Next, convert mol glucose to mol LiOH using the above equation for glucose and the equation for LiOH:

$$2\text{LiOH}(s) + CO_2(g) \rightarrow Li_2CO_3(s) + H_2O(l)$$

$$3.7\underline{3}19 \text{ mol glucose} \times \frac{6 \text{ mol } CO_2}{1 \text{ mol glucose}} \times \frac{2 \text{ mol LiOH}}{1 \text{ mol } CO_2} = 44.\underline{7}83 \text{ mol LiOH}$$

Finally, use the molar mass of LiOH to convert moles to mass:

$$44.783 \text{ mol LiOH} \times \frac{23.95 \text{ g LiOH}}{1 \text{ mol LiOH}} = 1.0\underline{7}25 \times 10^3 \text{ g} (1.07 \text{ kg}) \text{ LiOH per astronaut per day}$$

CHAPTER 7

Quantum Theory of the Atom

■ SOLUTIONS TO EXERCISES

Note on significant figures: If the final answer to a solution needs to be rounded off, it is given first with one nonsignificant figure, and the last significant figure is underlined. The final answer is then rounded to the correct number of significant figures. In multistep problems, intermediate answers are given with at least one nonsignificant figure; however, only the final answer has been rounded off.

7.1.　Rearrange the equation $c = \nu\lambda$, which relates wavelength to frequency and the speed of light (3.00×10^8 m/s):

$$\lambda = \frac{c}{\nu} = \frac{3.00 \times 10^8 \text{ m/s}}{3.91 \times 10^{14} \text{ /s}} = 7.6\underline{7}2 \times 10^{-7} = 7.67 \times 10^{-7} \text{ m, or } 767 \text{ nm}$$

7.2.　Rearrange the equation $c = \nu\lambda$, which relates frequency to wavelength and the speed of light (3.00×10^8 m/s). Recognize that 456 nm = 4.56×10^{-7} m.

$$\nu = \frac{c}{\lambda} = \frac{3.00 \times 10^8 \text{ m/s}}{4.56 \times 10^{-7} \text{ m}} = 6.5\underline{7}8 \times 10^{14} = 6.58 \times 10^{14} \text{ /s}$$

7.3.　First, use the wavelengths to calculate the frequencies from $c = \nu\lambda$. Then calculate the energies using $E = h\nu$.

$$\nu = \frac{c}{\lambda} = \frac{3.00 \times 10^8 \text{ m/s}}{1.0 \times 10^{-6} \text{ m}} = 3.\underline{0}0 \times 10^{14} \text{ /s}$$

$$\nu = \frac{c}{\lambda} = \frac{3.00 \times 10^8 \text{ m/s}}{1.0 \times 10^{-8} \text{ m}} = 3.\underline{0}0 \times 10^{16} \text{ /s}$$

$$\nu = \frac{c}{\lambda} = \frac{3.00 \times 10^8 \text{ m/s}}{1.0 \times 10^{-10} \text{ m}} = 3.\underline{0}0 \times 10^{18} \text{ /s}$$

$$E = h\nu = 6.63 \times 10^{-34} \text{ J•s} \times 3.00 \times 10^{14} \text{ /s} = 1.\underline{9}89 \times 10^{-19} = 2.0 \times 10^{-19} \text{ J (IR)}$$

$$E = h\nu = 6.63 \times 10^{-34} \text{ J•s} \times 3.00 \times 10^{16} \text{ /s} = 1.\underline{9}89 \times 10^{-17} = 2.0 \times 10^{-17} \text{ J (UV)}$$

$$E = h\nu = 6.63 \times 10^{-34} \text{ J•s} \times 3.00 \times 10^{18} \text{ /s} = 1.\underline{9}89 \times 10^{-15} = 2.0 \times 10^{-15} \text{ J (x ray)}$$

The x-ray photon (shortest wavelength) has the greatest amount of energy; the infrared photon (longest wavelength) has the least amount of energy.

7.4. From the formula for the energy levels, $E = -R_H/n^2$, obtain the expressions for both E_i and E_f. Then calculate the energy change for the transition from $n = 3$ to $n = 1$ by subtracting the lower value from the upper value. Set this equal to $h\nu$. The result is

$$\left[\frac{-R_H}{9}\right] - \left[\frac{-R_H}{1}\right] = \frac{8R_H}{9} = h\nu$$

The frequency of the emitted radiation is

$$\nu = \frac{8R_H}{9} = \frac{8}{9} \times \frac{2.179 \times 10^{-18}\text{ J}}{6.63 \times 10^{-34}\text{ J} \bullet \text{s}} = 2.9\underline{2}1 \times 10^{15} = 2.92 \times 10^{15}\text{ /s}$$

Since $\lambda = c/\nu$,

$$\lambda = \frac{3.00 \times 10^8\text{ m/s}}{2.92 \times 10^{15}\text{ /s}} = 1.0\underline{2}7 \times 10^{-7} = 1.03 \times 10^{-7}\text{ m, or 103 nm}$$

7.5. Calculate the frequency from $c = \nu\lambda$, recognizing that 589 nm is 5.89×10^{-7} m.

$$\nu = \frac{c}{\lambda} = \frac{3.00 \times 10^8\text{ m/s}}{5.89 \times 10^{-7}\text{ m}} = 5.0\underline{9}3 \times 10^{14} = 5.09 \times 10^{14}\text{ /s}$$

Finally, calculate the energy difference.

$$E = h\nu = 6.63 \times 10^{-34}\text{ J}\bullet\text{s} \times 5.093 \times 10^{14}\text{ /s} = 3.3\underline{7}66 \times 10^{-19} = 3.38 \times 10^{-19}\text{ J}$$

7.6. To calculate wavelength, use the mass of an electron ($m = 9.11 \times 10^{-31}$ kg), and Planck's constant ($h = 6.63 \times 10^{-34}$ J$\bullet$s, or 6.63×10^{-34} kg$\bullet$m^2/s).

$$\lambda = \frac{h}{mv} = \frac{6.63 \times 10^{-34}\text{ kg} \bullet \text{m}^2\text{/s}}{9.11 \times 10^{-31}\text{ kg} \times 2.19 \times 10^6\text{ m/s}} = 3.3\underline{2}3 \times 10^{-10}\text{ m (332 pm)}$$

7.7. a. The value of n must be a positive whole number greater than zero. Here, it is zero. Also, if n is zero, there are no allowed values for l and m_l.

b. The values for l can range only from zero to $(n - 1)$. Here, l has a value greater than n.

c. The values for m_l range from $-l$ to $+l$. Here, m_l has a value greater than l.

d. The value for m_s is either $+ \frac{1}{2}$ or $-\frac{1}{2}$. Here, it is zero.

■ ANSWERS TO CONCEPT CHECKS

7.1. The frequency and wavelength are inversely related. Therefore, if the frequency is doubled, the wavelength is halved. Red light has a wavelength around 700 nm, so doubling its frequency halves its wavelength to about 350 nm, which is in the ultraviolet range just beyond the visible spectrum.

7.2. Since the transitions are between adjacent levels, the energy-level diagram must look something like the following diagram, with the red transition between two close levels and the blue transition between two more widely spaced levels. (The three levels could be spaced so the red and blue transitions are interchanged, with the blue transition above the red one.)

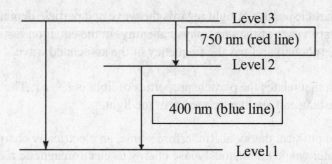

The transition from the top level to the lowest level would correspond to a transition that is greater in energy change than either of the other two transitions. Thus, the three transitions, from lowest to highest energy change, are in this order: red, blue, and the transition from the highest to lowest level. The last transition would have the highest frequency and therefore the shortest wavelength. It would lie just beyond the blue portion of the visible spectrum in the ultraviolet region.

7.3. The de Broglie relation says the wavelength of a particle is inversely proportional to both mass and speed. So, to maintain the wavelength constant while the mass increases would mean the speed would have to decrease. In going from a particle with the mass of an electron to one with that of a proton, the speed would have to decrease by a factor of about 2000 in order to maintain the same wavelength. The proton would have to have a speed approximately 2000 times slower than an electron of the same wavelength.

■ ANSWERS TO SELF-ASSESSMENT AND REVIEW QUESTIONS

7.1. Light is a wave, which is a form of electromagnetic radiation. In terms of waves, light can be described as a continuously repeating change, or oscillation, in electric and magnetic fields that can travel through space. Two characteristics of light are wavelength (often given in nanometers, nm) and frequency.

7.2. The relationship among the different characteristics of light waves is $c = \nu\lambda$, where ν is the frequency, λ is the wavelength, and c is the speed of light.

7.3. Starting with the shortest wavelengths, the electromagnetic spectrum consists of gamma rays, x rays, far ultraviolet (UV), near UV, visible light, near infrared (IR), far IR, microwaves, radar, and TV/FM radio waves (longest wavelengths).

7.4. The term *quantized* means the possible values of the energies of an atom are limited to only certain values. Planck was trying to explain the intensity of light of various frequencies emitted by a hot solid at different temperatures. The formula he arrived at was $E = nh\nu$, where E is energy, n is a whole number ($n = 1, 2, 3, \ldots$), h is Planck's constant, and ν is frequency.

7.5. *Photoelectric effect* is the term applied to the ejection of electrons from the surface of a metal or from other materials when light shines on it. Electrons are ejected only when the frequency (or energy) of light is larger than a certain minimum, or threshold, value that is constant for each metal. If a photon has a frequency equal to or greater than this minimum value, then it will eject one electron from the metal surface.

7.6. The wave–particle picture of light regards the wave and particle depictions of light as complementary views of the same physical entity. In the equation $E = h\nu$, E is the energy of a light particle (photon) and ν is the frequency of the associated wave.

7.7. The equation that relates the particle properties of light is $E = h\nu$. The symbol E is energy, h is Planck's constant, and ν is the frequency of the light.

7.8. According to physical theory at Rutherford's time, an electrically charged particle revolving around a center would continuously lose energy as electromagnetic radiation. As an electron in an atom lost energy, it would spiral into the nucleus (in about 10^{-10} s). Thus, the stability of the atom could not be explained.

7.9. According to Bohr, an electron in an atom can have only specific energy values. An electron in an atom can change energy only by going from one energy level (of allowed energy) to another energy level (of allowed energy). An electron in a higher energy level can go to a lower energy level by emitting a photon of an energy equal to the difference in energy. However, when an electron is in its lowest energy level, no further changes in energy can occur. Thus, the electron does not continuously radiate energy as was thought at Rutherford's time. These features solve the difficulty alluded to in Question 7.8.

7.10. Emission of a photon occurs when an electron in a higher energy level undergoes a transition to a lower energy level. The energy lost is emitted as a photon.

7.11. Absorption, the reverse of emission, occurs when a photon of a certain required energy is absorbed by a certain electron in an atom. The energy of the photon must be equal to the energy necessary to excite the electron of the atom from a lower energy level, usually the lowest, to a higher energy level.

7.12. The quantum corral, shown in Figure 7.21, shows evidence of electron waves. A practical example of diffraction is the operation of the scanning tunneling microscope.

7.13. The square of a wave function equals the probability of finding an electron within a region of space.

7.14. The uncertainty principle says we can no longer think of the electron as having a precise orbit in an atom similar to the orbit of the planets around the sun. This principle says it is impossible to know with absolute precision both the position and the speed of a particle such as an electron.

7.15. Quantum mechanics vastly changes Bohr's original picture of the hydrogen atom in that we can no longer think of the electron as having a precise orbit around the nucleus in this atom. Recall that Bohr's theory depended on the hydrogen electron having specific energy values and thus specific positions and speeds around the nucleus. But quantum mechanics and the uncertainty principle say it is impossible to know with absolute precision both the speed and the position of an electron. So Bohr's energy levels are only the most probable paths of the electrons.

7.16. a. The principal quantum number can have an integer value between one and infinity.

       b. The angular momentum quantum number can have any integer value between zero and $(n - 1)$.

c.   The magnetic quantum number can have any integer value between $-l$ and $+l$.

d.   The spin quantum number can be either $+\frac{1}{2}$ or $-\frac{1}{2}$.

7.17.   The notation is $4f$. This subshell contains seven orbitals.

7.18.   An s orbital has a spherical shape. A p orbital has two lobes positioned along a straight line through the nucleus at the center of the line (a dumbbell shape).

7.19.   The answer is d, an electron in the $n = 1$ level is higher in energy than an electron in the $n = 4$ level.

7.20.   The answer is a, I only.

7.21.   The answer is c, transition from the $n = 3$ to the $n = 1$ level.

7.22.   The answer is a, 8.66×10^{-6} m.

■ ANSWERS TO CONCEPTUAL PROBLEMS

7.25.   Wavelength and frequency are inversely related. Moreover, ultraviolet light is at higher frequency than yellow light. Doubling the frequency of a beam of light would give that beam a higher frequency than yellow light, whereas doubling the wavelength would give that beam a lower frequency than yellow light. Consequently, the beam with frequency doubled must be the one in the ultraviolet region. Here is another way to look at the problem. Energy is directly related to the frequency and inversely related to the wavelength. Thus, the beam whose frequency is doubled will increase in energy, whereas the beam whose wavelength is doubled will decrease in energy. Since yellow light is in the visible region of the spectrum, which is lower in energy than the ultraviolet region (Figure 7.5), the beam whose frequency is doubled will be higher in energy and thus in the UV region of the spectrum.

7.27.   That one color of light does not result in an ejection of electrons implies that that color has too little energy per photon. Of the two colors, red and green, red light has less energy per photon. Thus, you expect the experiment with red light to result in no ejection of photons, whereas the experiment with green light must be the one that ejects electrons. (Two red photons have more than enough energy to eject an electron, but this energy needs to be concentrated in only one photon to be effective.) In the photoelectric effect, one photon of light ejects at most one electron. Therefore, in the experiment with green light, one electron is ejected.

7.29.   Energy is inversely proportional to the wavelength of the radiation. The transition from the highest energy level to the lowest energy level would involve the greatest energy change and thus the shortest wavelength, x nm.

7.31.   A proton is approximately 2000 times the weight of an electron. Also, from the de Broglie relation, $l = h/mv$, you see that the wavelength is inversely proportional to both the mass and the speed of the particle. Considering the protons in parts b and c, since the mass is the same in both parts, the proton with the smaller speed, part b, will have a longer wavelength. Now, comparing the electron in part a with the proton in part b, since both have the same speed, the electron in part a with the smaller mass will have the longer wavelength. Therefore, the electron in part a will have the longest wavelength.

7.33.   a.   The frequency is directly proportional to the energy difference between the two transition levels ($\Delta E = h\nu$). The lowest frequency corresponds with the smallest energy difference. Thus the transition from $n = 3$ to $n = 2$ will emit the lowest-frequency light.

   b.   The highest frequency corresponds with the largest energy difference. Thus the $n = 3$ to $n = 5$ transition will require (absorb) the highest-frequency light.

   c.   Since the frequency is proportional to the energy difference between two transition levels, the energy difference is the same for absorption and transmission, and the color light is the same for both. Thus, green light is absorbed.

■ SOLUTIONS TO PRACTICE PROBLEMS

Note on significant figures: If the final answer to a solution needs to be rounded off, it is given first with one nonsignificant figure, and the last significant figure is underlined. The final answer is then rounded to the correct number of significant figures. In multistep problems, intermediate answers are given with at least one nonsignificant figure; however, only the final answer has been rounded off. Starting with Problem 7.35, the value 2.998×10^8 m/s will be used for the speed of light.

7.35.   Solve $c = \lambda\nu$ for λ:

$$\lambda = \frac{c}{\nu} = \frac{2.998 \times 10^8 \text{ m/s}}{1.365 \times 10^6 \text{ /s}} = 219.\underline{6}3 = 219.6 \text{ m}$$

7.37.   Solve $c = \lambda\nu$ for ν. Recognize that 478 nm = 478×10^{-9} m, or 4.78×10^{-7} m.

$$\nu = \frac{c}{\lambda} = \frac{2.998 \times 10^8 \text{ m/s}}{4.78 \times 10^{-7} \text{ m}} = 6.2\underline{7}1 \times 10^{14} = 6.27 \times 10^{14} \text{ /s}$$

7.39.   Radio waves travel at the speed of light, so divide the distance by c:

$$56 \times 10^9 \text{ m} \times \frac{1 \text{ s}}{2.998 \times 10^8 \text{ m}} = 1\underline{8}6.7 = 1.9 \times 10^2 \text{ s}$$

7.41.   To do the calculation, divide 1 meter by the number of wavelengths in 1 meter to find the wavelength of this transition. Then use the speed of light (with nine digits for significant figures) to calculate the frequency:

$$\lambda = \frac{1 \text{ m}}{1,650,763.73} = 6.05780\underline{2}106 \times 10^{-7} \text{ m} = 6.05780211 \times 10^{-7} \text{ m}$$

$$\nu = \frac{c}{\lambda} = \frac{2.99792458 \times 10^8 \text{ m/s}}{6.057802106 \times 10^{-7} \text{ m}} = 4.948865\underline{1}62 \times 10^{14} = 4.94886516 \times 10^{14} \text{ /s}$$

7.43.   Solve for E, using $E = h\nu$, and use four significant figures for h:

$$E = h\nu = (6.626 \times 10^{-34} \text{ J•s}) \times (1.365 \times 10^6 \text{ /s}) = 9.04\underline{4}4 \times 10^{-28} = 9.044 \times 10^{-28} \text{ J}$$

7.45. Recognize that 535 nm = 535×10^{-9} m = 5.35×10^{-7} m. Then calculate v and E.

$$v = \frac{c}{\lambda} = \frac{2.998 \times 10^8 \text{ m/s}}{5.35 \times 10^{-7} \text{ m}} = 5.6037 \times 10^{14} \text{ /s}$$

$$E = hv = (6.626 \times 10^{-34} \text{ J} \bullet \text{s}) \times (5.6037 \times 10^{14}/\text{s}) = 3.7113 \times 10^{-19} = 3.71 \times 10^{-19} \text{ J}$$

7.47. First, calculate the wavelength of this transition from the frequency using the speed of light:

$$\lambda = \frac{c}{v} = \frac{2.998 \times 10^8 \text{ m/s}}{3.84 \times 10^{14} \text{ /s}} = 7.8072 \times 10^{-7} = 7.81 \times 10^{-7} \text{ m (781 nm)}$$

Using Figure 7.5, note that 781 nm is just on the edge of the red end of the spectrum and is barely visible to the eye.

7.49. Solve the equation $E = -R_H/n^2$ for both E_5 and E_3; equate to hv, and solve for v.

$$\Delta E = hv = = E_5 - E_3 = \frac{-R_H}{5^2} - \frac{-R_H}{3^2} = \frac{-R_H}{25} - \frac{-R_H}{9} = \frac{16R_H}{225}$$

If you reversed the order and obtained a negative energy change, such a change actually corresponds to the relaxing atom. However, the frequency of the emitted radiation is related to the absolute energy released in the form of a photon, which must be a positive quantity:

$$v = \frac{16R_H}{225h} = \frac{16}{225} \times \frac{2.179 \times 10^{-18} \text{ J}}{6.626 \times 10^{-34} \text{ J} \bullet \text{s}} = 2.3338 \times 10^{14} = 2.34 \times 10^{14} \text{ /s}$$

7.51. Solve the equation $E = -R_H/n^2$ for both E_2 and E_1; solve for v, and convert to λ.

$$\Delta E = hv = E_2 - E_1 = \frac{-R_H}{2^2} - \frac{-R_H}{1^2} = \frac{-R_H}{4} - \frac{-R_H}{1} = \frac{3R_H}{4}$$

If you reversed the order and obtained a negative energy change, such a change actually corresponds to the relaxing atom. However, the frequency of the emitted radiation is related to the absolute energy released in the form of a photon, which must be a positive quantity

$$v = \frac{3R_H}{4h} = \frac{3}{4} \times \frac{2.179 \times 10^{-18} \text{ J}}{6.626 \times 10^{-34} \text{ J} \bullet \text{s}} = 2.4666 \times 10^{15} \text{ /s}$$

The wavelength can now be calculated.

$$\lambda = \frac{c}{v} = \frac{2.998 \times 10^8 \text{ m/s}}{2.466 \times 10^{15} \text{ /s}} = 1.2155 \times 10^{-7} = 1.22 \times 10^{-7} \text{ m (near UV)}$$

7.53. This is the highest energy transition from the $n = 6$ level, so the electron must undergo a transition to the $n = 1$ level. Solve the Balmer equation using Bohr's approach:

$$\Delta E = hv = E_6 - E_1 = \frac{-R_H}{6^2} - \frac{-R_H}{1^2} = \frac{-R_H}{36} - \frac{-R_H}{1} = \frac{35R_H}{36}$$

If you reversed the order and obtained a negative energy change, such a change actually corresponds to the relaxing atom. However, the frequency of the emitted radiation is related to the absolute energy released in the form of a photon, which must be a positive quantity:

$$v = \frac{35 R_H}{36h} = \frac{35}{36} \times \frac{2.179 \times 10^{-18} \text{ J}}{6.626 \times 10^{-34} \text{ J} \cdot \text{s}} = 3.197 \times 10^{15} \text{ /s}$$

The wavelength can now be calculated.

$$\lambda = \frac{c}{v} = \frac{2.998 \times 10^8 \text{ m/s}}{3.197 \times 10^{15} \text{ /s}} = 9.3769 \times 10^{-8} = 9.38 \times 10^{-8} \text{ m (93.8 nm)}$$

7.55.   Noting that 422.7 nm = 4.227×10^{-7} m, convert the 422.7 nm to frequency. Then convert the frequency to energy using $E = h\,v$.

$$v = \frac{c}{\lambda} = \frac{2.998 \times 10^8 \text{ m/s}}{4.227 \times 10^{-7} \text{ m}} = 7.0925 \times 10^{14} \text{ /s}$$

$$E = h\,v = (6.626 \times 10^{-34} \text{ J} \bullet \text{s}) \times 7.0925 \times 10^{14} \text{ /s}) = 4.6994 \times 10^{-19} = 4.699 \times 10^{-19} \text{ J}$$

7.57.   The mass of a neutron = 1.67493×10^{-27} kg. Its speed or velocity, v, of 4.15 km/s equals 4.15×10^3 m/s. Substitute these parameters into the de Broglie relation, and solve for λ:

$$\lambda = \frac{h}{mv} = \frac{6.626 \times 10^{-34} \text{ kg} \bullet \text{m}^2/\text{s}}{1.67493 \times 10^{-27} \text{ kg} \times 4.15 \times 10^3 \text{ m/s}} = 9.532 \times 10^{-11} = 9.53 \times 10^{-11} \text{ m}$$

A wavelength of 9.53×10^{-11} m (95.3 pm) would be in the x-ray region of the spectrum.

7.59.   The mass of an electron equals 9.109×10^{-31} kg. The wavelength, λ, given as 10.0 pm, is equivalent to 1.00×10^{-11} m. Substitute these parameters into the de Broglie relation, and solve for the speed, v.

$$v = \frac{h}{m\lambda} = \frac{6.626 \times 10^{-34} \text{ kg} \bullet \text{m}^2/\text{s}}{9.109 \times 10^{-31} \text{ kg} \times 1.00 \times 10^{-11} \text{ m}} = 7.2774 \times 10^7 = 7.27 \times 10^7 \text{ m/s}$$

7.61.   Substitute the 1.45×10^{-1} kg mass of the baseball and the 30.0 m/s velocity, v, into the de Broglie relation, and solve for wavelength (recall that 1 pm = 10^{-12} m).

$$\lambda = \frac{h}{mv} = \frac{6.626 \times 10^{-34} \text{ kg} \bullet \text{m}^2/\text{s}}{1.45 \times 10^{-1} \text{ kg} \times 30.0 \text{ m/s}} = 1.523 \times 10^{-34} = 1.52 \times 10^{-34} \text{ m} = 1.52 \times 10^{-22} \text{ pm}$$

Because this is much smaller than 100 pm, the wavelength is much smaller than the diameter of one atom.

7.63.   The possible values of l range from zero to $(n - 1)$, so l may be 0, 1, 2, or 3. The possible values of m_l range from $-l$ to $+l$. If $l = 3$, m_l may be $-3, -2, -1, 0, +1, +2$, or $+3$.

7.65.   For the M shell, $n = 3$; there are three subshells in this shell ($l = 0, 1$, and 2). A d subshell has $l = 2$; the number of orbitals in this subshell is 2(2) + 1 = 5 ($m_l = -2, -1, 0, 1$, and 2).

7.67. a. $6d$

   b. $5g$

   c. $4f$

   d. $6p$

7.69. a.   Not permissible; m_s can be only $+\frac{1}{2}$ or $-\frac{1}{2}$.

   b.   Not permissible; l can be only as large as $(n-1)$.

   c.   Not permissible; m_l cannot exceed $+2$ in magnitude.

   d.   Not permissible; n cannot be zero.

   e.   Not permissible; m_s can be only $+\frac{1}{2}$ or $-\frac{1}{2}$.

■ SOLUTIONS TO GENERAL PROBLEMS

7.71. Use $c = \nu\lambda$ to calculate frequency; then use $E = h\nu$ to calculate energy.

$$\nu = \frac{c}{\lambda} = \frac{2.998 \times 10^8 \text{ m/s}}{4.61 \times 10^{-7} \text{ m}} = 6.503 \times 10^{14} = 6.50 \times 10^{14} \text{ /s}$$

$$E = h\nu = (6.626 \times 10^{-34} \text{ J•s}) \times (6.503 \times 10^{14}\text{/s}) = 4.309 \times 10^{-19} = 4.31 \times 10^{-19} \text{ J}$$

7.73. Calculate the frequency corresponding to 4.10×10^{-19} J. Then convert that to wavelength.

$$\nu = \frac{E}{h} = \frac{4.10 \times 10^{-19} \text{ J}}{6.626 \times 10^{-34} \text{ J•s}} = 6.187 \times 10^{14} \text{ /s}$$

$$\lambda = \frac{c}{\nu} = \frac{2.998 \times 10^8 \text{ m/s}}{6.187 \times 10^{14} \text{ /s}} = 4.845 \times 10^{-7} = 4.85 \times 10^{-7} \text{ m} = 485 \text{ nm (blue-green)}$$

7.75. Solve for frequency using $E = h\nu$.

$$\nu = \frac{E}{h} = \frac{4.34 \times 10^{-19} \text{ J}}{6.626 \times 10^{-34} \text{ J•s}} = 6.549 \times 10^{14} = 6.55 \times 10^{14} \text{ /s}$$

7.77. First calculate E_p, the energy of the 345-nm photon, noting that it is equivalent to 3.45×10^{-7} m.

$$E_p = \frac{hc}{\lambda} = \frac{(6.626 \times 10^{-34} \text{ J•s})(2.998 \times 10^8 \text{ m/s})}{3.45 \times 10^{-7} \text{ m}} = 5.7578 \times 10^{-19} \text{ J}$$

Now, subtract the work function of Ca = 4.34×10^{-19} J (Problem 7.75) from E_p:

$$5.7578 \times 10^{-19} \text{ J} - 4.34 \times 10^{-19} \text{ J} = 1.4178 \times 10^{-19} \text{ J}$$

Note that for this situation, $E = \frac{1}{2}mv^2$. Recall that the mass of the electron is 9.1094×10^{-31} kg. Now calculate speed, v:

$$v = \sqrt{\frac{2E}{m}} = \sqrt{\frac{2 \times 1.4178 \times 10^{-19} \text{ J}}{9.1095 \times 10^{-31} \text{ kg}}} = 5.579 \times 10^5 = 5.58 \times 10^5 \text{ m/s}$$

7.79. This is a transition from the $n = 5$ level to the $n = 2$ level. Solve the Balmer equation using Bohr's approach.

$$E = h\nu = = E_5 - E_2 = \frac{-R_H}{5^2} - \frac{-R_H}{2^2} = \frac{-R_H}{25} - \frac{-R_H}{4} = \frac{21R_H}{100}$$

The wavelength can now be calculated.

$$\nu = \frac{21R_H}{100h} = \frac{21}{100} \times \frac{2.179 \times 10^{-18} \text{ J}}{6.626 \times 10^{-34} \text{ J} \cdot \text{s}} = 6.9059 \times 10^{14} \text{ /s}$$

$$\lambda = \frac{c}{\nu} = \frac{2.998 \times 10^8 \text{ m/s}}{6.9059 \times 10^{14} \text{ /s}} = 4.341 \times 10^{-7} = 4.34 \times 10^{-7} \text{ m (434 nm)}$$

7.81. Use 397 nm $= 3.97 \times 10^{-7}$ m, and convert to frequency and then to energy.

$$\nu = \frac{c}{\lambda} = \frac{2.998 \times 10^8 \text{ m/s}}{3.97 \times 10^{-7} \text{ m}} = 7.551 \times 10^{14} \text{ /s}$$

$$E = h\nu = (6.626 \times 10^{-34} \text{ J} \bullet \text{s}) \times (7.551 \times 10^{14}) = 5.0037 \times 10^{-19} \text{ J}$$

Substitute this energy into the Balmer formula, recalling that the Balmer series is an emission spectrum, so ΔE is negative:

$$E = E_2 - E_i = \frac{-R_H}{2^2} - \frac{-R_H}{n_i^2} = \frac{-R_H}{4} - \frac{-R_H}{n_i^2} = 5.0037 \times 10^{-19} \text{ J}$$

$$\frac{1}{4} - \frac{1}{n_i^2} = \frac{\Delta E}{-R_H} = \frac{-5.0037 \times 10^{-19} \text{ J}}{-2.179 \times 10^{-18} \text{ J}} = 0.22963$$

$$\frac{1}{n_i^2} = \frac{1}{4} - 0.22963 = 0.02036$$

$$n_i = \left[\frac{1}{0.02036} \right]^{\frac{1}{2}} = 7.007 = 7.0 \,(= n)$$

7.83. Employ the Balmer formula using $Z = 2$ for the He^+ ion.

$$E = h\nu = E_3 - E_2 = \frac{-(2^2)R_H}{3^2} - \frac{-(2^2)R_H}{2^2} = \frac{-4R_H}{9} - \frac{-4R_H}{4} = \frac{20R_H}{36}$$

The frequency of the radiation is

$$\nu = \frac{20R_H}{36h} = \frac{20}{36} \times \frac{2.179 \times 10^{-18} \text{ J}}{6.626 \times 10^{-34} \text{ J} \bullet \text{s}} = 1.8269 \times 10^{15} \text{ /s}$$

$$\lambda = \frac{c}{\nu} = \frac{2.998 \times 10^8 \text{ m/s}}{1.8269 \times 10^{15} \text{ /s}} = 1.6409 \times 10^{-7} = 1.641 \times 10^{-7} \text{ m (164.1 nm; near UV)}$$

7.85. First, use the wavelength of 10.0 pm (1.00×10^{-11} m) and the mass of 9.1094×10^{-31} kg to calculate the velocity, v. Then use the kinetic energy equation to calculate kinetic energy from velocity.

$$v = \frac{h}{m\lambda} = \frac{6.626 \times 10^{-34} \text{ kg} \cdot \text{m}^2/\text{s}}{9.1095 \times 10^{-31} \text{ kg} \times 1.00 \times 10^{-11} \text{ m}} = 7.2737 \times 10^7 \text{ m/s}$$

$$E = \tfrac{1}{2}mv^2 = \tfrac{1}{2} \times (9.1094 \times 10^{-31} \text{ kg}) \times (7.273 \times 10^7 \text{ m/s})^2 = 2.409 \times 10^{-15} \text{ J}$$

$$E_{\text{eV}} = 2.409 \times 10^{-15} \text{ J} \times \frac{1 \text{ eV}}{1.602 \times 10^{-19} \text{ J}} = 1.503 \times 10^4 = 1.50 \times 10^4 \text{ eV}$$

7.87. a. Five   b. Seven   c. Three   d. One

7.89. The possible subshells for the $n = 6$ shell are $6s$, $6p$, $6d$, $6f$, $6g$, and $6h$.

7.91. Gamma rays are a form of electromagnetic radiation similar to x rays, but the photons of gamma rays have higher energy. High-energy radiation kills bacteria and molds in foods by breaking up the DNA molecules within their cells.

7.93. When a photon of appropriate wavelength is used to flash the laser crystal, it stimulates a transition, and a photon of exactly the same wavelength as the original photon is emitted. In place of just one photon, there are now two photons. The net effect is to increase the intensity (or amplitude) of the light at this wavelength.

7.95. Tunneling depends on the probability interpretation of quantum mechanics. The probability of an electron in an atom being at a location far from atom A and near atom B is very small but not zero. This means that an electron that normally belongs to atom A can find itself near atom B without any extra energy having been supplied. The electron is said to have tunneled from one atom to another.

■ SOLUTIONS TO STRATEGY PROBLEMS

7.97. $\lambda = \dfrac{c}{v} = \dfrac{3.00 \times 10^8 \text{ m/s}}{7.76 \times 10^9 \text{ /s}} = 0.03865 \text{ m} = 0.0387 \text{ m}$

7.99. The energy required to heat the water is

$$E = s \times m \times \Delta t = (4.18 \text{ J/mol} \cdot {}^\circ\text{C})(1.00 \text{ g})(1.00{}^\circ\text{C}) = 4.18 \text{ J}$$

The microwave radiation has a wavelength of 12.2 cm (0.122 m), so the frequency and energy are

$$v = \frac{c}{\lambda} = \frac{3.00 \times 10^8 \text{ m/s}}{0.122 \text{ m}} = 2.459 \times 10^9 \text{ /s}$$

$$E = hv = (6.63 \times 10^{-34} \text{ J} \cdot \text{s})(2.459 \times 10^9 \text{ /s}) = 1.630 \times 10^{-24} \text{ J/photon}$$

Therefore, the number of photons needed to heat the water is

$$n = \frac{4.18 \text{ J}}{1.630 \times 10^{-24} \text{ J/photon}} = 2.563 \times 10^{24} = 2.56 \times 10^{24} \text{ photons}$$

7.101. The number of photons in each pulse is determined by dividing the energy of each pulse by the energy of each photon:

$$\#\,\text{photons} = \frac{\text{Energy /pulse}}{\text{Energy/photon}} = \frac{E_{pulse}}{E_{photon}}$$

The energy delivered by each pulse, E_{pulse}, is given in the problem statement:

$$E_{pulse} = 1.6\underline{0} \times 10^{-16} \; \frac{\text{J}}{\text{pulse}}$$

The energy of each 498 nm photon, E_{photon}, is

$$E_{photon} = h\nu = \frac{hc}{\lambda} = \frac{(6.626 \times 10^{-34} \; \frac{\text{J·s}}{\text{photon}})(2.998 \times 10^{8} \text{ m/s})}{498 \times 10^{-9} \text{ m}} = 3.98\underline{9} \times 10^{-19} \; \frac{\text{J}}{\text{photon}}$$

Therefore, the number of photons in each pulse is:

$$\#\,\text{photons} = \frac{E_{pulse}}{E_{photon}} = \frac{1.60 \times 10^{-16} \text{ J/pulse}}{3.98\underline{9} \times 10^{-19} \text{ J/photon}} = 40\underline{1}.1 = 401 \text{ photons /pulse}$$

7.103. The longest wavelength of light that can eject an electron from the calcium will be associated with a photon that has just enough energy to match the work function. Setting that energy equal to the energy of the photon, solve for the frequency and then find the wavelength

$$\nu = \frac{E}{h} = \frac{4.60 \times 10^{-19} \text{ J}}{6.63 \times 10^{-34} \text{ Js}} = 6.9\underline{3}8 \times 10^{14} \text{ /s}$$

$$\lambda = \frac{c}{\nu} = \frac{3.00 \times 10^{8} \text{ m/s}}{6.938 \times 10^{14} \text{ /s}} = 4.3\underline{2}3 \times 10^{-7} = 4.32 \times 10^{-7} \text{ m} = 432 \text{ nm}$$

7.105. The sum of the kinetic energy of the emitted electron, E_{kin}, and the work function of the metal, φ_{metal}, equals the energy of the photon, $E_{h\nu}$.

$$E_{h\nu} = E_{kin} + \varphi_{metal}$$

φ_{metal} is calculated by subtracting the kinetic energy of the electron, $E_{kin} = \frac{1}{2}mv^2$, from the energy of the photon, $E_{kin} = hc / \lambda$.

$$\varphi_{metal} = E_{h\nu} - E_{kin} = (hc/\lambda) - \frac{1}{2}mv^2$$

$$\varphi_{metal} = \frac{(6.626 \times 10^{-34} \text{ J} \bullet \text{s})(2.998 \times 10^{8} \text{ m/s})}{3.8\underline{9} \times 10^{-7} \text{ m}} - \frac{1}{2}(9.1094 \times 10^{-31} \text{ kg})(3.3\underline{4} \times 10^{5} \text{ m/s})^2$$

$$\varphi_{metal} = 5.1\underline{0}7 \times 10^{-19} \text{ J} - 5.0\underline{8}1 \times 10^{-20} \text{ J} = 4.5\underline{9}9 \times 10^{-19} \text{ J} = 4.60 \times 10^{-19} \text{ J}$$

A final conversion to eV units is made.

$$\varphi_{metal} = 4.599 \times 10^{-19} \text{ J} \left(\frac{1 \text{ eV}}{1.602 \times 10^{-19} \text{ J}} \right) = 2.870 = 2.87 \text{ eV}$$

The *CRC Handbook of Chemistry and Physics* provides the closest match value of 2.87 eV for the work function of calcium, Ca. The metal is most likely Ca.

7.107. Light of wavelength 1.03×10^{-7} m (103 nm) is in the ultraviolet region of the spectrum. The frequency and energy of this radiation are

$$\nu = \frac{c}{\lambda} = \frac{3.00 \times 10^8 \text{ m/s}}{1.03 \times 10^{-7} \text{ m}} = 2.912 \times 10^{15} \text{ /s}$$

$$E = h\nu = (6.63 \times 10^{-34} \text{ J} \cdot \text{s})(2.912 \times 10^{15} \text{ /s}) = 1.931 \times 10^{-18} \text{ J}$$

Now use the appropriate formula to determine the quantum number of the excited (n_i) level. Remember, ΔE is negative for an emission spectrum.

$$\Delta E = -R_H \left(\frac{1}{n_f^2} - \frac{1}{n_i^2} \right) = -R_H \left(\frac{1}{1^2} - \frac{1}{n_i^2} \right) = -R_H \left(1 - \frac{1}{n_i^2} \right)$$

$$1 - \frac{1}{n_i^2} = \frac{-\Delta E}{-R_H} = \frac{1.931 \times 10^{-18} \text{ J}}{2.179 \times 10^{-18} \text{ J}} = 0.8862$$

$$n_i = \sqrt{\frac{1}{1 - 0.8862}} = 2.964 = 2.96$$

Thus, the quantum number of the excited level is 3.

7.109. The shortest wavelength photon corresponds to that having the highest possible energy. This would occur if an electron relaxed from an infinitely high quantum state, for example $n = \infty$, to the ground state at n = 1. Employing the Balmer formula using $Z = 3$ for the Li^{2+} ion.

$$\Delta E = h\nu = E_1 - E_\infty = \frac{-(3^2)R_H}{1^2} - \frac{-(3^2)R_H}{\infty^2}$$

With an infinitely large denominator, the second term in this equation has a infinitesimally small value, essentially 0. Thus,

$$\Delta E = h\nu = E_1 - E_\infty = E_1 - 0 = \frac{-(3^2)R_H}{1^2}$$

$$\Delta E = \frac{hc}{\lambda} = \frac{-(3^2)(2.179 \times 10^{-18} \text{ J})}{1^2} = -1.9611 \times 10^{-17} \text{ J}$$

The negative result here relates to the energy change for the relaxing Li^{2+} ion. The emitted photon carries this energy away and the wavelength of that photon is

$$\lambda = \frac{hc}{-\Delta E} = \frac{(6.626 \times 10^{-34} \text{ J} \bullet \text{s})(2.998 \times 10^8 \text{ m/s})}{-1.9611 \times 10^{-17} \text{ J}} = 1.0129 \times 10^{-8} \text{ m} = 10.13 \text{ nm}$$

A photon of this wavelength would be found on the fringe of the x ray-UV region of the electromagnetic spectrum.

7.111.   First, calculate the mass of one oxygen molecule.

$$m = \frac{32.00 \text{ g O}_2}{1 \text{ mol}} \times \frac{1 \text{ mol}}{6.02 \times 10^{23} \text{ molec}} \times \frac{1 \text{ kg}}{1000 \text{ g}} = 5.314 \times 10^{-26} \text{ kg}$$

Now the de Broglie wavelength can be calculated.

$$\lambda = \frac{h}{mv} = \frac{6.63 \times 10^{-34} \text{ J} \bullet \text{s}}{(5.314 \times 10^{-26} \text{ kg})(479 \text{ m/s})} = 2.604 \times 10^{-11} = 2.60 \times 10^{-11} \text{ m (26.0 pm)}$$

This wavelength can be compared to the length of the molecule (242 pm) as follows.

$$\frac{26.04 \text{ pm}}{242 \text{ pm}} \times 100\% = 10.76\% = 10.8\%$$

Thus, the de Broglie wavelength is 10.8% of the length of the molecule.

7.113.   From the given wavelength, λ, the de Broglie relation can be used to determine the velocity of the electron, $v = h/m\lambda$. In turn, the electron's velocity and mass can be used to find the kinetic energy of the electron, $E_{kin} = \frac{1}{2}mv^2$.

$$v(\text{m/s}) = \frac{h}{m\lambda} = \frac{6.626 \times 10^{-34} \text{ J} \bullet \text{s}}{(9.1094 \times 10^{-31} \text{kg})(0.1476 \times 10^{-9} \text{ m})} = 4.9281 \times 10^6 \text{ m/s}$$

$$E_{kin} = \frac{1}{2}mv^2 = \frac{1}{2}(9.1094 \times 10^{-31}\text{kg})(4.9281 \times 10^6 \text{ m/s})^2 = 1.1061 \times 10^{-17} = 1.106 \times 10^{-17} \text{ J}$$

7.115.   For the $n = 5$ level, the sublevels are $5s$, $5p$, $5d$, $5f$, and $5g$. The numbers of orbitals for the sublevels are 1, 3, 5, 7, and 9, respectively. The total number of orbitals for the $n = 5$ level is therefore $1 + 3 + 5 + 7 + 9 = 25$. Thus, the degeneracy of the $n = 5$ level in the H atom is 25.

■ SOLUTIONS TO CUMULATIVE-SKILLS PROBLEMS

7.117.   First, use Avogadro's number to calculate the energy for one Cl_2 molecule.

$$\frac{239 \text{ kJ}}{1 \text{ mol}} \times \frac{1000 \text{ J}}{1 \text{ kJ}} \times \frac{1 \text{ mol}}{6.022 \times 10^{23} \text{ molecules}} = 3.9687 \times 10^{-19} \text{ J/molecule}$$

Then convert energy to frequency and finally to wavelength.

$$v = \frac{E}{h} = \frac{3.9687 \times 10^{-19} \text{ J}}{6.626 \times 10^{-34} \text{ J} \bullet \text{s}} = 5.9897 \times 10^{14} \text{ /s}$$

$$\lambda = \frac{c}{v} = \frac{2.998 \times 10^8 \text{ m/s}}{5.9897 \times 10^{14} \text{ /s}} = 5.0052 \times 10^{-7} \text{ m (501 nm; visible region)}$$

7.119. First, calculate the energy needed to heat the 0.250 L of water from 20.0°C to 100.0°C.

$$0.250 \text{ L} \times \frac{1000 \text{ g}}{1 \text{ L}} \times \frac{4.184 \text{ J}}{(\text{g} \cdot \text{°C})} \times (100.0 \text{ °C} - 20.0 \text{°C}) = 8.3\underline{6}8 \times 10^4 \text{ J}$$

Then calculate the frequency, the energy of one photon, and the number of photons.

$$\nu = \frac{c}{\lambda} = \frac{2.998 \times 10^8 \text{ m/s}}{0.125 \text{ m}} = 2.3\underline{9}8 \times 10^9 \text{ /s}$$

$$E \text{ of one photon} = h\nu = (6.626 \times 10^{-34} \text{ J} \cdot \text{s}) \times (2.398 \times 10^9 \text{/s}) = 1.5\underline{8}9 \times 10^{-24} \text{ J}$$

$$n = 8.368 \times 10^4 \text{ J} \times \frac{1 \text{ photon}}{1.589 \times 10^{-24} \text{ J}} = 5.2\underline{6}56 \times 10^{28} = 5.27 \times 10^{28} \text{ photons}$$

7.121. First, write the following equality for the energy to remove one electron, $E_{removal}$:

$$E_{removal} = E_{425 \text{ nm}} - E_k \text{ of ejected photon}$$

Use $E = h\nu$ to calculate the energy of the photon. Then recall that E_k, the kinetic energy, is $\frac{1}{2}mv^2$. Use this to calculate E_k.

$$E_{425 \text{ nm}} = \frac{hc}{\lambda} = \frac{(6.626 \times 10^{-34} \text{ J} \cdot \text{s})(2.998 \times 10^8 \text{ m/s})}{4.25 \times 10^{-7} \text{ m}} = 4.6\underline{7}40 \times 10^{-19} \text{ J}$$

$$E_k = \frac{1}{2}mv^2 = \frac{1}{2} \times (9.1094 \times 10^{-31} \text{ kg}) \times (4.88 \times 10^5 \text{ m/s})^2 = 1.0\underline{8}46 \times 10^{-19} \text{ J}$$

Subtract to find $E_{removal}$, and convert it to kJ/mol:

$$E_{removal} = 4.6740 \times 10^{-19} \text{ J} - (1.0847 \times 10^{-19} \text{ J}) = 3.5\underline{8}93 \times 10^{-19} = 3.59 \times 10^{-19} \text{ J/electron}$$

$$E_{removal} = \frac{3.5893 \times 10^{-19} \text{ J}}{1 \text{ e}^-} \times \frac{6.022 \times 10^{23} \text{ e}^-}{1 \text{ mol}} \times \frac{1 \text{ kJ}}{1000 \text{ J}} = 2.1\underline{6}1 \times 10^2$$

$$E_{removal} = 2.16 \times 10^2 \text{ kJ/mol}$$

7.123. First, calculate the energy, E_{kin}, in joules, using the product of voltage and charge:

$$E_{kin} = (4.00 \times 10^3 \text{ V}) \times (1.602 \times 10^{-19} \text{ C}) = 6.4\underline{0}8 \times 10^{-16} \text{ J}$$

Now, use the kinetic energy equation, $E_k = \frac{1}{2}mv^2$, and solve for velocity:

$$v = \sqrt{\frac{2E_{kin}}{m}} = \sqrt{\frac{2 \times 6.408 \times 10^{-16} \text{ J}}{9.1095 \times 10^{-31} \text{ kg}}} = 3.7\underline{5}08 \times 10^7 \text{ m/s}$$

$$\lambda = \frac{h}{mv} = \frac{6.626 \times 10^{-34} \text{ J} \cdot \text{s}}{(9.1095 \times 10^{-31} \text{ kg}) \times (3.7508 \times 10^7 \text{ m/s})} = 1.9\underline{3}9 \times 10^{-11}$$

$$= 1.94 \times 10^{-11} \text{ m (19.4 pm)}$$

CHAPTER 8

Electron Configurations and Periodicity

■ SOLUTIONS TO EXERCISES

Note on significant figures: If the final answer to a solution needs to be rounded off, it is given first with one nonsignificant figure, and the last significant figure is underlined. The final answer is then rounded to the correct number of significant figures. In multistep problems, intermediate answers are given with at least one nonsignificant figure; however, only the final answer has been rounded off.

8.1.   a.   Possible orbital diagram.

b.   Possible orbital diagram.

c.   Impossible orbital diagram; there are two electrons in a $2p$ orbital with the same spin.

d.   Possible electron configuration.

e.   Impossible electron configuration; only two electrons are allowed in an s subshell.

f.   Impossible electron configuration; only six electrons are allowed in a p subshell.

8.2.   Look at the periodic table. Start with hydrogen and go through the periods, writing down the subshells being filled, stopping with manganese ($Z = 25$). You obtain the following order:

Order: $1s$ $2s2p$ $3s3p$ $4s3d4p$

Period: first   second third   fourth

Now fill the subshells with electrons, remembering that you have a total of twenty-five electrons to distribute. You obtain

$1s^2 2s^2 2p^6 3s^2 3p^6 4s^2 3d^5$, or $1s^2 2s^2 2p^6 3s^2 3p^6 3d^5 4s^2$

8.3.   Arsenic is a main-group element in Period 4, Group VA, of the periodic table. The five outer electrons should occupy the $4s$ and $4p$ subshells; the five valence electrons have the configuration $4s^2 4p^3$.

8.4.   Because the sum of the $6s^2$ and $6p^2$ electrons gives four outer (valence) electrons, lead should be in Group IVA, which it is. Looking at the table, you find lead in Period 6. From its position, it would be classified as a main-group element.

8.5.   The electron configuration of phosphorus is $1s^2 2s^2 2p^6 3s^2 3p^3$. The orbital diagram is

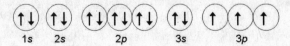

1s   2s   2p   3s   3p

8.6.   The radius tends to decrease across a row of the periodic table from left to right, and it tends to increase from the top of a column to the bottom. Therefore, in order of increasing radius,

Be < Mg < Na

8.7.   It is more likely that answer a, 1000 kJ/mol, is the ionization energy for iodine because ionization energies tend to decrease with atomic number in a group (I is below Cl in Group VIIA).

8.8.   Fluorine should have a more negative electron affinity because (1) carbon has only two electrons in the p subshell, (2) the 1− fluoride ion has a stable noble-gas configuration, and (3) the electron can approach the fluorine nucleus more closely than the carbon nucleus. This follows the general trend, which is toward more negative electron affinities from left to right in any period.

■ ANSWERS TO CONCEPT CHECKS

8.1.   The second-period elements are those in which the $2s$ and $2p$ orbitals fill. Each orbital can hold only one electron, so all four orbitals will be filled after four electrons. Therefore, the second period will have four elements.

8.2.   The s orbital fills in the first two elements of the period (Groups IA and IIA); then the p orbital starts to fill (Group IIIA). Thus, the first element is in Group IIA (Mg), and the next element is in Group IIIA (Al).

8.3.   From the information given, the element must be in Group IIA. These elements have positive electron affinities and also have large third ionization energies.

8.4.   A metalloid is an element near the staircase line in the periodic table (the green elements in the periodic table on the inside front cover of the text). The formula R_2O_5 suggests a Group VA element. There are two metalloids in Group VA, arsenic and antimony. That this is an acidic oxide indicates this metalloid has considerable nonmetal character. So, of the two metalloids, the one nearer the top of the column, arsenic, seems more likely. This agrees with the text, which notes that arsenic(V) oxide is acidic, whereas antimony(V) oxide is amphoteric.

■ ANSWERS TO SELF-ASSESSMENT AND REVIEW QUESTIONS

8.1.   In the original Stern-Gerlach experiment, a beam of silver atoms is directed into the field of a specially designed magnet. (The same can be done with hydrogen atoms.) The beam of atoms is split into two by the magnetic field; half are bent toward one magnetic pole face and the other half toward the other magnetic pole face. This effect shows that the atoms themselves act as magnets with a positive or a negative component, as indicated by the positive or negative spin quantum numbers.

8.2.   In effect, the electron acts as though it were a sphere of spinning charge (Figure 8.3). Like any circulating electric charge, it creates a magnetic field with a spin axis that has more than one possible direction relative to a magnetic field. Electron spin is subject to a quantum restriction to one of two directions corresponding to the m_s quantum numbers +1/2 and −1/2.

8.3. The Pauli exclusion principle limits the configurations of an atom by excluding configurations in which two or more electrons have the same four quantum numbers. For example, each electron in the same orbital must have different m_s values. This also implies that only two electrons occupy one orbital.

8.4. According to the principles discussed in Section 7.5, the number of orbitals in the g subshell ($l = 4$) is given by $2l + 1$ and is thus equal to 9 Because each orbital can hold a maximum of two electrons, the g subshell can hold a maximum of eighteen electrons.

8.5. The orbitals, in order of increasing energy up to and including the $3p$ orbitals (but not including the $3d$ orbitals), are as follows: $1s$, $2s$, $2p$, $3s$, and $3p$ (Figure 8.7).

8.6. The noble-gas core is an inner-shell configuration corresponding to one of the noble gases. The pseudo-noble-gas core is an inner-shell configuration corresponding to one of the noble gases together with $(n - 1)d^{10}$ electrons. Like the noble-gas core electrons, the d^{10} electrons are not involved in chemical reactions. The valence electron is an electron (of an atom) located outside the noble-gas core or pseudo-noble-gas core. It is an electron primarily involved in chemical reactions.

8.7. The orbital diagram for the $1s^2 2s^2 2p^4$ ground state of oxygen is

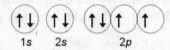

Another possible oxygen orbital diagram, but not a ground state, is

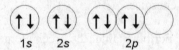

8.8. A diamagnetic substance is a substance that is not attracted by a magnetic field or is very slightly repelled by such a field. This property generally indicates the substance has only paired electrons. A paramagnetic substance is a substance that is weakly attracted by a magnetic field. This property generally indicates the substance has one or more unpaired electrons. Ground-state oxygen has two unpaired $2p$ electrons and is therefore paramagnetic.

8.9. In Groups IA and IIA, the outer s subshell is being filled: s^1 for Group IA and s^2 for Group IIA. In Groups IIIA to VIIIA, the outer p subshell is being filled: p^1 for IIIA, p^2 for IVA, p^3 for VA, p^4 for VIA, p^5 for VIIA, and p^6 for VIIIA. In the transition elements, the $(n - 1)d$ subshell is being filled from d^1 to d^{10} electrons. In the lanthanides and actinides, the f subshell is being filled from f^1 to f^{14} electrons.

8.10. Mendeleev arranged the elements in order of increasing atomic weight, an arrangement that was later changed to atomic numbers. His periodic table was divided into rows (periods) and columns (groups). In his first attempt, he left spaces for what he believed to be undiscovered elements. In his row 5, under aluminum and above indium in Group III, he left a blank space. This Group III element he called eka-aluminum, and he predicted its properties from those of aluminum and indium. Later, the French chemist de Boisbaudran discovered this element and named it gallium.

8.11.   In a plot of atomic radii versus atomic number (Figure 8.16), the major trends that emerge are the following: (1) Within each period (horizontal row), the atomic radius tends to decrease with increasing atomic number or nuclear charge. The largest atom in a period is thus the Group 1A atom, and the smallest atom in a period is thus the noble-gas atom. (2) Within each group (vertical column), the atomic radius tends to increase with the period number.

In a plot of ionization energy versus atomic number (Figure 8.18), the major trends are that (1) the ionization energy within a period increases with atomic number, and (2) the ionization energy within a group tends to decrease going down the group.

8.12.   The alkaline earth element with the smallest radius is beryllium (Be).

8.13.   Group VIIA (halogens) is the main group with the largest (and most negative) electron affinities. Configurations with filled subshells (ground states of the noble-gas elements) would form unstable negative ions when adding one electron per atom. Group VIIIA (noble gases) is the group of elements having only unstable negative ions.

8.14.   The Na^+ and Mg^{2+} ions are stable because they have the same electronic configuration as the noble gas neon. If Na^{2+} and Mg^{3+} ions were to exist, they would be very unstable because they would not have the same electronic configuration as a noble-gas structure and because of the energy needed to remove an electron from an inner shell.

8.15.   The elements tend to increase in metallic character from right to left in any period. They also tend to increase in metallic character down any column (group) of elements.

8.16.   A basic oxide is an oxide that reacts with acids. An example is calcium oxide, CaO. An acidic oxide is an oxide that reacts with bases. An example is carbon dioxide, CO_2.

8.17.   Rubidium is the alkali metal atom with a $5s^1$ configuration.

8.18.   Atomic number equals 117 (protons in last known element plus those needed to reach Group VIIA).

8.19.   The following elements are in Groups IIIA to VIA:

Group IIIA	Group IVA	Group VA	Group VIA
B: metalloid	C: nonmetal	N: nonmetal	O: nonmetal
Al: metal	Si: metalloid	P: nonmetal	S: nonmetal
Ga: metal	Ge: metalloid	As: metalloid	Se: nonmetal
In: metal	Sn: metal	Sb: metalloid	Te: metalloid
Tl: metal	Pb: metal	Bi: metal	Po: metal

Yes, each column displays the expected increasing metallic character.

8.20. The oxides of the following elements are listed as acidic, basic, or amphoteric:

Group IIIA	Group IVA	Group VA	Group VIA
B: acidic	C: acidic	N: acidic	O: amphoteric (H_2O)
Al: amphoteric	Si: acidic	P: acidic	S: acidic
Ga: amphoteric	Ge: acidic	As: acidic	Se: acidic
In: basic	Sn: amphoteric	Sb: amphoteric	Te: amphoteric
Tl: basic	Pb: amphoteric	Bi: basic	Po: amphoteric

8.21. $2K(s) + 2H_2O(l) \rightarrow 2KOH(aq) + H_2(g)$

8.22. Barium should be a soft, reactive metal. Barium should form the basic oxide, BaO. Barium metal, for example, would be expected to react with water according to the equation

$$Ba(s) + 2H_2O(l) \rightarrow Ba(OH)_2(aq) + H_2(g)$$

8.23. The two oxides of carbon are carbon monoxide, CO, and carbon dioxide, CO_2.

8.24.
    a.   White phosphorus

    b.   Sulfur

    c.   Bromine

    d.   Sodium

8.25. The answer is c, 3.

8.26. The answer is b, $[Ne]3s^2 3p^3$

8.27. The answer is a. For Be, you would expect the first two ionization potentials to be successively getting larger with the third ionization energy much larger than the first two. The first two electrons are taken from the valence shell; the third electron is much harder to ionize because it is removed from the core.

8.28. The answer is b, II only.

■ ANSWERS TO CONCEPTUAL PROBLEMS

8.31. This statement of the Pauli principle implies there can be two electrons with the same spin in a given orbital. Because an electron can have either one of two spins, any orbital can hold a maximum of four electrons. The first six elements of the periodic table would have the following electron configurations:

(1) $1s^1$

(2) $1s^2$

(3) $1s^3$

(4) $1s^4$

(5) $1s^4 2s^1$

(6) $1s^4 2s^2$

8.33. The elements are in Group IIA (only s electrons) and IIIB (d electrons). They are also in Period 5. Therefore, the elements are strontium (Sr) and yttrium (Y).

8.35. Keeping in mind that a filled orbital is usually a stable configuration for an atom, an element in this universe with five electrons would probably lose the two electrons in the second orbital and form a cation with a charge of positive two. The other possible option is for the atom to gain seven additional electrons to fill the second orbital. However, this is unlikely given that the nuclear charge would be relatively small, and electron-electron repulsions in such an atom would be large.

8.37. The elements that form oxides of the form RO_2 are in Groups IVA and VIA. However, the metalloid oxide in Group VIA is amphoteric. Therefore, the elements are in Group IVA. The metalloid is germanium (Ge), and the metal is tin (Sn). GeO_2 is the acidic oxide, and SnO_2 is the amphoteric oxide.

8.39. a. Only heavier elements of Group IIA form slightly stable negative ions whereas the lighter elements do not form negative ions; thus, elements in Group IIA have small electron affinities as a rule. The only other main group of elements that would be in question here would be the noble gases in Group VIIIA. Noble gases do not form negative ions.

b. The large difference between the second and third ionization energies means this would be a Group IIA element.

c. Luster and conductivity are properties of metals. Group IIA is the only main group that contains just metallic elements.

Considering the above, element "E" must be a Group IIA alkaline earth metal.

■ SOLUTIONS TO PRACTICE PROBLEMS

Note on significant figures: If the final answer to a solution needs to be rounded off, it is given first with one nonsignificant figure, and the last significant figure is underlined. The final answer is then rounded to the correct number of significant figures. In multistep problems, intermediate answers are given with at least one nonsignificant figure; however, only the final answer has been rounded off.

8.41.   a.   Not allowed; the paired electrons in the 2p orbital should have opposite spins.

        b.   Allowed; electron configuration is $1s^22s^22p^4$.

        c.   Not allowed; the electrons in the 1s orbital must have opposite spins.

        b.   Not allowed; the 2s orbital can hold at most two electrons, with opposite spins.

8.43.   a.   Impossible state; the 2p orbitals can hold no more than six electrons.

        b.   Possible state.

        c.   Impossible state; the 3s orbital can hold no more than two electrons.

        d.   Possible state; however, the 3p and 4s orbitals should be filled before the 3d orbital.

8.45.   The six possible orbital diagrams for $1s^22p^1$ are

8.47.   Iodine ($Z = 53$): $1s^22s^22p^63s^23p^63d^{10}4s^24p^64d^{10}5s^25p^5$

8.49.   Manganese ($Z = 25$): $1s^22s^22p^63s^23p^63d^54s^2$

8.51.   Bromine ($Z = 35$): $4s^24p^5$

8.53.   Zirconium ($Z = 40$): $4d^25s^2$

8.55.   The highest value of *n* is six, so thallium (Tl) is in the sixth period. The 5d subshell is filled, and there is a 6p electron, so Tl belongs in an A group. There are three valence electrons, so Tl is in Group IIIA. It is a main-group element.

8.57. Cobalt (Z = 27): [Ar]

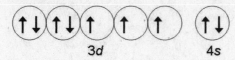

3d   4s

8.59. Potassium (Z = 19): [Ar]

4s

All the subshells are filled in the argon core; however, the 4s electron is unpaired, causing the ground state of the potassium atom to be a paramagnetic substance.

8.61. Atomic radius increases going down a column (group), from S to Se, and increases going from right to left in a row, from Se to As. Thus, the order by increasing atomic radius is S, Se, As.

8.63. Ionization energy increases going left to right in a row. Thus, the order by increasing ionization energy is Na, Al, Cl, Ar.

8.65. a. In general, the electron affinity becomes larger going from left to right within a period. Thus, Br has a larger electron affinity than As. When Br gains an electron it also results in a stable noble gas electron configuration.

        b. In general, a nonmetal has a larger electron affinity than a metal. Thus, F has a larger electron affinity than Li. When F gains an electron it also results in a stable noble gas electron configuration.

8.67. Chlorine forms the ClO_3^- ion, so bromine should form the BrO_3^- ion, and potassium forms the K^+ ion, so lithium should be Li^+. Thus, the expected formula of lithium bromate is $LiBrO_3$.

■ SOLUTIONS TO GENERAL PROBLEMS

8.69. Strontium: $1s^2 2s^2 2p^6 3s^2 3p^6 3d^{10} 4s^2 4p^6 5s^2$

8.71. Polonium: $6s^2 6p^4$

8.73. The orbital diagram for arsenic is

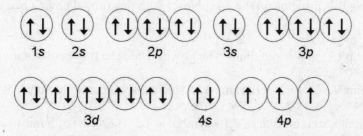

1s   2s   2p   3s   3p

3d   4s   4p

8.75. For eka-lead: [Rn] $5f^{14} 6d^{10} 7s^2 7p^2$. It is a metal; the oxide is eka-PbO or eka-PbO_2.

8.77. The ionization energy of Fr is ~370 kJ/mol (slightly less than that of Cs).

8.79.   Niobium: [Kr]

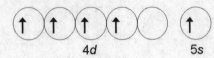

8.81.   a. Cl_2

b.   Na

c.   Sb

d.   Ar

8.83.   Element with $Z = 23$: $1s^2 2s^2 2p^6 3s^2 3p^6 3d^3 4s^2$. The element is in Group VB (three of the five valence electrons are d electrons) and in Period 4 (largest n is 4). It is a d-block transition element.

8.85.   Nuclear magnetic resonance depends upon the property of nuclear spin. Modern NMR uses the frequency range 300 MHz to 900 MHz.

8.87.   When an electron in the cathode ray hits a metal atom in the target, it can (if it has sufficient energy) knock an electron from an inner shell of the atom. This produces a metal ion with an electron missing from an inner orbital. This electron configuration is unstable, so an electron from an orbital of higher energy drops into the half-filled orbital, and a photon is emitted. The photon corresponds to electromagnetic radiation in the x-ray region.

8.89.   When you place a diamagnetic material in an external magnetic field, its electrons move so as to induce, or generate, a smaller magnetic field that is opposite in direction to the external field. This results in a repulsive force between the diamagnetic material and the external field. This repulsive force can be made upward to balance the downward force of gravity so the diamagnetic material can be levitated by a magnetic field.

■ SOLUTIONS TO STRATEGY PROBLEMS

8.91.   Diagram (a) violates Hund's rule in the $2p$ sublevel by not having all the spins in the same direction. Diagram (b) violates Pauli's principle in the $2s$ sublevel with both electrons having the same spin in the same orbital. Diagram (c) violates Pauli's principle in the $2p$ sublevel with one orbital having two electrons with the same spin. Diagram (d) does not violate either condition. Diagram (e) violates Pauli's principle in the $3p$ sublevel with one orbital having two electrons with the same spin.

8.93.   The element is in Group IA, so it is rubidium. The ground-state electron configuration is $[Kr]5s^1$.

8.95.   The element is in Group VIA, so it is tellurium. The valence-shell configuration is $5s^2 5p^4$.

8.97.   The element is in Period 5, so it is tellurium. Its symbol is Te. The value of b must be 4.

8.99.   If the electron configuration $1s^2 2s^2 2p^5 3s^2 3p^2$ is for a neutral atom (M), it must be an   excited state atom (M^*) because there are only 5 electrons in the $2p$ sublevel. Allowing one of the $3p$ electrons to transition (by way of relaxation) to the $2p$ sublevel results in the following change:

$$M^* (1s^2 2s^2 2p^5 3s^2 3p^2) \rightarrow M (1s^2 2s^2 2p^6 3s^2 3p^1) + h\nu$$

The resulting electron configuration $1s^2 2s^2 2p^6 3s^2 3p^1$ is the electron configuration for an atom in period 3 and group IIIA. The element is aluminum, Al. The second electron configuration given in the problem statement, i.e., $1s^2 2s^2 2p^6 3s^2 3p^5$, has no partly filled sublevels below the last sublevel so it is a ground state electron configuration associated with an atom in period 3 and Group VIIA. The element is chlorine, Cl. Since Al forms the 3+ ion and chlorine forms the 1- ion, the formula of the compound of these elements is $AlCl_3$.

8.101. The alkaline earths in Group IIA are moderately reactive metals. The element in this group that has a referenced melting point near 850 °C is calcium, Ca. An element that is a green gas under normal conditions is chlorine, Cl_2. When Cl_2 reacts with Ca, calcium chloride, $CaCl_2$ forms as a white solid.

$$Ca(s) + Cl_2(g) \rightarrow CaCl_2(s)$$

Calcium chloride dissolves in water to form $Ca^{2+}(aq)$ and $Cl^-(aq)$ ions.

$$CaCl_2(s) + xH_2O \rightarrow Ca^{2+}(aq) + Cl^-(aq)$$

When carbon dioxide gas, $CO_2(g)$, is bubbled into water, it forms a solution of carbonic acid, a polyprotic acid which dissociates stepwise to form some carbonate ions.

$$CO_2(g) + H_2O(l) \rightarrow H_2CO_3(aq)$$

$$H_2CO_3(aq) + H_2O(l) \rightarrow HCO_3^-(aq) + H_3O^+(aq)$$

$$HCO_3^-(aq) + H_2O(l) \rightarrow CO_3^{2-}(aq) + H_3O^+(aq)$$

The presence of Ca^{2+}(aq) produces a reaction with the carbonate ions yielding a white precipitate of calcium carbonate, $CaCO_3$.

$$Ca^{2+}(aq) + CO_3^{2-}(aq) \rightarrow CaCO_3(s)$$

In summary, the white solid is $CaCl_2(s)$ and the white precipitate is $CaCO_3(s)$.

8.103. Element 120 is expected to be associated with the alkaline earth metal family in Group IIA. Applying the Aufbau principle, element 120 should have a ground state electron configuration of $[Uuo]8s^2$. Here, [Uuo] represents the shorthand e^- configuration of element 118. Note the similarity in the valence shell configuration with the other alkaline earth metals (ns^2).

8.105. The main-group atom in Period 5 with the smallest radius is xenon. The trend in atomic radius is to decrease as you go from left to right across a period. This is because electrons are being added to the same valence shell, but the charge on the nucleus is increasing. The net effect is to pull the valence electrons closer to the nucleus. The orbital diagram for xenon is

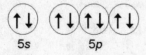

8.107. The element in Period 6 that forms the ion R^{2+} and forms the oxides RO and RO_2 is lead (Group IVA). The element that immediately follows lead is bismuth ($Z = 83$) and is in Group VA. The orbital diagram for the ground-state valence-shell electrons is

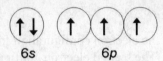

8.109. Applying Hess's law, we add the thermochemical equation associated with the dissociation process given in the problem statement to the thermochemical equation associated with Cl's electron affinity as follows:

$Cl_2(g)$	$\rightarrow$	$2Cl(g)$	$\Delta H = +240$ kJ/mol
$2Cl(g) + 2e^-$	$\rightarrow$	$2Cl^-(g)$	$2 \times (\Delta H = -349$ kJ/mol)
$Cl_2(g) + 2e^-$	$\rightarrow$	$2Cl^-(g)$	$\Delta H = -458$ kJ/mol

The net result in line 3 above shows that 2 electrons are being added to a Cl_2 molecule to produce two Cl^- ions. The negative enthalpy change of -458 kJ/mol shows the process to be exothermic.

■ SOLUTIONS TO CUMULATIVE-SKILLS PROBLEMS

8.111. The equation is

$$Ba(s) + 2H_2O(l) \rightarrow Ba(OH)_2(aq) + H_2(g)$$

Using the equation, calculate the moles of H_2; then use the ideal gas law to convert to volume.

$$\text{mol } H_2 = 2.50 \text{ g Ba} \times \frac{1 \text{ mol Ba}}{137.33 \text{ g Ba}} \times \frac{1 \text{ mol } H_2}{1 \text{ mol Ba}} = 0.018204 \text{ mol}$$

$$V = \frac{nRT}{P} = \frac{(0.018204 \text{ mol})(0.082057 \text{ L} \cdot \text{atm/K} \cdot \text{mol})(294.2 \text{ K})}{(748/760) \text{ atm}} = 0.44651 \text{ L (447 mL)}$$

8.113. Radium is in Group IIA; hence, the radium cation is Ra^{2+}, and its oxide is RaO. Use the atomic weights to calculate the percentage of Ra in RaO.

$$\text{Percent Ra} = \frac{226 \text{ amu Ra}}{226 \text{ amu Ra } + 16.00 \text{ amu O}} \times 100\% = 93.\underline{38} = 93.4\% \text{ Ra}$$

8.115. Convert 5.00 mg (0.00500 g) Na to moles of Na; then convert to energy using the first ionization energy of 496 kJ/mol Na.

$$\text{mol Na} = 0.00500 \text{ g Na} \times \frac{1 \text{ mol Na}}{22.99 \text{ g Na}} = 2.1\underline{7}4 \times 10^{-4} \text{ mol Na}$$

$$2.1\underline{7}4 \times 10^{-4} \text{ mol Na} \times \frac{496 \text{ kJ}}{1 \text{ mol Na}} = 0.10\underline{7}8 = 0.108 \text{ kJ} = 108 \text{ J}$$

8.117. Use the Bohr formula, where $n_f = \infty$ and $n_i = 1$.

$$\Delta E = -R_H \left[\frac{1}{\infty^2} - \frac{1}{1^2} \right] = -R_H[-1] = R_H = \frac{2.179 \times 10^{-18} \text{ J}}{1 \text{ H atom}}$$

$$I.E. = \frac{2.179 \times 10^{-18} \text{ J}}{1 \text{ H atom}} \times \frac{6.022 \times 10^{23} \text{ H atoms}}{1 \text{ mol H}} = \frac{1.31\underline{2}19 \times 10^6 \text{ J}}{1 \text{ mol H}}$$

$$I.E. = 1.312 \times 10^3 \text{ kJ/mol H}$$

8.119. Add the three equations after reversing the equation for the lattice energy and its ΔH:

$Na(g)$	$\rightarrow$	$Na^+(g) + e^-$	$\Delta H = +496$ kJ/mol
$Cl(g) + e^-$	$\rightarrow$	$Cl^-(g)$	$\Delta H = -349$ kJ/mol
$Na^+(g) + Cl^-(g)$	$\rightarrow$	$NaCl(s)$	$-1(\Delta H = 786$ kJ/mol$)$
$Na(g) + Cl(g)$	$\rightarrow$	$NaCl(s)$	$\Delta H = -639$ kJ/mol

CHAPTER 9

Ionic and Covalent Bonding

■ SOLUTIONS TO EXERCISES

9.1.   The Lewis symbol for oxygen is $:\overset{\cdot\cdot}{\underset{\cdot\cdot}{O}}\cdot$ and the Lewis symbol for magnesium is $\cdot\,Mg\,\cdot$. The magnesium atom loses two electrons, and the oxygen atom accepts two electrons. You can represent this electron transfer as follows:

9.2.   The electron configuration of the Ca atom is $[Ar]4s^2$. By losing two electrons, the atom assumes a 2+ charge and the argon configuration, $[Ar]$. The Lewis symbol is Ca^{2+}. The S atom has the configuration $[Ne]3s^23p^4$. By gaining two electrons, the atom assumes a 2− charge and the argon configuration $[Ne]3s^23p^6$ and is the same as $[Ar]$. The Lewis symbol is

$$\left[\,:\overset{\cdot\cdot}{\underset{\cdot\cdot}{S}}:\,\right]^{2-}$$

9.3.   The electron configuration of lead (Pb) is $[Xe]4f^{14}5d^{10}6s^26p^2$. The electron configuration of Pb^{2+} is $[Xe]4f^{14}5d^{10}6s^2$.

9.4.   The electron configuration of manganese $(Z = 25)$ is $[Ar]3d^54s^2$. To find the ion configuration, remove first the $4s$ electrons, then the $3d$ electrons. In this case, only two electrons need to be removed. The electron configuration of Mn^{2+} is $[Ar]3d^5$.

9.5. S^{2-} has a larger radius than S. The anion has more electrons than the atom. The electron-electron repulsion is greater; hence, the valence orbitals expand. The anion radius is larger than the atomic radius.

9.6.   The ionic radii increase down any column because of the addition of electron shells. All of these ions are from the Group IIA family; therefore, $Mg^{2+} < Ca^{2+} < Sr^{2+}$.

9.7. Cl^-, Ca^{2+}, and P^{3-} are isoelectronic with an electron configuration equivalent to $[Ar]$. In an isoelectronic sequence, the ionic radius decreases with increasing nuclear charge. Therefore, in order of increasing ionic radius, we have Ca^{2+}, Cl^-, and P^{3-}.

9.8.   The absolute values of the electronegativity differences are C–O, 1.0; C–S, 0.0; and H–Br, 0.7. Therefore, C–O is the most polar bond.

9.9.   First, calculate the total number of valence electrons. C has four, Cl has seven, and F has seven. The total number is $4 + (2 \times 7) + (2 \times 7) = 32$. The expected skeleton consists of a carbon atom surrounded by Cl and F atoms. Distribute the electron pairs to the surrounding atoms to satisfy the octet rule. All 32 electrons (16 pairs) are accounted for.

$$
\begin{array}{c}
\ddot{} \\
: \text{Cl} : \\
:\ddot{\text{F}} : \text{C} : \ddot{\text{F}} : \\
: \text{Cl} : \\
\ddot{}
\end{array}
$$

9.10.   The total number of electrons in CO_2 is $4 + (2 \times 6) = 16$. Because carbon is more electropositive than oxygen, it is expected to be the central atom. Distribute the electrons to the surrounding atoms to satisfy the octet rule.

$$: \ddot{\text{O}} : \text{C} : \ddot{\text{O}} :$$

All sixteen electrons have been used, but note that there are only four electrons on carbon. This is four electrons short of a complete octet, which suggests the existence of double bonds. Move a pair of electrons from each oxygen to the carbon-oxygen bonds.

$$\ddot{\text{O}} :: \text{C} :: \ddot{\text{O}} \qquad \text{or} \qquad \ddot{\text{O}} = \text{C} = \ddot{\text{O}}$$

9.11.   a.   There are $(3 \times 1) + 6 = 9$ valence electrons in H_3O. The H_3O^+ ion has one less electron than is provided by the neutral atoms because the charge on the ion is 1+. Hence, there are eight valence electrons in H_3O^+. The electron-dot formula is

$$
\left[
\begin{array}{c}
\text{H} \\
\ddot{} \\
\text{H} : \ddot{\text{O}} : \text{H}
\end{array}
\right]^+
$$

b.   Cl has seven valence electrons, and O has six valence electrons. The total number of valence electrons from the neutral atoms is $7 + (2 \times 6) = 19$. The charge on the ClO_2^- is 1−, which provides one more electron than the neutral atoms. This makes a total of 20 valence electrons. The electron-dot formula for ClO_2^- is

$$
\left[
: \ddot{\text{O}} : \ddot{\text{Cl}} : \ddot{\text{O}} :
\right]^-
$$

9.12.   The resonance formulas for NO_3^- are

$$
\left[
\begin{array}{c}
: \ddot{\text{O}} : \\
: \ddot{\text{O}} : \text{N} : \ddot{\text{O}} :
\end{array}
\right]^-
\longleftrightarrow
\left[
\begin{array}{c}
: \ddot{\text{O}} : \\
: \ddot{\text{O}} :: \text{N} : \ddot{\text{O}} :
\end{array}
\right]^-
\longleftrightarrow
\left[
\begin{array}{c}
: \ddot{\text{O}} : \\
: \ddot{\text{O}} : \text{N} :: \ddot{\text{O}} :
\end{array}
\right]^-
$$

9.13. The number of valence electrons in SF₄ is $6 + (4 \times 7) = 34$. The skeleton structure is a sulfur atom surrounded by fluorine atoms. After the electron pairs are placed on the F atoms to satisfy the octet rule, two electrons remain.

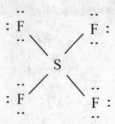

These additional two electrons are put on the sulfur atom because it had *d* orbitals and, therefore, can expand its octet.

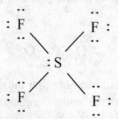

9.14. Be has two valence electrons, and Cl has seven valence electrons. The total number of valence electrons is $2 + (2 \times 7) = 16$ in the BeCl₂ molecule. Be, a Group IIA element, can have fewer than eight electrons around it. The electron-dot formula of BeCl₂ is

$$: \overset{\cdot\cdot}{\underset{\cdot\cdot}{Cl}} : Be : \overset{\cdot\cdot}{\underset{\cdot\cdot}{Cl}} :$$

9.15. The total number of electrons in H₃PO₄ is $3 + 5 + 24 = 32$. Assume a skeleton structure in which the phosphorus atom is surrounded by the more electronegative four oxygen atoms. The hydrogen atoms are then attached to the oxygen atoms. Distribute the electron pairs to the surrounding atoms to satisfy the octet rule. If you assume all single bonds (structure on the left), the formal charge on the phosphorus is 1+ and the formal charge on the top oxygen is 1−. Using the principle of forming a double bond with a pair of electrons on the atom with the negative formal charge, you obtain the structure on the right. The formal charge on all oxygens in this structure is zero; the formal charge on phosphorus is $5 - 5 = 0$. This is the better structure.

9.16. The bond length can be predicted by adding the covalent radii of the two atoms. For O–H, we have 66 pm + 31 pm = 97 pm.

9.17. As the bond order increases, the bond length decreases. Since the C=O is a double bond, we would expect it to be the shorter one, 123 pm.

9.18.

One C=C bond, four C–H bonds, and three O=O bonds are broken. There are four C=O bonds and four O–H bonds formed.

$$\Delta H = \{[614 + (4 \times 413) + (3 \times 498)] - [(4 \times 804) + (4 \times 463)]\} \text{ kJ} = -1308 \text{ kJ}$$

■ ANSWERS TO CONCEPT CHECKS

9.1.　a.　The 2+ ions are common in transition elements, but it is the outer s electrons that are lost to form these ions in compounds. Iron, whose configuration is $[Ar]3d^6 4s^2$, would be expected to lose two $4s$ electrons to give the configuration $[Ar]3d^6$ for the Fe^{2+} ion in compounds. The configuration given in the problem is for an excited state; you would not expect to see it in compounds.

　　b.　Nitrogen, whose ground-state atomic configuration is $[He]2s^2 2p^3$, would be expected to form an anion with a noble-gas configuration by gaining three electrons. This would give the anion N^{3-} with the configuration $[He]2s^2 2p^6$. You would not expect to see the anion N^{2-} in compounds.

　　c.　The zinc atom has the ground-state configuration $[Ar]3d^{10} 4s^2$. The element is often considered to be a transition element. In any case, you would expect the atom to form compounds by losing its $4s$ electrons to give Zn^{2+} with the pseudo-noble-gas configuration $[Ar]3d^{10}$. This is the ion configuration given in the problem.

　　d.　The configuration of the ground-state sodium atom is $[He]2s^2 2p^6 3s^1$. You would expect the atom to lose one electron to give the Na^+ ion with the noble-gas configuration $[He]2s^2 2p^6$. You would not expect to see compounds with the Na^{2+} ion.

　　e.　The ground state of the calcium atom is $[Ne]3s^2 3p^6 4s^2$. You would expect the atom to lose its two outer electrons to give Ca^{2+} with the noble-gas configuration $[Ne]3s^2 3p^6$, which is the configuration given in the problem.

9.2.　a.　There are two basic points to consider in assessing the validity of each of the formulas given in the problem. One is whether the formula has the correct skeleton structure. You expect the F atoms to be bonded to the central N atoms because the F atoms are more electronegative. The second point is the number of dots in the formula. This should equal the total number of electrons in the valence shell of the atoms (five for each nitrogen atom and seven for each fluorine atom), which is $(2 \times 5) + (2 \times 7) = 24$, or twelve pairs. The number showing in the formula here is thirteen, which is incorrect.

　　b.　This formula has the correct skeleton structure and the correct number of dots. All of the atoms have octets, so the formula would appear to be correct. As a final check, however, you might try drawing the formula beginning with the skeleton structure. In drawing an electron-dot formula, after connecting atoms by single bonds (a single electron pair), you would place electron pairs around the outer atoms (the F atoms in this formula) to give octets. After doing that, you would have used up nine electron pairs (three for the single bonds and three for each F atom to fill out its octet). This leaves three pairs, which you might distribute as follows:

$$: \overset{..}{\underset{..}{F}} : \overset{..}{N} : \overset{..}{N} : \overset{..}{\underset{..}{F}} :$$

One of the nitrogen atoms (the one on the right) does not have an octet. The lack of an octet on this atom suggests trying for a double bond. This suggests that you move one of the lone pairs on the left N atom into one of the adjacent bonding regions. Moving this lone pair into the N–N region would give a symmetrical result, whereas moving the lone pair into the F–N region would not. The text notes that the atoms often showing multiple bonds are C, N, O, and S. The formula given here with a nitrogen-nitrogen double bond appears quite reasonable.

c. This formula is similar to the previous one, b, but the double bond is between the F and N atoms. In this case, however, there are 10 electrons around the left F and only 6 electrons around the right N. Both of these violate the octet rule for Period 2 elements. This formula is incorrect.

d. This formula is similar to the one drawn earlier in describing how one would get to the formula in b. The left N atom does not have an octet, which suggests you move a lone pair on the other N atom into the N–N bond region to give a double bond.

e. This formula does not have the correct skeleton structure.

f. This formula has the correct skeleton structure and the correct total number of electron dots, but neither N atom has an octet. In fact, there is no bond between the two N atoms.

9.3. a. This model and corresponding Lewis structure, H:C:::N:, has the expected skeleton structure. (H must be an exterior atom, but either C or N might be in the center; however, you expect the more electropositive, or less electronegative, atom, C, to be in this position). This formula also has the correct number of electron dots ($1 + 4 + 5 = 10$, or 5 pairs). Finally, the formal charge of each atom is zero. Therefore, this model should be an accurate representation of the HCN molecule.

b. This structure has the more electronegative atom, N, in the central position; you don't expect this to be the correct structure. You can also look at this from the point of view of formal charges. This formula has a 1+ charge on the N atom and a 1− charge on the C atom. You would not expect the more electronegative atom to have the positive formal charge. Moreover, the previous formula, a, has zero charges for each atom, which would be preferred.

c. If you draw the Lewis structure, you will see that each atom has an octet, but the formula has too many electron pairs (seven instead of five). You can remove two pairs and still retain octets if you move two lone pairs into the bonding region, to give a triple bond.

d. If you draw the Lewis structure, you will see that each atom has an octet, but the formula has too many electron pairs (six instead of five). You would arrive at a similar conclusion using formal charges. The formal charges are 0 for H, 1− for C, and 1− for N. Since these don't add to 0 in relation to the neutral molecule, the formula must be incorrect.

■ ANSWERS TO SELF-ASSESSMENT AND REVIEW QUESTIONS

9.1. As an Na atom approaches a Cl atom, the outer electron of the Na atom is transferred to the Cl atom. The result is an Na^+ and a Cl^- ion. Positively charged ions attract negatively charged ions, so, finally, the NaCl crystal consists of Na^+ ions surrounded by six Cl^- ions surrounded by six Na^+ ions.

9.2. Ions tend to attract as many ions of opposite charge about them as possible. The result is that ions tend to form crystalline solids rather than molecular substances.

9.3. The energy terms involved in the formation of an ionic solid from atoms are the ionization energy of the metal atom, the electron affinity of the nonmetal atom, and the energy of the attraction of the ions forming the ionic solid. The energy of the solid will be low if the ionization energy of the metal is low, the electron affinity of the nonmetal is high, and the energy of the attraction of the ions is large.

9.4. The lattice energy for potassium bromide is the change in energy that occurs when $KBr(s)$ is separated into isolated $K^+(g)$ and $Br^-(g)$ ions in the gas phase.

$$KBr(s) + \text{lattice energy} \rightarrow K^+(g) + Br^-(g)$$

9.5. A monatomic cation with a charge equal to the group number corresponds to the loss of all valence electrons. This loss of electrons would give a noble-gas configuration, which is especially stable. A monatomic anion with a charge equal to the group number minus eight would have a noble-gas configuration.

9.6. Most of the transition elements have configurations in which the outer s subshell is doubly occupied. These electrons will be lost first, and we might expect each to be lost with almost equal ease, resulting in +2 ions.

9.7. If we assume the ions are spheres that are just touching, the distances between centers of the spheres will be related to the radii of the spheres. For example, in LiI, we assume that the −1 ions are large spheres that are touching. The distance between centers of the I^- ions equals two times the radius of the I^- ion.

9.8. In going across a period, the cations decrease in radius. When we reach the anions, there is an abrupt increase in radius, and then the radii again decrease. Ionic radii increase going down any column of the periodic table.

9.9. As the H atoms approach one another, their $1s$ orbitals begin to overlap. Each electron can then occupy the space around both atoms; that is, the two electrons are shared by the atoms.

9.10.

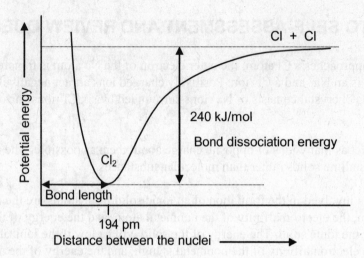

9.11. An example is thionyl chloride, $SOCl_2$:

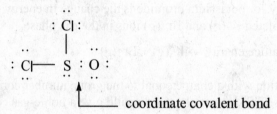

Note that the O atom has eight electrons around it; that is, it has two more electrons than the neutral atom. These two electrons must have come from the S atom. Thus, this bond is a coordinate covalent bond.

9.12. In many atoms of the main-group elements, bonding uses an *s* orbital and the three *p* orbitals of the valence shell. These four orbitals are filled with eight electrons, thus accounting for the octet rule.

9.13. Electronegativity increases from left to right (with the exception of the noble gases) and decreases from top to bottom in the periodic table.

9.14. The absolute difference in the electronegativities of the two atoms in a bond gives a rough measure of the polarity of the bond.

9.15. Resonance is used to describe the electron structure of a molecule in which bonding electrons are delocalized. In a resonance description, the molecule is described in terms of two or more Lewis formulas. If we want to retain Lewis formulas, resonance is required because each Lewis formula assumes that a bonding pair of electrons occupies the region between two atoms. We must imagine that the actual electron structure of the molecule is a composite of all resonance formulas.

9.16. Molecules having an odd number of electrons do not obey the octet rule. An example is nitrogen monoxide, NO. The other exceptions fall into two groups. In one group are molecules with an atom having fewer than eight valence electrons around it. An example is borane, BH_3. In the other group are molecules with an atom having more than eight valence electrons around it. An example is sulfur hexafluoride, SF_6.

9.17.   As the bond order increases, the bond length decreases. For example, the average carbon-carbon single-bond length is 154 pm, whereas the carbon-carbon double-bond length is 134 pm, and the carbon-carbon triple-bond length is 120 pm.

9.18.   Bond enthalpy is the average enthalpy change for the breaking of a bond in a molecule. The enthalpy of a reaction for gaseous reactions can be determined by summing the bond enthalpies of all the bonds that are broken and subtracting the sum of the bond enthalpies of all the bonds that are formed.

9.19.   The answer is a, $BaCO_3$.

9.20.   The answer is e, $S^- > S > S^+$.

9.21.   The answer is d, $1s^2 2s^2 2p^5$.

9.22.   The answer is a, sulfur.

■ ANSWERS TO CONCEPTUAL PROBLEMS

9.25.   Because the compound that forms is a combination of a metal and a nonmetal, we would expect it to be ionic. If we assume that metal atoms tend to lose electrons to obtain filled shells, then the metal atom X would lose three electrons from the $n = 2$ level, forming the X^{3+} cation. We can expect the nonmetal atom Y to gain electrons to obtain a filled shell, so it requires an additional electron to fill the $n = 1$ level, forming the Y^- anion. To produce an ionic compound with an overall charge of zero, the compound formed from these two elements would be XY_3.

9.27.   The smaller atom on the left (yellow) becomes a larger ion on the right, while the larger atom on the left (blue) becomes the smaller ion on the right. Since cations are smaller than their parent atom, and anions are larger than their parent atom, the cation on the right is the smaller ion (blue), and the anion is the larger ion (yellow). Finally, since metals tend to form cations, and nonmetals form anions, the metal on the left is the larger atom (blue), and the nonmetal is the smaller atom (yellow).

9.29.   a.   Incorrect. The atoms in this formula do not obey the octet rule. The formula has the correct number of valence electrons, so this suggests a multiple bond between the N atoms.

    b.   Correct. The central atom is surrounded by more electronegative atoms, as you would expect, and each atom obeys the octet rule.

    c.   Incorrect. The skeleton structure is acceptable (the central atom is surrounded by more electronegative atoms), but you would expect the double bond to be between C and O rather than between C and F (C, N, O, and S form multiple bonds). You would come to this same conclusion using rules of formal charge. (The formula has a formal charge of 1+ on F and 1− on O, whereas you would expect these formal charges to be interchanged, with the negative charge on the F atom, which is more electronegative.)

    d.   Incorrect. The skeleton structure is OK, but the carbon atom has ten valence electrons about it. This suggests that you replace the two carbon-oxygen double bonds by one carbon-oxygen double bond (because there is one extra pair of electrons on the C atom). The most symmetrical location of the double bond uses the oxygen atom not bonded to an H atom. Also, only this formula has zero formal charges on all atoms.

9.31.   a.   To arrive at a skeleton structure, you decide which is the central atom. (It cannot be H). The C atom is less electronegative than the Cl atom, so you place it as the central atom and surround it by the other atoms.

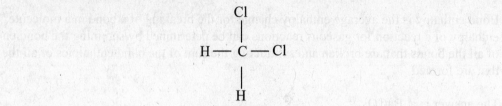

b. HNO_2 is an oxyacid in which O atoms bond to the central atom with the H bonded to O. The central atom must be N (the only other atom), so the skeletal structure is

H—O—N—O

c.   You place the least electronegative atom (N) as the central atom and bond it to the other atoms.

F—N—O

d.   N is less electronegative than O. The most symmetrical structure would be the two N atoms in the center with two O atoms bonded to each N atom.

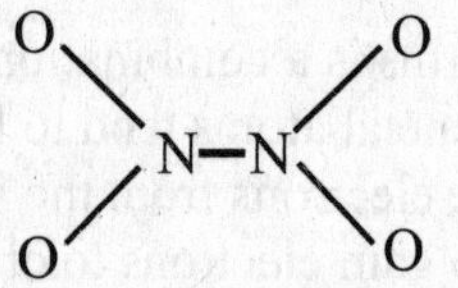

$$\begin{array}{ccc} O & & O \\ \diagdown & & \diagup \\ & N\!-\!N & \\ \diagup & & \diagdown \\ O & & O \end{array}$$

9.33.   a.   In order to be a neutral ionic compound, element X must have a charge of 3−. In an ionic compound, calcium forms the Ca^{2+} cation. The combination of Ca^{2+} and X^{3-} would form the ionic compound with the formula Ca_3X_2.

b.   Since element X formed an ionic compound with sodium metal, it is probably a nonmetal with a high electron affinity. When a nonmetal with a high electron affinity combines with a metal such as calcium, an ionic compound is formed.

■ SOLUTIONS TO PRACTICE PROBLEMS

9.35.   a.   P has the electron configuration $[Ne]3s^2 3p^3$. It has five electrons in its valence shell. The Lewis formula is

$\cdot \overset{\displaystyle \cdot\cdot}{\underset{\displaystyle \cdot}{P}} \cdot$

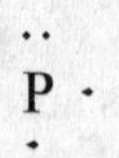

b. P^{3-} has three more valence electrons than P. It now has eight electrons in its valence shell. The Lewis formula is

$\left[\overset{\displaystyle \cdot\cdot}{\underset{\displaystyle \cdot\cdot}{:\, P \,:}} \right]^{3-}$

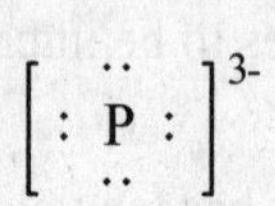

c.   Ga has the electron configuration $[Ar]3d^{10}4s^2 4p^1$. It has three electrons in its valence shell. The Lewis formula is

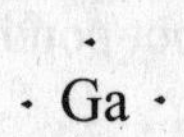

$\cdot\, Ga \,\cdot$

d. Ga^{3+} has three fewer valence electrons than Ga. It now has zero electrons in its valence shell. The Lewis formula is

$$Ga^{3+}$$

9.37.   a.   If the calcium atom loses two electrons, and the bromine atoms gain one electron each, all three atoms will assume noble-gas configurations. This can be represented as follows.

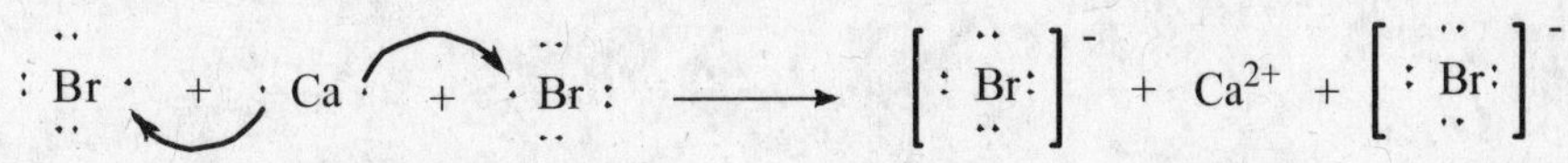

b.   If the potassium atom loses one electron, and the iodine atom gains one electron, both atoms will assume a noble-gas configuration. This can be represented as follows.

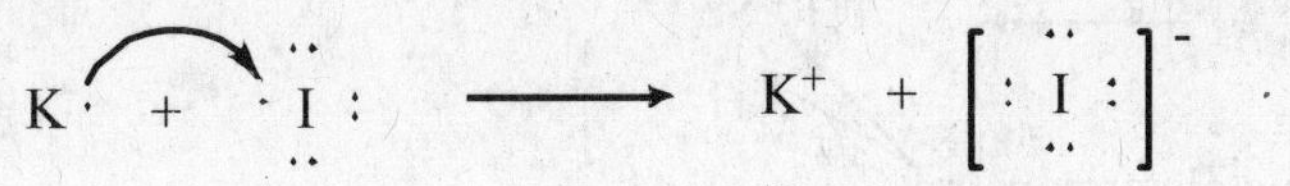

9.39.

a.   As: $1s^2 2s^2 2p^6 3s^2 3p^6 3d^{10} 4s^2 4p^3$

b. As^{3+}: $1s^2 2s^2 2p^6 3s^2 3p^6 3d^{10} 4s^2$

c.   Se: $1s^2 2s^2 2p^6 3s^2 3p^6 3d^{10} 4s^2 4p^4$

d. Se^{2-}: $1s^2 2s^2 2p^6 3s^2 3p^6 3d^{10} 4s^2 4p^6$

9.41.   Bi: $[Xe]4f^{14} 5d^{10} 6s^2 6p^3$

Bi^{3+}:   The three $6p$ electrons are lost from the valence shell.
$[Xe]4f^{14} 5d^{10} 6s^2$

9.43.   The 2+ ion is formed by the loss of electrons from the $4s$ subshell.

Ni^{2+}: $[Ar]3d^8$

The 3+ ion is formed by the loss of electrons from the $4s$ and $3d$ subshells.

Ni^{3+}: $[Ar]3d^7$

9.45.   a. $Sr^{2+} < Sr$

The cation is smaller than the neutral atom because it has lost all its valence electrons; hence, it has one less shell of electrons. The electron-electron repulsion is reduced, so the orbitals shrink because of the increased attraction of the electrons to the nucleus.

b. $Br < Br^-$

The anion is larger than the neutral atom because it has more electrons. The electron-electron repulsion is greater, so the valence orbitals expand to give a larger radius.

9.47. $S^{2-} < Se^{2-} < Te^{2-}$

All have the same number of electrons in the valence shell. The radius increases with the increasing number of filled shells.

9.49. Smallest Na^+ ($Z = 11$), F^- ($Z = 9$), N^{3-} ($Z = 7$) Largest

These ions are isoelectronic. The atomic radius increases with the decreasing nuclear charge (Z).

9.51.

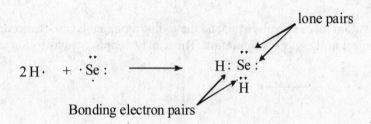

9.53. Arsenic is in Group VA on the periodic table and has five valence electrons. Bromine is in Group VIIA and has seven valence electrons. Arsenic forms three covalent bonds, and bromine forms one covalent bond. Therefore, the simplest compound would be $AsBr_3$.

9.55. a. P, N, O

Electronegativity increases from left to right and from bottom to top in the periodic table.

b. Na, Mg, Al

Electronegativity increases from left to right within a period.

c. Al, Si, C

Electronegativity increases from left to right and from bottom to top in the periodic table.

9.57. $X_O - X_P = 3.5 - 2.1 = 1.4$

$X_{Cl} - X_C = 3.0 - 2.5 = 0.5$

$X_{Br} - X_{As} = 2.8 - 2.0 = 0.8$

The bonds arranged by increasing difference in electronegativity are C–Cl, As–Br, P–O.

9.59. The atom with the greater electronegativity has the partial negative charge.

a. P – O

    δ+   δ–

b. C – Cl

    δ+   δ–

c. As – Br

    δ+   δ–

9.61.   a.   Total number of valence electrons = 7 + 7 = 14. Br–Br is the skeleton. Distribute the remaining 12 electrons.

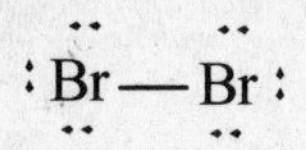

$$:\ddot{Br}\!-\!\ddot{Br}:$$

b.   Total valence electrons = (2 × 1) + 6 = 8. The skeleton is H–Se–H. Distribute the remaining 4 electrons.

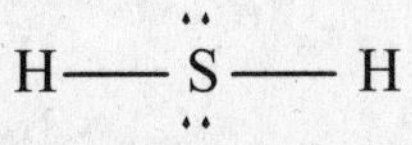

$$H\!-\!\ddot{S}\!-\!H$$

c.   Total valence electrons = (3 × 7) + 5 = 26. The skeleton is on the left below; after distributing the remaining 20 electrons the structure on the right results.

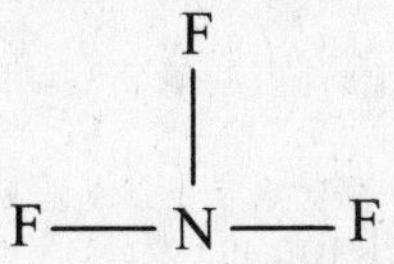

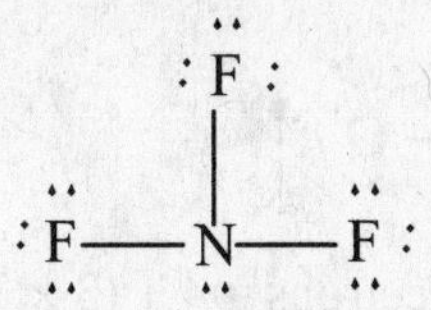

9.63.   a.   Total valence electrons = 2 × 5 = 10. The skeleton is P–P. Distribute the remaining electrons symmetrically:

$$:\ddot{P}\!-\!\ddot{P}:$$

Neither P atom has an octet. There are 4 fewer electrons than needed. This suggests the presence of a triple bond. Make one lone pair from each P a bonding pair.

$$:P\!\equiv\!P:$$

b.   Total valence electrons = 4 + 6 + (2 × 7) = 24. The skeleton is

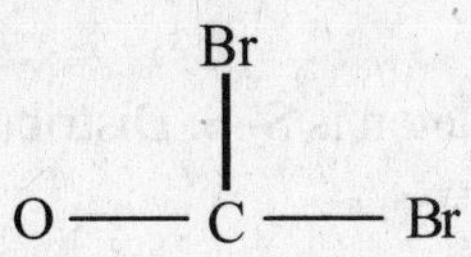

$$
\begin{array}{c}
Br \\
| \\
O\!-\!C\!-\!Br
\end{array}
$$

Distribute the remaining 18 electrons.

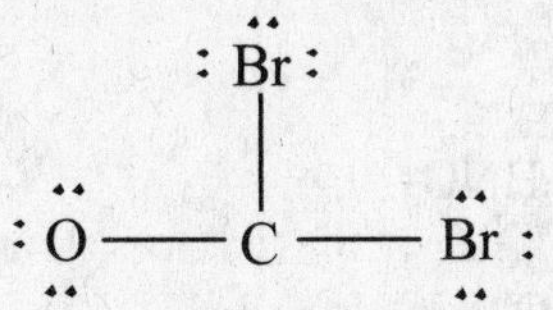

$$
\begin{array}{c}
:\ddot{Br}: \\
| \\
:\ddot{O}\!-\!C\!-\!\ddot{Br}:
\end{array}
$$

Note that carbon is two electrons short of an octet. This suggests the presence of a double bond. The most likely double bond is between C and O.

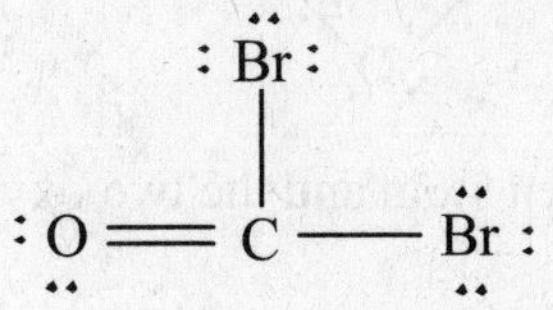

$$
\begin{array}{c}
:\ddot{Br}: \\
| \\
:\ddot{O}\!=\!C\!-\!\ddot{Br}:
\end{array}
$$

c.   Total valence electrons = $1 + 5 + (2 \times 6) = 18$. The skeleton is most likely H–O–N–O. Distribute the remaining 12 electrons:

$$H \underline{\quad} \overset{\cdot\cdot}{\underset{\cdot\cdot}{O}} \underline{\quad} N \underline{\quad} \overset{\cdot\cdot}{\underset{\cdot\cdot}{O}} \colon$$

Note that the N atom does not have an octet. It is two electrons short. The double bond resulting in the lowest formal charges is between N and the end O.

$$H \underline{\quad} \overset{\cdot\cdot}{\underset{\cdot\cdot}{O}} \underline{\quad} \overset{\cdot\cdot}{N} = \overset{\cdot\cdot}{O} \colon$$

9.65.   a.   Total valence electrons = $7 + 6 + 1 = 14$. The skeleton is Cl–O. Distribute the remaining 12 electrons.

$$\left[\colon\!\overset{\cdot\cdot}{\underset{\cdot\cdot}{Cl}} \underline{\quad} \overset{\cdot\cdot}{\underset{\cdot\cdot}{O}} \colon \right]^{-}$$

b.   Total valence electrons = $4 + (3 \times 7) + 1 = 26$. The skeleton is

$$\begin{array}{c} Cl \\ | \\ Cl \underline{\quad} Sn \underline{\quad} Cl \end{array}$$

Distribute the remaining 20 electrons so that each atom has an octet.

$$\left[\begin{array}{c} \colon\!\overset{\cdot\cdot}{Cl}\!\colon \\ | \\ \colon\!\overset{\cdot\cdot}{\underset{\cdot\cdot}{Cl}} \underline{\quad} Sn \underline{\quad} \overset{\cdot\cdot}{\underset{\cdot\cdot}{Cl}}\!\colon \end{array} \right]^{-}$$

c.   Total valence electrons = $(2 \times 6) + 2 = 14$. The skeleton is S–S. Distribute the remaining 12 electrons.

$$\left[\colon\!\overset{\cdot\cdot}{\underset{\cdot\cdot}{S}} \underline{\quad} \overset{\cdot\cdot}{\underset{\cdot\cdot}{S}} \colon \right]^{2-}$$

9.67.   a.   There are two possible resonance structures for HNO_3.

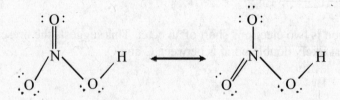

One electron pair is delocalized over the nitrogen atom and the two oxygen atoms.

b.   There are three possible resonance structures for SO₃.

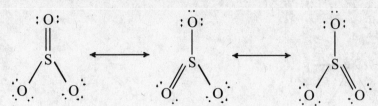

One pair of electrons is delocalized over the region of the three sulfur-oxygen bonds.

9.69.

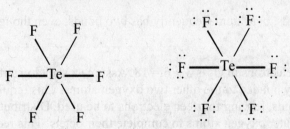

One pair of electrons is delocalized over the O–N–O bonds.

9.71.   a.   Total valence electrons = 8 + (2 × 7) = 22. The skeleton is F–Xe–F. Place six electrons around each fluorine atom to satisfy its octet.

$$: \ddot{F} \!-\!\!- Xe \!-\!\!- \ddot{F} :$$

There are three electron pairs remaining. Place them on the xenon atom.

$$: \ddot{F} \!-\!\!- \ddot{Xe} \!-\!\!- \ddot{F} :$$

b.   Total valence electrons = 6 + (4 × 7) = 34. The skeleton is below left; 24 electrons are then distributed to the F atoms with the last 2 electrons placed on the central Se atom (at right).

$$\begin{array}{c} F \\ | \\ F \!-\!\!- Se \!-\!\!- F \\ | \\ F \end{array}$$

$$\begin{array}{c} :\ddot{F}: \\ | \\ :\ddot{F} \!-\!\!- \ddot{Se} \!-\!\!- \ddot{F}: \\ | \\ :\ddot{F}: \end{array}$$

c.   Total valence electrons = 6 + (6 × 7) = 48. The skeleton is below left. The structure on the right results after the remaining 36 electrons are distributed to the fluorine atoms.

$$\begin{array}{c} F \quad\quad F \\ \diagdown \;\; \diagup \\ F \!-\!\!- Te \!-\!\!- F \\ \diagup \;\; \diagdown \\ F \quad\quad F \end{array}$$

$$\begin{array}{c} :\ddot{F}: \quad :\ddot{F}: \\ \diagdown \;\; \diagup \\ :\ddot{F} \!-\!\!- Te \!-\!\!- \ddot{F}: \\ \diagup \;\; \diagdown \\ :\ddot{F}: \quad :\ddot{F}: \end{array}$$

d.   Total valence electrons = $8 + (5 \times 7) - 1 = 42$. The skeleton is

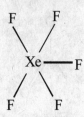

Use 30 of the remaining 32 electrons on the fluorine atoms to complete their octets. The remaining 2 electrons form a lone pair on the central Xe atom.

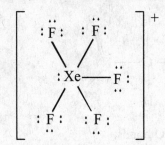

9.73.   a.   Total valence electrons = $3 + (3 \times 7) = 24$. The skeleton is below left. Distribute the remaining 18 electrons to the Cl atoms to get the structure on the right. Although boron has only 6 electrons, it has the normal number of covalent bonds.

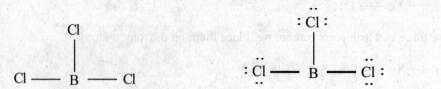

b.   Total valence electrons = $3 + (2 \times 7) - 1 = 16$. The skeleton is Cl–Tl–Cl. Distribute the remaining 12 electrons.

$$\left[\; :\overset{..}{\underset{..}{Cl}} \text{ —— } Tl \text{ —— } \overset{..}{\underset{..}{Cl}}: \; \right]^{+}$$

Tl has only 4 electrons around it.

c.   Total valence electrons = $2 + (2 \times 7) = 16$. The skeleton is Br–Be–Br. Distribute the remaining 12 electrons.

$$:\overset{..}{\underset{..}{Br}} \text{ —— } Be \text{ —— } \overset{..}{\underset{..}{Br}}:$$

In covalent compounds, beryllium frequently has two bonds, even though it does not have an octet.

9.75.   a.   The total number of electrons in O_3 is $3 \times 6 = 18$. Assume a skeleton structure in which one oxygen atom is singly bonded to the other two oxygen atoms. This requires four electrons for the two single bonds, leaving fourteen electrons to be used. Distribute three electron pairs to each of the outer oxygen atoms to complete their octets. This requires twelve more electrons, leaving two electrons to distribute. Since this is two electrons short of an octet, move a pair of electrons from one of the outer oxygen atoms to give an oxygen-oxygen double bond. One of the possible resonance structures is shown below; the other structure would have the double bond written between the left and central oxygen atoms.

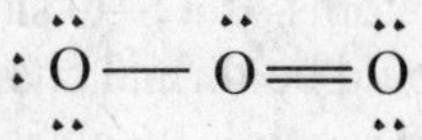

$$: \overset{..}{\underset{..}{O}} \!\!-\!\! \overset{..}{O} \!\!=\!\! \overset{..}{\underset{..}{O}}$$

Starting with the left oxygen, the formal charge of this oxygen is $6 - 1 - 6 = -1$. The formal charge of just the central oxygen is $6 - 3 - 2 = +1$. The formal charge of the right oxygen is $6 - 2 - 4 = 0$. The sum of all three is 0.

b. The total number of electrons in CO is $4 + 6 = 10$. Assume a skeleton structure in which the oxygen atom is singly bonded to the carbon atom. This requires two electrons for the single bond and leaves eight electrons. Distribute these remaining electrons around the atoms. Since four more electrons are needed to complete octets on both atoms, move two electron pairs to give a carbon-oxygen triple bond.

The structure is

$$: C \!\equiv\! O :$$

The formal charge of the carbon is $4 - 3 - 2 = -1$. The formal charge of the oxygen is $6 - 3 - 2 = +1$. The sum of both is 0.

c. The total number of electrons in HNO_3 is $1 + 5 + 18 = 24$. Assume a skeleton structure in which the nitrogen atom is singly bonded to two oxygen atoms and doubly bonded to one oxygen. This requires two electrons for the O–H single bond and leaves eight electrons to be used for the N bonds.

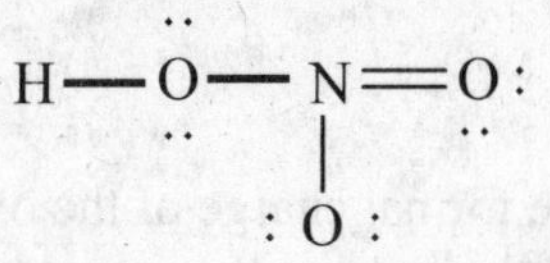

$$H \!-\! \overset{..}{\underset{..}{O}} \!-\! \underset{\displaystyle \underset{..}{\overset{|}{\underset{..}{O}}}}{N} \!\!=\!\! \overset{..}{\underset{..}{O}} :$$

The formal charge of the nitrogen is $5 - 4 - 0 = +1$. The formal charge of the hydrogen is $1 - 1 - 0 = 0$. The formal charge of the oxygen bonded to the hydrogen is $6 - 2 - 4 = 0$. The formal charge of the other singly bonded oxygen is $6 - 1 - 6 = -1$. The formal charge of the doubly bonded oxygen is $6 - 2 - 4 = 0$.

9.77. a. The total number of electrons in SOF_2 is $6 + 6 + 14 = 26$. Assume a skeleton structure in which the sulfur atom is singly bonded to the two fluorine atoms. If a S–O single bond is assumed, 26 electrons are needed. However, there would be formal charges of +1 on the sulfur and −1 on the oxygen. Using a S=O double bond requires only 26 electrons and results in zero formal charge.

$$: \overset{..}{\underset{..}{F}} \!-\! \underset{\displaystyle \underset{..}{\overset{\|}{\underset{..}{O}}}}{S} \!-\! \overset{..}{\underset{..}{F}} :$$

The formal charge on each of the two fluorine atoms is $7 - 1 - 6 = 0$. The formal charge on the oxygen is $6 - 2 - 4 = 0$. The formal charge on the sulfur is $6 - 4 - 2 = 0$.

b.   The total number of electrons in H_2SO_3 is $2 + 6 + 18 = 26$. Assume a skeleton structure in which the sulfur atom is singly bonded to the three oxygen atoms. Then form single bonds from the two hydrogen atoms to each of two oxygen atoms. If a S–O single bond is assumed, 26 electrons are needed. However, there would be formal charges of +1 on the sulfur and −1 on the oxygen. A S=O double bond also requires 26 electrons but results in zero formal charge on all atoms.

$$H—\overset{\cdot\cdot}{\underset{\cdot\cdot}{O}}—\overset{\cdot\cdot}{S}—\overset{\cdot\cdot}{\underset{\cdot\cdot}{O}}—H$$
$$\overset{\|}{\underset{:\,O\,:}{}}$$

The formal charge of each hydrogen is $1 − 1 = 0$. The formal charge of each oxygen bonded to a hydrogen is $6 − 2 − 4 = 0$. The formal charge of the oxygen doubly bonded to the sulfur is $6 − 2 − 4 = 0$. The formal charge of the sulfur is $6 − 4 − 2 = 0$.

c.   The total number of electrons in $HClO_2$ is $1 + 7 + 12 = 20$. Assume a skeleton structure in which the chlorine atom is singly bonded to the two oxygen atoms, and the hydrogen is singly bonded to one of the oxygen atoms. If all Cl–O single bonds are assumed, 20 electrons are needed, but the chlorine exhibits a formal charge of +1 and one oxygen exhibits a formal charge of −1.

Hence, a pair of electrons on the oxygen without the hydrogen is used to form a Cl=O double bond.

$$H—\overset{\cdot\cdot}{\underset{\cdot\cdot}{O}}—\overset{\cdot\cdot}{Cl}:$$
$$\overset{\|}{\underset{:\,O\,:}{}}$$

The formal charge of hydrogen is $1 − 1 = 0$. The formal charge of the oxygen bonded to hydrogen is $6 − 2 − 4 = 0$. The formal charge of the oxygen that is not bonded to the hydrogen is $6 − 2 − 4 = 0$. The formal charge of the chlorine is $7 − 3 − 4 = 0$.

9.79. $r_F = 57$ pm

$r_P = 107$ pm

$d_{P–F} = r_F + r_P = 57\ \text{pm} + 107\ \text{pm} = 164\ \text{pm}$

9.81.   a. $d_{C–H} = r_C + r_H = 76\ \text{pm} + 31\ \text{pm} = 107\ \text{pm}$

b. $d_{S–Cl} = r_S + r_{Cl} = 105\ \text{pm} + 102\ \text{pm} = 207\ \text{pm}$

c. $d_{Br–Cl} = r_{Br} + r_{Cl} = 120\ \text{pm} + 102\ \text{pm} = 222\ \text{pm}$

d. $d_{Si–O} = r_{Si} + r_O = 111\ \text{pm} + 66\ \text{pm} = 177\ \text{pm}$
The calculated bond distances agree very well with the experimental values.

9.83.   Methylamine   147 pm   Single C–N bond is longer.

Acetonitrile   116 pm   Triple C–N bond is shorter.

9.85.

In the reaction, a C=C double bond is converted to a C–C single bond. An H–Br bond is broken, and one C–H bond and one C–Br bond are formed.

$$\Delta H \cong BE(\text{C=C}) + BE(\text{H–Br}) - BE(\text{C–C}) - BE(\text{C–H}) - BE(\text{C–Br})$$

$$= (614 + 366 - 348 - 413 - 276) \text{ kJ} = -57 \text{ kJ}$$

■ SOLUTIONS TO GENERAL PROBLEMS

9.87.　a.　Strontium is a metal, and oxygen is a nonmetal. The binary compound is likely to be ionic. Strontium, in Group IIA, forms Sr^{2+} ions; oxygen, from Group VIA, forms O^{2-} ions. The binary compound has the formula SrO and is named strontium oxide.

　　b.　Carbon and bromine are both nonmetals; hence, the binary compound is likely to be covalent. Carbon usually forms four bonds, and bromine usually forms one bond. The formula for binary compound is CBr_4. It is called carbon tetrabromide.

　　c.　Gallium is a metal, and fluorine is a nonmetal. The binary compound is likely to be ionic. Gallium is in Group IIIA and forms Ga^{3+} ions. Fluorine is in Group VIIA and forms F^- ions. The binary compound is GaF_3 and is named gallium(III) fluoride.

　　d.　Nitrogen and bromine are both nonmetals; hence, the binary compound is likely to be covalent. Nitrogen usually forms three bonds, and bromine usually forms one bond. The formula for the binary compound is NBr_3. It is called nitrogen tribromide.

9.89.　Total valence electrons = $6 + (3 \times 6) + 2 = 26$. The skeleton is

Distribute the remaining 20 electrons to complete the octets of oxygen and selenium atoms.

The formula for aluminum selenite is $Al_2(SeO_3)_3$.

9.91.   Total valence electrons = $1 + 7 + (3 \times 6) = 26$. The skeleton is

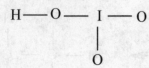

Distribute the remaining 18 electrons to satisfy the octet rule. The structure on the right has no formal charge.

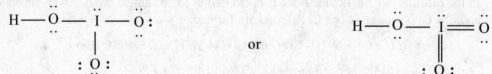 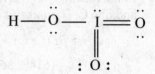

9.93.   Total valence electrons = $5 + (2 \times 1) + 1 = 8$. The skeleton is H–N–H. Distribute the remaining 4 electrons to complete the octet of the nitrogen atom.

$$\left[H \underset{\cdot\cdot}{\overset{\cdot\cdot}{—N—}} H \right]^{-}$$

9.95.   Total valence electrons = $5 + (2 \times 6) - 1 = 16$. The skeleton is O–N–O. Distribute the remaining electrons on the oxygen atoms.

$$: \overset{\cdot\cdot}{\underset{\cdot\cdot}{O}} — N — \overset{\cdot\cdot}{\underset{\cdot\cdot}{O}} :$$

The nitrogen atom is short four electrons. Use two double bonds, one with each oxygen.

$$\left[: \overset{\cdot\cdot}{O} = N = \overset{\cdot\cdot}{O} : \right]^{+}$$

9.97.

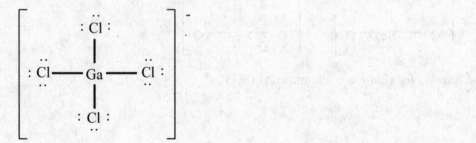

a.

b.

c.

d. 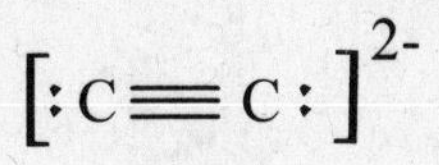 $$\left[: C \equiv C :\right]^{2-}$$

9.99.   a.   Total valence electrons = 5 + (3 × 7) = 26. The skeleton is

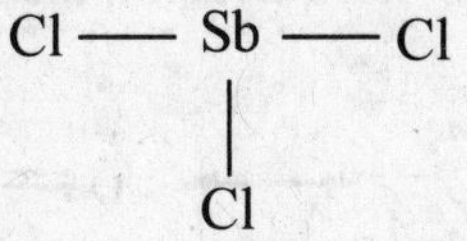

$$Cl — Sb — Cl$$
$$|$$
$$Cl$$

Distribute the remaining 20 electrons to the chlorine atoms and the antimony atom to complete their octets.

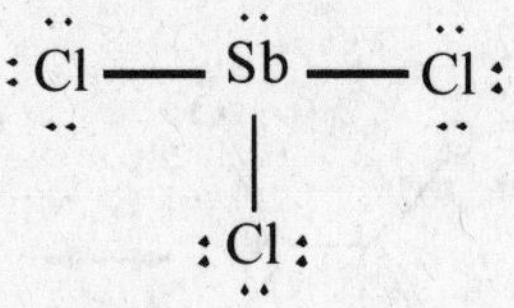

$$: \ddot{C}l — \ddot{S}b — \ddot{C}l :$$
$$|$$
$$: \ddot{C}l :$$

b.   Total valence electrons = 7 + 4 + 5 = 16. The skeleton is I–C–N. Distribute the remaining 12 electrons.

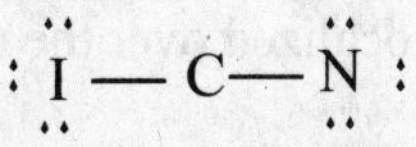

$$: \ddot{I} — C — \ddot{N} :$$

Notice the carbon atom is four electrons short of an octet. Make a triple bond between C and N from four nonbonding electrons on the nitrogen.

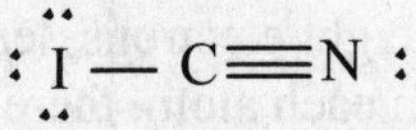

$$: \ddot{I} — C \equiv N :$$

c.   Total valence electrons = 7 + (3 × 7) = 28. The skeleton is

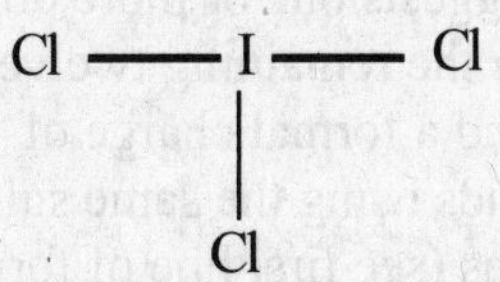

$$Cl — I — Cl$$
$$|$$
$$Cl$$

Distribute 18 of the remaining 22 electrons to complete the octets of the chlorine atoms. The 4 remaining electrons form two sets of lone pairs on the central iodine atom.

$$: \ddot{C}l — \ddot{I} — \ddot{C}l :$$
$$|$$
$$: \ddot{C}l :$$

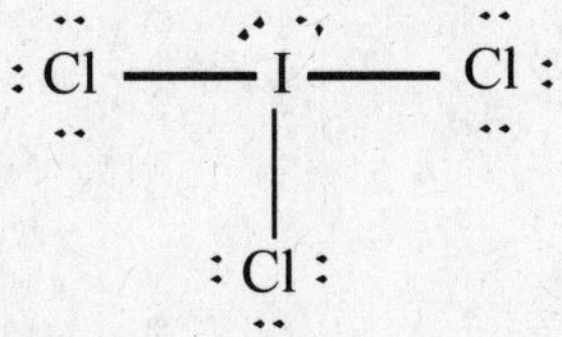

d.   Total valence electrons = 7 + (5 × 7) = 42. The skeleton is below left. Use 30 of the remaining 32 electrons to complete the octets of the F atoms. The 2 electrons remaining form a lone pair on the central iodine atom (structure on right):

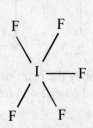

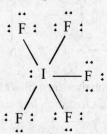

9.101. a. One possible electron-dot structure is

$$: O = Se - O :$$

Because the selenium-oxygen bonds are expected to be equivalent, the structure must be described in resonance terms.

$$: O = Se - O : \longleftrightarrow : O - Se = O : \longleftrightarrow : O = Se = O :$$

The electrons are delocalized over the selenium atom and the two oxygen atoms.

b. The possible electron-dot structures are

At each end of the molecule, a pair of electrons is delocalized over the region of the nitrogen atom and the two oxygen atoms.

9.103. The compound S_2N_2 will have a four-membered ring structure. Calculate the total number of valence electrons of sulfur and nitrogen, which will be $6 + 6 + 5 + 5 = 22$. Writing the skeleton of the four-membered ring with single S–N bonds will use up eight electrons, leaving fourteen electrons for electron pairs. After writing an electron pair on each atom, there will be six electrons left for three electron pairs. No matter where these electrons are written, either a nitrogen or a sulfur will be left with less than eight electrons. This suggests one or more double bonds are needed. If only one S=N double bond is written, writing the remaining twelve electrons as six electron pairs will give the sulfur in the S=N double bond a formal charge of 1+ (see second line of formulas on next page). Writing two S=N double bonds using the same sulfur for both double bonds will give a formal charge of zero for all four atoms (see first line of formulas). The first two resonance formulas below have a zero formal charge on all atoms. However, one of the sulfur atoms does not obey the octet rule.

In the four resonance formulas at the bottom, all of the atoms obey the octet rule, but there is a positive formal charge on one sulfur atom and a negative formal charge on one nitrogen atom.

9.105.   The possible electron-dot structures are

Because double bonds are shorter, the terminal N–O bonds that resonate between single and double bonds are 118 pm, and the central N–O single bonds are 136 pm.

9.107. $\Delta H = BE(\text{H–H}) + BE(\text{O=O}) - 2BE(\text{H–O}) - BE(\text{O–O}) = (436 + 498 - 2 \times 463 - 146)$ kJ
   $= -138$ kJ

9.109. $\Delta H = BE(\text{N=N}) + BE(\text{F–F}) - BE(\text{N–N}) - 2BE(\text{N–F}) = (418 + 159 - 163 - 2 \times 272)$ kJ $= -130.$ kJ

9.111.   Ionic materials like NaCl are solids at room temperature, with high melting points. The molten liquid, which is clear, is very corrosive. Ionic materials consist of small, spherical ions that pack closely together. Thus, the ions interact strongly, giving a solid with a high melting point. Room-temperature ionic liquids, which are also clear, consist of large, nonspherical cations with various anions. The large, bulky cation keeps the ions from packing closely, yielding a substance with weak interactions and a low melting point.

9.113.   The decomposition of nitroglycerin (see page 350) is given by

$$4C_3H_5(ONO_2)_3(l) \rightarrow 6N_2(g) + 12CO_2(g) + 10H_2O(g) + O_2(g)$$

The stability of the products results from their strong bonds, which are much stronger than those in nitroglycerin. In particular, nitrogen has a strong nitrogen-nitrogen triple bond and carbon dioxide has two strong carbon-oxygen double bonds.

9.115.   A chemical bond acts like a stiff spring connecting nuclei in a molecule that vibrate relative to each other. The vibration of molecules is revealed in their absorption of infrared radiation. The frequency of radiation absorbed equals the frequencies of nuclear vibrations.

■ SOLUTIONS TO STRATEGY PROBLEMS

9.117.   Structure a is incorrect. Al^{3+} ion has zero valence electrons. The rest are valid Lewis structures.

9.119.

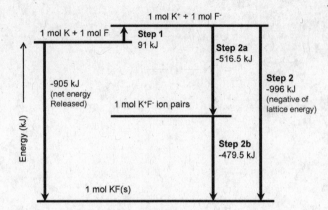

Step 1 $= E_{ionization} + E.A. = 419$ kJ/mol $+ (-328)$ kJ/mol $= 91$ kJ/mol

Step 2a $= E_{ion\ pair\ formation} = -516.5$ kJ/mol (by way of Coulomb's law given on page 338 and using ionic radii for K^+ and F^- found in Table 9.3 (see problem 9.124 below example calculation)

Step 2b $= E_{ion\ pair\ solidification} = -(|\Delta H_f^o(KF)| + $ Step 1 $- |$Step 2a$|) = -479.5$ kJ/mol

The sublimation energy for $K(s) \rightarrow K(g)$ is obtained directly from Appendix C. It is the standard heat of formation of $K(g)$, or 89.00 kJ/mol.

9.121. Both a (Ar) and d (Cl^-) are isoelectronic with the potassium ion, K^+. The electron configuration in each of these cases is $[Ne]3s^23p^6$.

9.123. a. Cl^- b. Ca^+ c. Ni^{2+} d. Ge^{2+} e. Br^-

9.125. $X_F - X_{Sr} = 4.0 - 1.0 = 3.0$

$X_F - X_{Sn} = 4.0 - 1.8 = 2.2$

The difference in electronegativities is higher in SrF_2. Thus, SrF_2 would be expected to be more ionic than SnF_2. Because ionic compounds are usually characterized with high melting points, the substantially lower melting point given in the problem statement likely corresponds to the melting point of SnF_2(tin(II) fluoride).

9.127. Only b (CO_2) contains only double bonds.

9.129. If M is Fe, then the electron configuration of X is $[Ar]3d^{10}4s^24p^4$. If M is Co, the electron configuration of X is exactly the same as for iron.

9.131. Total valence electrons $= (3 \times 1) + 5 + (4 \times 6) = 32$. The skeleton is

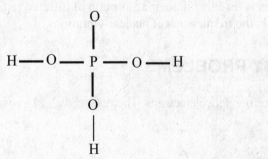

Distribute the remaining 18 electrons to satisfy the octet rule. The formula on the left below has the central phosphorus atom with a formal charge of 1+ and the top oxygen atom with a formal charge of 1−. (Each of the other atoms have zero formal charge.) By moving one lone pair from the top oxygen into a bonding position with the central phosphorus atom which can accommodate an expanded octet, the formula on the right results. Because all of the atoms in the formula on the right have zero formal charges, this formula most closely approximates the actual electron distribution in phosphoric acid.

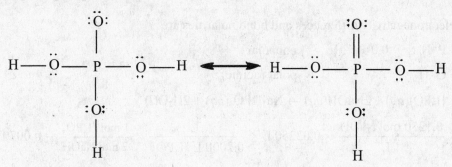

9.133. The reaction is $X_2 + Y_2 \rightarrow 2XY$. The enthalpy of the reaction is

$$\Delta H°_{rxn} = 2\Delta H°_f[XY] - \Delta H°_f[X_2] - \Delta H°_f[Y_2] = 2\Delta H°_f[XY] - 0 - 0 = 2\Delta H°_f[XY]$$

Bonding energies can also be used to approximate the enthalpy of the reaction as follows:

$$\Delta H°_{rxn} \cong BE[X–X] + BE[Y–Y] - 2BE[X–Y]$$

Combining the two reaction enthalpy expressions gives

$$2\Delta H°_f[XY] = BE[X–X] + BE[Y–Y] - 2BE[X–Y]$$

$$BE[X–Y] = \frac{BE[X-X] + BE[Y-Y] - 2\Delta H°_f[XY]}{2 \text{ mol}} = \frac{414 \text{ kJ} + 159 \text{ kJ} - 2(-336 \text{ kJ})}{2 \text{ mol}}$$

$$BE[X–Y] = 62\underline{2}.5 = 623 \text{ kJ/mol}$$

9.135. The total number of electrons in HONO is $1 + (2 \times 6) + 5 = 18$. Assume a skeleton structure as given in the problem statement in which the nitrogen atom is bonded between the oxygen atoms and the hydrogen atom is bonded to an oxygen atom. This skeleton structure uses requires 6 electrons. To satisfy the octet on the N and O atoms, 14 electrons are required. However, only 12 electrons remain to be distributed. Therefore a double bond is required between the central N atom and one of the oxygen atoms. The two possible formulas are as follows:

$$\text{H}-\ddot{\text{O}}-\text{N}=\ddot{\text{O}} \longleftrightarrow \text{H}-\ddot{\text{O}}=\text{N}-\ddot{\text{O}}:$$
$$\phantom{\text{H}-}146 \quad 120 \qquad\qquad\qquad \oplus \qquad\quad \ominus$$
$$\phantom{\text{H}-}\text{pm} \quad \text{pm}$$

Each of the atoms in the left formula have formula charges equal to zero. The formula on the right has the left-most O atom carrying a formal charge of 1+ and the right-most O atom carrying a formal charge of 1−. Thus, based on formal charges, the formula on the left likely approximates the electron distribution in HONO. Because double bonds are shorter than single bonds, the N=O double bond on the right is assigned the experimental bond length of 120 pm and the O−N single bond on the left is assigned the experimental bond length of 146 pm.

■ SOLUTIONS TO CUMULATIVE-SKILLS PROBLEMS

Note on significant figures: The final answer to each cumulative-skills problem is given first with one nonsignificant figure (the rightmost significant figure is underlined) and then is rounded to the correct number of figures. Intermediate answers usually also have at least one nonsignificant figure. Atomic weights, except for that of hydrogen, are rounded to two decimal places.

9.137. The electronegativity differences and bond polarities are

P–H   0.0   nonpolar

O–H   1.4   polar (acidic)

$H_3PO_3(aq) + 2NaOH(aq) \rightarrow Na_2HPO_3(aq) + 2H_2O(l)$

$$\frac{0.1250 \text{ mol NaOH}}{1 \text{ L}} \times 0.02250 \text{ L} \times \frac{1}{0.2000 \text{ L } H_3PO_3} \times \frac{1 \text{ mol } H_3PO_3}{2 \text{ mol NaOH}} = 0.0070312$$

$$= 0.007031 \ M \ H_3PO_3$$

9.139. After assuming a 100.0-g sample, convert to moles:

$$10.9 \text{ g Mg} \times \frac{1 \text{ mol Mg}}{24.3 \text{ g Mg}} = 0.4485 \text{ mol Mg}$$

$$31.8 \text{ g Cl} \times \frac{1 \text{ mol Cl}}{35.453 \text{ g Cl}} = 0.89696 \text{ mol Cl}$$

$$57.3 \text{ g O} \times \frac{1 \text{ mol O}}{16.00 \text{ g O}} = 3.581 \text{ mol O}$$

Divide by 0.4485:

$$\text{Mg: } \frac{0.4485}{0.4485} = 1; \text{ Cl: } \frac{0.89696}{0.4485} = 2.00; \text{ O: } \frac{3.581}{0.4485} = 7.98$$

The simplest formula is $MgCl_2O_8$. However, since $Cl_2O_8^{2-}$ is not a well-known ion, write the simplest formula as $Mg(ClO_4)_2$, magnesium perchlorate. The Lewis formulas are Mg^{2+} and

9.141. After assuming a 100.0-g sample, convert to moles:

$$25.0 \text{ g C} \times \frac{1 \text{ mol C}}{12.01 \text{ g C}} = 2.0\underline{8}1 \text{ mol C}$$

$$2.1 \text{ g H} \times \frac{1 \text{ mol H}}{1.008 \text{ g H}} = 2.\underline{0}8 \text{ mol H}$$

$$39.6 \text{ g F} \times \frac{1 \text{ mol F}}{18.99 \text{ g F}} = 2.0\underline{8}5 \text{ mol F}$$

$$33.3 \text{ g O} \times \frac{1 \text{ mol O}}{16.00 \text{ g O}} = 2.0\underline{8}1 \text{ mol O}$$

The simplest formula is CHOF. Because the molecular mass of 48.0 divided by the formula mass of 48.0 is one, the molecular formula is also CHOF. The Lewis formula is

9.143. First, calculate the number of moles in one liter:

$$n = \frac{PV}{RT} = \frac{1.00 \text{ atm} \times 1.00 \text{ L}}{0.0821 \text{ L} \cdot \text{atm/ (K} \cdot \text{mol)} \times 424 \text{ K}} = 0.028\underline{7}27 \text{ mol}$$

$$MW = \frac{\text{g}}{\text{mol}} = \frac{7.49 \text{ g}}{0.028727 \text{ mol}} = 26\underline{0}.7 \text{ g/mol}$$

$$MW = 26\underline{0}.7 \text{ amu} = 118.71 \text{ amu Sn} + n \times (35.453 \text{ amu Cl})$$

$$n = \frac{260.7 - 118.71}{35.453} = 4.0\underline{0}50$$

The formula is $SnCl_4$. It is molecular because the electronegativity difference between Sn and Cl is 1.3, and because it is a liquid, and is volatile at 151°C. The Lewis formula is

9.145.

$$HCN(g) \quad \rightarrow \quad H(g) \; + \; C(g) \; + \; N(g)$$

(135.1 218.0 716.7 472.7) ΔH_f (kJ/mol)

ΔH_{rxn} = 1272.3 kJ/mol

$BE(C \equiv N$) = ΔH_{rxn} − BE(C–H) = [1272.3 − 411] kJ/mol = 86$\underline{1}$.3

= 861 kJ/mol (Table 9.5 has 891 kJ/mol.)

9.147. Use the O–H bond and its bond enthalpy of 463 kJ/mol to calculate X_O.

$$BE(O\text{–}H) = 1/2[BE(H\text{–}H) + BE(O\text{–}O)] + k(X_O − X_H)^2$$

463 kJ/mol = 1/2(436 kJ/mol + 146 kJ/mol) + 98.6 kJ $(X_O − X_H)^2$

Collecting the terms gives

$$\frac{463 - 291}{98.6} = (X_O − X_H)^2$$

Taking the square root of both sides gives

1.3$\underline{2}$1 = 1.32 = $(X_O − X_H)$

Assuming X_H = 2.1, X_O = 2.1 + 1.32 = 3.$\underline{4}$2 = 3.4.

9.149. $X = \dfrac{\text{I.E.} + \text{E.A.}}{2} = \dfrac{[1251 + 349] \text{ kJ/mol}}{2} = 800.0$ kJ/mol

$\dfrac{800.0 \text{ kJ/mol}}{2\underline{3}0 \text{ kJ/mol}} = 3.\underline{4}7 = 3.5$ (Pauling's X = 3.0)

CHAPTER 10

Molecular Geometry and Chemical Bonding Theory

■ SOLUTIONS TO EXERCISES

10.1.   a.   A Lewis structure of ClO_3^- is

$$
\left[
\begin{array}{c}
: \overset{..}{O} : \\
| \\
: \overset{..}{\underset{..}{O}} - \underset{..}{Cl} - \overset{..}{\underset{..}{O}} :
\end{array}
\right]^{-}
$$

There are four electron pairs in a tetrahedral arrangement about the central atom. Three pairs are bonding, and one pair is nonbonding. The expected geometry is trigonal pyramidal.

b.   The Lewis structure of OF_2 is

$$: \overset{..}{\underset{..}{F}} - \overset{..}{\underset{..}{O}} - \overset{..}{\underset{..}{F}} :$$

There are four electron pairs in a tetrahedral arrangement about the central atom. Two pairs are bonding, and two pairs are nonbonding. The expected geometry is bent.

c.   The Lewis structure of SiF_4 is

$$
\begin{array}{ccc}
: \overset{..}{\underset{..}{F}} & & \overset{..}{\underset{..}{F}} : \\
& Si & \\
: \overset{..}{\underset{..}{F}} & & \overset{..}{\underset{..}{F}} :
\end{array}
$$

There are four bonding electron pairs in a tetrahedral arrangement around the central atom. The expected geometry is tetrahedral.

10.2.   First, distribute the valence electrons to the bonds and the chlorine atoms. Then distribute the remaining electrons to iodine.

$$: \ddot{C}l \longrightarrow \ddot{I} \longrightarrow \ddot{C}l :$$
$$|$$
$$: \ddot{C}l :$$

The five electron pairs around iodine should have a trigonal bipyramidal arrangement with two lone pairs occupying equatorial positions. The molecule is T-shaped.

10.3.   Both trigonal pyramidal (b) and T-shaped (c) geometries are consistent with a nonzero dipole moment. In trigonal planar geometry, the Br–F contributions to the dipole moment would cancel.

10.4.   On the basis of symmetry, SiF_4 (b) would be expected to have a dipole moment of zero. The bonds are all symmetrical about the central atom.

10.5.   The Lewis structure for ammonia, NH_3, is

$$H \longrightarrow \ddot{N} \longrightarrow H$$
$$|$$
$$H$$

There are four pairs of electrons around the nitrogen atom. According to the VSEPR model, these are arranged tetrahedrally around the nitrogen atom, and you should use sp^3 hybrid orbitals. Each N–H bond is formed by the overlap of a $1s$ orbital of a hydrogen atom with one of the singly occupied sp^3 hybrid orbitals of the nitrogen atom. This gives the following bonding description for NH_3:

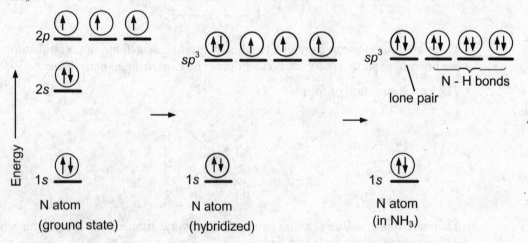

10.6.   The Lewis structure for PCl_5 is

$$: \ddot{C}l : \quad : \ddot{C}l :$$
$$P \longrightarrow \ddot{C}l :$$
$$: \ddot{C}l : \quad : \ddot{C}l :$$

The phosphorus atom has five single bonds and no lone pairs around it. This suggests that you use sp^3d hybrid orbitals on phosphorus. Each chlorine atom (valence-shell configuration $3s^2 3p^5$) has one singly occupied $3p$ orbital. The P–Cl bonds are formed by the overlap of a phosphorus sp^3d hybrid orbital with a singly occupied chlorine $3p$ orbital. The hybridization of phosphorus can be represented as follows:

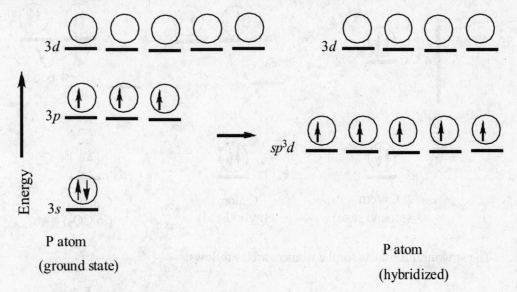

The bonding description of phosphorus in PCl_5 is

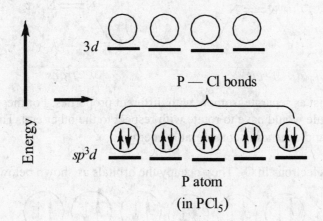

10.7. The Lewis structure of CO_2 is

$$\ddot{O} = C = \ddot{O}$$

The double bonds are each a π bond plus a σ bond. Hybrid orbitals are needed to describe the two σ bonds. This suggests sp hybridization. Each sp hybrid orbital on the carbon atom overlaps with a $2p$ orbital on one of the oxygen atoms to form a σ bond.

The π bonds are formed by the overlap of a $2p$ orbital on the carbon atom with a $2p$ orbital on one of the oxygen atoms. Hybridization and bonding of the carbon atom are shown as follows:

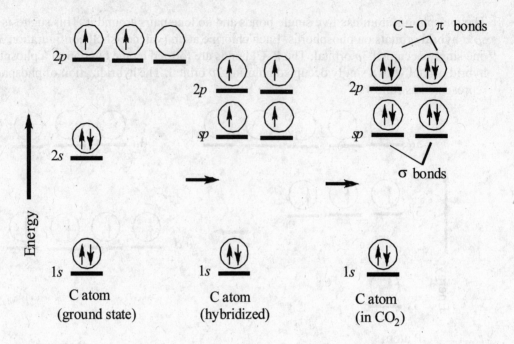

10.8.   The structural formulas for the isomers are as follows:

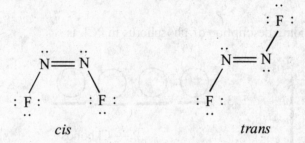

These compounds exist as separate isomers with different properties. For these to interconvert, one end of the molecule would have to rotate with respect to the other end. This would require breaking the π bond and expending considerable energy.

10.9.   There are $2 \times 6 = 12$ electrons in C_2. They occupy the orbitals as shown below.

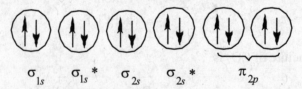

The electron configuration is $KK(\sigma_{2s})^2(\sigma_{2s}*)^2(\pi_{2p})^4$. There are no unpaired electrons; therefore, C_2 is diamagnetic. There are eight bonding and four antibonding electrons. The bond order is $\frac{1}{2}(8 - 4) = 2$.

10.10.   There are $6 + 8 = 14$ electrons in CO. The orbital diagram is

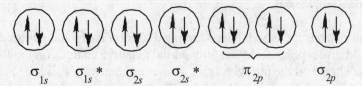

$$\sigma_{1s} \quad \sigma_{1s}* \quad \sigma_{2s} \quad \sigma_{2s}* \quad \pi_{2p} \quad \sigma_{2p}$$

The electron configuration is $KK(\sigma_{2s})^2(\sigma_{2s}*)^2(\pi_{2p})^4(\sigma_{2p})^2$. There are ten bonding and four antibonding electrons. The bond order is $\frac{1}{2}(10 - 4) = 3$. There are no unpaired electrons; hence, CO is diamagnetic.

ANSWERS TO CONCEPT CHECKS

10.1.   The VSEPR model predicts that four electron pairs about any atom in a molecule will distribute themselves to give a tetrahedral arrangement. Any three of these electron pairs would have a trigonal pyramidal arrangement. The geometry of a molecule having a central atom with three atoms bonded to it would be trigonal pyramidal.

10.2.   A molecule, AX_3, could have one of three geometries: it could be trigonal planar, trigonal pyramidal, or T-shaped. Assuming the three groups attached to the central atom are alike, as indicated by the formula, the planar geometry should be symmetrical, so even if the A–X bonds are polar, their polarities would cancel to give a nonpolar molecule (dipole moment of zero). This would not be the case in the trigonal pyramidal geometry. In that situation, the bonds all point to one side of the molecule. It is possible for such a molecule to have a lone pair that points away from the bonds and whose polarity might fortuitously cancel the bond polarities, but an exact cancellation is not likely. In general, you should expect the trigonal pyramidal molecule to have a nonzero dipole moment, but a zero dipole is possible. The argument for the T-shaped geometry is similar to that for the trigonal pyramidal geometry. The bonds point in a plane, but toward one side of the molecule. Unless the sum of the bond polarities was fortuitously canceled by the polarities from the lone pairs, this geometry would have a nonzero dipole moment. This means that molecule Y is likely to be trigonal planar, but trigonal pyramidal or T-shaped geometries are possible. Molecule Z cannot have a trigonal planar geometry; it must be either trigonal pyramidal or T-shaped.

10.3.   Assuming there are no lone pairs, the atom has four electron pairs and, therefore, an octet of electrons about it. The single bond and the triple bond each require a sigma bond orbital for a total of two such orbitals. This suggests *sp* hybrids on the central atom.

ANSWERS TO SELF-ASSESSMENT AND REVIEW QUESTIONS

10.1.   The VSEPR model is used to predict the geometry of molecules. The electron pairs around an atom are assumed to arrange themselves to reduce electron repulsion. The molecular geometry is determined by the positions of the bonding electron pairs.

10.2.   The arrangements are linear, trigonal planar, tetrahedral, trigonal bipyramidal, and octahedral.

10.3.   A lone pair is "larger" than a bonding pair; therefore, it will occupy an equatorial position, where it encounters less repulsion than if it were in an axial position.

10.4. The bonds could be polar, but if they are arranged symmetrically, the molecule will be nonpolar. The bond dipoles will cancel.

10.5. Nitrogen trifluoride has three N–F bonds arranged to form a trigonal pyramid. These bonds are polar and would give a polar molecule with partial negative charges on the fluorine atoms and a partial positive charge on the nitrogen atom. However, there is also a lone pair of electrons on nitrogen that is directed away from the bonds. The result is that the lone pair nearly cancels the polarity of the bonds and gives a molecule with a very small dipole moment.

10.6. Certain orbitals, such as p orbitals and hybrid orbitals, have lobes in given directions. Bonding to these orbitals is directional; that is, the bonding is in preferred directions. This explains why the bonding gives a particular molecular geometry.

10.7. The angle is 109.5°.

10.8. A sigma bond has a cylindrical shape about the bond axis. A *pi* bond has a distribution of electrons above and below the bond axis.

10.9. In ethylene, C_2H_4, the changes on a given carbon atom may be described as follows:

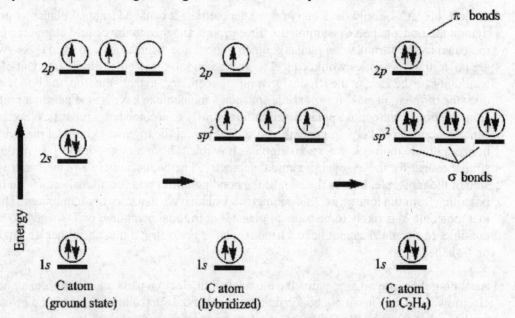

An sp^2 hybrid orbital on one carbon atom overlaps a similar hybrid orbital on the other carbon atom to form a σ bond. The remaining hybrid orbitals on the two carbon atoms overlap $1s$ orbitals from the hydrogen atoms to form four C–H bonds. The unhybridized $2p$ orbital on one carbon atom overlaps the unhybridized $2p$ orbital on the other carbon atom to form a π bond. The σ and π bonds together constitute a double bond.

10.10. Both of the unhybridized $2p$ orbitals, one from each carbon atom, are perpendicular to their CH_2 planes. When these orbitals overlap each other, they fix both planes in the same plane. The two ends of the molecule cannot twist around without breaking the π bond, which requires considerable energy. Therefore, it is possible to have stable molecules with the following structures:

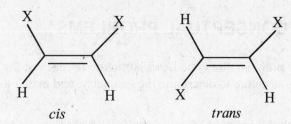

cis   trans

Because these have the same molecular formulas, they are isomers. In this case, they are called *cis-trans* isomers, or geometrical isomers.

10.11. In a bonding orbital, the probability of finding electrons between the two nuclei is high. For this reason, the energy of the bonding orbital is lower than that of the separate atomic orbitals. In an antibonding orbital, the probability of finding electrons between the two nuclei is low. For this reason, the energy of the antibonding orbital is higher than that of the separate atomic orbitals.

10.12. The factors determining the strength of interaction of two atomic orbitals are (1) the energy difference between the interacting orbitals and (2) the magnitude of their overlap.

10.13. When two $2s$ orbitals overlap, they interact to form a bonding orbital, σ_{2s}, and an antibonding orbital, $\sigma_{2s}{}^*$. The bonding orbital is at lower energy than the antibonding orbital.

10.14. When two $2p$ orbitals overlap along their axes, they interact to form one σ_{2p} bonding orbital and one $\sigma_{2p}{}^*$ antibonding orbital. When they overlap sideways, they form π_{2p} and $\pi_{2p}{}^*$ molecular orbitals.

10.15. A σ bonding orbital is formed by the overlap of the $1s$ orbital on the H atom with the $2p$ orbital on the F atom. This H–F orbital is made up primarily of the fluorine orbital.

10.16. The O_3 molecule consists of a framework of localized orbitals and of delocalized *pi* molecular orbitals. The localized framework is formed from sp^2 hybrid orbitals on each atom. Thus, an O–O bond is formed by the overlap of a hybrid orbital on the left O atom with a hybrid orbital on the center O atom. Another O–O bond is formed by the overlap of another hybrid orbital on the right O atom with a hybrid orbital on the center O atom. The remaining hybrid orbitals are occupied by lone pairs of electrons. Also, there is one unhybridized p orbital on each of the atoms. These p orbitals are perpendicular to the plane of the molecule and overlap sidewise to give three pi molecular orbitals that are delocalized. The two orbitals of lowest energy are occupied by pairs of electrons.

10.17. The answer is e, a little less than 109.5°.

10.18. The answer is d, square pyramidal.

10.19. The answer is b, H_2S.

10.20. The answer is e, 5/2.

■ ANSWERS TO CONCEPTUAL PROBLEMS

10.23. In order to solve this problem, draw the Lewis structure for each of the listed molecules. In each case, use your Lewis structure to determine the geometry, and match this geometry with the correct model.

    a. SeO_2 is angular and has an AX_2 geometry. This is represented by model (ii).

    b. $BeCl_2$ is linear and has an AX_2 geometry. This goes with model (i).

    c. PBr_3 is trigonal pyramidal and has an AX_3 geometry. This goes with model (iv).

    d. BCl_3 is trigonal planar and has an AX_3 geometry. This is represented by model (iii).

10.25. In a CH_3CH_3 molecule, each C atom has four electron pairs arranged tetrahedrally. Within this molecule, each CH_3 considered as a separate group has a trigonal pyramidal geometry (with three C–H bonding pairs and a fourth pair from the C–C bond around the C atom). The :CH3 molecule retains this trigonal pyramidal geometry, having three bonding pairs and one lone pair around the C atom. The CH_3 molecule, however, has only three electron pairs around the C atom. Initially, as the CH_3 molecule breaks away from the ethane molecule, it has the trigonal pyramidal geometry it had in the ethane molecule. However, the repulsions of the bonding electron pairs on the CH_3 molecule are no longer balanced by the fourth pair (from the C–C bond), so the molecule flattens out to form a trigonal planar geometry.

10.27. First, determine the geometry of each molecule using VSEPR theory. Then compare to the orbital pictures for the correct number of bonding and nonbonding orbitals.

    a. BeF_2 is an AX_2 molecule having linear geometry depicted by orbital drawing (i).

    b. SiF_4 is an AX_4 molecule having tetrahedral geometry depicted by orbital drawing (iii).

    c. SeF_4 is an AX_4 molecule having seesaw geometry depicted by orbital drawing (iv).

    d. RnF_4 is an AX_4 molecule with square planar geometry depicted by orbital drawing (v).

10.29. The reaction with Br_2 indicates that $C_2H_2Br_2$ has a double bond. There are three possible isomers of $C_2H_2Br_2$ having double bonds:

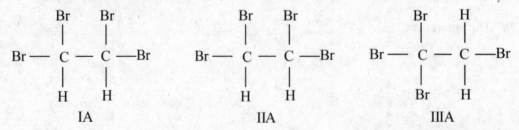

Compounds II and III have dipole moments. The addition of Br_2, with one Br going to each C atom, yields the following products:

Products IA and IIA are identical and arise from compounds I and II. Thus, the original two compounds, one not having a dipole moment, the other having a dipole moment, but both reacting with bromine to give the same product, are compounds I and II, respectively.

10.31. First, determine the geometry about atoms a, b, and c using VSEPR theory. Then compare to the geometry in each drawing.

   a.   The bonding configuration about atom a (carbon) is AX_4 with tetrahedral   geometry. This is depicted by drawing (ii).

   b.   The bonding configuration about atom b (carbon) is AX_3 with trigonal planar geometry. This is depicted by drawing (iv).

   c.   The bonding configuration about atom c (oxygen) is AX_2 with bent geometry. This is depicted by drawing (i).

■ SOLUTIONS TO PRACTICE PROBLEMS

10.33. The number of electron pairs, number of lone pairs, and geometry are for the central atom.

Electron-Dot Structure	General Formula	Number of Electron Pairs	Number of Lone Pairs	Geometry
	AX_4	4	0	Tetrahedral
	AX_4	4	2	Bent
	AX_3	3	0	Trigonal planar
	AX_4	4	1	Trigonal pyramidal

10.35. The number of electron pairs, number of lone pairs, and geometry are for the central atom.

Electron-Dot Structure	General Formula	Number of Electron Pairs	Number of Lone Pairs	Geometry
	AX_4	4	1	Trigonal pyramidal
	AX_4	4	0	Tetrahedral
	AX_2	2	0	Linear
	AX_4	4	1	Trigonal pyramidal

10.37. a. CCl_4 is tetrahedral, VSEPR predicts that the bond angles will be 109°, and you would expect them to be this angle.

b. SCl_2 is bent, and VSEPR theory predicts bond angles of 109°, but you would expect the Cl–S–Cl bond angle to be less.

c. $COCl_2$ is trigonal planar. VSEPR theory predicts 120° bond angles. The C–O bond is a double bond, so you would expect the Cl–C–O bond to be more than 120° and the Cl–C–Cl bond to be less than 120°.

d. AsH_3 is trigonal pyramidal, and VSEPR theory predicts bond angles of 109°, but you would expect the H–As–H bond angle to be less.

$$
\begin{array}{c}
H \\
| \\
H - As - H \\
\end{array}
$$

10.39.   The number of electron pairs, number of lone pairs, and geometry are for the central atom.

Electron-Dot Structure	General Formula	Number of Electron Pairs	Number of Lone Pairs	Geometry
$F-P(F)(F)(F)-F$	AX_5	5	0	Trigonal bipyramidal
$F-Br(F)-F$	AX_5	5	2	T-shaped
$Br(F)(F)(F)(F)$	AX_6	6	1	Square pyramidal
$S(Cl)(Cl)(Cl)(Cl)$	AX_5	5	1	Seesaw

10.41. The number of electron pairs, number of lone pairs, and geometry are for the central atom.

Electron-Dot Structure	General Formula	Number of Electron Pairs	Number of Lone Pairs	Geometry
	AX_5	5	0	Trigonal bipyramidal
	AX_6	6	0	Octahedral
	AX_5	5	3	Linear
	AX_6	6	2	Square planar

10.43. a.   Trigonal pyramidal and T-shaped. Trigonal planar would have a dipole moment of zero.

b.   Bent. Linear would have a dipole moment of zero.

10.45. a. CS_2 has a linear geometry and has no dipole moment.

b. TeF_2 has a bent geometry and has a dipole moment.

c. $SeCl_4$ has a seesaw geometry and has a dipole moment.

d. XeF_4 has a square planar geometry and has no dipole moment.

10.47. a. SF_2 is a bent molecule. The sulfur atom is sp^3 hybridized.

b. ClO_3^- is a trigonal pyramidal molecular ion. The chlorine atom is sp^3 hybridized.

10.49. a. $SeCl_2$ is a bent molecule. The Se atom is sp^3 hybridized.

b. NO_2^- is a bent ion. The N atom is sp^2 hybridized.

c. CO_2 is a linear molecule. The C atom is sp hybridized.

d. COF_2 is a trigonal planar molecule. The C atom is sp^2 hybridized.

10.51. a.   The Lewis structure is

$$: \ddot{C}l —— Hg —— \ddot{C}l :$$

The presence of two single bonds and no lone pairs suggests sp hybridization. Thus, the Hg atom with the configuration $[Xe]4f^{14}5d^{10}6s^2$ is promoted to $[Xe]4f^{14}5d^{10}6s^16p^1$, then sp hybridized. An Hg–Cl bond is formed by overlapping the Hg sp hybrid orbital with a $3p$ orbital of Cl.

b.   The Lewis structure is

$$
\begin{array}{c}
: \ddot{C}l : \\
| \\
: \ddot{C}l — \underset{..}{P} — \ddot{C}l :
\end{array}
$$

The presence of three single bonds and one lone pair suggests sp^3 hybridization of the P atom. Three hybrid orbitals each overlap a $3p$ orbital of a Cl atom to form a P–Cl bond. The fourth hybrid orbital contains the lone pair.

10.53. a.   Xenon has eight valence electrons. Each F atom donates one electron to give a total of ten electrons, or five electron pairs, around the Xe atom. The hybridization is sp^3d.

b.   Bromine has seven valence electrons. Each F atom donates one electron to give a total of twelve electrons, or six electron pairs, around the Br atom. The hybridization is sp^3d^2.

c.   Phosphorus has five valence electrons. The Cl atoms each donate one electron to give a total of ten electrons, or five electron pairs, around the P atom. The hybridization is sp^3d.

d.   Chlorine has seven valence electrons, to which may be added one electron from each F atom minus one electron for the charge on the ion. This gives a total of ten electrons, or five electron pairs, around chlorine. The hybridization is sp^3d.

10.57. a.   The structural formula of formaldehyde is

Because the C is bonded to three other atoms, it is assumed to be sp^2 hybridized. One $2p$ orbital remains unhybridized. The carbon–hydrogen bonds are σ bonds formed by the overlap of an sp^2 hybrid orbital on C with a $1s$ orbital on H. The remaining sp^2 hybrid orbital on C overlaps with a $2p$ orbital on O to form a σ bond. The unhybridized $2p$ orbital on C overlaps with a parallel $2p$ orbital on O to form a π bond. Together, the σ and π bonds constitute a double bond.

b.   The nitrogen atoms are *sp* hybridized. A σ bond is formed by the overlap of an *sp* hybrid orbital from each N. The remaining *sp* hybrid orbitals contain lone pairs of electrons. The two unhybridized 2*p* orbitals on one N overlap with the parallel unhybridized 2*p* orbitals on the other N to form two π bonds.

10.59.   Each of the N atoms has a lone pair of electrons and is bonded to two atoms. The N atoms are sp^2 hybridized. The two possible arrangements of the O atoms relative to one another are shown below. Because the π bond between the N atoms must be broken to interconvert these two forms, it is to be expected that the hyponitrite ion will exhibit *cis–trans* isomerism.

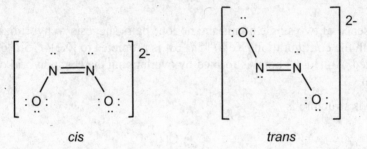

                   cis   *trans*

10.61.   a.   Total electrons = $2 \times 5 = 10$.

The electron configuration is $KK(\sigma_{2s})^2(\sigma_{2s}*)^2(\pi_{2p})^2$.

Bond order = $\frac{1}{2}(n_b - n_a) = \frac{1}{2}(6 - 4) = 1$

The B_2 molecule is stable. It is paramagnetic because the two electrons in the π_{2p} subshell occupy separate orbitals.

b.   Total electrons = $(2 \times 5) - 1 = 9$.

The electron configuration is $KK(\sigma_{2s})^2(\sigma_{2s}*)^2(\pi_{2p})^1$.

Bond order = $\frac{1}{2}(n_b - n_a) = \frac{1}{2}(5 - 4) = 1/2$

The B_2^+ molecular ion should be stable and is paramagnetic because there is one unpaired electron in the π_{2p} subshell.

c.   Total electrons = $(2 \times 8) + 1 = 17$.

The electron configuration is $KK(\sigma_{2s})^2(\sigma_{2s}*)^2(\pi_{2p})^4(\sigma_{2p})^2(\pi_{2p}*)^3$.

Bond order = $\frac{1}{2}(n_b - n_a) = \frac{1}{2}(10 - 7) = 3/2$

The O_2^- molecular ion should be stable and is paramagnetic because there is one unpaired electron in the $\pi_{2p}*$ subshell.

10.63.   Total electrons = $6 + 7 + 1 = 14$.

The electron configuration is $KK(\sigma_{2s})^2(\sigma_{2s}*)^2(\pi_{2p})^4(\sigma_{2p})^2$.

Bond order = $\frac{1}{2}(n_b - n_a) = \frac{1}{2}(10 - 4) = 3$

The CN^- ion is diamagnetic.

■ SOLUTIONS TO GENERAL PROBLEMS

10.65. The number of electron pairs, number of lone pairs, and geometry are for the central atom.

Electron-Dot Structure	General Formula	Number of Electron Pairs	Number of Lone Pairs	Geometry
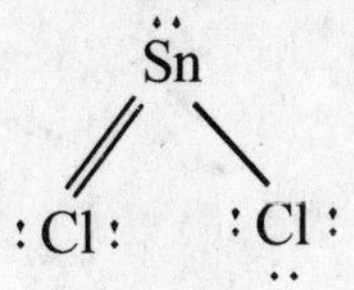	AX_3	3	1	Bent
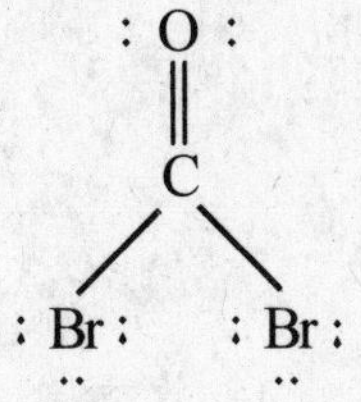	AX_3	3	0	Trigonal planar
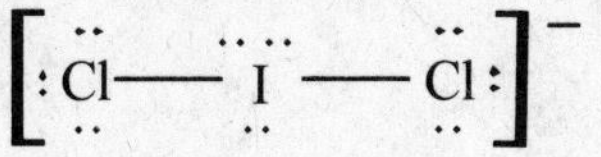	AX_5	5	3	Linear
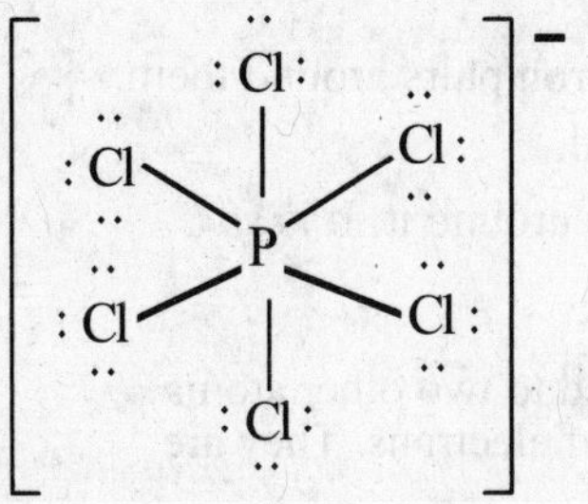	AX_6	6	0	Octahedral

10.67. None of the given molecules or ions are linear.

a. 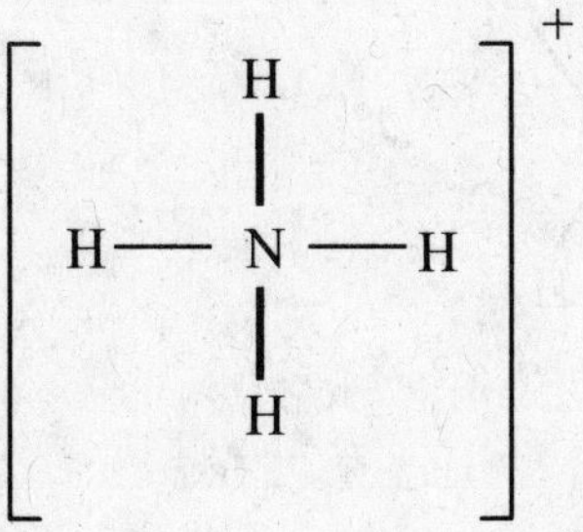 Tetrahedral

b. 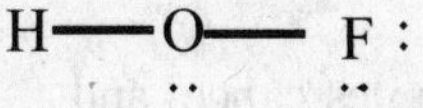 Bent, or angular

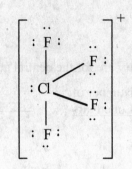

c.   Seesaw

d. 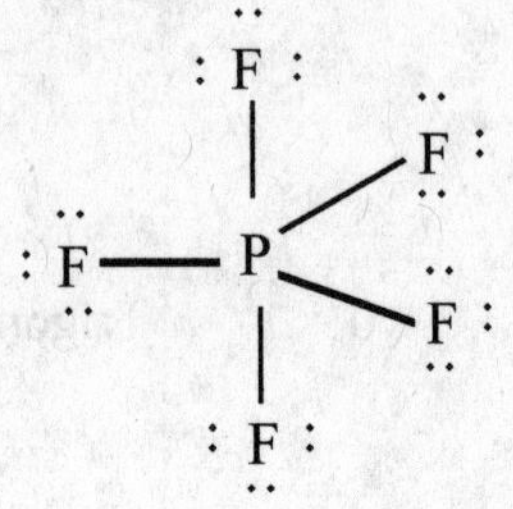   Trigonal bypyramidal

10.69.

a.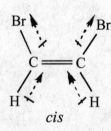

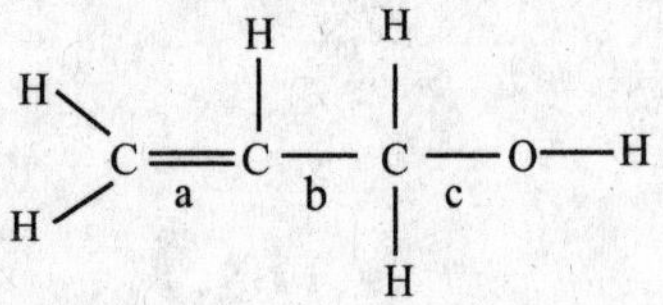

C_a and C_b: Three electron pairs around them. They are sp^2 hybridized.

C_c: Four electron pairs around it. It is sp^3 hybridized.

b.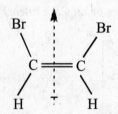

Both C atoms are bonded to two other atoms and have no lone pairs of electrons. They are sp hybridized.

10.71.

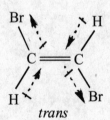

has a net dipole

cis

has no net dipole. The two C–Br bond dipoles cancel and the two C–H bond dipoles cancel.

trans

10.73. All four hydrogen atoms of $H_2C=C=CH_2$ cannot lie in the same plane because the second $C=C$ bond forms perpendicular to the plane of the first $C=C$ bond. By looking at Figure 10.26, you can see how this is so. The second $C=C$ bond forms in the plane of the C–H bonds. Thus, the plane of the C–H bonds on the right side will be perpendicular to the plane of the C–H bonds on the left side. This is shown below using the π orbitals of the two $C=C$ double bonds.

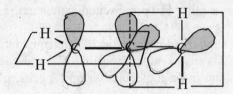

10.75. Total electrons = $2 + 1 - 1 = 2$.

The electron configuration is $(\sigma_{1s})^2$.

Bond order = $\frac{1}{2}(n_b - n_a) = \frac{1}{2}(2) = 1$

The HeH^+ ion is expected to be stable.

10.77. Total electrons = $(2 \times 6) + 2 = 14$.

The electron configuration is $KK(\sigma_{2s})^2(\sigma_{2s}*)^2(\pi_{2p})^4(\sigma_{2p})^2$.

Bond order = $\frac{1}{2}(n_b - n_a) = \frac{1}{2}(10 - 4) = 3$

10.79. The molecular orbital configuration of O_2 is $KK(\sigma_{2s})^2(\sigma_{2s}*)^2(\pi_{2p})^4(\sigma_{2p})^2(\pi_{2p}*)^2$. O_2^+ has one electron less than O_2. The difference is in the number of electrons in the $\pi_{2p}*$ antibonding orbital. This means that the bond order is larger for O_2^+ than for O_2.

O_2: Bond order = $\frac{1}{2}(n_b - n_a) = \frac{1}{2}(10 - 6) = 2$

O_2^+: Bond order = $\frac{1}{2}(n_b - n_a) = \frac{1}{2}(10 - 5) = 5/2$

It is expected that the species with the higher bond order, O_2^+, has the shorter bond length. In O_2^-, there is one more electron than in O_2. This additional electron occupies a $\pi_{2p}*$ orbital. Increasing the number of electrons in antibonding orbitals decreases the bond order; hence, O_2^- should have a longer bond length than O_2.

10.81. As shown in Figure 10.34, the occupation of molecular orbitals by the N_2 valence electrons is

$KK(\sigma_{2s})^2(\sigma_{2s}*)^2(\pi_{2p})^4(\sigma_{2p})^2(\pi_{2p}*)^0$

To form the first excited state of N_2, a σ_{2p} electron is promoted to the $\pi_{2p}*$ orbital, giving

$KK(\sigma_{2s})^2(\sigma_{2s}*)^2(\pi_{2p})^4(\sigma_{2p})^1(\pi_{2p}*)^1$

The differences in properties are as follows:

Magnetic character: The ground state is diamagnetic (all electrons paired), and the excited state is paramagnetic.

Bond order: ground state order = ½(8 − 2) = 3

excited state order = ½(7 − 3) = 2

Bond dissociation energy: ground-state energy = 942 kJ; excited-state energy is less than 942 kJ (excited state does not possess a stable triple bond like the ground state)

Bond length: ground-state length = 110 pm; excited-state length is more than 110 pm.

10.83. A person's two hands are similar but not identical. A person's left hand is a mirror image of the other hand, yet the two hands are nonsuperimposible. The presence of handedness in molecules depends on the fact that atoms in the molecules occupy specific places in 3-D space.

10.85. Color vision is possible because three types of cone cells exist: one type absorbs light in the red region of the spectrum, another absorbs in the green region, and a third absorbs in the blue region. The chemical substance primarily responsible for human vision is 11-*cis*-retinal. In each of the different cone cells, 11-*cis*-retinal is attached to a different protein molecule, which affects the region of light that is absorbed by retinal.

10.87. Ozone in the stratosphere absorbs ultraviolet radiation between 200 and 300 nm, which is important to life on earth. Radiation from the sun contains ultraviolet rays that are harmful to the DNA of biological organisms. Oxygen, O_2, absorbs the most energetic of these ultraviolet rays in the earth's upper atmosphere, but only ozone in the stratosphere absorbs the remaining ultraviolet radiation that is destructive to life on earth.

■ SOLUTIONS TO STRATEGY PROBLEMS

10.89. N_2: Triple bond; bond length = 110 pm. Geometry is linear; *sp* hybrid orbitals are needed for one lone pair and one σ bond.

N_2F_2: Double bond; bond length = 122 pm. Geometry is trigonal planar; sp^2 hybrid orbitals are needed for one lone pair and two σ bonds.

N_2H_4: Single bond; bond length = 145 pm. Geometry is tetrahedral; sp^3 hybrid orbitals are needed for one lone pair and three σ bonds.

10.91. The electron dot formula for $C_2{}^{2-}$ is

$$\left[\, : \text{C} \equiv \text{C} : \, \right]^{2-}$$

The valence bond description of the bonding is a triple bond, involving a σ bond formed by the overlap of a *sp* hybrid orbital on each carbon, and two π bonds formed by the overlap of the two unhybridized 2*p* orbitals on each carbon. Each atom obeys the octet rule, and there is a formal charge of −1 on each carbon. The molecular orbital description is based on a total of 14 electrons for the ion, leading to a configuration of $KK(\sigma_{2s})^2(\sigma_{2s}*)^2(\pi_{2p})^4(\sigma_{2p})^2$. The bond order is ½(8 − 2) = 3. This agrees with the valence bond description.

10.93. In BF_3NH_3, both the boron atom and the nitrogen atom are in a tetrahedral geometry, with sp^3 hybrid orbitals. In terms of valence bond theory, the bond between boron and fluorine is a σ bond, formed by the overlap of an sp^3 orbital on boron with an sp^3 orbital on nitrogen. For the reactant molecules, BF_3 is trigonal planar with sp^2 hybrid orbitals, and NH_3 is trigonal pyramidal with sp^3 hybrid orbitals.

10.95.

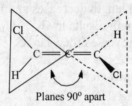

The two C_a atoms are bonded two three atoms with no lone pairs. They are sp^2 hybridized with trigonal planar geometry. The central C_b atom is bonded to two atoms with no lone pairs. It is sp hybridized with a linear geometry.

The central C_b atom uses one sp_x orbital to form a σ bond when overlapping with the sp^2 hybrid orbital on the left C_a atom and the other sp_x orbital to form a σ bond when overlapping with the sp^2 hybrid orbital on the right C_a atom. The left π bond is formed by sideways overlap of the unhybridized p_z orbitals present on both the central C_b and left C_a atoms. The right π bond is formed by sideways overlap of the unhybridized p_y orbitals present on both the central C_b and right C_a atoms.

Because of allene's π bonding network, the two terminal CH_2 groups occupy planes that are offset from one another by 90°. As a result, the Cl atoms in the derivative molecule 1,3-dichloroallene will not be symmetrical with respect to one another and a net dipole will be present. (In the depiction below, the solid triangle is in the plane of this document and the dotted triangle is in the plane that is perpendicular to the plane of this document.)

Planes 90° apart

Thus, 1,3-dichloroallene is a polar molecule.

10.97. The electron dot formula for I_3^- (formal charges, if any, are given below the atoms) is

$$\left[:\ddot{I} - \ddot{I} - \ddot{I}: \right]^-$$
1-

The central I atom in I_3^- has two single bonds and three lone pairs around it. This suggests sp^3d hybridization. Since repulsions between lone pairs are minimized when placed in the equatorial position of the trigonal bipyramid electron pair geometry, the geometry of the molecular ion is linear. Each I–I bond is formed by the overlap of an sp^3d hybrid orbital on the central I with a $5p$ orbital from a terminal I. There are no other reasonable resonance structures for I_3^-.

Including resonance structures, the electron dot formula for the N_3^- ion is

$$\left[:\ddot{N} - N \equiv N: \right]^- \longleftrightarrow \left[:N \equiv N - \ddot{N}: \right]^- \longleftrightarrow \left[\ddot{N} = N = \ddot{N} \right]^-$$
2- 1+   1+ 2-   1- 1+ 1-

Dominant structure

In each case the central N atom in N_3^- has two bonding regions of electron density and no lone pairs. This suggests sp hybridization with a linear molecular geometry. Since the structure to the right has the smaller formal charges it is likely to be the dominating structure.

10.99. The Lewis electron dot formula for PF_3Br_2 is

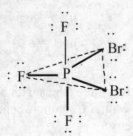

There are five bonded atoms and no lone pairs. This suggests dsp^3 hybridization with trigonal bipyramidal geometry. Because bromine atoms are considerably larger than fluorine atoms, they will likely occupy equatorial positions instead of axial positions.

10.101. Total electrons for $C_2 = 2 \times 6 = 12$. The molecular orbital configuration for C_2 is $KK(\sigma_{2s})^2(\sigma_{2s}*)^2(\pi_{2p})^4$ leads to a bond order 2 (B.O. = ½(8 − 4) = 2).

Total electrons for $C_2^+ = 2 \times 6 - 1 = 11$. The molecular orbital configuration for C_2^+ is $KK(\sigma_{2s})^2(\sigma_{2s}*)^2(\pi_{2p})^3$ leads to a bond order 3/2 (B.O. = ½(7 − 4) = 3/2).

Total electrons for $C_2^{2-} = 2 \times 6 + 2 = 14$. The molecular orbital configuration for C_2^{2-} is $KK(\sigma_{2s})^2(\sigma_{2s}*)^2(\pi_{2p})^4(\sigma_{2p})^2$ leads to a bond order 3 (B.O. = ½(10 − 4) = 3).

As bond order increases, bond length decreases and bond enthalpy increases. Arranging the species by increasing bond length results in $C_2^{2-} < C_2 < C_2^+$. Arranging the species in increasing bond enthalpies results in the reverse order, i.e., $C_2^+ < C_2 < C_2^{2-}$.

10.103. The structures for the compounds are

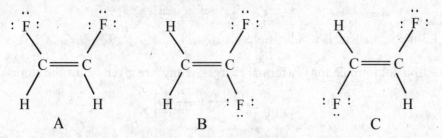

10.105. The molecular orbital description of an O_2 molecule is $KK(\sigma_{2s})^2(\sigma_{2s}*)^2(\pi_{2p})^4(\sigma_{2p})^2(\pi_{2p}*)^2$. In the $\pi_{2p}*$ orbital, both electrons must be in the same orbital for all electrons to be paired. The ground state would have one electron in each of the two $\pi_{2p}*$ orbitals. In both cases, the bond order is 2, but the excited state is diamagnetic, whereas the ground state is paramagnetic.

10.107. The Lewis formula for formaldehyde is

Because the C is bonded to three other atoms, it is assumed to be sp^2 hybridized. One $2p$ orbital remains unhybridized. The carbon–hydrogen bonds are σ bonds formed by the overlap of an sp^2 hybrid orbital on C with a $1s$ orbital on H. The remaining sp^2 hybrid orbital on C overlaps with a

2*p* orbital on O to form a σ bond. The unhybridized 2*p* orbital on C overlaps with a parallel 2*p* orbital on O to form the π bond.

In molecular orbital theory, the carbon–oxygen double bond has a σ and a π molecular orbital that are occupied by electrons. There is also a π^* orbital that is unoccupied in the ground state. The transition at 270 nm (UV region) is due to an electron moving from the occupied π orbital to the unoccupied π^* orbital to give an excited state.

■ SOLUTIONS TO CUMULATIVE-SKILLS PROBLEMS

Note on significant figures: If the final answer to a solution needs to be rounded off, it is given first with one nonsignificant figure, and the last significant figure is underlined. The final answer is then rounded to the correct number of significant figures. In multistep problems, intermediate answers are given with at least one nonsignificant figure; however, only the final answer has been rounded off.

10.109. After assuming a 100.0-g sample, convert to moles:

$$60.4 \text{ g Xe} \times \frac{1 \text{ mol Xe}}{131.29 \text{ g Xe}} = 0.46\underline{0}05 \text{ mol Xe}$$

$$22.1 \text{ g O} \times \frac{1 \text{ mol O}}{16.00 \text{ g O}} = 1.3\underline{8}1 \text{ mol O}$$

$$17.5 \text{ g F} \times \frac{1 \text{ mol F}}{18.99 \text{ g F}} = 0.92\underline{1}5 \text{ mol F}$$

Divide by 0.460 :

$$\text{Xe: } \frac{0.460}{0.460} = 1; \text{ O: } \frac{1.381}{0.460} = 3.00; \text{ F: } \frac{0.9215}{0.460} = 2.00$$

The simplest formula is XeO_3F_2. This is also the molecular formula. The Lewis formula is

Number of electron pairs = 5, number of lone pairs = 0; hence, the geometry is trigonal bipyramidal. Because xenon has five single bonds, it will require five orbitals to describe the bonding. This suggests sp^3d hybridization.

10.111. $U(s) + ClF_n \rightarrow UF_6 + ClF(g)$

$$\text{mol } UF_6 = 3.53 \text{ g } UF_6 \times \frac{1 \text{ mol } UF_6}{352.07 \text{ g } UF_6} = 0.0100\underline{3} \text{ mol } UF_6$$

$$\text{mol } ClF = n = \frac{PV}{RT} = \frac{2.50 \text{ atm} \times 0.343 \text{ L}}{0.082057 \text{ L} \cdot \text{atm/ (K} \cdot \text{mol)} \times 348 \text{ K}} = 0.0300\underline{3} \text{ mol } ClF$$

0.010 mol UF_6 = 0.060 mol F, and 0.030 mol ClF = 0.030 mol F; therefore, the total moles of F from ClF_n = 0.090 mol F. Because mol ClF_n must equal mol ClF, mol ClF_n = 0.030 mol and n = 0.090 mol F ÷ 0.030 mol ClF_n = 3. The Lewis formula is

$$: \overset{..}{\underset{..}{F}} \!\! - \!\! \overset{.\,.}{\underset{|}{Cl}} \!\! - \!\! \overset{..}{\underset{..}{F}} :$$
$$: \overset{}{\underset{..}{F}} :$$

Number of electron pairs = 5, number of lone pairs = 2; hence, the geometry is T-shaped. Because chlorine has five electron pairs, it will require five orbitals to describe the bonding. This suggests sp^3d hybridization.

10.113. HNO_3 resonance formulas:

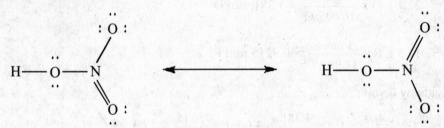

The geometry around the nitrogen is trigonal planar; therefore, the hybridization is sp^2.

Formation reaction: $H_2(g) + 3O_2(g) + N_2(g) \rightarrow 2HNO_3(g)$

$2 \times \Delta H_f^\circ = [BE(H-H) + 3BE(O_2) + BE(N_2)] - [2BE(H-O) + 4BE(N-O) + 2BE(N=O)]$

$2 \times \Delta H_f^\circ = [(436 + 3 \times 498 + 945) - (2 \times 463 + 4 \times 201 + 2 \times 607) \text{ kJ}]$

$\Delta H_f^\circ = -69 \text{ kJ/2 mol} = -3\underline{4}.5 \text{ kJ/mol}$

Resonance energy = $-3\underline{4}.5$ kJ/mol $- (-135$ kJ/mol$) = 10\underline{0}.5 = 101$ kJ/mol

CHAPTER 11

States of Matter; Liquids and Solids

■ SOLUTIONS TO EXERCISES

Note on significant figures: If the final answer to a solution needs to be rounded off, it is given first with one nonsignificant figure, and the last significant figure is underlined. The final answer is then rounded to the correct number of significant figures. In multistep problems, intermediate answers are given with at least one nonsignificant figure; however, only the final answer has been rounded off.

11.1.   First, calculate the heat required to vaporize 1.00 kg of ammonia:

$$1.00 \text{ kg NH}_3 \times \frac{1000 \text{ g}}{1 \text{ kg}} \times \frac{1 \text{ mol NH}_3}{17.03 \text{ g NH}_3} \times \frac{23.4 \text{ kJ}}{1 \text{ mol}} = 13\underline{7}4.04 \text{ kJ}$$

The amount of water at 0°C that can be frozen to ice at 0°C with this heat is

$$13\underline{7}4.04 \text{ kJ} \times \frac{1 \text{ mol H}_2\text{O}}{6.01 \text{ kJ}} \times \frac{18.01 \text{ g H}_2\text{O}}{1 \text{ mol H}_2\text{O}} = 41\underline{1}7.54\text{g} = 4.12 \text{ kg H}_2\text{O}$$

11.2.   Use the two-point form of the Clausius-Clapeyron equation to calculate P_2:

$$\ln \frac{P_2}{760 \text{ mmHg}} = \frac{26.8 \times 10^3 \text{ J/mol}}{8.31 \text{ J/(K} \cdot \text{mol)}} \left[\frac{1}{319 \text{ K}} - \frac{1}{308 \text{ K}} \right]$$

$$= 3225 \text{ K} \left[\frac{-1.\underline{1}2 \times 10^{-4}}{\text{K}} \right] = -0.3\underline{6}106$$

Converting to antilogs gives

$$\frac{P_2}{760 \text{ mmHg}} = \text{antilog}(-0.3\underline{6}106) = e^{-0.3\underline{6}106} = 0.6\underline{9}693$$

$$P_2 = 0.6\underline{9}693 \times 760 \text{ mmHg} = 5\underline{2}9.6 = 5.3 \times 10^2 \text{ mmHg}$$

11.3.   Use the two-point form of the Clausius-Clapeyron equation to solve for ΔH_{vap}:

$$\ln \frac{757 \text{ mmHg}}{522 \text{ mmHg}} = \frac{\Delta H_{vap}}{8.31 \text{ J/(K} \cdot \text{mol)}} \left[\frac{1}{368 \text{ K}} - \frac{1}{378 \text{ K}} \right]$$

$$0.37\underline{1}69 = \frac{\Delta H_{vap}}{8.31 \text{ J/(K} \cdot \text{mol)}} \left[\frac{7.2 \times 10^{-5}}{\text{K}} \right]$$

$$\Delta H_{vap} = \underline{4}.3 \times 10^4 \text{ J/mol } (4 \times 10^1 \text{ kJ/mol})$$

11.4.   a.   Liquefy methyl chloride by a sufficient increase in pressure below 144°C.

   b.   Liquefy oxygen by compressing to 50 atm below −119°C.

11.5.   a.   Propanol has a hydrogen atom bonded to an oxygen atom. Therefore, hydrogen bonding is expected. Because propanol is polar (from the O–H bond), we also expect dipole-dipole forces. Weak London forces exist, too, because such forces exist between all molecules.

   b.   Linear carbon dioxide is not polar, so only London forces exist among CO_2 molecules.

   c.   Bent sulfur dioxide is polar, so we expect dipole-dipole forces; we also expect the usual London forces.

11.6.   The order of increasing vapor pressure is butane (C_4H_{10}), propane (C_3H_8), and ethane (C_2H_6). Because London forces tend to increase with increasing molecular mass, we would expect the molecule with the highest molecular mass to have the lowest vapor pressure.

11.7.   Because ethanol has an H atom bonded to an O atom, strong hydrogen bonding exists in ethanol but not in methyl chloride. Hydrogen bonding explains the lower vapor pressure of ethanol compared to methyl chloride.

11.8.   a.   Zinc, a metal, is a metallic solid.

   b.   Sodium iodide, an ionic substance, exists as an ionic solid.

   c.   Silicon carbide, a compound in which carbon and silicon might be expected to form covalent bonds to other carbon and silicon atoms, exists as a covalent network solid.

   d.   Methane, at room temperature a gaseous molecular compound with covalent bonds, freezes as a molecular solid.

11.9.   Only $MgSO_4$ is an ionic solid; C_2H_5OH, CH_4, and CH_3Cl form molecular solids; thus $MgSO_4$ should have the highest melting point. Of the molecular solids, CH_4 has the lowest molecular mass (16.0 amu) and would be expected to have the lowest melting point. Both C_2H_5OH and CH_3Cl have approximately the same molecular masses (46.0 amu vs. 50.5 amu), but C_2H_5OH exhibits strong hydrogen bonding and, therefore, would be expected to have the higher melting point. The order of increasing melting points is CH_4, CH_3Cl, C_2H_5OH, and $MgSO_4$.

11.10.   Each of the four corners of the cell contains one atom, which is shared by a total of four unit cells. Therefore, the corners contribute one whole atom.

$$\frac{\text{Atoms}}{\text{Unit cell}} = 4 \text{ corners} \times \frac{1/4 \text{ atom}}{1 \text{ corner}} = 1 \text{ atom}$$

11.11.   Use the edge length to calculate the volume of the unit cell. Then, use the density to determine the mass of one atom. Divide the molar mass by the mass of one atom.

$$V = (3.509 \times 10^{-10} \text{ m})^3 = 4.3\underline{2}1 \times 10^{-29} \text{ m}^3$$

$$d = \frac{0.534 \text{ g}}{1 \text{ cm}^3} \times \left[\frac{100 \text{ cm}}{1 \text{ m}}\right]^3 = 5.34 \times 10^5 \text{ g/m}^3$$

Mass of 1 unit cell $= d \times V = (5.34 \times 10^5 \text{ g/m}^3) \times (4.321 \times 10^{-29} \text{ m}^3) = 2.3\underline{0}74 \times 10^{-23} \text{ g}$

There are two atoms in a body-centered cubic unit cell; thus, the mass of one lithium atom is

$$\tfrac{1}{2} \times 2.3074 \times 10^{-23}\ g = 1.1537 \times 10^{-23}\ g$$

The known atomic mass of lithium is 6.941 amu, so Avogadro's number is

$$N_A = \frac{6.941\ g/mol}{1.1537 \times 10^{-23}\ g/atom} = 6.016 \times 10^{23} = 6.02 \times 10^{23}\ atoms/mol$$

11.12. Use Avogadro's number to convert the molar mass of potassium to the mass per one atom.

$$\frac{39.0983\ g\ K}{1\ mol\ K} \times \frac{1\ mol\ K}{6.022 \times 10^{23}\ atoms} = \frac{6.4925 \times 10^{-23}\ g\ K}{1\ atom}$$

There are two K atoms per unit cell; therefore, the mass per unit cell is

$$\frac{6.4925 \times 10^{-23}\ g\ K}{1\ atom} \times \frac{2\ atoms}{1\ unit\ cell} = \frac{1.2985 \times 10^{-22}\ g}{1\ unit\ cell}$$

The density of 0.856 g/cm³ is equal to the mass of one unit cell divided by its unknown volume, V. After solving for V, determine the edge length from the cube root of the volume.

$$0.856\ g/cm^3 = \frac{1.2985 \times 10^{-22}\ g}{V}$$

$$V = \frac{1.2985 \times 10^{-22}\ g}{0.856\ g/cm^3} = 1.517 \times 10^{-22}\ cm^3\ (1.517 \times 10^{-28}\ m^3)$$

Edge length $= \sqrt[3]{1.517 \times 10^{-28}\ m^3} = 5.333 \times 10^{-10} = 5.33 \times 10^{-10}\ m\ (533\ pm)$

■ ANSWERS TO CONCEPT CHECKS

11.1. a. (1) At $t = 0$, since the system is not at equilibrium and there are no H_2O molecules in the gaseous state, you would expect the rate of evaporation to exceed the rate of condensation. At $t = 1$, since evaporation has proceeded at a greater rate than condensation, there must now be fewer molecules in the liquid state, resulting in a lower level of $H_2O(l)$.

(2) At $t = 1$, since some of the H_2O has gone into the vapor state, the vapor pressure must be higher.

(3) At $t = 1$, since evaporation has occurred, there must be more molecules in the vapor state.

(4) At $t = 1$, since the system has not reached equilibrium you would expect the rate of evaporation to exceed the rate of condensation.

(5)

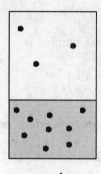

$t = 1$

b. (1) Between $t = 1$ and $t = 2$, the system has still not reached equilibrium. Therefore, because the rate of evaporation continues to exceed the rate of condensation, you would expect the water level to be lower.

(2) Prior to reaching equilibrium at $t = 2$, you would continue to observe a rate of evaporation greater than the rate of condensation, resulting in a higher vapor pressure than $t = 1$.

(3) Since evaporation has been occurring at a greater rate than condensation between points $t = 1$ and $t = 2$, you would expect more molecules in the vapor state at $t = 2$.

(4) When the system has reached equilibrium at $t = 2$, the rate of evaporation equals the rate of condensation.

(5)

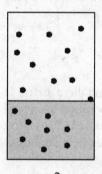

$t = 2$

11.2. You would have to cook the egg for a longer time. The reason is that, since the boiling temperature is lower, it would take longer for the egg to become hard, a chemical process (which slows down at lower temperature).

11.3. a. Because A has stronger intermolecular forces than B, A will boil at a higher temperature. Statement (a) is true.

b. Because A has stronger intermolecular forces than B, A will be more viscous than B. Statement (b) is false.

c. Because B has weaker intermolecular forces than A, it will require a lower temperature to freeze. Statement (c) is true.

d. Because A has stronger intermolecular forces than B, its vapor pressure will be lower than the vapor pressure of B at any given temperature. Statement (d) is true.

e. Because A and B measurably different intermolecular forces of attraction, they will most likely melt at different temperatures. Statement (e) is true.

11.4. a. If the first reaction occurred, the mixture of hydrogen and oxygen that resulted would form an explosive mixture. At 100°C, 2 moles of water make 61.2 L of gaseous water. In the incorrect reaction, 2 moles of water produce 91.8 L of gaseous products.

b. Since you would be breaking strong chemical bonds and forming relatively weak bonds, the enthalpy for the first reaction (the wrong reaction) would be many times greater (more positive) than for the second reaction.

c. Apply Hess's law. The enthalpy for the wrong reaction would be equal to two times the negative of ΔH_f^o for $H_2O(l)$ plus the heat required to raise the temperature of 2 moles of water from 25°C to 100°C.

11.5. a. First, consider the B balls (small). There are four atoms, each completely inside the cell. Thus, there are four B atoms per cell. Next, there are fourteen A atoms (large). Of these, eight are in corners, and contribute ⅛ to the cell. Six atoms are in faces, and contribute ½ to the cell. Thus, there are $8 \times (⅛) + 6 \times (½) = 4$ A atoms per cell. The ratio of A atoms to B atoms is 4 to 4, or 1 to 1. Thus, the formula of the compound is AB.

b. Since all of the B atoms are completely within the cell, the shape of the cell is determined by the A atoms only. It is a face-centered cubic unit cell.

■ ANSWERS TO SELF-ASSESSMENT AND REVIEW QUESTIONS

11.1. The six different phase transitions, with examples in parentheses, are melting (snow melting), sublimation (dry ice subliming directly to carbon dioxide gas), freezing (water freezing), vaporization (water evaporating), condensation (dew forming on the ground), and gas-solid condensation or deposition (frost forming on the ground).

11.2. Iodine can be purified by heating it in a beaker covered with a dish containing ice or ice water. Only pure iodine should sublime, crystallizing on the cold bottom surface of the dish above the iodine. The common impurities in iodine do not sublime nor do they vaporize significantly.

11.3. The vapor pressure of a liquid is the partial pressure of the vapor over the liquid, measured at equilibrium. In molecular terms, vapor pressure involves molecules of a liquid vaporizing from the liquid phase, colliding with any surface above the liquid, and exerting pressure on it. The equilibrium is a dynamic one because molecules of the liquid are continually leaving the liquid phase and returning to it from the vapor phase.

11.4. Steam at 100°C will melt more ice than the same mass of water at 100°C because it contains much more energy in the form of its heat of vaporization. It will transfer this energy to the ice and condense in doing so. The condensed steam and the water will both transfer heat to the ice as the temperature then drops.

11.5.   The heat of fusion is smaller than the heat of vaporization because melting requires only enough energy for molecules to escape from their sites in the crystal lattice, leaving other molecular attractions intact. In vaporization, sufficient energy must be added to break almost all molecular attractions and also to do the work of pushing back the atmosphere.

11.6.   Evaporation leads to cooling of a liquid because the gaseous molecules require heat to evaporate; as they leave the other liquid molecules, they remove the heat energy required to vaporize them. This leaves less energy in the liquid, the temperature of which then drops.

11.7.   As the temperature increases for a liquid and its vapor in the closed vessel, the two, which are separated by a meniscus, gradually become identical. The meniscus first becomes fuzzy and then disappears altogether as the temperature reaches the critical temperature. Above this temperature, only the vapor exists.

11.8.   A permanent gas can be liquefied only by lowering the temperature below its critical temperature while compressing the gas.

11.9.   The pressure in the cylinder of nitrogen at room temperature (above its critical temperature of $-147°C$) decreases continuously as gas is released because the number of molecules in the vapor phase, which governs the pressure, decreases continuously. The pressure in the cylinder of propane at room temperature (below its critical temperature) is constant because liquid propane and gaseous propane exist at equilibrium in the cylinder. The pressure will remain constant at the vapor pressure of propane until only gaseous propane remains. At that point, the pressure will decrease until all of the propane is gone.

11.10.   The vapor pressure of a liquid depends on the intermolecular forces in the liquid phase since the ease with which a molecule leaves the liquid phase depends on how strongly it is attracted to the other molecules. If such molecules attract each other strongly, the vapor pressure will be relatively low; if they attract each other weakly, the vapor pressure will be relatively high.

11.11.   Surface tension makes a liquid act as though it had a skin, because for an object to break through the surface, the surface area must increase. This requires energy, so there is some resistance to the object breaking through the surface.

11.12.   London forces, also known as dispersion forces, originate between any two molecules that are weakly attracted to each other by means of small instantaneous dipoles that occur as a result of the varying positions of the electrons during their movement about their nuclei.

11.13.   Hydrogen bonding is a weak to moderate attractive force that exists between a hydrogen atom covalently bonded to a very electronegative atom, X (N, O, or F), and a lone pair of electrons on another small, electronegative atom, Y. (X and Y may be the same or different elements.) Hydrogen bonding in water involves a hydrogen atom of one water molecule bonding to a lone pair of electrons on the oxygen atom of another water molecule.

11.14.   Molecular substances have relatively low melting points because the forces broken by melting are weak intermolecular attractions in the solid state, not strong bonding attractions.

11.15.   A crystalline solid has a well-defined, orderly structure; an amorphous solid has a random arrangement of structural units.

11.16. In a face-centered cubic cell, there are atoms at the center of each face of the unit cell in addition to those at the corners.

11.17. The structure of thallium(I) iodide is a simple cubic lattice for both the metal ions and the anions. Thus, the structure consists of two interpenetrating cubic lattices of cation and anion.

11.18. The coordination number of Cs^+ in CsCl is 8; the coordination number of Na^+ in NaCl is 6; and the coordination number of Zn^{2+} in ZnS is 4.

11.19. Starting with the edge length of a cubic crystal, we can calculate the volume of a unit cell by cubing the edge length. Next, knowing the density of the crystalline solid, we can calculate the mass of the atoms in the unit cell. Then, the mass of the atoms in the unit cell is divided by the number of atoms in the unit cell, to give the mass of one atom. Dividing the mass of one mole of the crystal by the mass of one atom yields a value for Avogadro's number.

11.20. X rays can strike a crystal and be reflected at various angles; at most angles the reflected waves will be out of phase and will interfere destructively. At certain angles, however, the reflected waves will be in phase and will interfere constructively, giving rise to a diffraction pattern.

11.21. The answer is e, cooling the H_2O sample from 105°C to 84°C.

11.22. The answer is d, sublime.

11.23. The answer is c, London (dispersion) forces.

11.24. The answer is b, 6.40×10^7 pm^3.

■ ANSWERS TO CONCEPTUAL PROBLEMS

11.27. a. The molecules of A would have the majority of molecules in the gas phase because at this temperature, liquid A has the higher fraction of molecules that have sufficient kinetic energy and can vaporize.

   b. The molecules with the strongest intermolecular attractions will have the fewest molecules in the gas phase because a higher kinetic energy is needed to overcome the attractions. Since molecules of C have the smallest fraction of molecules with sufficient kinetic energy, they have the strongest intermolecular attractions.

   c. The molecules with the strongest intermolecular attractions will have the lowest vapor pressure. Thus, molecules of C would have the lowest vapor pressure.

11.29. The water the farmers spray above and on their fruit is warmer than the temperature of the fruit on the trees. Therefore, as the temperature of the air drops, it absorbs heat from the water, converting it into ice, before absorbing any heat from the fruit. The heat released when the liquid-to-solid phase change occurs prevents the fruit from freezing.

11.31. a.   Considering the A atoms, there are nine A atoms per cell. Of these, eight are in corners and contribute ⅛ per cell, and one is completely inside the cell. Thus there are $8 \times (⅛) + 1 \times (1)$ = 2 A atoms per cell. Next, considering the B atoms, there are six per cell. Of these, four are in faces and contribute ½ per cell, and two are completely inside the cell. Thus, there are $4 \times (½) + 2 \times (1) = 4$ B atoms per unit cell. The ratio of A atoms to B atoms is 2 to 4, or 1 to 2. Thus, the formula of the compound is AB_2.

b.   The A atoms are in the arrangement of a body-centered cell.

11.33. As the water evaporates, molecules with higher kinetic energy escape the liquid and leave behind molecules with lower energy. The result is a drop in temperature of the liquid. Since the cup is well insulated, the energy lost with the evaporated molecules is not rapidly replaced.

11.35. This question can be answered by looking at the packing efficiencies of the three types of crystals: simple cubic, 52.4% body-centered cubic, 68% and face-centered cubic, 74%.

a.   The highest density would correspond to the type of crystal with the highest packing efficiency. Of the three types of crystals, the face-centered cubic has the highest packing efficiency (74%) and thus has the highest density.

b.   The most empty space corresponds to the type of crystal with the lowest packing efficiency. Of the three types of crystals, the simple cubic has the lowest packing efficiency (52.4%) and therefore the most empty space.

■ SOLUTIONS TO PRACTICE PROBLEMS

Note on significant figures: If the final answer to a solution needs to be rounded off, it is given first with one nonsignificant figure, and the last significant figure is underlined. The final answer is then rounded to the correct number of significant figures. In multistep problems, intermediate answers are given with at least one nonsignificant figure; however, only the final answer has been rounded off.

11.37. a. Vaporization   b. Freezing of eggs and sublimation of ice

c. Condensation   d. Gas-solid condensation, deposition

e. Freezing

11.39. Dropping a line from the intersection of a 350-mmHg line with the diethyl ether curve in Figure 11.7 intersects the temperature axis at about 10°C.

11.41. The total amount of energy provided by the heater in 4.54 min is

$$4.54 \text{ min} \times \frac{60 \text{ s}}{1 \text{ min}} \times \frac{3.48 \text{ J}}{\text{s}} = 94\underline{7}.95 \text{ J} \ (0.94\underline{7}95 \text{ kJ})$$

The heat of fusion per mole of I_2 is

$$\frac{0.9479 \text{ kJ}}{15.5 \text{ g I}_2} \times \frac{2 \times 126.9 \text{ g I}_2}{\text{mol I}_2} = 15.\underline{5}2 = \frac{15.5 \text{ kJ}}{\text{mol I}_2}$$

11.43. The heat absorbed per 2.25 g of isopropyl alcohol, C_3H_8O, is

$$2.25 \text{ g } C_3H_8O \times \frac{1 \text{ mol } C_3H_8O}{60.09 \text{ g } C_3H_8O} \times \frac{42.1 \text{ kJ}}{1 \text{ mol } C_3H_8O} = 1.5\underline{7}6 = 1.58 \text{ kJ}$$

11.45. Because all the heat released by freezing the water is used to evaporate the remaining water, you must first calculate the amount of heat released in the freezing:

$$9.31 \text{ g } H_2O \times \frac{\text{mol } H_2O}{18.02 \text{ g } H_2O} \times \frac{6.01 \text{ kJ}}{\text{mol } H_2O} = 3.1\underline{0}505 \text{ kJ}$$

Finally, calculate the mass of H_2O that was vaporized by the 3.10505 kJ of heat:

$$3.10505 \text{ kJ} \times \frac{18.02 \text{ g } H_2O}{1 \text{ mol } H_2O} \times \frac{1 \text{ mol } H_2O}{44.9 \text{ kJ}} = 1.2\underline{4}6 = 1.25 \text{ g } H_2O$$

11.47. Calculate how much heat is released by cooling 64.3 g of H_2O from 55°C to 15°C.

$$\text{Heat released} = (64.3 \text{ g})(15°C - 55°C)\left(\frac{4.18 \text{ J}}{1 \text{ g} \cdot °C}\right) = -1.\underline{0}7509 \times 10^4 \text{ J} = -1\underline{0}.7509 \text{ kJ}$$

The heat released is used first to melt the ice and then to warm the liquid from 0°C to 15°C. Let the mass of ice equal y grams. Then, for fusion, and for warming, we have

$$\text{Fusion: } (y \text{ g } H_2O) \times \frac{1 \text{ mol } H_2O}{18.02 \text{ g } H_2O} \times \frac{6.01 \text{ kJ}}{1 \text{ mol } H_2O} = 0.33\underline{3}5 \, y \text{ kJ}$$

$$\text{Warming: } (y \text{ g } H_2O)(15°C - 0°C)\left(\frac{4.18 \text{ J}}{1 \text{ g} \cdot °C}\right) = 6\underline{2}.70 \, y \text{ J } (0.06\underline{2}70 \, y \text{ kJ})$$

Because the total heat required for melting and warming must equal the heat released by cooling, equate the two, and solve for y.

$$10.7509 \text{ kJ} = 0.3335y \text{ kJ} + 0.0627y \text{ kJ} = y(0.3335 + 0.0627) \text{ kJ}$$

$$y = 10.7509 \text{ kJ} \div 0.39\underline{6}2 \text{ kJ} = 2\underline{7}.13 \text{ (grams)} = 27 \text{ g of ice added}$$

11.49. At the normal boiling point, the vapor pressure of a liquid is 760.0 mmHg. Use the Clausius-Clapeyron equation to find P_2 when $P_1 = 760.0$ mmHg, $T_1 = 334.85$ K (61.7°C), and $T_2 = 309.35$ K (36.2°C). Also use $\Delta H_{vap} = 31.4 \times 10^3$ J/mol.

$$\ln \frac{P_2}{P_1} = \frac{\Delta H_{vap}}{R}\left(\frac{1}{T_1} - \frac{1}{T_2}\right)$$

$$\ln \frac{P_2}{760 \text{ mmHg}} = \frac{31.4 \times 10^3 \text{ J/mol}}{8.31 \text{ J/K} \cdot \text{mol}}\left(\frac{1}{334.85 \text{ K}} - \frac{1}{309.35 \text{ K}}\right) = -0.930\underline{1}8$$

Taking antilogs of both sides gives

$$\frac{P_2}{760 \text{ mmHg}} = e^{-0.93018} = 0.39\underline{4}4$$

$$P_2 = 0.3944 \times 760 \text{ mmHg} = 29\underline{9}.8 = 3.00 \times 10^2 \text{ mmHg } (300. \text{ mmHg})$$

11.51. From the Clausius-Clapeyron equation,

$$\Delta H_{vap} = R\left(\frac{T_2 T_1}{T_2 - T_1}\right)\left[\ln\frac{P_2}{P_1}\right] = [8.31\ \text{J/(K•mol)}]\left[\frac{(553.2\ \text{K})(524.2\ \text{K})}{(553.2 - 524.2)\ \text{K}}\right]\left[\ln\frac{760.0\ \text{mmHg}}{400.0\ \text{mmHg}}\right]$$

$$= 5.3\underline{3}36 \times 10^4\ \text{J/mol} = 53.3\ \text{kJ/mol}$$

11.53. a. At point A, the substance will be a gas.   b. The substance will be a gas.

c. The substance will be a liquid.   d. No

11.55. The phase diagram for oxygen is shown below. It is plotted from these points: triple point = −219°C, boiling point = −183°C, and critical point = −118°C. The graph is not drawn to scale.

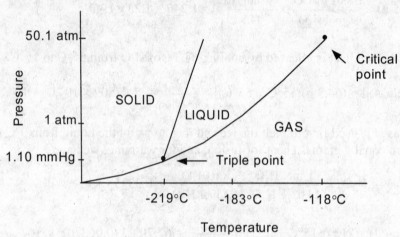

11.57. Liquefied at 25°C: SO_2 and C_2H_2. To liquefy CH_4, lower its temperature below −82°C, and then compress it. To liquefy CO, lower its temperature below −140°C, and then compress it.

11.59. Br_2 phase diagram:

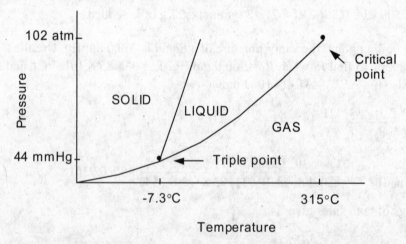

a. Circle "solid." The pressure of 40 mmHg is lower than the pressure at the triple point, so the liquid phase cannot exist.

b. Circle "liquid." The pressure of 400 mmHg is above the triple point, so the gas will to a liquid.

11.61. Yes, the heats of vaporization of 0.9, 5.6, and 20.4 kJ/mol (for H_2, N_2, and Cl_2, respectively) increase in the order of the respective molecular masses of 2.016, 28.02, and 71.0. (London forces increase in order of increasing molecular mass.)

11.63. a. London forces
   b. London and dipole-dipole forces, hydrogen bonding
   c. London and dipole-dipole forces
   d. London forces

11.65. The order is $CCl_4 < SiCl_4 < GeCl_4$ (in order of increasing molecular mass).

11.67. CCl_4 has the lowest vapor pressure because it has the largest molecular mass and the greatest London forces even though $HCCl_3$ and H_3CCl have dipole-dipole interactions.

11.69. The order of increasing vapor pressure is $HOCH_2CH_2OH$, FCH_2CH_2OH, FCH_2CH_2F. There is no hydrogen bonding in the third molecule; the second molecule can hydrogen-bond at only one end; and the first molecule can hydrogen-bond at both ends for the strongest interaction.

11.71. The order is $CH_4 < C_2H_6 < CH_3OH < HOCH_2CH_2OH$. The weakest forces are the London forces in CH_4 and C_2H_6, which increase with molecular mass. The next-strongest interaction is in CH_3OH, which can hydrogen-bond at only one end of the molecule. The strongest interaction is in the $HOCH_2CH_2OH$ molecule, which can hydrogen-bond at both ends.

11.73. a. Metallic   b. Metallic   c. Covalent network   d. Molecular   e. Ionic

11.75. a. Metallic   b. Covalent network (like diamond)   c. Molecular   d. Molecular

11.77. The order is $(C_2H_5)_2O < C_4H_9OH < KCl < CaO$. Melting points increase in the order of attraction between molecules or ions in the solid state. Hydrogen bonding in C_4H_9OH causes it to melt at a higher temperature than $(C_2H_5)_2O$. Both KCl and CaO are ionic solids with much stronger attraction than the organic molecules. In CaO, the higher charges in particular and (less so) the smaller ion sizes cause the lattice energy to be higher than in KCl.

11.79. a. Low-melting and brittle
   b. High-melting, hard, and brittle
   c. Malleable and electrically conducting
   d. Hard and high-melting

11.81. a. LiCl   b. SiC   c. CHI_3 d. Co

11.83. In a simple cubic lattice with one atom at each lattice point, there are atoms only at the corners of unit cells. Each corner is shared by eight unit cells, and there are eight corners per unit cell. Therefore, there is one atom per unit cell.

11.85. Calculate the volume of the unit cell, change density to g/m³, and then convert volume to mass, using density:

$$\text{Volume} = (2.866 \times 10^{-10} \text{ m})^3 = 2.354 \times 20^{-29} \text{ m}^3$$

$$\frac{7.87 \text{ g}}{1 \text{ cm}^3} \times \left(\frac{100 \text{ cm}}{1 \text{ m}}\right)^3 = 7.87 \times 10^6 \text{ g/m}^3$$

$$\text{Mass of one cell} = (7.87 \times 10^6 \text{ g/m}^3) \times (2.354 \times 10^{-29} \text{ m}^3) = 1.8\underline{5}26 \times 10^{-22} \text{ g}$$

Because Fe is a body-centered cubic cell, there are two Fe atoms in the cell, and

$$\text{Mass of one Fe atom} = (1.8526 \times 10^{-22} \text{ g}) \div 2 = 9.2\underline{6}3 \times 10^{-23} \text{ g}$$

Using the molar mass to calculate the mass of one Fe atom, you find the agreement is good:

$$\frac{55.85 \text{ g Fe}}{1 \text{ mol Fe}} \times \frac{1 \text{ mol Fe}}{6.022 \times 10^{23} \text{ Fe atoms}} = 9.2\underline{7}43 \times 10^{-23} \text{ g/Fe atom}$$

11.87. There are four Cu atoms in the face-centered cubic structure, so the mass of one cell is

$$4 \text{ Cu atoms} \times \frac{1 \text{ mol Cu}}{6.022 \times 10^{23} \text{ Cu atoms}} \times \frac{63.5 \text{ g Cu}}{1 \text{ mol Cu}} = 4.2\underline{1}8 \times 10^{-22} \text{ g}$$

$$\text{Cell volume} = \frac{4.218 \times 10^{-22} \text{ g}}{8.93 \text{ g/cm}^3} = 4.7\underline{2}3 \times 10^{-23} \text{ cm}^3$$

All edges are the same length in a cubic cell, so the edge length, l, is

$$l = \sqrt[3]{V} = \sqrt[3]{4.723 \times 10^{-23} \text{ cm}^3} = 3.6\underline{1}4 \times 10^{-8} = 3.61 \times 10^{-8} \text{ cm (361 pm)}$$

11.89. Calculate the volume from the edge length of 407.9 pm (4.079×10^{-8} cm), and then use it to calculate the mass of the unit cell:

$$\text{Cell volume} = (4.079 \times 10^{-8} \text{ cm}^3 = 6.7869 \times 10^{-23} \text{ cm}^3$$

$$\text{Cell mass} = (19.3 \text{ g/cm}^3)(6.7869 \times 20^{-23} \text{ cm}^3) = 1.3\underline{0}98 \times 10^{-21} \text{ g}$$

Calculate the mass of one gold atom:

$$1 \text{ Au atom} \times \frac{1 \text{ mol Au}}{6.022 \times 10^{23} \text{ Au atoms}} \times \frac{196.97 \text{ g Au}}{1 \text{ mol Au}} = 3.27\underline{0}8 \times 10^{-22} \text{ g}$$

$$\frac{1.3098 \times 10^{-21} \text{ g}}{1 \text{ unit cell}} \times \frac{1 \text{ Au atom}}{3.2708 \times 10^{-22} \text{ g Au}} = \frac{4.0\underline{0}4 \text{ Au atoms}}{\text{unit cell}}$$

Since there are four atoms per unit cell, it is face-centered cubic.

11.91. Calculate the volume from the edge (316.5 pm = 3.165×10^{-8} cm). Use it to calculate the mass:

$$\text{Cell volume} = (3.165 \times 10^{-8} \text{ cm})^3 = 3.17\underline{0}5 \times 10^{-23} \text{ cm}^3$$

For a body-centered cubic lattice, there are two atoms per cell, so their mass is

$$2 \text{ W atoms} \times \frac{1 \text{ mol W}}{6.022 \times 10^{23} \text{ W atoms}} \times \frac{183.8 \text{ g W}}{1 \text{ mol W}} = 6.10\underline{4}3 \times 10^{-22} \text{ g W}$$

$$\text{Density} = \frac{6.1043 \times 10^{-22} \text{ g W}}{3.1705 \times 10^{-23} \text{ cm}^3} = 19.2\underline{5}3 = 19.25 \text{ g/cm}^3$$

11.93. Use Avogadro's number to calculate the number of atoms in 1.74 g ($= d \times 1.000 \text{ cm}^3$):

$$1.74 \text{ g Mg} \times \frac{1 \text{ mol Mg}}{24.305 \text{ g Mg}} \times \frac{6.022 \times 10^{23} \text{ Mg atoms}}{1 \text{ mol Mg}} = 4.3\underline{1}1 \times 10^{22} \text{ Mg atoms}$$

Because the space occupied by the Mg atoms = 0.741 cm^3, each atom's volume is

$$\text{Volume 1 Mg atom} = \frac{0.741 \text{ cm}^3}{4.3\underline{1}1 \times 10^{22} \text{ Mg atoms}} = 1.7\underline{1}9 \times 10^{-23} \text{ cm}^3$$

$$\text{Volume} = \frac{4\pi r^3}{3}$$

so

$$r = \sqrt[3]{\frac{3V}{4\pi}} = \sqrt[3]{\frac{3}{4\pi}(1.7\underline{1}9 \times 10^{-23} \text{ cm}^3)} = 1.6\underline{0}1 \times 10^{-8} = 1.60 \times 10^{-8} \text{ cm} (= 160. \text{ pm})$$

■ SOLUTIONS TO GENERAL PROBLEMS

11.95. Water vapor deposits directly to solid water (frost) without forming liquid water. After heating, most of the frost melted to liquid water, which then vaporized to water vapor. Some of the frost may have sublimed directly to water vapor.

11.97. From Table 5.6, the vapor pressures are 18.7 mmHg at 21°C and 12.8 mmHg at 15°C. If the moisture did not begin to condense until the air had been cooled to 15°C, then the partial pressure of water in the air at 21°C must have been 12.8 mmHg. The relative humidity is

$$\text{Percent relative humidity} = \frac{12.8 \text{ mmHg}}{18.7 \text{ mmHg}} \times 100\% = 68.\underline{4}4 = 68.4 \text{ percent}$$

11.99. After labeling the problem data as shown below, use the Clausius-Clapeyron equation to obtain ΔH_{vap}, which can then be used to calculate the boiling point.

At $T_1 = 299.3$ K, $P_1 = 100.0$ mmHg; at $T_2 = 333.8$ K, $P_2 = 400.0$ mmHg

$$\ln \frac{400.0 \text{ mmHg}}{100.0 \text{ mmHg}} = \frac{\Delta H_{vap}}{8.3145 \text{ J/(K} \cdot \text{mol})} \left[\frac{1}{299.3 \text{ K}} - \frac{1}{333.8} \right]$$

$$1.38\underline{6}2 = \Delta H_{vap} (4.1\underline{5}3 \times 10^{-5} \text{ mol/J})$$

$$\Delta H_{vap} = 33.\underline{3}8 \times 10^3 \text{ J/mol } (33.4 \text{ kJ/mol})$$

Now, use this value of ΔH_{vap} and the following data to calculate the boiling point:

At $T_1 = 299.3$ K, $P_1 = 100.0$ mmHg; at T_2 (boiling pt.), $P_2 = 760$ mmHg

$$\ln \frac{760.0 \text{ mmHg}}{100.0 \text{ mmHg}} = \frac{33.4 \times 10^3 \text{ J/mol}}{8.3145 \text{ J/(K} \bullet \text{mol)}} \left[\frac{1}{299.3 \text{ K}} - \frac{1}{T_2} \right]$$

$$2.0281 = 4.0171 \times 10^3 \text{ K} \left[\frac{1}{299.3 \text{ K}} - \frac{1}{T_2} \right]$$

$$\frac{1}{T_2} = \frac{1}{299.3 \text{ K}} - \frac{2.0281}{4.0171 \times 10^3 \text{ K}} = 2.8363 \times 10^{-3}/\text{K}$$

$$T_2 = 352.58 = 352.6 \text{ K } (79.4 \text{ °C})$$

11.101. a.   As this gas is compressed at 20°C, it will condense into a liquid because 20°C is above the triple point but below the critical point.

   b.   As this gas is compressed at −70°C, it will condense directly to the solid phase because the temperature of −70°C is below the triple point.

   c.   As this gas is compressed at 40°C, it will not condense because 40°C is above the critical point.

11.103. In propanol, hydrogen bonding exists between the hydrogen of the OH group and the lone pair of electrons of oxygen of the OH group of an adjacent propanol molecule. For two adjacent propanol molecules, the hydrogen bond may be represented as follows:

   C_3H_7 –O–H•••O(H)C_3H_7

11.105. Ethylene glycol molecules are capable of hydrogen bonding to each other, whereas pentane molecules are not. The greater intermolecular forces in ethylene glycol are reflected in greater resistance to flow (viscosity) and high boiling point.

11.107. Aluminum (Group IIIA) forms a metallic solid. Silicon (Group IVA) forms a covalent network solid. Phosphorus (Group VA) forms a molecular solid. Sulfur (Group VIA) forms a molecular (amorphous) solid.

11.109. a.   Lower: KCl. The lattice energy should be lower for ions with a lower charge. A lower lattice energy implies a lower melting point.

   b.   Lower: CCl_4. Both are nonpolar and form molecular solids, so the compound with the lower molecular mass should have weaker London forces and, therefore, the lower melting point.

   c.   Lower: Zn. Melting points for Group IIB metals are lower than for metals near the middle of the transition-metal series.

   d.   Lower: C_2H_5Cl. Ethyl chloride cannot hydrogen-bond, but acetic acid can. The compound with the weaker intermolecular forces has the lower melting point.

11.111. The face-centered cubic structure means one atom is at each lattice point. All edges are the same length in such a structure, so the volume is

$$\text{Volume} = l^3 = (3.839 \times 10^{-8} \text{ cm})^3 = 5.6579 \times 10^{-23} \text{ cm}^3$$

$$\text{Mass of unit cell} = dV = (22.42 \text{ g/cm}^3)(5.6579 \times 10^{-23} \text{ cm}^3) = 1.2685 \times 10^{-21} \text{ g}$$

There are four atoms in a face-centered cubic cell, so

$$\text{Mass of one Ir atom} = \text{mass of unit cell} \div 4 = (1.2685 \times 10^{-21} \text{ g}) \div 4 = 3.1712 \times 10^{-22} \text{ g}$$

$$\text{Molar mass of Ir} = (3.1712 \times 10^{-22} \text{ g/Ir atom}) \times (6.022 \times 10^{23} \text{ Ir atoms/mol})$$

$$= 190.97 = 191.0 \text{ g/mol (The atomic mass} = 191.0 \text{ amu.)}$$

11.113. From Problem 11.87, the cell edge length (l) is 361.4 pm. There are four copper atom radii along the diagonal of a unit-cell face. Because the diagonal square $= l^2 + l^2$ (Pythagorean theorem),

$$4r = \sqrt{2 l^2} = \sqrt{2} \, l, \text{ or } r = \frac{\sqrt{2}}{4} (361.4 \text{ pm}) = 127.8 = 128 \text{ pm}$$

11.115. The body diagonal (diagonal passing through the center of the cell) is four times the radius, r, of a sphere. Also, from the geometry of a cube and the Pythagorean theorem, the body diagonal equals $\sqrt{3} \, l$, where l is the edge length of the unit cell. Thus

$$4r = \sqrt{3} \, l \qquad \text{or} \qquad l = \frac{4r}{\sqrt{3}}$$

Because the unit cell contains two spheres, the volume occupied by the spheres is

$$V_{\text{spheres}} = 2 \times \frac{4}{3} \pi r^3$$

and

$$V_{\text{cell}} = l^3 = \left[\frac{4r}{\sqrt{3}} \right]^3 = \frac{64r^3}{3\sqrt{3}}$$

Finally, to obtain the percent volume of the cell occupied, divide V_{spheres} by V_{cell}:

$$\text{Percent } V = \frac{V_{\text{spheres}}}{V_{\text{cell}}} \times 100\% = \frac{2\left[\dfrac{4\pi r^3}{3} \right]}{\dfrac{64r^3}{3\sqrt{3}}} \times 100\% = \frac{\pi\sqrt{3}}{8} \times 100\% = 68.01 = 68.0\%$$

11.117. a. Except for an unusually high boiling point for HF, the boiling point increases as the size (number of electrons in the atom or molecule) increases for the hydrogen halides and the noble gases. The London forces or dispersion forces increase.

b. Hydrogen bonding occurs between the H–F molecules and is much stronger than the London forces.

c. In addition to the dispersion forces, the hydrogen halides are polar (have dipole moments), so there are dipole-dipole interactions.

11.119. a.   Diamond and silicon carbide are covalent network solids with strong covalent bonds between all the atoms. Graphite is a layered structure, and the forces holding the layers together are weak dispersion forces.

b.   Silicon dioxide is a giant molecule with an infinite array of O–S–O bonds. Each silicon is bonded to four oxygen atoms in a covalent network solid. Carbon dioxide is a discrete, nonpolar molecule.

11.121. a. CO_2 consists of discrete nonpolar molecules that are held together in the solid by weak dispersion forces. SiO_2 is a covalent network solid with all the atoms held together by strong covalent bonds.

b.   HF(l) has extensive hydrogen bonding among the molecules. HCl(l) boils much lower because it doesn't have hydrogen bonding.

c. SiF_4 is a larger molecule (it has more electrons than CF_4), so it has stronger dispersion forces and a higher boiling point than CF_4. Both molecules are tetrahedrally symmetrical and, therefore, nonpolar.

11.123. In a tank of carbon dioxide under pressure (for example, in a CO_2 fire extinguisher), the substance normally exists as the liquid in equilibrium with its gas phase. At 35°C (above 31°C), the two phases, gas and liquid, are replaced by a single fluid phase. Thus the carbon dioxide in the tank is above its critical temperature and pressure and exists as the supercritical fluid.

11.125. Van der Waals forces exist between any two surfaces but are extremely weak unless relatively large areas of the two surfaces come quite close together. The toe of a gecko is covered with fine hairs, each hair having a thousand or so split ends. As the gecko walks across a surface, it presses these stalks of hairs against the surface. The intimate contact of a billion or so split ends of hairs with the surface results in a large attractive force, holding the gecko fast. This is not true for your finger, where the contact between the surfaces is much less.

11.127. The nematic liquid crystals consist of rodlike, polar molecules in a phase that is intermediate in order between that of a liquid and that of a crystalline solid. The molecules tend to align or orient themselves in the same direction along their long axes, like matches in a matchbox, but they occupy random positions within the substance. Thus, nematic liquid crystals have orientation order but no position order.

11.129. The Bragg equation, $n\lambda = 2d \sin \theta$, relates the wavelength of x rays, λ, to the distance between atomic planes, d, and the angle of reflection, θ. Note that reflections occur at several angles, corresponding to different values of n (n = 1, 2, 3, …).

11.131. Water has several unusual properties that set it apart from other substances. For example, its solid phase, ice, is less dense than liquid water, whereas for most substances the solid phase is more dense than the liquid. In addition, water has an unusually large heat capacity. The unusual properties of water are largely linked to its ability to form hydrogen bonds. For example, ice is less dense than liquid water because ice has an open, hydrogen-bonded structure. Each oxygen atom in the structure of ice is surrounded tetrahedrally by four hydrogen atoms: two that are close and covalently bonded to give the H_2O molecule, and two others that are farther away and held by hydrogen bonds. The tetrahedral angles give rise to a three-dimensional structure that contains open space. The solvent properties of water are also unusual. Water is both a polar substance and a hydrogen-bonding molecule. As a result, water dissolves many substances, including ionic and polar compounds. These properties make water the premier solvent, biologically and industrially.

■ SOLUTIONS TO STRATEGY PROBLEMS

11.133. a. $n = \dfrac{PV}{RT} = \dfrac{(750.0/760 \text{ atm})(20.00 \text{ L})}{(0.082058 \text{ L} \cdot \text{atm/K} \cdot \text{mol})(293.15 \text{ K})} = 0.820\underline{4}78 = 0.8205 \text{ mol N}_2$

b. $353.6 \times 10^{-3} \text{ g} \times \dfrac{1 \text{ mol H}_2\text{O}}{18.0153 \text{ g}} = 0.0196\underline{2}78 = 0.01963 \text{ mol H}_2\text{O}$

The water evaporated and was pushed out of the flask by the nitrogen.

c. During the experiment, the total number of moles of gas that exited the flask is

$n_{\text{tot}} = 0.820478 \text{ mol N}_2 + 0.0196278 \text{ mol H}_2\text{O} = 0.840\underline{1}1 \text{ mol}$

The partial pressure of nitrogen is

$P_{\text{N}_2} = X_{\text{N}_2} P_{\text{tot}} = \dfrac{0.820478 \text{ mol N}_2}{0.84011 \text{ mol}} \times 750.0 \text{ mmHg} = 732.\underline{4}7 = 732.5 \text{ mmHg}$

d. The vapor pressure of water is

$P_{\text{H}_2\text{O}} = P_{\text{tot}} - P_{\text{N}_2} = 750.0 \text{ mmHg} - 732.5 \text{ mmHg} = 17.5 \text{ mmHg}.$

Appendix B gives the vapor pressure of water at 20 °C as 17.5 mmHg, so the calculated value agrees with this value.

11.135. There are three triple points in the phase diagram for sulfur. The triple point at 95°C and 1×10^{-5} atm has the phases rhombic solid, monoclinic solid, and vapor in equilibrium. At 119°C and 6×10^{-5} atm, the phases present are monoclinic solid, liquid, and vapor. The triple point at 151°C and 1290 atm has the phases rhombic solid, monoclinic solid, and liquid in equilibrium. If you cooled liquid sulfur, the solid phase that would freeze out would be monoclinic. It is not the normal phase of solid sulfur, which is rhombic. The rhombic form of solid sulfur cannot form from the liquid except at very high pressures. Only the triple point at 151°C and 1290 atm has the two phases in equilibrium with each other.

11.137. a. At room temperature, carbon dioxide is below its critical temperature, so it would be present in two different phases: liquid and gas. Thus, inside the tank you would expect to see a liquid phase separated from a gaseous phase by a meniscus.

b. The pressure of carbon dioxide would remain constant at the vapor pressure at 20°C for the gas. It would remain the same as long as liquid carbon dioxide was present. As soon as all of the liquid carbon dioxide disappeared, the pressure of the gas would begin to drop, eventually reaching a gauge pressure of zero.

11.139. a. CH_3CHO is a polar molecule, so it has London forces and dipole-dipole forces present. $CH_3CH_2CH_3$ is a nonpolar molecule and has only London forces present. CH_3CH_2OH is a polar molecule with London forces, dipole-dipole forces, and hydrogen bonding.

b. The heat of vaporization increases with increasing intermolecular forces. Since CH_3CHO has stronger intermolecular forces than $CH_3CH_2CH_3$ and weaker intermolecular forces than CH_3CH_2OH, you would expect it to have a heat of vaporization of 25.8 kJ/mol.

c. Use the Clapeyron equation to find the vapor pressure at 15°C.

$$\ln \frac{P_2}{P_1} = \frac{\Delta H_{vap}}{R} \left(\frac{1}{T_1} - \frac{1}{T_2} \right);$$

$$\ln \frac{P_2}{760 \text{ mmHg}} = \frac{25.8 \times 10^3 \text{ J/mol}}{8.3145 \text{ J/K} \cdot \text{mol}} \left(\frac{1}{294 \text{ K}} - \frac{1}{288 \text{ K}} \right) = -0.2198$$

Taking antilogs of both sides gives

$$\frac{P_2}{760 \text{ mmHg}} = e^{-0.2198} = 0.8027; \ P_2 = 0.8027 \times 760 \text{ mmHg} = 610.1 = 6.1 \times 10^2 \text{ mmHg}$$

11.141. a. The rhenium atoms (smaller spheres) are occupying each corner in the unit cell, each atom contributing ⅛ rhenium atom to the unit cell. This gives ⅛(8), or one Re atom per unit cell. The oxygen atoms (larger spheres) are occupying each edge in the unit cell. There are twelve edges in the cell, and each atom on an edge contributes ¼ oxygen atom to the unit cell. This gives ¼(12), or three O atoms per unit cell.

b. Each unit cell has one Re atom and three O atoms for a formula unit of ReO_3, which is red.

11.143. a. Since a smaller amount of substance B has melted, substance B must have stronger intermolecular attractions than substance A.

b. A smaller heat of fusion corresponds to the substance having weaker intermolecular attractions, or substance A.

c. The substance expected to boil at a higher temperature would be the substance having stronger intermolecular attractions, or substance B.

11.145. a. Energy transfer from the puddle to the street occurs after sunset, or during the night. As the outside temperature drops from 3.4 °C to -4.5 °C, the puddle initially cools and loses heat, then loses more heat during freezing, and finally cools again to lose additional heat. These energy losses go into the surroundings, or the underlying street and the overhanging air.

b. Because the highest and lowest temperatures remain the same for each day of the cycle, after the puddle loses heat during the night , it gains an equal amount of heat during the day for a net energy flow of 0 J between the puddle and the surroundings.

c. Because the highest and lowest temperatures remain the same for each day of the cycle, after the puddle gains heat during the day, it loses an equal amount of heat during the night for a net energy clow of 0 J between the puddle and the surroundings.

11.147. a. The thermochemical phase changes for water are as follows:

Melting water: $H_2O(s) \rightarrow H_2O(l)$; $\Delta H_{fus} = 6.01$ kJ/mol

Vaporizing water: $H_2O(l) \rightarrow H_2O(g)$; $\Delta H_{vap} = 40.7$ kJ/mol

Using Hess's law to sum these two processes results in the sublimation process:

Subliming water: $H_2O(s) \rightarrow H_2O(g)$; $\Delta H_{sub} = \Delta H_{fus} + \Delta H_{vap} = 46.7$ kJ/mol

Since sublimation simultaneously involves the energies of both fusing and vaporizing water, more heat will be required to sublime a 1.0 g sample of $H_2O(l)$ at -10 °C than to vaporize a 1.0 g sample of $H_2O(s)$ at 100 °C .

b.   Here we compare the absolute relative heats associated with condensing (an exothermic process) and melting (an endothermic process) a given amount of water. On a molar basis, more energy (ΔH_{vap}) is associated with condensing a given amount of water than melting the same amount of water (ΔH_{fus}). Thus, the amount of heat released when condensing a 0.5 g sample of $H_2O(l)$ at 60°C will be greater than the amount of heat absorbed when melting a 0.5 g sample of $H_2O(s)$ at 0°C.

c.   Regardless of the different oven temperatures, since both ovens are at least 100°C both water samples will remain at the initial boiling point of water (100°C) until the entire samples have been vaporized. Only after complete vaporization will any further increase in temperature occur for the sample in the 200°C oven. Because we are interested only in the energy required for vaporization, less energy will be required to vaporize the 50 g sample of water than for the 100 g of water.

■ SOLUTIONS TO CUMULATIVE-SKILLS PROBLEMS

11.149. Use the ideal gas law to calculate n, the number of moles of N_2:

$$N_2: n = \frac{PV}{RT} = \frac{(745/760 \text{ atm})(5.40 \text{ L})}{(0.082057 \text{ L} \cdot \text{atm/K} \cdot \text{mol})(293.2 \text{ K})} = 0.22\underline{0}0 \text{ mol}$$

$$C_3H_8O: n = 0.6149 \text{ g } C_3H_8O \times \frac{1 \text{ mol } C_3H_8O}{60.094 \text{ g } C_3H_8O} = 0.0102\underline{3}2 \text{ mol}$$

$$X_{C_3H_8O} = \frac{0.0102\underline{3}2 \text{ mol } C_3H_8O}{(0.0102\underline{3}2 \text{ mol} + 0.22\underline{0}0 \text{ mol})} = 0.044\underline{4}4 \text{ mole fraction}$$

Partial $P = 0.044\underline{4}4 \times 745 \text{ mmHg} = 33.\underline{1}1 \text{ mmHg} = 33.1 \text{ mmHg}$

Vapor pressure of C_3H_8O = 33.1 mmHg

11.151. Calculate the moles of HCN in 10.0 mL of the solution (density = 0.687 g HCN/mL HCN):

$$10.0 \text{ mL HCN} \times \frac{0.687 \text{ g HCN}}{1 \text{ mL HCN}} \times \frac{1 \text{ mol HCN}}{27.03 \text{ g HCN}} = 0.25\underline{4}2 \text{ mol HCN}$$

$0.25\underline{4}2 \text{ mol HCN}(l) \rightarrow \quad 0.25\underline{4}2 \text{ mol HCN}(g)$

$(\Delta H_f° = 108.9 \text{ kJ/mol}) \quad (\Delta H_f° = 135.1 \text{ kJ/mol})$

$\Delta H° = 0.25\underline{4}2 \text{ mol} \times [135.1 \text{ kJ/mol} - 108.9 \text{ kJ/mol}] = 6.6\underline{6}0 = 6.66 \text{ kJ}$

11.153. First, convert the mass to moles. Then multiply by the molar heat capacity and the temperature change to determine the heat required to raise the solid's temperature up to its melting point. Next use the heat of fusion to determine the heat required to melt the solid at its melting point. Finally add these two heats together:

$$12.5 \text{ g } P_4 \times \frac{1 \text{ mol } P_4}{123.88 \text{ g } P_4} = 0.10\underline{0}9 \text{ mol } P_4$$

$$0.1009 \text{ mol } P_4 \times \frac{95.4 \text{ J}}{\text{°C} \cdot \text{mol } P_4} \times (44.1°C - 25.0°C) = 18\underline{3}.9 \text{ J} = 0.18\underline{3}9 \text{ kJ}$$

$$0.1009 \text{ mol } P_4 \times 2.63 \text{ kJ/mol } P_4 = 0.26\underline{5}4 \text{ kJ}$$

Total heat = 0.18$\underline{3}$9 kJ + 0.26$\underline{5}$4 kJ = 0.44$\underline{9}$3 = 0.449 kJ = 449 J

11.155. Use the ideal gas law to calculate the total number of moles of monomer and dimer:

$$n = \frac{PV}{RT} = \frac{(436/760)\text{atm} \times 1.000 \text{ L}}{[0.082057 \text{ L} \cdot \text{atm}/(\text{K} \cdot \text{mol})] \times 373.75 \text{ K}} = 0.0187\underline{0}6 \text{ mol (monomer + dimer)}$$

$$(0.0187\underline{0}6 \text{ mol monomer + dimer}) \times \frac{0.630 \text{ mol dimer}}{1 \text{ mol dimer + monomer}} = 0.011\underline{7}8 \text{ mol dimer}$$

0.0187$\underline{0}$6 mol both − 0.011$\underline{7}$8 mol dimer = 0.006$\underline{9}$3 mol monomer

$$\text{Mass dimer} = 0.011\underline{7}8 \text{ mol dimer} \times \frac{120.1 \text{ g dimer}}{1 \text{ mol dimer}} = 1.4\underline{1}4 \text{ g dimer}$$

$$\text{Mass monomer} = 0.006\underline{9}3 \text{ mol monomer} \times \frac{60.05 \text{ g monomer}}{1 \text{ mol monomer}} = 0.4\underline{1}6 \text{ g monomer}$$

$$\text{Density} = \frac{1.4\underline{1}4 \text{ g} + 0.4\underline{1}6 \text{ g}}{1.000 \text{ L}} = 1.8\underline{3}0 = 1.83 \text{ g/L vapor}$$

CHAPTER 12

Solutions

■ SOLUTIONS TO EXERCISES

Note on significant figures: If the final answer to a solution needs to be rounded off, it is given first with one nonsignificant figure, and the last significant figure is underlined. The final answer is then rounded to the correct number of significant figures. In multistep problems, intermediate answers are given with at least one nonsignificant figure; however, only the final answer has been rounded off.

12.1.   An example of a solid solution prepared from a liquid and a solid is a dental filling made of liquid mercury and solid silver.

12.2.   The C_4H_9OH molecules will be more soluble in water because their –OH ends can form hydrogen bonds with water.

12.3.   The Na^+ ion has a larger energy of hydration because its ionic radius is smaller, giving Na^+ a more concentrated electric field than K^+.

12.4.   Write Henry's law ($S = k_H P$) for 159 mmHg (P_2), and divide it by Henry's law for 1 atm, or 760 mmHg (P_1). Then substitute the experimental values of P_1, P_2, and S_1 to solve for S_2.

$$\frac{S_2}{S_1} = \frac{k_H P_2}{k_H P_1} = \frac{P_2}{P_1}$$

Solving for S_2 gives

$$S_2 = \frac{P_2 S_1}{P_1} = \frac{(159 \text{ mmHg})(0.0404 \text{ g O}_2/\text{L})}{760 \text{ mmHg}} = 8.4\underline{5}2 \times 10^{-3} = 8.45 \times 10^{-3} \text{ g O}_2/\text{L}$$

12.5.   The mass of HCl in 20.2% HCl (0.202 = fraction of HCl) is

$$0.202 \times 35.0 \text{ g} = 7.0\underline{7}0 = 7.07 \text{ g HCl}$$

The mass of H_2O in 20.2% HCl is

$$35.0 \text{ g solution} - 7.07 \text{ g HCl} = 27.\underline{9}3 = 27.9 \text{ g H}_2O$$

12.6.   Calculate the moles of toluene using its molar mass of 92.14 g/mol:

$$35.6 \text{ g toluene} \times \frac{1 \text{ mol toluene}}{92.14 \text{ g toluene}} = 0.38\underline{6}3 \text{ mol toluene}$$

To calculate molality, divide the moles of toluene by the mass in kg of the solvent (C_6H_6):

$$\text{Molality} \times \frac{0.3863 \text{ mol toluene}}{0.125 \text{ kg solvent}} = 3.09\underline{0}4 = 3.09 \ m \text{ toluene}$$

12.7.   The number of moles of toluene = 0.3863 (previous exercise); the number of moles of benzene is

$$125 \text{ g benzene} \times \frac{1 \text{ mol benzene}}{78.11 \text{ g benzene}} = 1.6003 \text{ mol benzene}$$

The total number of moles is 1.6003 + 0.3863 = 1.9866, and the mole fractions are

$$\text{Mole fraction benzene} \times \frac{1.6003 \text{ mol benzene}}{1.9866 \text{ mol}} = 0.80554 = 0.806$$

$$\text{Mole fraction toluene} \times \frac{0.3863 \text{ mol toluene}}{1.9866 \text{ mol}} = 0.1944 = 0.194$$

The sum of the mole fractions = 1.000.

12.8.   This solution contains 0.120 moles of methanol dissolved in 1.00 kg of ethanol. The number of moles in 1.00 kg of ethanol is

$$1.00 \times 10^3 \text{ g } C_2H_5OH \times \frac{1 \text{ mol } C_2H_5OH}{46.07 \text{ g } C_2H_5OH} = 21.706 \text{ mol } C_2H_5OH$$

The total number of moles is 21.706 + 0.120 = 21.826, and the mole fractions are

$$\text{Mole fraction } C_2H_5OH = \frac{21.706 \text{ mol } C_2H_5OH}{21.826 \text{ mol}} = 0.994501 = 0.995$$

$$\text{Mole fraction } CH_3OH = \frac{0.120 \text{ mol } CH_3OH}{21.826 \text{ mol}} = 0.005498 = 0.00550$$

The sum of the mole fractions is 1.000.

12.9.   One mole of solution contains 0.250 mol methanol and 0.750 mol ethanol. The mass of this amount of ethanol, the solvent, is

$$0.750 \text{ mol } C_2H_5OH \times \frac{46.07 \text{ g } C_2H_5OH}{1 \text{ mol } C_2H_5OH} = 34.55 \text{ g } C_2H_5OH \text{ (0.03455 kg)}$$

The molality of methanol in the ethanol solvent is

$$\frac{0.250 \text{ mol } CH_3OH}{0.03455 \text{ kg } C_2H_5OH} = 7.2358 = 7.24 \text{ } m \text{ } CH_3OH$$

12.10.   Assume an amount of solution contains 1 kg of water. The mass of urea in this mass is

$$3.42 \text{ mol urea} \times \frac{60.05 \text{ g urea}}{1 \text{ mol urea}} = 205.4 \text{ g urea}$$

The total mass of solution is 205.4 + 1000.0 g = 1205.4 g. The volume and molarity are

$$\text{Volume of solution} = 1205.4 \text{ g} \times \frac{1 \text{ mL}}{1.045 \text{ g}} = 1153.49 \text{ mL} = 1.15349 \text{ L}$$

$$\text{Molarity} = \frac{3.42 \text{ mol urea}}{1.15349 \text{ L solution}} = 2.9649 \text{ mol/L} = 2.96 \text{ } M$$

12.11. Assume a volume equal to 1.000 L of solution. Then

$$\text{Mass of solution} = 1.029 \text{ g/mL} \times (1.000 \times 10^3 \text{ mL}) = 1029 \text{ g}$$

$$\text{Mass of urea} = 2.00 \text{ mol urea} \times \frac{60.05 \text{ g urea}}{1 \text{ mol urea}} = 120.1 \text{ g urea}$$

$$\text{Mass of water} = (1029 - 120.1) \text{ g} = 90\underline{8}.9 \text{ g water} (0.90\underline{8}9 \text{ kg})$$

$$\text{Molality} = \frac{2.00 \text{ mol urea}}{0.9089 \text{ kg solvent}} = 2.2\underline{0}04 = 2.20 \text{ } m \text{ urea}$$

12.12. Calculate the moles of naphthalene and the moles of chloroform:

$$0.515 \text{ g C}_{10}\text{H}_8 \times \frac{1 \text{ mol C}_{10}\text{H}_8}{128.17 \text{ g C}_{10}\text{H}_8} = 0.00401\underline{8} \text{ mol C}_{10}\text{H}_8$$

$$60.8 \text{ g CHCl}_3 \times \frac{1 \text{ mol CHCl}_3}{119.38 \text{ g CHCl}_3} = 0.50\underline{9}29 \text{ mol CHCl}_3$$

The total number of moles is $0.004018 + 0.50929 = 0.51\underline{3}3$ mol, and the mole fraction of chloroform is

$$\text{Mole fraction CHCl}_3 = \frac{0.50929 \text{ mol CHCl}_3}{0.5133 \text{ mol}} = 0.99\underline{2}1$$

$$\text{Mole fraction C}_{10}\text{H}_8 = \frac{0.004018 \text{ mol C}_{10}\text{H}_8}{0.5133 \text{ mol}} = 0.00782\underline{8}$$

The vapor-pressure lowering is

$$\Delta P = P° \, X_{\text{C}_{10}\text{H}_8} = (156 \text{ mmHg})(0.007828) = 1.2\underline{2}1 = 1.22 \text{ mmHg}$$

Use Raoult's law to calculate the vapor pressure of chloroform:

$$P = P° \, X_{\text{CHCl}_3} = (156 \text{ mmHg})(0.9921) = 15\underline{4}.7 = 155 \text{ mmHg}$$

12.13. Solve for c_m in the freezing-point-depression equation ($\Delta T = K_f c_m$; K_f in Table 12.3):

$$c_m = \frac{\Delta T}{K_f} = \frac{0.150°\text{C}}{1.858°\text{C}/m} = 0.80\underline{7}3 \text{ } m$$

Use the molal concentration to solve for the mass of ethylene glycol:

$$\frac{0.08073 \text{ mol glycol}}{1 \text{ kg solvent}} \times 0.0378 \text{ kg solvent} = 0.003\underline{0}51 \text{ mol glycol}$$

$$0.003051 \text{ mol glycol} \times \frac{62.1 \text{ g glycol}}{1 \text{ mol glycol}} = 1.8\underline{9}4 \times 10^{-1} = 1.89 \times 10^{-1} \text{ g glycol}$$

12.14. Calculate the moles of ascorbic acid (vitamin C) from the molality, and then divide the mass of 0.930 g by the number of moles to obtain the molar mass:

$$\frac{0.0555 \text{ mol vit. C}}{1 \text{ kg H}_2\text{O}} \times 0.0950 \text{ kg H}_2\text{O} = 0.005272 \text{ mol vit C}$$

$$\frac{0.930 \text{ g vit. C}}{0.005272 \text{ mol vit. C}} = 17\underline{6}.4 = 176 \text{ g/mol}$$

The molecular mass of ascorbic acid, or vitamin C, is 176 amu.

12.15. The molal concentration of white phosphorus is

$$c_m = \frac{\Delta T}{K_b} = \frac{0.159°\text{C}}{2.40°\text{C}/m} = 0.066\underline{2}5 \ m$$

The number of moles of white phosphorus (P_x) present in this solution is

$$\frac{0.06625 \text{ mol P}_x}{1 \text{ kg CS}_2} \times 0.0250 \text{ kg CS}_2 = 0.00165\underline{6} \text{ mol P}_x$$

The molar mass of white phosphorus equals the mass divided by moles:

$$0.205 \text{ g} \div 0.001656 \text{ mol} = 12\underline{3}.77 = 124 \text{ g/mol}$$

Thus, the molecular mass of P_x is 124 amu. The number of P atoms in the molecule of white phosphorus is obtained by dividing the molecular mass by the atomic mass of P:

$$\frac{123.77 \text{ amu P}_x}{30.97 \text{ amu P}} = 3.99\underline{6}5 = 4.00$$

Hence, the molecular formula is P_4 ($x = 4$).

12.16. The number of moles of sucrose is

$$5.0 \text{ g sucrose} \times \frac{1 \text{ mol sucrose}}{342.3 \text{ g sucrose}} = 0.01\underline{4}6 \text{ mol sucrose}$$

The molarity of the solution is

$$\frac{0.0146 \text{ mol sucrose}}{0.100 \text{ L}} = 0.1\underline{4}6 \ M \text{ sucrose}$$

The osmotic pressure, π, is equal to MRT and is calculated as follows:

$$\frac{0.146 \text{ mol sucrose}}{1 \text{ L}} \times \frac{0.0821 \text{ L} \cdot \text{atm}}{\text{K} \cdot \text{mol}} \times 293 \text{ K} = 3.\underline{5}1 = 3.5 \text{ atm}$$

12.17. The number of ions from each formula unit is i. Here,

$$i = 1 + 2 = 3$$

The boiling-point elevation is

$$\Delta T_b = K_b c_m = 3 \times \frac{0.512°C}{m} \times 0.050 \ m = 0.07\underline{6}81 = 0.077°C$$

The boiling point of aqueous $MgCl_2$ is 100.077°C.

12.18. $AlCl_3$ would be most effective in coagulating colloidal sulfur because of the greater magnitude of charge on the Al ion (3+).

■ ANSWERS TO CONCEPT CHECKS

12.1. In each case, the component present in the greatest amount is the solvent.

   a.   Mo is the solute, and Cr is the solvent.

   b. $MgCl_2$ is the solute, and water is the solvent.

   c. N_2 and O_2 are the solutes, and Ar is the solvent.

12.2. Because compound X has no dipole-dipole attractions of any kind, its attractive forces must be dispersion forces. If compound X has stronger dispersion forces than the hydrogen bonding forces exhibited by compound Y, X must be a relatively large nonpolar molecule. Compound X will be soluble in the nonpolar solvent but insoluble in water, a polar solvent. If compound Y has stronger hydrogen bonding forces than dispersion forces, Y must be a relatively small yet polar molecule containing H bonded to N, O, or F. Compound Y will be soluble in water but insoluble in the nonpolar solvent.

12.3. The two main factors to consider when trying to determine the solubility of an ionic compound in water are ionic size and lattice energy. In this case, the lattice energy for the two compounds is the same; you can discount its effects. Since a smaller cation will have a more concentrated electric field leading to a larger energy of hydration, you would expect that if AB_2 has a smaller cation, then AB_2 will have a greater energy of hydration and AB_2 will be the more soluble compound.

12.4. As the altitude increases, the atmospheric pressure decreases, and thus the partial pressure of oxygen decreases. Above 3500 m, the partial pressure of oxygen in air has decreased to the point that not enough will dissolve in the water to sustain the fish.

12.5. In order to boil at a lower temperature than water, the vapor pressure of the solution (water + liquid) must be greater than that of water. To make this solution, you must add a liquid that is both soluble in water and chemically similar to water. It must have a higher vapor pressure than water and a boiling point lower than 100°C. One possible liquid is ethanol, with a boiling point of 78.3°C (Table 12.3).

12.6. By the principle of osmosis, in a brine solution, water will flow out of the pickle (lower concentration of ions) into the brine (higher concentration of ions). If the pickles were stored in a water solution, the water (lower concentration of ions) would flow into the pickle (higher concentration of ions) and cause it to swell up and probably burst.

12.7.   These are water solutions of identical volume (normal boiling point 100°C) containing different numbers of moles of solute. The boiling point of a solution can be determined by the formula $\Delta T_b = iK_b m$. The solution with the largest ΔT_b will have the highest boiling point. Since K_b is a constant, this will be the compound with the largest factor of $i \bullet m$. Also, since the volume is constant, the factor reduces to $i \bullet$ moles. Ideally, all of the compounds will dissolve completely, so NaCl and KBr have $i = 2$, and Na_2SO_4 and $MgCl_2$ have $i = 3$.

This gives

> For NaCl, $i \bullet$ moles = $2 \times 1.5 = 3.0$
>
> For Na_2SO_4, $i \bullet$ moles = $3 \times 1.3 = 3.9$
>
> For $MgCl_2$, $i \bullet$ moles = $3 \times 2.0 = 6.0$
>
> For KBr, $i \bullet$ moles = $2 \times 2.0 = 4.0$

The result is given from highest boiling point to lowest boiling point:

> $MgCl_2 >$ KBr $> Na_2SO_4 >$ NaCl

12.7.   Iron(III) hydroxide is a hydrophobic colloid. As the colloid forms in water, an excess of iron(III) ion (Fe^{3+}) is present on the surface, giving each crystal an excess positive charge. These positively charged crystals repel one another, so aggregation to larger particles of iron(III) hydroxide is prevented. When the electrodes are dipped into the colloidal solution, iron(III) hydroxide precipitates because electrons from the negative electrode neutralize the excess positive charge on the iron(III) hydroxide, allowing larger particles to form (precipitate).

■ ANSWERS TO SELF-ASSESSMENT AND REVIEW QUESTIONS

12.1.   An example of a gaseous solution is air, in which nitrogen (78%) acts as a solvent for a gas such as oxygen (21%). Recall that the solvent is the component that is present in greater amount. An example of a liquid solution containing a gas is any carbonated beverage in which water acts as the solvent for carbon dioxide gas. Ethanol in water is an example of a liquid-liquid solution. An example of a solid solution is any gold-silver alloy.

12.2.   The two factors that explain differences in solubilities are (1) the natural tendency of substances to mix together, or the natural tendency of substances to become disordered, and (2) the relative forces of attraction between solute species (or solvent species) compared to that between the solute and solvent species. The strongest interactions are always achieved.

12.3.   This is not a case of "like dissolves like." There are strong hydrogen-bonding forces between the water molecules. For the octane to mix with water, hydrogen bonds must be broken and replaced by the much weaker London forces between water and octane. Thus, octane does not dissolve in water, because the maximum forces of attraction among molecules are obtained if it does not dissolve.

12.4.   In most cases, the wide differences in solubility can be explained in terms of the different energies of attraction between ions in the crystal and between ions and water. Hydration energy is used to measure the attraction of ions for water molecules, and lattice energy is used to measure the attraction of positive ions for negative ions in the crystal lattice. An ionic substance is soluble when the hydration energy is much larger than the lattice energy. An ionic substance is insoluble when the lattice energy is much larger than the hydration energy.

12.5. A sodium chloride crystal dissolves in water because of two factors. The positive Na^+ ion is strongly attracted to the oxygen (negative end of the water dipole) and dissolves as $Na^+(aq)$. The negative Cl^- ion is strongly attracted to the hydrogens (positive end of the water dipole) and dissolves as $Cl^-(aq)$.

12.6. When the temperature (energy of a solution) is increased, the solubility of an ionic compound usually increases. A number of salts are exceptions to this rule, particularly a number of calcium salts such as calcium acetate, calcium sulfate, and calcium hydroxide (although the solubilities of calcium bromide, calcium chloride, calcium fluoride, and calcium iodide all increase with temperature).

12.7. Calcium chloride is an example of a salt that releases heat when it dissolves (exothermic heat of solution). Ammonium nitrate is an example of a salt that absorbs heat when it dissolves (endothermic heat of solution).

12.8. As the temperature of the solution is increased by heating, the concentration of the dissolved gas would decrease.

12.9. A carbonated beverage must be stored in a closed container because carbonated beverages must contain more carbon dioxide than is soluble in water at atmospheric pressure. It is possible to add carbon dioxide under pressure to a closed container before it is sealed and increase the solubility of carbon dioxide. This is an illustration of Le Châtelier's principle, which states that the equilibrium between gaseous and dissolved carbon dioxide is shifted in favor of the dissolved carbon dioxide by an increase in pressure.

12.10. According to Le Châtelier's principle, a gas is more soluble in a liquid at higher pressures because, when the gas dissolves in the liquid, the system decreases in volume, tending to decrease the applied pressure. However, when a solid dissolves in a liquid, there is very little volume change. Thus, pressure has very little effect on the solubility of a solid in a liquid.

12.11. The four ways to express the concentration of a solute in a solution are (1) molarity, which is moles per liter; (2) mass percentage of solute, which is the percentage by mass of solute contained in a given mass of solution; (3) molality, which is the moles of solute per kilogram of solvent; and (4) mole fraction, which is the moles of the component substance divided by the total moles of solution.

12.12. The vapor pressure of the solvent of the dilute solution is larger than the vapor pressure of the solvent of the more concentrated solution (Raoult's law). Thus, the more dilute solution loses solvent and becomes more concentrated while the solvent molecules in the vapor state condense into the concentrated solution, making it more dilute. After sufficient time has passed, the vapor pressure of the solvent in the closed container will reach a steady value (equilibrium), at which time the concentration of solute will be the same in the two solutions.

12.13. In fractional distillation, the vapor that first appears over a solution will have a greater mole fraction of the more volatile component. If a portion of this is vaporized and condensed, the liquid will be still richer in the more volatile component. After successive distillation stages, eventually the more volatile component will be obtained in pure form (Figure 12.20).

12.14. The boiling point of the solution is higher because the nonvolatile solute lowers the vapor pressure of the solvent. Thus, the temperature must be increased to a value greater than the boiling point of the pure solvent to achieve a vapor pressure equal to atmospheric pressure.

12.15. One application is the use of ethylene glycol in automobile radiators as antifreeze; the glycol-water mixture usually has a freezing point well below the average low temperature during the winter. A second application is spreading sodium chloride on icy roads in the winter to melt the ice. The ice usually melts, because at equilibrium, a concentrated solution of NaCl usually freezes at a temperature below that of the roads.

12.16. If a pressure greater than the osmotic pressure of the ocean water is applied, the natural osmotic flow can be reversed. Then, the water solvent flows from the ocean water through a membrane to a more dilute solution or to pure water, leaving behind the salt and other ionic compounds from the ocean in a more concentrated solution.

12.17. Part of the light from the sun is scattered in the direction of an observer by fine particles in the clouds (Tyndall effect) rather than being completely absorbed by the clouds. The scattered light becomes visible against the darker background of dense clouds.

12.18. Fog is an aerosol, whipped cream is a foam, mayonnaise is an emulsion, solid silver chloride dispersed in water is a sol, and fruit jelly is a gel.

12.19. The polar –OH group on glycerol allows it to interact (hydrogen-bond) with the polar water molecules, which means it is like water and, therefore, will dissolve in water. Benzene is a nonpolar molecule, which indicates that it is not "like" water and, therefore, will not dissolve in water.

12.20. Soap removes oil from a fabric by absorbing the oil into the hydrophobic centers of the soap micelles and off the surface of the fabric. Rinsing removes the micelles from contact with the fabric and leaves only water on the fabric, which can then be dried.

12.21. The answer is a, 6.50×10^{-2} mol.

12.22. The answer is c, 8.66 m.

12.23. The answer is e, 25.3 g/mol.

12.24. The answer is a, the solution would freeze at a lower temperature than pure water.

■ ANSWERS TO CONCEPTUAL PROBLEMS

12.27. The amount of oxygen dissolved in water decreases as the temperature increases. Thus, at the lower temperatures, there is enough oxygen dissolved in the water to support both bass and trout. But as the temperature rises above 23°C, there is not enough dissolved oxygen in the warm water to support the trout, which need more O_2 than bass.

12.29. The two main factors to consider when trying to determine the solubility of an ionic compound in water are ionic size and lattice energy. Ionic size is inversely related to the energy of hydration; the smaller the ion, the greater the energy of hydration. Keep in mind that the greater the energy of hydration, the more likely it is for a compound to dissolve. The amount of lattice energy is directly related to the solubility of the compound; the lower the lattice energy, the more likely it is for the compound to dissolve.

Taking into account these factors, in order to increase the solubility of a compound you need to decrease the ionic size and decrease the lattice energy. Since the energy of hydration of the Y^+ ion is greater than that of the X^+ ion (making XZ less soluble), in order for XZ to be more soluble than YZ, the lattice energy must be less for the XZ compound.

12.31. Smoke particles carry a small net charge that prevents them from forming larger particles that would settle to the bottom of the smokestack. The charged smoke particles are neutralized by the current, which then allows them to aggregate into large particles. These large particles are too big to be carried out of the stack.

12.33. Vinegar is a solution of acetic acid (solute) and water (solvent). Because the salt concentration is higher outside the lettuce leaf than inside, water will pass out of the lettuce leaf into the dressing via osmosis. The result is that the lettuce will wilt.

12.35. To answer these questions, it is necessary to determine the relative concentrations of solute particles in each beaker. With equal moles and equal volumes, the solution concentration will be directly proportional to the van't Hoff factor, i, for that compound. Urea, a nonelectrolyte, has $i = 1$. NaCl, which is ionic, has $i = 2$, and $CaCl_2$, which is also ionic, has $i = 3$.

   a. The highest boiling point will correspond to the largest boiling-point elevation, ΔT_b. Since $\Delta T_b = iK_bm$, the largest ΔT_b will correspond to the highest value of i. Thus, the solution with $CaCl_2$ ($i = 3$) will have the highest boiling point.

   b. The highest freezing point will correspond to the smallest freezing-point depression, ΔT_f. Since $\Delta T_f = iK_fm$, the smallest ΔT_f will correspond to the smallest value of i. Thus, the solution with urea ($i = 1$) will have the highest freezing point.

■ SOLUTIONS TO PRACTICE PROBLEMS

Note on significant figures: If the final answer to a solution needs to be rounded off, it is given first with one nonsignificant figure, and the last significant figure is underlined. The final answer is then rounded to the correct number of significant figures. In multistep problems, intermediate answers are given with at least one nonsignificant figure; however, only the final answer has been rounded off. Atomic masses are rounded to two decimal places, except for that of hydrogen.

12.37. An example of a liquid solution prepared by dissolving a gas in a liquid is household ammonia, which consists of ammonia (NH_3) gas dissolved in water.

12.39. Boric acid would be more soluble in ethanol because this acid is polar and is more soluble in a more polar solvent. It can also hydrogen-bond to ethanol but not to benzene.

12.41. The order of increasing solubility is $H_2O < CH_2OHCH_2OH < C_{10}H_{22}$. The solubility in nonpolar hexane increases with the decreasing polarity of the solute.

12.43. The Al^{3+} ion has both a greater charge and a smaller ionic radius than Mg^{2+}, so Al^{3+} should have a greater energy of hydration.

12.45. The order is $Ba(IO_3)_2 < Sr(IO_3)_2 < Ca(IO_3)_2 < Mg(IO_3)_2$. The iodate ion is fairly large, so the lattice energy for all these iodates should change to a smaller degree than the hydration energy of the cations. Therefore, solubility should increase with decreasing cation radius.

12.47. Using Henry's law, let S_1 = the solubility at 1.00 atm (P_1), and S_2 = the solubility at 5.50 atm (P_2).

$$S_2 = \frac{P_2 S_1}{P_1} = \frac{(5.50 \text{ atm})(0.161 \text{ g}/100 \text{ mL})}{1.00 \text{ atm}} = 0.88\underline{5}5 = 0.886 \text{ g}/100 \text{ mL}$$

12.49. First, calculate the mass of KI in the solution; then calculate the mass of water needed.

$$\text{Mass KI} = 72.5 \text{ g} \times \frac{5.00 \text{ g KI}}{100 \text{ g solution}} = 3.6\underline{2}5 = 3.63 \text{ g KI}$$

$$\text{Mass H}_2\text{O} = 72.5 \text{ g soln} - 3.625 \text{ g KI} = 68.\underline{8}75 = 68.9 \text{ g H}_2\text{O}$$

Dissolve 3.63 g KI in 68.9 g of water.

12.51. Multiply the mass of KI by 100 g of solution per 5.00 g KI (reciprocal of percentage).

$$0.258 \text{ g KI} \times \frac{100 \text{ g solution}}{5.00 \text{ g KI}} = 5.1\underline{6}0 = 5.16 \text{ g solution}$$

12.53. Convert mass of vanillin ($C_8H_8O_3$, molar mass 152.14 g/mol) to moles, convert mg of ether to kg, and divide for molality.

$$0.0391 \text{ g vanillin} \times \frac{1 \text{ mol vanillin}}{152.14 \text{ g vanillin}} = 2.5\underline{7}0 \times 10^{-4} \text{ mol vanillin}$$

$$168.5 \text{ mg ether} \times 1 \text{ kg}/10^6 \text{ mg} = 168.5 \times 10^{-6} \text{ kg ether}$$

$$\text{Molality} = \frac{2.570 \times 10^{-4} \text{ mol vanillin}}{168.5 \times 10^{-6} \text{ kg ether}} = 1.5\underline{2}52 = 1.53 \text{ } m \text{ vanillin}$$

12.55. Convert mass of fructose ($C_6H_{12}O_6$, molar mass 180.16 g/mol) to moles, and then multiply by one kg H_2O per 0.125 mol fructose (the reciprocal of molality).

$$1.75 \text{ g fructose} \times \frac{1 \text{ mol fructose}}{180.16 \text{ g fructose}} \times \frac{1 \text{ kg H}_2\text{O}}{0.125 \text{ mol fructose}} = 0.0777\underline{0} \text{ kg } (77.7 \text{ g H}_2\text{O})$$

12.57. Convert masses to moles, and then calculate the mole fractions.

$$65.0 \text{ g alc.} \times \frac{1 \text{ mol alc.}}{60.09 \text{ g alc.}} = 1.0\underline{8}17 \text{ mol alc.}$$

$$35.0 \text{ g H}_2\text{O} \times \frac{1 \text{ mol H}_2\text{O}}{18.02 \text{ g H}_2\text{O}} = 1.9\underline{4}22 = 1.94 \text{ mol H}_2\text{O}$$

$$\text{Mole fraction alc.} = \frac{\text{mol alc.}}{\text{total mol}} = \frac{1.0817 \text{ mol}}{3.0239 \text{ mol}} = 0.35\underline{7}7 = 0.358$$

$$\text{Mole fraction } H_2O = \frac{\text{mol } H_2O}{\text{total mol}} = \frac{1.9422 \text{ mol}}{3.0239 \text{ mol}} = 0.64\underline{2}2 = 0.642$$

Alternatively, since the sum of the mole fractions must add to 1, the mole fraction of water could have been obtained by subtracting the mole fraction of alcohol from 1:

$$\text{Mole fraction } H_2O = 1.000 - \text{Mole fraction alc.} = 1.000 - 0.358 = 0.642$$

12.59. In the solution, for every 0.650 mol of NaClO there is 1.00 kg, or 1.00×10^3 g, of H_2O, so

$$1.00 \times 10^3 \text{ g } H_2O \times \frac{1 \text{ mol } H_2O}{18.02 \text{ g } H_2O} = 55.\underline{4}9 \text{ mol } H_2O$$

Total mol $= 55.\underline{4}9 \text{ mol } H_2O + 0.650 \text{ mol NaClO} = 56.\underline{1}4 \text{ mol}$

$$\text{Mole fraction NaClO} = \frac{\text{mol NaClO}}{\text{total mol}} = \frac{0.650 \text{ mol}}{56.\underline{1}4 \text{ mol}} = 0.011\underline{5}7 = 0.0116$$

12.61. The total moles of solution $= 3.31 \text{ mol } H_2O + 1.00 \text{ mol HCl} = 4.31 \text{ mol}$

$$\text{Mole fraction HCl} = \frac{1 \text{ mol HCl}}{4.31 \text{ mol}} = 0.23\underline{2}01 = 0.232$$

$$3.31 \text{ mol } H_2O \times \frac{18.02 \text{ g } H_2O}{1 \text{ mol } H_2O} \times \frac{1 \text{ kg } H_2O}{10^3 \text{ g } H_2O} = 5.9\underline{6}5 \times 10^{-2} \text{ kg } H_2O$$

$$\text{Molality} = \frac{1.00 \text{ mol HCl}}{5.965 \times 10^{-2} \text{ kg } H_2O} = 16.\underline{7}6 = 16.8 \text{ } m$$

12.63. The mass of 1.000 L of solution is 1.022 kg. In the solution, there is 0.580 mol $H_2C_2O_4$ (OA) for every 1.0000 kg of water. Convert this number of moles to mass.

$$0.580 \text{ mol OA} \times \frac{90.04 \text{ g OA}}{1 \text{ mol OA}} \times \frac{1 \text{ kg OA}}{10^3 \text{ g OA}} = 0.052\underline{2}2 \text{ kg OA}$$

The total mass of the solution containing 1.000 kg H_2O and 0.580 mol OA is calculated as follows:

$$\text{Mass} = 1.0000 \text{ kg } H_2O + 0.05222 \text{ kg OA} = 1.05\underline{2}22 \text{ kg}$$

Use this to relate the mass of 1.000 L (1.022 kg) of solution to the amount of solute:

$$1.022 \text{ kg solution} \times \frac{0.580 \text{ mol OA}}{1.05222 \text{ kg solution}} = 0.56\underline{3}3 \text{ mol OA}$$

$$\text{Molality} = \frac{0.5633 \text{ mol OA}}{1.00 \text{ L solution}} = 0.56\underline{3}3 = 0.563 \text{ } M$$

12.65. In 1.000 L of vinegar, there is 0.763 mol of acetic acid. The total mass of the 1.000-L solution is 1.004 kg. Start by calculating the mass of acetic acid (AA) in the solution.

$$0.763 \text{ mol AA} \times \frac{60.05 \text{ g AA}}{1 \text{ mol AA}} = 45.\underline{8}2 \text{ g AA } (0.045\underline{8}2 \text{ kg AA})$$

The mass of water may be found by difference:

$$\text{Mass H}_2\text{O} = 1.004 \text{ kg soln} - 0.04582 \text{ kg AA} = 0.95\underline{8}2 \text{ kg H}_2\text{O}$$

$$\text{Molality} = \frac{0.763 \text{ mol AA}}{0.9582 \text{ kg H}_2\text{O}} = 0.79\underline{6}2 = 0.796 \ m$$

12.67. To find the mole fraction of sucrose, first find the amounts of both sucrose (suc.) and water:

$$20.2 \text{ g sucrose} \times \frac{1 \text{ mol sucrose}}{342.30 \text{ g sucrose}} = 0.059\underline{0}1 \text{ mol sucrose}$$

$$70.1 \text{ g H}_2\text{O} \times \frac{1 \text{ mol H}_2\text{O}}{18.02 \text{ g H}_2\text{O}} = 3.8\underline{9}0 \text{ mol H}_2\text{O}$$

$$X_{\text{sucrose}} = \frac{0.05901 \text{ mol sucrose}}{(3.890 + 0.05901) \text{ mol}} = 0.014\underline{9}4$$

From Raoult's law, the vapor pressure (P) and lowering (ΔP) are

$$P = P^{\circ}_{\text{H}_2\text{O}} \ X_{\text{H}_2\text{O}} = P^{\circ}_{\text{H}_2\text{O}} \ (1 - X_{\text{suc.}}) = (42.2 \text{ mmHg})(1 - 0.01494) = 41.\underline{5}69 = 41.6 \text{ mmHg}$$

$$\Delta P = P^{\circ}_{\text{H}_2\text{O}} \ X_{\text{suc.}} = (42.2 \text{ mmHg})(0.01494) = 0.63\underline{0}6 = 0.631 \text{ mmHg}$$

12.69. Find the molality of glycerol (gly.) in the solution first:

$$0.150 \text{ g gly.} \times \frac{1 \text{ mol gly.}}{92.095 \text{ g gly.}} = 0.0016\underline{2}8 \text{ mol gly.}$$

$$\text{Molality} = \frac{0.001628 \text{ mol gly.}}{0.0200 \text{ kg solvent}} = 0.0814\underline{3}7 \ m$$

Substitute $K_b = 0.512°\text{C}/m$ and $K_f = 1.858 °\text{C}/m$ (Table 12.3) into equations for ΔT_b and ΔT_f:

$$\Delta T_b = K_b m = 0.512°\text{C}/m \times 0.081437 \ m = 0.041\underline{6}9°\text{C}$$

$$T_b = 100.000 + 0.04169 = 100.04\underline{1}69 = 100.042°\text{C}$$

$$\Delta T_f = K_f m = 1.858°\text{C}/m \times 0.081437 \ m = 0.151\underline{3}1°\text{C}$$

$$T_f = 0.000 - 0.15131 = -0.15\underline{1}31 = -0.151°\text{C}$$

12.71. Calculate ΔT_f, the freezing-point depression, and, using $K_f = 1.858°\text{C}/m$ (Table 12.3), the molality, c_m.

$$\Delta T_f = 0.000°\text{C} - (-0.086°\text{C}) = 0.086°\text{C}$$

$$c_m = \frac{\Delta T_f}{K_f} = \frac{0.086°\text{C}}{1.858°\text{C}/m} = 4.\underline{6}28 \times 10^{-2} = 4.6 \times 10^{-2} \ m$$

12.73. Find the moles of unknown solute from the definition of molality:

$$\text{Mol}_{\text{solute}} = m \times \text{kg solvent} = \frac{0.0698 \text{ mol}}{1 \text{ kg solvent}} \times 0.002135 \text{ kg solvent} = 1.4\underline{9}0 \times 10^{-4} \text{ mol}$$

$$\text{Molar mass} = \frac{0.0182 \text{ g}}{1.490 \times 10^{-4} \text{ mol}} = 12\underline{2}.1 = 122 \text{ g/mol}$$

The molecular mass is 122 amu.

12.75. Calculate ΔT_f, the freezing-point depression, and, using $K_f = 8.00°C/m$, the molality, c_m.

$$\Delta T_f = 26.84°C - 25.70°C = 1.14°C$$

$$c_m = \frac{\Delta T_f}{K_f} = \frac{1.14°C}{8.00°C/m} = 0.14\underline{2}5 \text{ } m$$

Find the moles of solute by rearranging the definition of molality:

$$\text{Mol} = m \times \text{kg solvent} = \frac{0.1425 \text{ mol}}{1 \text{ kg solvent}} \times 103 \times 10^{-6} \text{ kg solvent} = 1.4\underline{6}7 \times 10^{-5} \text{ mol}$$

$$\text{Molar mass} = \frac{2.39 \times 10^{-3} \text{ g}}{1.467 \times 10^{-5} \text{ mol}} = 16\underline{2}.8 = 163 \text{ g/mol}$$

The molecular mass is 163 amu.

12.77. Use the equation for osmotic pressure (π) to solve for the molarity of the solution.

$$M = \frac{\pi}{RT} = \frac{1.47 \text{ mmHg} \times \left(\dfrac{1 \text{ atm}}{760 \text{ mmHg}}\right)}{(0.0821 \text{ L} \cdot \text{atm/K} \cdot \text{mol})(21 + 273)\text{K}} = 8.0\underline{1}3 \times 10^{-5} \text{ mol/L}$$

Now, find the number of moles in 106 mL (0.106 L) using the molarity.

$$0.106 \text{ L} \times \frac{8.013 \times 10^{-5} \text{ mol}}{1 \text{ L}} = 8.4\underline{9}4 \times 10^{-6} \text{ mol}$$

$$\text{Molar mass} = \frac{0.582 \text{ g}}{8.494 \times 10^{-6} \text{ mol}} = 6.8\underline{5}2 \times 10^{4} = 6.85 \times 10^{4} \text{ g/mol}$$

The molecular mass is 6.85×10^{4} amu.

12.79. Begin by noting that $i = 3$. Then calculate ΔT_f from the product of iK_fc_m:

$$3 \times \frac{1.858°C}{m} \times 0.0075 \text{ } m = 0.04\underline{1}8°C$$

The freezing point = $0.000°C - 0.0418°C = -0.04\underline{1}8 = -0.042°C$.

12.81.　Begin by calculating the molarity of $Cr(NH_3)_5Cl_3$.

$$1.40 \times 10^{-2} \text{ g } Cr(NH_3)_5Cl_3 \times \frac{1 \text{ mol } Cr(NH_3)_5Cl_3}{243.5 \text{ g } Cr(NH_3)_5Cl_3} = 5.7\underline{4}9 \times 10^{-5} \text{ mol } Cr(NH_3)_5Cl_3$$

$$\text{Molarity} = \frac{5.749 \times 10^{-5} \text{ mol } Cr(NH_3)_5Cl_3}{0.0250 \text{ L}} = 0.0022\underline{9}9 \text{ } M$$

Now find the hypothetical osmotic pressure, assuming $Cr(NH_3)_5Cl_3$ does not ionize:

$$\pi = MRT = (2.30 \times 10^{-3} \text{ } M) \times \frac{0.0821 \text{ L} \cdot \text{atm}}{\text{K} \cdot \text{mol}} \times 298 \text{ K} \times \frac{760 \text{ mmHg}}{1 \text{ atm}} = 42.\underline{7}6 \text{ mmHg}$$

The measured osmotic pressure is greater than the hypothetical osmotic pressure. The number of ions formed per formula unit equals the ratio of the measured pressure to the hypothetical pressure:

$$i = \frac{119 \text{ mmHg}}{42.76 \text{ mmHg}} = 2.7\underline{8}3 \cong 3 \text{ ions/formula unit}$$

You will learn later that transition metals often form complexes containing ligands. In this case, 6 ligands (i.e., five NH_3 and one Cl^-) octahedrally bind to the central Cr^{3+} ion to form the $[Cr(NH_3)Cl]^{2+}$ complex ion. The other two Cl^- ions combine with the complex to form the neutral ionic compound $[Cr(NH_3)Cl]Cl_2$ having 3 ions/formula unit.

12.85.　Because the As_2S_3 particles are negatively charged, the effective coagulation requires a highly charged cation, so $Al_2(SO_4)_3$ is the best choice.

■ SOLUTIONS TO GENERAL PROBLEMS

12.87.　Using Henry's law $[S_2 = S_1 \times (P_2/P_1)$, where $P_1 = 1.00$ atm$]$, find the solubility of each gas at P_2, its partial pressure. For N_2, $P_2 = 0.800 \times 1.00$ atm $= 0.800$ atm; for O_2, $P_2 = 0.200$ atm.

$$N_2: S_1 \times \frac{P_2}{P_1} = (0.0175 \text{ g/L } H_2O) \times \frac{0.800 \text{ atm}}{1.00 \text{ atm}} = 0.0140\underline{0} \text{ g/L } H_2O$$

$$O_2: S_2 \times \frac{P_2}{P_1} = (0.0393 \text{ g/L } H_2O) \times \frac{0.200 \text{ atm}}{1.00 \text{ atm}} = 0.00786\underline{0} \text{ g/L } H_2O$$

In 1.00 L of the water, there are 0.0140 g of N_2 and 0.00786 g of O_2. If the water is heated to drive off both dissolved gases, the gas mixture that is expelled will contain 0.0140 g of N_2 and 0.00786 g of O_2.

Convert both masses to moles using the molar masses:

$$0.0140 \text{ g } N_2 \times \frac{1 \text{ mol } N_2}{28.01 \text{ g } N_2} = 4.9\underline{9}8 \times 10^{-4} \text{ mol}$$

$$0.00786 \text{ g } O_2 \times \frac{1 \text{ mol } O_2}{32.00 \text{ g } O_2} = 2.4\underline{5}6 \times 10^{-4} \text{ mol}$$

Now calculate the mole fraction of each gas:

$$X_{N_2} = \frac{mol\ N_2}{total\ mol} = \frac{4.998 \times 10^{-4}\ mol}{(4.998 + 2.456) \times 10^{-4}\ mol} = 0.670\underline{5}1 = 0.671$$

$$X_{O_2} = 1 - X_{N_2} = 1 - 0.670\underline{5}1 = 0.329\underline{4}9 = 0.329$$

12.89. Assume a volume of 1.000 L whose mass is then 1.024 kg. Use the percent composition given to find the mass of each of the components of the solution.

$$1.024\ kg\ soln \times \frac{8.50\ kg\ NH_4Cl}{100.00\ kg\ soln} = 0.087\underline{0}4\ kg\ NH_4Cl$$

Mass of H_2O = 1.024 kg soln − 0.08704 kg NH_4Cl = 0.93\underline{7}0 kg H_2O

Convert mass of NH_4Cl and water to moles:

$$87.\underline{0}4\ g\ NH_4Cl \times \frac{1\ mol\ NH_4Cl}{53.49\ g\ NH_4Cl} = 1.6\underline{2}7\ mol\ NH_4Cl$$

$$93\underline{7}.0\ g\ H_2O \times \frac{1\ mol\ H_2O}{18.015\ g\ H_2O} = 52.\underline{0}1\ mol\ H_2O$$

$$Molarity = \frac{mol\ NH_4Cl}{L\ solution} = \frac{1.627\ mol}{1.00\ L} = 1.6\underline{2}7 = 1.63\ M$$

$$Molality = \frac{mol\ NH_4Cl}{kg\ H_2O} = \frac{1.627\ mol}{0.9370\ kg\ H_2O} = 1.7\underline{3}6 = 1.74\ m$$

$$X_{NH_4Cl} = \frac{mol\ NH_4Cl}{total\ moles} = \frac{1.627\ mol}{(52.01 + 1.627)\ mol} = 0.030\underline{3}3 = 0.0303$$

12.91. In 1.00 mol of gas mixture, there are 0.51 mol of propane (pro.) and 0.49 mol of butane (but.). First, calculate the masses of these components.

$$0.51\ mol\ pro. \times \frac{44.10\ g\ pro.}{1\ mol\ pro.} = 22.\underline{4}91\ g\ pro.$$

$$0.49\ mol\ but. \times \frac{58.12\ g\ but.}{1\ mol\ but.} = 28.\underline{4}78\ g\ but.$$

The mass of 1.00 mol of gas mixture is the sum of the masses of the two components:

22.491 g pro. + 28.478 g but. = 50.\underline{9}69 g mixture

Therefore, in 50.\underline{0}969 g of the mixture, there are 22.\underline{4}91 g of propane and 28.\underline{4}78 g of butane.

For a sample with a mass of 55 g,

$$55\ g\ mixture \times \frac{22.491\ g\ pro.}{50.969\ g\ mixture} = 24.\underline{3} = 24\ g\ propane$$

$$55\ g\ mixture \times \frac{28.478\ g\ but.}{50.969\ g\ mixture} = 30.\underline{7} = 31\ g\ butane$$

12.93. $P_{ED} = P°_{ED}(X_{ED}) = 173$ mmHg $(0.30) = 5\underline{1}.90$ mmHg

$P_{PD} = P°_{PD}(X_{PD}) = 127$ mmHg $(0.70) = 8\underline{8}.90$ mmHg

$P = P_{ED} + P_{PD} = 5\underline{1}.90 + 8\underline{8}.90 = 14\underline{0}.80 = 141$ mmHg

12.95. Calculate the moles of $KAl(SO_4)_2 \bullet 12H_2O$ using its molar mass of 474.4 g/mol, and use this to calculate the three concentrations.

    a.   The moles of $KAl(SO_4)_2 \bullet 12H_2O$ are calculated below, using the abbreviation "Hyd" for the formula of $KAl(SO_4)_2 \bullet 12H_2O$.

$$\text{moles Hyd} = 0.1015 \text{ g Hyd} \times \frac{1 \text{ mol Hyd}}{474.4 \text{ g Hyd}} = 0.000213\underline{9}54 = 0.0002140 \text{ mol}$$

Note that 1 mol of $KAl(SO_4)_2 \bullet 12H_2O$ contains 1 mole of $KAl(SO_4)_2$, so the molarity of $KAl(SO_4)_2$ can be calculated using the moles of $KAl(SO_4)_2 \bullet 12H_2O$.

$$\frac{\text{mol}}{\text{L}} = \frac{0.0002140 \text{ mol Hyd}}{1.000 \text{ L soln}} \times \frac{1 \text{ mol KAl(SO}_4)_2}{1 \text{ mol Hyd}} = 0.0002140 \text{ } M \text{ KAl(SO}_4)_2$$

    b.   The molarity of the SO_4^{2-} ion will be twice that of the $KAl(SO_4)_2$.

$$\frac{\text{mol SO}_4^{2-}}{\text{L}} = 0.000213\underline{9}54 \text{ } M \text{ KAl(SO}_4)_2 \times \frac{2 \text{ mol SO}_4^{2-}}{1 \text{ mol KAl(SO}_4)_2} = 0.0004279 \text{ } M$$

    c.   Since the density of the solution is 1.00 g/mL, the mass of 1.000 L of solution is 10$\underline{0}$0. g. Of this, 0.1015 g is solute. Because the solute has 12 waters of hydration, 0.04625 g of the solute mass is water. Therefore the mass of just $KAl(SO_4)_2$ is (0.1015 g − 0.04625 g) = 0.055$\underline{2}$4 g. Using this information the mass of solvent is calculated as follows:

$$1000. \text{ g} - (0.1015 \text{ g} - 0.04625 \text{ g}) = 99\underline{9}.94 \text{ g} = 0.99\underline{9}94 \text{ kg H}_2\text{O}$$

The molality of $KAl(SO_4)_2$ can now be calculated.

$$\text{Molality} = \frac{\text{mol KAl(SO}_4)_2}{\text{kg H}_2\text{O}} = \frac{2.14\underline{0} \times 10^{-4} \text{ mol}}{0.99\underline{9}94 \text{ kg}} = 2.1\underline{4}0 \times 10^{-4} = 2.14 \times 10^{-4} \text{ } M$$

12.97. In 1.00 kg of a saturated solution of urea, there are 0.41 kg of urea (a molecular solute) and 0.59 kg of water. First, convert the mass of urea to moles.

$$0.41 \times 10^3 \text{ g urea} \times \frac{1 \text{ mol urea}}{60.06 \text{ g urea}} = 6.\underline{8}26 \text{ mol urea}$$

Then find the molality of the urea in the solution:

$$\text{Molality} = \frac{\text{mol urea}}{\text{kg H}_2\text{O}} = \frac{6.826 \text{ mol urea}}{0.59 \text{ kg}} = 1\underline{1}.57 \text{ } m$$

$$\Delta T_f = K_f c_m = (1.858°C/m)(11.57 \text{ } m) = 2\underline{1}.4°C$$

$$T_f = 0.0°C - 21.4°C = -2\underline{1}.4 = -21°C$$

12.99. $M = \dfrac{\pi}{RT} = \dfrac{7.7 \text{ atm}}{(0.0821 \text{ L} \bullet \text{atm/K} \bullet \text{mol})(37 + 273)\text{K}} = 0.3\underline{0}2 = 0.30 \text{ mol/L}$

12.101. Consider the equation $\Delta T_f = iK_fc_m$. For $CaCl_2$, $i = 3$; for glucose, $i = 1$. Because $c_m = 0.10$ for both solutions, the product of i and c_m will be larger for $CaCl_2$, as will ΔT_f. The solution of $CaCl_2$ will thus have the lower freezing point.

12.103. Assume there is 1.000 L of the solution, which will contain 18 mol H_2SO_4, mass 98.09 g/mol. The mass of the solution is

$$\text{Mass solution} = \frac{18 \text{ mol} \times 98.09 \text{ g/mol}}{0.98} = 1\underline{8}02 \text{ g}$$

Thus, the density of the solution is

$$d = \frac{1\underline{8}02 \text{ g}}{1000 \text{ mL}} = 1.\underline{8}02 = 1.8 \text{ g/mL}$$

The mass of water in the solution is

$$\text{Mass } H_2O = 1\underline{8}02 \text{ g} \times 0.02 = \underline{3}6.0 \text{ g} = 0.0\underline{3}60 \text{ kg}$$

Thus, the molality of the solution is

$$m = \frac{18 \text{ mol } H_2SO_4}{0.0\underline{3}60 \text{ Kg}} = \underline{5}00 = 5 \times 10^2 \, m$$

12.105. Use the freezing-point-depression equation to find the molality of the solution. The freezing point of pure cyclohexane is 6.55°C, and $K_f = 20.0°C/m$. Thus

$$m = \frac{\Delta T_f}{K_f} = \frac{(6.55 - 5.28)°C}{20.0°C/m} = 0.063\underline{5}0 \, m$$

The moles of the compound are

$$\text{Moles of compound} = \frac{0.06350 \text{ mol}}{1 \text{ kg solvent}} \times 0.00538 \text{ kg} = 3.4\underline{1}6 \times 10^{-4} \text{ mol}$$

The molar mass of the compound is

$$\text{Molar mass} = \frac{0.125 \text{ g}}{3.416 \times 10^{-4} \text{ mol}} = 36\underline{5}.9 \text{ g/mol}$$

The moles of the elements in 100 g of the compound are

$$\text{Moles of Mn} = 28.17 \text{ g Mn} \times \frac{1 \text{ mol}}{54.94 \text{ g Mn}} = 0.512\underline{7}4 \text{ mol}$$

$$\text{Moles of C} = 30.80 \text{ g C} \times \frac{1 \text{ mol}}{12.01 \text{ g C}} = 2.56\underline{4}5 \text{ mol}$$

$$\text{Moles of O} = 41.03 \text{ g O} \times \frac{1 \text{ mol}}{16.00 \text{ g O}} = 2.56\underline{4}4 \text{ mol}$$

This gives mole ratios of 1 mol Mn to 5 mol C to 5 mol O. Therefore, the empirical formula of the compound is MnC_5O_5. The mass of this formula unit is approximately 195 amu. Since the molar mass of the compound is 366. g/mol, the value of n is

$$n = \frac{366 \text{ g/mol}}{195 \text{ g/unit}} = 1.88 \approx 2$$

Therefore, the formula of the compound is $Mn_2C_{10}O_{10}$.

12.107. a.   Use the freezing-point-depression equation to find the molality of the solution. The freezing point of pure water is 0°C and $K_f = 1.858$°C/m. Thus

$$m = \frac{\Delta T_f}{K_f} = \frac{[0 - (-2.2)]°C}{1.858°C/m} = 1.\underline{1}84 \ m$$

The moles of the compound are

$$\text{Moles of compound} = \frac{1.184 \text{ mol}}{1 \text{ kg solvent}} \times 0.100 \text{ kg} = 0.1\underline{1}84 \text{ mol}$$

The molar mass of the compound is

$$\text{Molar mass} = \frac{18.0 \text{ g}}{0.1184 \text{ mol}} = 1\underline{5}2.0 \text{ g/mol}$$

The moles of the elements in 100 g of the compound are

$$\text{Moles of C} = 48.64 \text{ g C} \times \frac{1 \text{ mol}}{12.01 \text{ g C}} = 4.05\underline{0}0 \text{ mol}$$

$$\text{Moles of H} = 8.16 \text{ g H} \times \frac{1 \text{ mol}}{1.008 \text{ g H}} = 8.09\underline{5} \text{ mol}$$

$$\text{Moles of O} = 43.20 \text{ g O} \times \frac{1 \text{ mol}}{16.00 \text{ g O}} = 2.70\underline{0}0 \text{ mol}$$

This gives mole ratios of 1.5 mol C to 3 mol H to 1 mol O. Multiplying by 2 gives ratios of 3 mol C to 6 mol H to 2 mol O. Therefore, the empirical formula of the compound is $C_3H_6O_2$. The mass of this formula unit is approximately 74 amu. Since the molar mass of the compound is 152.0. g/mol, the value of n is

$$n = \frac{1\underline{5}2.0 \text{ g/mol}}{74 \text{ g/unit}} = 2.05 \approx 2$$

Therefore, the formula of the compound is $C_6H_{12}O_4$.

b.   The molar mass of the compound is (to the nearest tenth of a gram)

$$6(12.01) + 12(1.008) + 4(16.00) = 148.\underline{1}56 = 148.2 \text{ g/mol}$$

12.109. Use the freezing-point-depression equation to find the molality of the solution. The freezing point of pure water is 0°C, and $K_f = 1.86°C/m$. Thus

$$m = \frac{\Delta T_f}{K_f} = \frac{[0-(-2.3)]°C}{1.86°C/m} = 1.\underline{2}4 \ m$$

Since this is a relatively dilute solution, we can assume the molarity and molality of the fish blood are approximately equal. The calculated molarity is for the total number of particles, assuming they behave ideally.

$$\pi = MRT = 1.\underline{2}4 \text{ mol/L} \times 0.08206 \text{ L•atm/K•mol} \times 298.2 \text{ K} = 3\underline{0}.3 = 30. \text{ atm}$$

12.111. Hemoglobin is the substance in red blood cells that carries oxygen. Hemoglobin is normally present in solution within the red blood cells. But in people with sickle-cell anemia, the unoxygenated hemoglobin readily comes out of solution. It produces a fibrous precipitate that deforms the cell, giving it the characteristic sickle shape. Normal and sickle-cell hemoglobins are almost exactly alike, except that each β chain of the hemoglobin responsible for sickle-cell anemia differs from normal hemoglobin in one place. In this place, the normal hemoglobin has the group that helps confer water solubility on the molecule because of the polarity of the group and its ability to form hydrogen bonds.

12.113. Like a soap ion, a phospholipid has a hydrophobic end (the two hydrocarbon groups) and a hydrophilic end (an ionic portion containing a phosphate group, $-PO_4^-$). Like soap ions, phospholipid molecules in water tend to associate so that their hydrophilic (or ionic) heads dip into the water, with their hydrophobic (or hydrocarbon) tails pointing away. However, the hydrocarbon tails of a phospholipid molecule are too bulky to associate into micelles and instead form a bilayer, a layer two molecules thick.

■ SOLUTIONS TO STRATEGY PROBLEMS

12.115. a.   The highest boiling point will correspond to the largest boiling-point elevation, ΔT_b. Since $\Delta T_b = iK_bm$, and the solutions contain the same solute having the same i value, the largest ΔT_b will correspond to the solution having the highest molality or highest concentration. Thus, the solution that boils at 100.15°C is the more concentrated solution.

b.   The lowest freezing point will correspond to the largest freezing-point depression, ΔT_f. Since $\Delta T_f = iK_fm$, and the solutions contain the same solute having the same i value, the largest ΔT_f will correspond to the having the highest molality or highest concentration. As explained in (a), the solution that boils 100.15°C is the more concentrated solution and will be the solution that has the lowest freezing point.

c.   Because the boiling point elevation depends on the intensive property of molality, splitting the solution into portions will result in portions having the same boiling point elevation they had before the split.

The volumes that the sample was split into in part (c) are irrelevant when determining the correct answer to part (c).

12.117. a. Because osmotic pressure is directly proportional to the concentration of a nonvolatile solute, increasing the concentration of the solute will result in a higher osmotic pressure. Statement a is true.

b. Because the boiling point elevation of an aqueous solution directly proportional to the concentration of a nonvolatile solute, increasing the concentration of the solute will result in a higher boiling point elevation and a higher boiling point. Statement b is true.

c. As water evaporates from an aqueous solution containing a nonvolatile solute, the remaining solution becomes more concentrated in the solute. As a result, the mole fraction of the water and the vapor pressure of the solution both decrease. Statement c is true.

d. Because the solution is known to contain a nonvolatile solute, it will exhibit a freezing point depression and freeze at a temperature below $0^{\circ}C$ at 1.0 atm. Statement d is true.

e. Adding pure water to the solution will cause the molality of the nonvolatile solute particles to decrease. As a result the solution will exhibit a smaller boiling point elevation and boil at a lower temperature. Statement d is true.

12.119. a. The ratio $mass_{solute}/mass_{solution}$ is the fractional amount of solute to solution. If this ratio is multiplied by 10^6 the result is stated in terms of parts per million, or *ppm*. Likewise, if this ratio is multiplied by 10^2 the result is stated in parts per hundred, or more commonly in percentage terms. Given the EPA limit of 2 *ppm* for Ba, it is a simple matter to convert this to percentage terms.

$$2\,ppm = \frac{mass_{solute}}{mass_{solution}} \times 10^6 \quad\text{or}\quad \frac{2\,ppm}{10^6} = \frac{mass_{solute}}{mass_{solution}} = 2 \times 10^{-6}$$

$$\frac{mass_{solute}}{mass_{solution}} \times 100 = 2 \times 10^{-6} \times 100 = 2 \times 10^{-4} \text{ parts per hundred} = 2 \times 10^{-4}\ \%$$

Thus, the maximum mass percentage of Ba allowed in drinking water is 2×10^{-4} %.

b. First assume you have 1 L of solution. If the density of the solution is 1.00 g/mL, the mass of the solution is 1.00×10^3 g. Using this mass in the defining equation allows us to calculate the mass of Ba in the solution and thus the moles of Ba in the solution. Dividing the moles of Ba by 1 L gives the molarity of the Ba in the solution.

$$2\,ppm = \frac{mass_{Ba}}{mass_{solution}} \times 10^6$$

$$mass_{Ba} = \frac{2\,ppm}{10^6} \times mass_{solution} = \frac{2\,ppm}{10^6} \times 1.00 \times 10^3 \text{ g} = 0.002 \text{ g Ba}$$

$$mol\ Ba = 0.00\underline{2} \text{ g Ba} \times \frac{1 \text{ mol Ba}}{137.3 \text{ g Ba}} = 1.\underline{4} \times 10^{-5} \text{ mol Ba}$$

$$\text{molarity of Ba} = \frac{mol\ Ba}{\text{liters of solution}} = \frac{1.\underline{4} \times 10^{-5} \text{ mol Ba}}{1 \text{ L}}$$

$$\text{molarity of Ba} = 1.\underline{4} \times 10^{-5} = 1 \times 10^{-5}\ M \text{ Ba}$$

c. In part b we calculated that 1 L of solution contains 0.002 g Ba, or 2 mg of Ba. Thus, the concentration of Ba in mg per liter is 2 mg/L. This is a useful conversion to remember for dilute aqueous solutions, or solutions having densities very close to that of pure water. That is, once you have a concentration in *ppm*, if needed you can immediately interchange units of mg/L for *ppm*, and vice versa.

12.121. Moles solute $= \dfrac{\Delta T_f}{K_f} \times$ kg solvent $= \dfrac{1.34°C}{1.858°C/m} \times 0.878$ kg $= 0.63\underline{3}2$ mol

$$\text{Molar mass} = \frac{\text{mass}}{\text{moles}} = \frac{79.3 \text{ g}}{0.6332 \text{ mol}} = 12\underline{5}.2 = 125 \text{ g/mol}$$

The molecular mass of the compound is 125 amu.

12.123. $S_2 = S_1 \times \dfrac{P_2}{P_1} = 15.6$ g/L $\times \dfrac{24.6 \text{ atm}}{2.14 \text{ atm}} = 17\underline{9}.3 = 179$ g/L

If the temperature of the liquid were increased, the solubility of the gas would decrease.

12.125. The molar mass of potassium chloride (KCl) is 74.55 g/mol. The mass required is

$$(0.110 \ m) \times (0.372 \text{ kg}) \times (74.55 \text{ g/mol}) = 3.0\underline{5}0 = 3.05 \text{ g}$$

12.127. First calculate the moles of each substance. The molar mass of ethanol (C_2H_5OH) is 46.068 g/mol, and the molar mass of water is 18.015 g/mol.

$$\text{Moles of } C_2H_5OH = 4.76 \text{ g} \times \frac{1 \text{ mol}}{46.068 \text{ g}} = 0.10\underline{3}3 \text{ mol}$$

$$\text{Moles of } H_2O = 50.0 \text{ g} \times \frac{1 \text{ mol}}{18.015 \text{ g}} = 2.7\underline{7}54 \text{ mol}$$

The mole fraction of ethanol can now be calculated.

$$X_{C_2H_5OH} = \frac{\text{mol } C_2H_5OH}{\text{total mol}} = \frac{0.1033 \text{ mol}}{0.1033 \text{ mol} + 2.775 \text{ mol}} = 0.035\underline{8}9 = 0.0359$$

12.129. Assume 1 L of solution. The molar mass of magnesium chloride ($MgCl_2$) is 95.21 g/mol. The mass of magnesium chloride, the mass of water, and the mass of the solution are

$$\text{Mass } MgCl_2 = 0.797 \text{ mol} \times \frac{95.21 \text{ g}}{1 \text{ mol}} = 75.\underline{8}82 \text{ g}$$

$$\text{Mass solution} = d \times V = 1.108 \text{ g/mL} \times 1000 \text{ mL} = 1108 \text{ g}$$

$$\text{Mass water} = 1108 \text{ g} - 75.882 \text{ g} = 103\underline{2}.11 \text{ g} = 1032 \text{ g} = 1.032 \text{ kg}$$

The molality can now be calculated.

$$\text{Molality} = \frac{0.797 \text{ mol}}{1.032 \text{ kg}} = 0.77\underline{2}3 = 0.772 \ m$$

■ SOLUTIONS TO CUMULATIVE-SKILLS PROBLEMS

12.131. First, determine the initial moles of each ion present in the solution before any reaction has occurred. There are five ions present: Na^+, $2 \times 0.375 = 0.750$ mol; CO_3^{2-}, 0.375 mol; Ca^{2+}, 0.125 mol; Ag^+, 0.200 mol; and NO_3^-, $0.200 + 2 \times 0.125 = 0.450$ mol. Two precipitates form: $CaCO_3$ and Ag_2CO_3. The balanced net ionic equations for their formation are

$$Ca^{2+}(aq) + CO_3^{2-}(aq) \quad \rightarrow \quad CaCO_3(s)$$

$$2Ag^+(aq) + CO_3^{2-}(aq) \quad \rightarrow \quad Ag_2CO_3(s)$$

There is sufficient CO_3^{2-} to precipitate all of the Ca^{2+} and all of the Ag^+ ions. The moles of excess CO_3^{2-} are calculated as follows: $0.375 - 0.125 - 1/2 \times 0.200 = 0.150$ mol remaining. Since the volume is 2.000 L, the molarities of the various ions are

M of CO_3^{2-} left = 0.150 mol ÷ 2.000 L = 0.0750 M

M of NO_3^- left = 0.450 mol ÷ 2.000 L = 0.225 M

M of Na^+ left = 0.750 mol ÷ 2.000 L = 0.375 M

12.133. The sum of the heats of hydration of Na^+ and Cl^- is calculated as follows:

$Na^+(g) + Cl^-(g)$	$\rightarrow$	$NaCl(s)$	$\Delta H = -787$ kJ/mol
$NaCl(s)$	$\rightarrow$	$Na^+(aq) + Cl^-(aq)$	$\Delta H = +4.0$ kJ/mol
$Na^+(g) + Cl^-(g)$	$\rightarrow$	$Na^+(aq) + Cl^-(aq)$	$\Delta H = -783$ kJ/mol

The heat of hydration of Na^+ is next calculated with the additional information:

$Na^+(g) + Cl^-(g)$	$\rightarrow$	$Na^+(aq) + Cl^-(aq)$	$\Delta H = -783$ kJ/mol
$Cl^-(aq)$	$\rightarrow$	$Cl^-(g)$	$\Delta H = +338$ kJ/mol
$Na^+(g)$	$\rightarrow$	$Na^+(aq)$	$\Delta H = -445$ kJ/mol

12.135. $15.0 \text{ g MgSO}_4 \bullet 7H_2O \times \dfrac{1 \text{ mol}}{246.5 \text{ g}} = 0.060\underline{8}52 \text{ mol MgSO}_4 \bullet 7H_2O$

$0.060\underline{8}52 \text{ mol MgSO}_4 \bullet 7H_2O \times \dfrac{7 \text{ mol H}_2O}{1 \text{ mol hydrate}} \times \dfrac{18.015 \text{ g H}_2O}{1 \text{ mol H}_2O} = 7.6\underline{7}4 \text{ g H}_2O$

$\text{kg H}_2O = (100.0 \text{ g H}_2O + 7.6\underline{7}4 \text{ g H}_2O) \times \dfrac{1 \text{ kg H}_2O}{1000 \text{ g H}_2O} = 0.107\underline{6}7 \text{ kg H}_2O$

$m = \dfrac{0.060\underline{8}52 \text{ mol MgSO}_4}{0.107\underline{6}7 \text{ kg H}_2O} = 0.56\underline{5}2 \text{ mol/kg} = 0.565 \ m$

12.137. $15.0 \text{ g CuSO}_4 \cdot 5\text{H}_2\text{O} \times \dfrac{1 \text{ mol}}{249.7 \text{ g}} = 0.060\underline{0}7 \text{ mol CuSO}_4 \cdot 5\text{H}_2\text{O, or CuSO}_4$

$100 \text{ g soln} \times \dfrac{1 \text{ mL soln}}{1.167 \text{ g soln}} \times \dfrac{1 \text{ L}}{1000 \text{ mL}} = 0.08569\underline{0} \text{ L}$

$M = \dfrac{0.060\underline{0}7 \text{ mol CuSO}_4}{0.085690 \text{ L}} = 0.70\underline{1}0 = 0.701 \text{ mol/L}$

12.139. $0.159°\text{C} \times \dfrac{m}{1.858°\text{C}} = 0.085\underline{5}8 \ m = \dfrac{0.085\underline{5}8 \text{ mol AA} + \text{H}_3\text{O}^+ + \text{A}^-}{1000 \text{ g (or 1000 mL) H}_2\text{O}}$

The ionization reaction is as follows:

$$\text{HC}_2\text{H}_3\text{O}_2 + \text{H}_2\text{O} \rightarrow \text{H}_3\text{O}^+ + \text{C}_2\text{H}_3\text{O}_2^-$$

$\quad$ AA $\quad\quad\quad\quad\quad\quad\quad\quad\quad$ A$^-$

Note that 0.0830 mol AA leads to 0.085$\underline{5}$8 mol/L (AA + H$_3$O$^+$ + A$^-$). By the stoichiometry of the reaction, the moles of H$_3$O$^+$ equals the moles of A$^-$.

Moles of H$^+$ = 0.085$\underline{5}$8 − 0.0830 = 0.002$\underline{5}$8 mol

Percent dissoc. $= \dfrac{\text{mol H}^+}{\text{mol AA}} \times 100\% = \dfrac{0.002\underline{5}8 \text{ mol}}{0.0830 \text{ mol}} \times 100\% = 3.\underline{1}1 = 3.1 \ \%$

12.141. Calculate the empirical formula first, using the masses of C, O, and H in 1.000 g:

$1.434 \text{ g CO}_2 \times \dfrac{12.01 \text{ g C}}{44.01 \text{ g CO}_2} = 0.39\underline{1}3 \text{ g C}$

$0.783 \text{ g H}_2\text{O} \times \dfrac{2.016 \text{ g H}}{18.015 \text{ g H}_2\text{O}} = 0.087\underline{6}2 \text{ g H}$

g O = 1.000 g − 0.39$\underline{1}$3 g − 0.087$\underline{6}$2 g = 0.52$\underline{1}$1 g O

Mol C = 0.3913 g C × 1 mol/12.01 g = 0.03258 mol C (lowest integer = 1)

Mol H = 0.08762 g H × 1 mol/1.008 g = 0.08692 mol H (lowest integer = 8/3)

Mol O = 0.5211 g O × 1 mol/16.00 g = 0.03257 mol O (lowest integer = 1)

This gives mole ratios of 1 mol C to 2.67 mol H to 1 mol O. Multiplying by 3 gives ratios of 3 mol C to 8 mol H to 3 mol O. Therefore, the empirical formula of the compound is $\text{C}_3\text{H}_8\text{O}_3$. The formula mass from the freezing point is calculated by first finding the molality:

0.0894°C × (m/1.858°C) = 0.04811 = (0.048$\underline{1}$1 mol/1000 g H$_2$O)

(0.04811 mol/1000 g H$_2$O) × 25.0 g H$_2$O = 0.0012$\underline{0}$3 mol (in 25.0 g H$_2$O)

Molar mass = M_m = 0.1107 g/0.001203 mol = 92.$\underline{0}$2 g/mol

Because 92.0 amu is the empirical formula mass, the molecular formula is also $\text{C}_3\text{H}_8\text{O}_3$.

CHAPTER 13

Rates of Reaction

■ SOLUTIONS TO EXERCISES

Note on significant figures: If the final answer to a solution needs to be rounded off, it is given first with one nonsignificant figure, and the last significant figure is underlined. The final answer is then rounded to the correct number of significant figures. In multistep problems, intermediate answers are given with at least one nonsignificant figure; however, only the final answer has been rounded off.

13.1.   Rate of formation of $NO_2F = \Delta[NO_2F]/\Delta t$. Rate of reaction of $NO_2 = -\Delta[NO_2]/\Delta t$. Divide each rate by the coefficient of the corresponding substance in the equation:

$$\frac{1}{2}\frac{\Delta[NO_2F]}{\Delta t} = -\frac{1}{2}\frac{\Delta[NO_2]}{\Delta t}; \text{ or } \frac{\Delta[NO_2F]}{\Delta t} = -\frac{\Delta[NO_2]}{\Delta t}$$

13.2. $\text{Rate} = -\dfrac{\Delta[I^-]}{\Delta t} = -\dfrac{\Delta[0.00101 \text{ M} - 0.00169 \text{ M}]}{8.00 \text{ s} - 2.00 \text{ s}} = 1.\underline{1}3 \times 10^{-4} = 1.1 \times 10^{-4} \ M/\text{s}$

13.3.   The order with respect to CO is zero and with respect to NO_2 is 2. The overall order is 2, the sum of the exponents in the rate law.

13.4.   By comparing Experiments 1 and 2, you see the rate is quadrupled when the $[NO_2]$ is doubled. Thus, the reaction is second order in NO_2, and the rate law is

Rate = $k[NO_2]^2$

The rate constant may be found by substituting experimental values into the rate-law expression. Based on values from Experiment 1,

$$k = \frac{\text{rate}}{[NO_2]^2} = \frac{7.1 \times 10^{-5} \text{ mol/(L} \cdot \text{s)}}{(0.010 \text{ mol/L})^2} = 0.7\underline{1}0 = 0.71 \text{ L/(mol} \bullet \text{s)}$$

13.5.   a.   For $[N_2O_5]$ after 6.00×10^2 s, use the first-order rate law, and solve for the concentration at time t:

$$\ln \frac{[N_2O_5]_t}{[1.65 \times 10^{-2} \text{ M}]} = -(4.80 \times 10^{-4} \text{ /s})(6.00 \times 10^2 \text{ s}) = -0.288\underline{0}$$

Take the antilog of both sides to get

$$\frac{[N_2O_5]_t}{[1.65 \times 10^{-2} \text{ M}]} = e^{-0.2880} = 0.749\underline{7}6$$

Hence,

$$[N_2O_5]_t = 1.65 \times 10^{-2} \ M \times 0.74976 = 0.012\underline{3}7 = 0.0124 \text{ mol/L}$$

b. Substitute the values into the rate equation to get

$$\ln \frac{10.0\%}{100.0\%} = -(4.80 \times 10^{-4}/\text{s}) \times t$$

Taking the log on the left side gives $\ln(0.100) = -2.30258$. Hence,

$$-2.30258 = -(4.80 \times 10^{-4}/\text{s}) \times t$$

or,

$$t = \frac{2.30258}{4.80 \times 10^{-4}/\text{s}} = 4797 = 4.80 \times 10^{3} \text{ s } (80.0 \text{ min})$$

13.6. Substitute $k = 9.2/\text{s}$ into the equation relating k and $t_{\frac{1}{2}}$.

$$t_{\frac{1}{2}} = \frac{0.693}{k} = \frac{0.693}{9.2/\text{s}} = 0.0753 = 0.075 \text{ s}$$

By definition, the half-life is the amount of time it takes to decrease the amount of substance present by one-half. Thus, it takes 0.0753 s for the concentration to decrease by 50% and another 0.0753 s for the concentration to decrease by 50% of the remaining 50% (to 25% left), for a total of 0.1506, or 0.151 s.

13.7. Solve for E_a by substituting the given values into the two-temperature Arrhenius equation:

$$\ln \frac{2.14 \times 10^{-2}}{1.05 \times 10^{-3}} = \frac{E_a}{8.31 \text{ J/(mol} \cdot \text{K})} \left(\frac{1}{759 \text{ K}} - \frac{1}{836 \text{ K}} \right)$$

$$3.0146 = \frac{E_a}{8.31 \text{ J/(mol} \cdot \text{K})} \left(1.21 \times 10^{-4} / \text{K} \right)$$

$$E_a = \frac{3.0146 \times 8.31 \text{ J/mol}}{1.21 \times 10^{-4}} = 2.06 \times 10^{5} = 2.1 \times 10^{5} \text{ J/mol}$$

Solve for the rate constant, k_2, at 865 K by using the same equation and using $E_a = 2.06 \times 10^{5}$ J/mol:

$$\ln \frac{k_2}{2.14 \times 10^{-2}/\left(M^{\frac{1}{2}} \cdot \text{s} \right)} = \frac{2.06 \times 10^{5} \text{ J/mol}}{8.31 \text{ J/(mol} \cdot \text{K})} \left(\frac{1}{836 \text{ K}} - \frac{1}{865 \text{ K}} \right) = 0.994$$

Taking antilogarithms,

$$\frac{k_2}{2.14 \times 10^{-2}/\left(M^{\frac{1}{2}} \cdot \text{s} \right)} = e^{0.994} = 2.7$$

$$k_2 = 2.7 \times (2.14 \times 10^{-2})/(M^{\frac{1}{2}} \bullet \text{s}) = 5.8 \times 10^{-2} = 6 \times 10^{-2} \ (M^{\frac{1}{2}} \bullet \text{s})$$

13.8. The net chemical equation is the overall sum of the two elementary reactions:

$$H_2O_2 + I^- \longrightarrow H_2O + IO^-$$

$$\underline{H_2O_2 + IO^- \longrightarrow H_2O + O_2 + I^-}$$

$$2H_2O_2 \longrightarrow 2H_2O + O_2$$

The IO^- is an intermediate because it is produced in Step 1 and later consumed in Step 2; I^- is a catalyst because it is temporarily used in Step 1 but then regenerated in Step 2. Neither appears in the net equation.

13.9. The reaction is bimolecular because it is an elementary reaction that involves two molecules.

13.10. For $NO_2 + NO_2 \rightarrow N_2O_4$, the rate law is

$$Rate = k[NO_2]^2$$

(The rate must be proportional to the concentration of both reactant molecules.)

13.11. The first step is the slow, rate-determining step. Therefore, the rate law predicted by the mechanism given is

$$Rate = k_1 [H_2O_2][I^-]$$

13.12. According to the rate-determining (slow) step, the rate law is

$$Rate = k_2[NO_3][NO]$$

Eliminate NO_3 from the rate law by looking at the first step, which is fast and reaches equilibrium. At equilibrium, the forward rate and the reverse rate are equal.

$$k_1[NO][O_2] = k_{-1}[NO_3]$$

Therefore, $[NO_3] = (k_1/k_{-1})[NO][O_2]$, so

$$Rate = \frac{k_2k_1}{k_{-1}} [NO]^2[O_2] = k[NO]^2[O_2]$$

where $k_2(k_1/k_{-1})$ has been replaced by k, which represents the experimentally observed rate constant.

■ ANSWERS TO CONCEPT CHECKS

13.1. a. Since the slope is steeper at point A, point A must be a faster instantaneous rate.

b. Since the curve is not a flat line, the rate of reaction must be constantly changing over time. Therefore, the rate for the reaction cannot be constant at all points in time.

13.2. a. Keeping in mind that all reactant species must be present in some concentration for a reaction to occur, the reaction with $[Q] = 0$ is the slowest because no reaction occurs. The other two reactions are equal in rate because the reaction is zero order with respect to $[Q]$; as long as there is some amount of Q present, the reaction rate depends on the $[R]$, which is constant in this case.

b. Since $[Q]^o = 1$, you can rewrite the rate law as follows: $Rate = k[R]^2$.

13.3. a. A possible rate law is Rate of aging = $(diet)^w(exercise)^x(sex)^y(occupation)^z$. Your rate law probably will be different; however, the general form should be the same.

b. You will need a sample of people who have all the factors the same except one. For example, using the equation given in part a, you could determine the effect of diet if you had a sample of people who were the same sex, exercised the same amount, and had the same occupation. You would need to isolate each factor in this fashion to determine the exponent on each factor.

    c.   The exponent on the smoking factor would be 2 since you see a fourfold rate increase: $[2]^2 = 4$.

13.4.   The half-life of a first-order reaction is constant over the course of the reaction. The half-life of a second-order reaction depends on the initial concentration and becomes longer as time elapses. Thus, the reaction must be second order because the half-life increases from 20 s to 40 s after time has elapsed.

13.5.   a.   Since the "hump" is larger, the A + B reaction has a higher activation energy.

    b.   Since the activation energy is lower, the E + F reaction would have the larger rate constant. Keep in mind the inverse relationship between the activation energy, E_a, and the rate constant, k.

    c.   Since, in both cases, energy per mole of the reactants is greater than that of the products, both reactions are exothermic.

13.6.   a.   Her finding should increase the rate since the activation energy, E_a, is inversely related to the rate constant, k; a decrease in E_a results in an increase in the value of k.

    b.   This is possible because the rate law does not have to reflect the overall stoichiometry of the reaction.

    c.   No. Since the rate law is based on the slow step of the mechanism, it should be Rate = $k[Y]^2$.

■ ANSWERS TO SELF-ASSESSMENT AND REVIEW QUESTIONS

13.1.   The four variables that can affect rate are (1) the concentrations of the reactants, although in some cases a particular reactant's concentration does not affect the rate; (2) the presence and concentration of a catalyst; (3) the temperature of the reaction; and (4) the surface area of any solid reactant or solid catalyst.

13.2.   The rate of reaction of HBr can be defined as the decrease in HBr concentration (or the increase in Br_2 product formed) over the time interval, Δt:

$$\text{Rate} = -\tfrac{1}{4}\frac{\Delta[HBr]}{\Delta t} = \tfrac{1}{2}\frac{\Delta[Br_2]}{\Delta t} \text{ or } -\frac{\Delta[HBr]}{\Delta t} = 2\frac{\Delta[Br_2]}{\Delta t}$$

13.3.   Two physical properties used to determine the rate are color, or absorption of electromagnetic radiation, and pressure. If a reactant or product is colored, or absorbs a different type of electromagnetic radiation than the other species, then measurement of the change in color (change in absorption of electromagnetic radiation) may be used to determine the rate. If a gas reaction involves a change in the number of gaseous molecules, measurement of the pressure change may be used to determine the rate.

13.4.   Use the general example of a rate law in Section 13.3, where A and B react to give D and E with C as a catalyst:

$$\text{Rate} = k\,[A]^m\,[B]^n\,[C]^p$$

Note that the exponents m, n, and p are the orders of the individual reactants and catalyst. Assuming that m and n are positive numbers, the rate law predicts that increasing the concentrations of A and/or B will increase the rate. In addition, the rate will be increased by increasing the surface of the solid catalyst (making it as finely divided as possible, etc.). Finally, increasing the temperature will increase the rate constant, k, and increase the rate.

13.5.   An example that illustrates that exponents have no relationship to coefficients is the reaction of nitrogen monoxide and hydrogen from Example 13.12 in the text.

$$2NO + 2H_2 \rightarrow N_2 + 2H_2O.$$

The experimental rate law given there is

$$\text{Rate} = k[NO]^2[H_2]$$

Thus, the exponent for hydrogen is 1, not 2 like the coefficient, and the overall order is 3, not 4 like the sum of the coefficients.

13.6.   The rate law for this reaction of iodide ion, arsenic acid, and hydrogen ion is

$$\text{Rate} = k[I^-][H_3AsO_4]\,[H^+]$$

The overall order is $1 + 1 + 1 = 3$ (third order).

13.7.   Use m to symbolize the reaction order as is done in the text. Then, from the table for m and the change in rate in the text, m is 2 when the rate is quadrupled (increased fourfold). Using the equation in the text gives the same result:

$$2^m = \text{new rate/old rate} = 4/1; \text{ thus, } m = 2$$

13.8.   Use m to symbolize the reaction order as is done in the text. The table for m and the change in rate in the text cannot be used in this case. When $m = 0.5$, the new rate should be found using the equation in the text:

$$2^{0.50} = \sqrt{2} = 1.41 = \text{new rate/old rate}$$

Thus, the new rate is 1.41 times the old rate.

13.9.   Use the half-life concept to answer the question without an equation. If the half-life for the reaction of A(g) is 25 s, then the time for A(g) to decrease to 1/4 the initial value is two half-lives, or $2 \times 25 = 50$ s. The time for A(g) to decrease to 1/8 the initial value is three half-lives, or $3 \times 25 = 75$ s.

13.10.   The half-life equation for a first-order reaction is $t_{1/2} = 0.693/k$. The half-life for the reaction is constant, independent of the reactant concentration. For a second-order reaction, the half-life equation is $t_{1/2} = 1/(k[A]_o)$, and it depends on the initial reactant concentration.

13.11.   According to transition-state theory, the two factors that determine whether a collision results in reaction or not are (1) the molecules must collide with the proper orientation to form the activated complex, and (2) the activated complex formed must have a kinetic energy greater than the activation energy.

13.12. The potential-energy diagram for the exothermic reaction of A and B to give activated complex $AB^{\ddagger}$ and products C and D is given below.

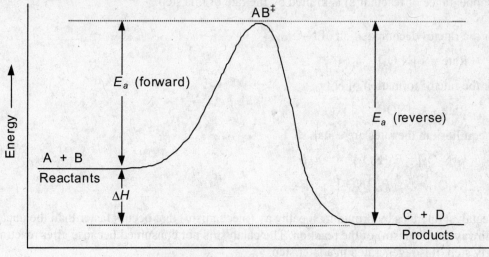

13.13. The activated complex for the reaction of NO_2 with NO_3 to give NO, NO_2, and O_2 has the structure below (dashed lines represent bonds about to form or break):

$$O–N--O--O--N(–O)_2$$

13.14. The Arrhenius equation expressed with the base e is

$$k = A \, e^{-E_a/RT}$$

The A term is the frequency factor and is equal to the product of p and Z from collision theory. The term p is the fraction of collisions with properly oriented reactant molecules, and Z is the frequency of collisions. Thus, A is the number of collisions with the molecules properly oriented. The E_a term is the activation energy, the minimum energy of collision required for two molecules to react. The R term is the gas constant, and T is the absolute temperature.

13.15. In the reaction of $NO_2(g)$ with $CO(g)$, an example of an intermediate is the temporary formation of NO_3 from the reaction of two NO_2 molecules in the first step:

$$NO_2 + NO_2 \rightarrow NO_3 + NO$$

$$NO_3 + CO \rightarrow NO_2 + CO_2$$

13.16. It is generally impossible to predict the rate law from the equation alone, because most reactions consist of several elementary steps whose combined result is summarized in the rate law. If these elementary steps are unknown, the rate law cannot be predicted.

13.17. The mechanism cannot be $2NO_2Cl \rightarrow 2NO_2 + Cl_2$ because the reaction is first order in NO_2Cl. The order in NO_2Cl would have to reflect the total number of molecules (two) for the proposed mechanism, but it does not.

13.18.   The characteristic of the rate-determining step in a mechanism is that it is, relatively speaking, the slowest step of all the elementary steps (even though it may occur in seconds). Thus, the rate of disappearance of reactant(s) is limited by the rate of this step.

13.19.   For the rate of decomposition of N_2O_4,

$$\text{Rate} = k_1[N_2O_4]$$

For the rate of formation of N_2O_4,

$$\text{Rate} = k_{-1}[NO_2]^2$$

At equilibrium the rates are equal, so

$$k_1[N_2O_4] = k_{-1}[NO_2]^2$$

$$[N_2O_4] = (k_{-1}/k_1)\,[NO_2]^2$$

13.20.   A catalyst operates by providing a pathway (mechanism) that occurs faster than the uncatalyzed pathway (mechanism) of the reaction. The catalyst is not consumed because after reacting in an early step, it is regenerated in a later step.

13.21.   In physical adsorption, molecules adhere to a surface through *weak* intermediate forces, whereas in chemisorption, the molecules adhere to the surface by *stronger* chemical bonding.

13.22.   In the first step of catalytic hydrogenation of ethylene, the ethylene and hydrogen molecules diffuse to the catalyst surface and undergo chemisorption. Then the *pi* electrons of ethylene form temporary bonds to the metal catalyst, and the hydrogen molecule breaks into two hydrogen atoms. The hydrogen atoms next migrate to an ethylene held in position on the metal catalyst surface, forming ethane. Finally, because it cannot bond to the catalyst, the ethane diffuses away from the surface.

13.23.   The answer is c, $[A] = 0.0250\ M$, $[B] = 0.0400\ M$.

13.24.   The answer is e, I and III only.

13.25.   The answer is e; if the rate law for the reaction is Rate = $k[E]^2[F]$, then doubling the concentration of E will cause the rate to increase by a factor of 4 (4 times faster).

13.26.   The answer is c, doubling the $[C]_o$ while keeping the $[A]_o$ and $[B]_o$ constant.

■ ANSWERS TO CONCEPTUAL PROBLEMS

13.29.   a.   You can write the rate expression in terms of the depletion of A:

$$\text{Rate of depletion of A} = -\frac{\Delta[A]}{\Delta t}$$

or you can write the rate expression in terms of the formation of B:

$$\text{Rate of formation of B} = +\frac{\Delta[B]}{\Delta t}$$

b. No. Consider the stoichiometry of the reaction, which indicates that the rate of depletion of A would be faster than the rate of formation of B; for every 3 moles of A that are consumed, 2 moles of B would be formed.

c. Taking into account the stoichiometry of the reaction, the two rate expressions that would give an equal rate when calculated over the same time interval are

$$\text{Rate} = -\frac{\Delta[A]}{3\Delta t} = \frac{\Delta[B]}{2\Delta t}$$

13.31. a. The rate law for a second-order reaction is Rate $= k[A]^2$.

b. The faster reaction rate will correspond to the container with the higher concentration of A. Both containers contain the same number of A particles, but the volume of the container on the right is only one-half the volume of the other. Therefore, the initial concentration of A in the container on the right is double the initial concentration of A in the left container. Thus, the reaction will be faster in the smaller container on the right.

c. For a second-order reaction, the relationship among the half-life, rate constant, and initial concentration of A is

$$t_{\frac{1}{2}} = \frac{1}{k[A]_o}$$

Since the half-life is inversely proportional to the initial concentration, the shorter half-life will correspond to the higher initial concentration of A, which is in the right container.

d. The relative rates of the reactions can be determined as follows. Since the initial concentration of A in the container on the right is double the initial concentration of A in the left container, the ratio of the rate in the right container to that on the left is

$$\frac{\text{Rate}_R}{\text{Rate}_L} = \frac{k[A]_{o,R}^2}{k[A]_{o,L}^2} = \left(\frac{[A]_{o,R}}{[A]_{o,L}}\right)^2 = \left(\frac{2[A]_{o,L}}{[A]_{o,L}}\right)^2 = 2^2 = 4$$

Thus, the reaction rate in the right container is four times the reaction rate of the container on the left.

e. Since both containers start with the same number of A particles, and the reaction rate is faster in the right container, more A particles will have reacted in this container, so it will contain fewer atoms.

13.33. a. If the concentration is tripled but there is no effect on the rate, the order of the reaction must be zero. Thus, $x = 0$.

b. If the concentration is doubled and the rate doubles, it is a first-order reaction. Thus, $x = 1$.

c. If the concentration is tripled and the rate goes up by a factor of 27, it is a third-order reaction. Thus, $x = 3$.

13.35. a. The rate has a constant value in region C because the slope of the curve is constant (flat) in this region.

b. The rate is the fastest in region A because the slope of the curve is steepest in this region.

13.37. A number of answers will work as long as you match one of the existing concentrations of A. For example: [A] $= 2.0\ M$ with [B] $= 2.0\ M$, or [A] $= 1.0\ M$ with [B] $= 2.0\ M$.

■ SOLUTIONS TO PRACTICE PROBLEMS

Note on significant figures: If the final answer to a solution needs to be rounded off, it is given first with one nonsignificant figure, and the last significant figure is underlined. The final answer is then rounded to the correct number of significant figures. In multistep problems, intermediate answers are given with at least one nonsignificant figure; however, only the final answer has been rounded off.

13.39. For the reaction $2NO_2 \rightarrow 2NO + O_2$, the rate of decomposition of NO_2 and the rate of formation of O_2 are, respectively,

$$Rate = -\Delta[NO_2]/\Delta t$$

$$Rate = \Delta[O_2]/\Delta t$$

To relate the two rates, divide each rate by the coefficient of the corresponding substance in the chemical equation and equate them.

$$-\frac{1}{2}\frac{\Delta[NO_2]}{\Delta t} = \frac{\Delta[O_2]}{\Delta t}$$

13.41. For the reaction $5Br^- + BrO_3^- + 6H^+ \rightarrow 3Br_2 + 3H_2O$, the rate of decomposition of Br^- and the rate of decomposition of BrO_3^- are, respectively,

$$Rate = -\Delta[Br^-]/\Delta t$$

$$Rate = -\Delta[BrO_3^-]/\Delta t$$

To relate the two rates, divide each rate by the coefficient of the corresponding substance in the chemical equation and equate them.

$$\frac{1}{5}\frac{\Delta[Br^-]}{\Delta t} = \frac{\Delta[BrO_3^-]}{\Delta t}$$

13.43. $Rate = -\dfrac{\Delta[NH_4NO_2]}{\Delta t} = -\dfrac{[0.0432\,M - 0.500\,M]}{[3.00\,hr - 0.00\,hr]} = 2.2\underline{7} \times 10^{-2} = 2.3 \times 10^{-2}\,M/hr$

13.45. $Rate = -\dfrac{\Delta[Azo.]}{\Delta t} = -\dfrac{[0.0101\,M - 0.0150\,M]}{7.00\,min - 0.00\,min} \times \dfrac{1\,min}{60\,sec} = 1.1\underline{6} \times 10^{-5} = 1.2 \times 10^{-5}\,M/s$

13.47. If the rate law is $Rate = k[H_2S][Cl_2]$, the order with respect to H_2S is 1 (first order), and the order with respect to Cl_2 is also 1 (first-order). The overall order is $1 + 1 = 2$, second-order.

13.49. If the rate law is $Rate = k[MnO_4^-][H_2C_2O_4]$, the order with respect to MnO_4^- is 1 (first order), the order with respect to $H_2C_2O_4$ is 1 (first order), and the order with respect to H^+ is zero. The overall order is 2, second order.

13.51. The reaction rate doubles when the concentration of CH_3NNCH_3 is doubled, so the reaction is first order in azomethane. The rate equation should have the form

$$Rate = k[CH_3NNCH_3]$$

Substituting values for the rate and concentration yields a value for k:

$$k = \frac{\text{rate}}{[\text{Azo.}]} = \frac{2.8 \times 10^{-6} \ M/s}{1.13 \times 10^{-2} \ M} = 2.\underline{4}7 \times 10^{-4} = 2.5 \times 10^{-4}/s$$

13.53. Doubling [NO] quadruples the rate, so the reaction is second order in NO. Doubling $[H_2]$ doubles the rate, so the reaction is first order in H_2. The rate law should have the form

Rate = $k[\text{NO}]^2[H_2]$

Substituting values for the rate and concentrations yields a value for k:

$$k = \frac{\text{rate}}{[\text{NO}]^2[H_2]} = \frac{2.6 \times 10^{-5} \ M/s}{[6.4 \times 10^{-3} \ M]^2[2.2 \times 10^{-3} \ M]} = 2.\underline{8}8 \times 10^2 = 2.9 \times 10^2/M^2s$$

13.55. By comparing Experiments 1 and 2, you see that tripling $[\text{ClO}_2]$ increases the rate ninefold; that is, $3^m = 9$, so $m = 2$ (and the reaction is second order in ClO_2). From Experiments 2 and 3, you see that tripling $[\text{OH}^-]$ triples the rate, so the reaction is first order in OH^-. The rate law is

Rate = $k[\text{ClO}_2]^2[\text{OH}^-]$

Substituting values for the rate and concentrations yields a value for k:

$$k = \frac{\text{rate}}{[\text{ClO}_2]^2[\text{OH}^-]} = \frac{0.0248 \ M/s}{[0.060 \ M]^2[0.030 \ M]} = 2.\underline{2}9 \times 10^2 = 2.3 \times 10^2/M^2s$$

13.57. Let $[\text{SO}_2\text{Cl}_2]_o = 0.0248 \ M$ and $[\text{SO}_2\text{Cl}_2]_t$ = the concentration after 2.0 hr. Substituting these and $k = 2.2 \times 10^{-5}/s$ into the first-order rate equation gives

$$\ln \frac{[\text{SO}_2\text{Cl}_2]_t}{[0.0248 \ M]} = -(2.2 \times 10^{-5}/s)\left(2.0 \ \text{hr} \times \frac{3600 \ s}{1 \ \text{hr}}\right) = -0.1\underline{5}84$$

Taking the antilog of both sides gives

$$\frac{[\text{SO}_2\text{Cl}_2]_t}{[0.0248 \ M]} = e^{-0.1584} = 0.8\underline{5}35$$

Solving for $[\text{SO}_2\text{Cl}_2]_t$ gives

$$[\text{SO}_2\text{Cl}_2]_t = 0.8\underline{5}25 \times [0.0248 \ M] = 0.02\underline{1}16 = 0.021 = 2.1 \times 10^{-2} \ M$$

13.59. The second-order integrated rate law is

$$\frac{1}{[A]_t} = kt + \frac{1}{[A]_o}$$

Using a rate constant value of 0.225 L/(mol•s) and an initial concentration of 0.293 mol/L, after 35.4 s the concentration of A is

$$\frac{1}{[A]_t} = 0.225 \ \text{L/(mol•s)} \times 35.4 \ s + \frac{1}{0.293 \ \text{mol/L}}$$

$$\frac{1}{[A]_t} = 7.9\underline{6}5 \text{ L/mol} + 3.4\underline{1}2 \text{ L/mol} = 11.3\underline{7}7 \text{ L/mol}$$

$$[A]_t = \frac{1}{11.377 \text{ L/mol}} = 0.0878\underline{8}9 = 0.08789 \ M$$

This answer results only if you precisely follow significant figure rules. However, significant figure rules are only approximate at best. A more detailed evaluation of the precision of measurement in this problem would likely yield a less precise value of 0.088 M. How this is accomplished is beyond the scope of this presentation.

13.61. First, find the rate constant, k, by substituting experimental values into the first-order rate equation. Let [Et. Cl.]$_o$ = 0.00100 M, [Et. Cl.]$_t$ = 0.00067 M, and t = 155 s. Solving for k yields

$$k = -\frac{\ln \frac{[0.00067 \ M]_t}{[0.00100 \ M]_o}}{155 \text{ s}} = 2.\underline{5}83 \times 10^{-3}\text{/s}$$

Now let [Et. Cl.]$_t$ = the concentration after 256 s, [Et. Cl.]$_o$ again = 0.00100 M, and use the value of k of $1.5\underline{6}4 \times 10^{-3}$/s to calculate [Et. Cl.]$_t$.

$$\ln \frac{[\text{Et. Cl.}]_t}{[0.00100 \ M]} = -(2.584 \times 10^{-3}\text{/s})(256 \text{ s}) = -0.6\underline{6}14$$

Converting both sides to antilogs gives

$$\frac{[\text{Et. Cl.}]_t}{[0.00100 \ M]} = 0.5\underline{1}61$$

$$[\text{Et. Cl.}]_t = 0.5161 \times [0.00100 \ M] = 5.\underline{1}6 \times 10^{-4} = 5.2 \times 10^{-4} \ M$$

Solving gives $k = 5.0\underline{8}8 \times 10^{-4}$/s. Now let [Cyb.]$_t$ = the concentration after 875 s and [Cyb.]$_o$ =

13.63. For a first-order reaction, divide 0.693 by the rate constant to find the half-life:

$$t_{1/2} = 0.693/(6.3 \times 10^{-4}\text{/s}) = 1.\underline{1}0 \times 10^3 = 1.1 \times 10^3 \text{ s } (1\underline{8}.3 \text{ min})$$

Now, use the half-life to determine the concentrations. When the concentration decreases to 50.0% of its initial value, this is equal to the half-life.

$$t_{50.0\% \text{ left}} = t_{1/2} = 1.10 \times 10^3 \text{ s}$$

When the concentration decreases to 25.0% of its initial value, this is equal to two half-lives.

$$t_{25.0\% \text{ left}} = t_{1/4 \text{ left}} = 2 \times t_{1/2} = 2 \times (1.10 \times 10^3 \text{ s}) = 2.\underline{2}0 \times 10^3 \text{ s } (37 \text{ min})$$

13.65. For a first-order reaction, divide 0.693 by the rate constant to find the half-life:

$$t_{1/2} = 0.693/(2.0 \times 10^{-6}\text{/s}) = 3.\underline{4}65 \times 10^5 \text{ s } (9\underline{6}.25 \text{ or } 96 \text{ hr})$$

$$t_{25\% \text{ left}} = t_{1/4 \text{ left}} = 2 \times t_{1/2} = 2 \times 96.25 \text{ hr} = 19\underline{2}.5 = 1.9 \times 10^2 \text{ hr}$$

$$t_{12.5\% \text{ left}} = t_{1/8 \text{ left}} = 3 \times t_{1/2} = 3 \times 96.25 \text{ hr} = 28\underline{8}.75 = 2.9 \times 10^2 \text{ hr}$$

$$t_{6.25\% \text{ left}} = t_{1/16 \text{ left}} = 4 \times t_{1/2} = 4 \times 96.25 \text{ hr} = 3\underline{8}5.0 = 3.9 \times 10^2 \text{ hr}$$

$$t_{3.125\% \text{ left}} = t_{1/32 \text{ left}} = 5 \times t_{1/2} = 5 \times 96.25 \text{ hr} = 4\underline{8}1.25 = 4.8 \times 10^2 \text{ hr}$$

13.67. The half-life for a second-order reaction is

$$t_{1/2} = \frac{1}{k[A]_o}$$

Using a rate constant of 0.413 L/(mol•s) and an initial A concentration of 5.25×10^{-3} mol/L, the half-life is

$$t_{1/2} = \frac{1}{(0.413 \text{ L/(mol•s)})(5.25 \times 10^{-3} \text{ mol/L})} = 46\underline{1}.2 = 461 \text{ s}$$

13.69. Use the first-order rate equation, and solve for time, t. Let $[Cr^{3+}]_o = 100.0\%$; then the concentration at time t, $[Cr^{3+}]_t$, = (100.0% − 85.0%, or 15.0%). Use $k = 2.0 \times 10^{-6}$/s.

$$\ln\frac{[15.0]}{[100.0]} = -(2.0 \times 10^{-6}\text{/s})\, t$$

$$t = -\frac{\ln(0.150)}{2.0 \times 10^{-6}\text{/s}} = 9.\underline{4}8 \times 10^{5} \text{ s, or } 2.6 \times 10^{2} \text{ hr}$$

13.71. The rate law for a zero-order reaction is

$$[A] = -kt + [A]_o.$$

Using a rate constant of 8.1×10^{-2} mol/(L•s) and an initial concentration of 0.10 M, the time it would take for the concentration to change to 1.0×10^{-2} M is

$$1.0 \times 10^{-2}\, M = -8.1 \times 10^{-2} \text{ mol/(L•s)} \times t + 0.10\, M$$

$$t = \frac{0.10 \text{ M} - 1.0 \times 10^{-2} \text{ M}}{8.1 \times 10^{-2} \text{ M/s}} = \underline{1}.1 = 1 \text{ s}$$

13.73. For the first-order plot, follow Figure 13.9, and plot ln $[ClO_2]$ versus the time in seconds. The data used for plotting are

t, sec	$[ClO_2]$, M	$\ln_e [ClO_2]$
0.00	4.77×10^{-4}	−7.647
1.00	4.31×10^{-4}	−7.749
2.00	3.91×10^{-4}	−7.846
3.00	3.53×10^{-4}	−7.949
5.00	2.89×10^{-4}	−8.149
10.00	1.76×10^{-4}	−8.645
30.00	2.4×10^{-5}	−10.63
50.00	3.2×10^{-5}	−12.65

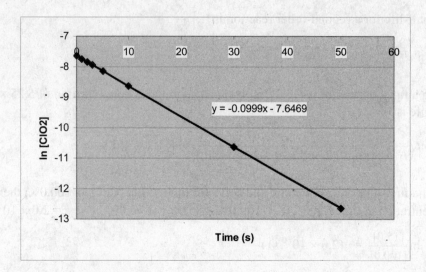

The plot yields a straight line, demonstrating the reaction is first order in [ClO_2]. The least squares slope of -0.0999 given in the above plot can also be approximated from the difference between the last point and the first point:

$$\text{Slope} = \frac{[(-12.65) - (-7.647)]}{[50.00 - 0.00]\text{s}} = -0.10\underline{0}1/\text{s}$$

Just as the slope, m, was obtained for the plot in Figure 13.9, you can also equate m to $-k$, and calculate k as follows:

$$k = -\text{slope} = 0.10\underline{0}1 = 0.100/\text{s}$$

13.75. The potential-energy diagram, not drawn to scale, is below. Because the activation energy for the forward reaction is +10 kJ, and $\Delta H° = -200$ kJ, the activation energy for the reverse reaction is +210 kJ.

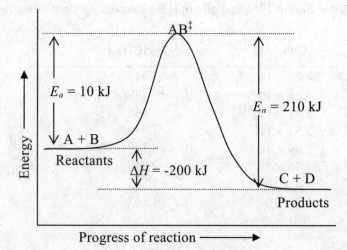

13.77. Solve the two-temperature Arrhenius equation for E_a by substituting $T_1 = 308$ K (from 35°C), $k_1 = 1.4 \times 10^{-4}/\text{s}$, $T_2 = 318$ K (from 45°C), and $k_2 = 5.0 \times 10^{-4}/\text{s}$:

$$\ln\frac{5.0 \times 10^{-4}}{1.4 \times 10^{-4}} = \frac{E_a}{8.31\text{ J/(mol} \cdot \text{K)}}\left(\frac{1}{308\text{ K}} - \frac{1}{318\text{ K}}\right)$$

Rearranging E_a to the left side and calculating $[1/308 - 1/318]$ give

$$E_a = \frac{8.31 \text{ J/K} \times \ln(3.5714)}{1.0209 \times 10^{-4}/\text{K}} = 1.037 \times 10^5 = 1.0 \times 10^5 \text{ J/mol}$$

To find the rate at 55°C (328 K), use the first equation. Let k_2 in the numerator be the unknown and solve:

$$\ln\frac{k_2}{1.4 \times 10^{-4}} = \frac{1.037 \times 10^5 \text{ J/mol}}{8.31 \text{ J/(mol}\cdot\text{K)}}\left(\frac{1}{308 \text{ K}} - \frac{1}{328 \text{ K}}\right) = 2.468$$

$$\frac{k_2}{1.4 \times 10^{-4}} = 11.80$$

$$k_2 = 11.80 \times (1.4 \times 10^{-4}/\text{s}) = 1.652 \times 10^{-3} = 1.7 \times 10^{-3}/\text{s}$$

13.79. Because the rate constant is proportional to the rate of a reaction, tripling the rate at 25°C means that the rate constant at 25°C is also tripled. Thus, $k_{35} = 3k_{25}$, and the latter can be substituted for k_{25} in the Arrhenius equation:

$$\ln\frac{3 k_{25}}{k_{25}} = \frac{E_a}{8.31 \text{ J/(mol}\cdot\text{K)}}\left(\frac{1}{298 \text{ K}} - \frac{1}{308 \text{ K}}\right)$$

$$1.0986 = (1.311 \times 10^{-5} \text{ mol/J})\, E_a$$

$$E_a = \frac{1.0986}{1.311 \times 10^{-5} \text{ mol/J}} = 8.38 \times 10^4 \text{ J/mol} = 84 \text{ kJ/mol}$$

13.81. For plotting $\ln k$ versus $1/T$, the data below are used:

k	$\ln k$	$1/T$ (1/K)
0.527	−0.64055	1.686×10^{-3}
0.776	−0.25360	1.658×10^{-3}
1.121	0.11422	1.631×10^{-3}
1.607	0.47436	1.605×10^{-3}

The plot yields an approximately straight line. The slope of the line is calculated from the difference between the last and the first points:

$$\text{Slope} = \frac{(0.47436) - (-0.64055)}{[1.605 \times 10^{-3} - 1.686 \times 10^{-3}]/\text{K}} = -13764 \text{ K}$$

Because the slope $= -E_a/R$, you can solve for E_a using $R = 8.31$ J/K:

$$\frac{-E_a}{8.31 \text{ J/(K}\cdot\text{mol)}} = -13764 \text{ K}$$

$$E_a = 13764 \text{ K} \times 8.31 \text{ J/K} = 1.143 \times 10^5 \text{ J/mol, or } 1.1 \times 10^2 \text{ kJ/mol}$$

13.83. The $NOCl_2$ is a reaction intermediate that is produced in the first reaction and consumed in the second. The overall reaction is the sum of the two elementary reactions:

$$NO + Cl_2 \quad \rightarrow \quad NOCl_2$$

$$\underline{NOCl_2 + NO \quad \rightarrow \quad 2NOCl}$$

$$2NO + Cl_2 \quad \rightarrow \quad 2NOCl$$

13.85. a.   Bimolecular

b.   Bimolecular

c.   Unimolecular

d.   Termolecular

13.87. a.   Only O_3 occurs on the left side of the equation, so the rate law is

$$Rate = k[O_3]$$

b.   Both $NOCl_2$ and NO occur on the left side of the equation, so the rate law is

$$Rate = k[NOCl_2][NO]$$

13.89. Step 1 of the isomerization of cyclopropane, C_3H_6, is slow, so the rate law for the overall reaction will be the rate law for this step, with $k_1 = k$, the overall rate constant:

$$Rate = k[C_3H_6]^2$$

13.91. Step 2 of this reaction is slow, so the rate law for the overall reaction would appear to be the rate law for this step:

$$Rate = k_2[I]^2[H_2]$$

However, the rate law includes an intermediate, the I atom, and cannot be used unless the intermediate is eliminated. This can be done only using an equation for Step 1. At equilibrium, you can write the following equality for Step 1:

$$k_1[I_2] = k_{-1}[I]^2$$

Rearranging and then substituting for the $[I]^2$ term yield

$$[I]^2 = [I_2]\frac{k_1}{k_{-1}}$$

$$Rate = k_2(k_1/k_{-1})[I_2][H_2] = k[I_2][H_2] \ (k = \text{the overall rate constant})$$

13.93. The Br^- ion is the catalyst. It is consumed in the first step and regenerated in the second step. It speeds up the reaction by providing a pathway with a lower activation energy than that of a reaction pathway involving no Br^-. The overall reaction is obtained by adding the two steps:

$$2H_2O_2 \rightarrow 2H_2O + O_2$$

Bromide ion is added to the mixture to give the catalytic activity, and BrO^- is an intermediate.

■ SOLUTIONS TO GENERAL PROBLEMS

13.95. All rates of reaction are calculated by dividing the decrease in concentration by the difference in times; hence, only the setup for the first rate (after 10 minutes) is given below. This setup is

$$\text{Rate (10 min)} = -\frac{(1.29-1.50) \times 10^{-2} \text{ M}}{(10-0) \text{ min}} \times \frac{1 \text{ min}}{60 \text{ s}} = 3.5 \times 10^{-6} \text{ M/s}$$

A summary of the times and rates is given in the table.

Time, min	Rate
10	$3.\underline{50} \times 10^{-6} = 3.5 \times 10^{-6}$ M/s
20	$3.\underline{17} \times 10^{-6} = 3.2 \times 10^{-6}$ M/s
30	$2.\underline{50} \times 10^{-6} = 2.5 \times 10^{-6}$ M/s

13.97. The calculation of the average concentration and the division of the rate by the average concentration are the same for all three time intervals. Thus, only the setup for the first interval is given:

$$k_{10 \text{ min}} = \frac{\text{rate}}{\text{avg. conc.}} = \frac{3.50 \times 10^{-6} \text{ M/s}}{\left[\frac{(1.50 + 1.29) \times 10^{-2} \text{ M}}{2}\right]} = 2.5\underline{08} \times 10^{-4}/\text{s}$$

A summary of the times, rate constants, and average rate constant is given in the table.

Time	Rate	k
10 min	3.50×10^{-6} M/s	$2.\underline{5}08 \times 10^{-4}/\text{s}$
20 min	3.17×10^{-6} M/s	$2.\underline{6}52 \times 10^{-4}/\text{s}$
30 min	2.50×10^{-6} M/s	$2.\underline{4}39 \times 10^{-4}/\text{s}$
-----	---- average k	$2.\underline{5}33 \times 10^{-4} = 2.5 \times 10^{-4}/\text{s}$

13.99. Use the first-order rate equation $k = 1.26 \times 10^{-4}/\text{s}$, the initial methyl acetate $[MA]_o = 100\%$, and $[MA]_t = (100\% - 65\%, \text{ or } 35\%)$.

$$t = -\frac{\ln\frac{35\%}{100\%}}{1.26 \times 10^{-4}/\text{s}} = 8.3\underline{3}19 \times 10^3 = 8.33 \times 10^3 \text{ s}$$

13.101. Use $k = 1.26 \times 10^{-4}/\text{s}$, and substitute into the $t_{1/2}$ equation:

$$t_{1/2} = \frac{0.693}{k} = \frac{0.693}{1.26 \times 10^{-4}/\text{s}} = 5.5\underline{00} \times 10^3 = 5.50 \times 10^3 \text{ s (1.53 hr)}$$

13.103. First, find the rate constant from the first-order rate equation, substituting the initial concentration of $[\text{comp.}]_o = 0.0350$ M, and the $[\text{comp.}]_t = 0.0250$ M.

$$\ln\frac{0.0250 \text{ M}}{0.0350 \text{ M}} = -k (65 \text{ s})$$

Rearranging and solving for k give

$$k = -\frac{\left(\ln\frac{0.0250\ M}{0.0350\ M}\right)}{65\ s} = 5.\underline{1}8 \times 10^{-3}/s$$

Now, arrange the first-order rate equation to solve for $[\text{comp.}]_t$; substitute the above value of k, again using $[\text{comp.}]_o = 0.0350\ M$.

$$\ln\frac{[\text{comp.}]_t}{0.0350\ M} = -(5.\underline{1}8 \times 10^{-3}/s)(75\ s) = -0.3\underline{8}8$$

Taking the antilog of both sides gives

$$\frac{[\text{comp.}]_t}{0.0350\ M} = e^{-0.388} = 0.6\underline{7}8;\ [\text{comp}]_t = 0.6\underline{7}8 \times [0.0350\ M]_o = 0.02\underline{3}7 = 0.024\ M$$

13.105. a. The rate constant for a second-order reaction is related to the half-life by

$$k = \frac{1}{t_{1/2}[A]_o}$$

Using a half-life of 5.92×10^{-2} s and an initial A concentration of 0.50 mol/L, the rate constant is

$$k = \frac{1}{(5.92 \times 10^{-2}\ s)(0.50\ mol/L)} = 3\underline{3}.78 = 34\ L/(mol\bullet s)$$

b. The second-order integrated rate law is

$$\frac{1}{[A]_t} = kt + \frac{1}{[A]_o}$$

Using an initial concentration of C_4H_8 (A) of 0.010 M, after 3.6×10^2 s, the concentration will be

$$\frac{1}{[A]_t} = 33.78\ L/(mol\bullet s)(3.6 \times 10^2\ s) + \frac{1}{0.010\ mol/L}$$

$$\frac{1}{[A]_t} = 1\underline{2},162\ L/mol + 1\underline{0}0.0\ L/mol = 1\underline{2},262\ L/mol$$

$$[A]_t = \frac{1}{12,262\ L/mol} = 8.\underline{1}55 \times 10^{-5} = 8.2 \times 10^{-5}\ M$$

13.107. The second-order integrated rate law is

$$\frac{1}{[A]_t} = kt + \frac{1}{[A]_o}$$

The starting concentration of NO_2 (A) is 0.050 M. Using a rate constant of 0.775 L/(mol•s), after 2.5×10^2 s the concentration of NO_2 will be

$$\frac{1}{[A]_t} = 0.775\ L/(mol\bullet s)(2.5 \times 10^2\ s) + \frac{1}{0.050\ mol/L}$$

$$\frac{1}{[A]_t} = 1\underline{9}3 \text{ L/mol} + 2\underline{0}.0 \text{ L/mol} = 2\underline{1}3. \text{ L/mol}$$

$$[A]_t = \frac{1}{213 \text{ L/mol}} = 4.\underline{6}7 \times 10^{-3} = 4.7 \times 10^{-3} \, M$$

The half-life is

$$t_{1/2} = \frac{1}{k[A]_o}$$

Using a rate constant of 0.775 L/(mol•s) and an initial A concentration of 0.050 mol/L, the half-life is

$$t_{1/2} = \frac{1}{(0.775 \text{ L/(mol} \cdot \text{s})(0.050 \text{ mol/L})} = 25.80 = 26 \text{ s}$$

13.109. The $\ln[CH_3NNCH_3]$ and time data for the plot are tabulated below.

t min	$\ln[CH_3NNCH_3]$
0	−4.1997
10	−4.3505
20	−4.5098
30	−4.6564

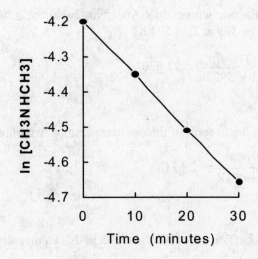

The slope, m, is calculated from the graph:

$$m = \frac{(-4.6564)-(-4.1997)}{(30-0) \text{ min}} = -0.015\underline{2}2 \text{ /min}$$

Because the slope also $= -k$, this gives

$$k = -(-0.01522/\text{min})(1 \text{ min}/60 \text{ s}) = 2.\underline{5}3 \times 10^{-4} = 2.5 \times 10^{-4}/\text{s}$$

13.111. The rate law for a zero-order reaction is

$$[A] = -kt + [A]_o.$$

Using a rate constant of 3.7×10^{-6} mol/(L•s) and an initial concentration of 5.0×10^{-4} M, the time it would take for the concentration to drop to 5.0×10^{-5} M is

$$5.0 \times 10^{-5}\ M = -8.1 \times 10^{-2}\ \text{mol/(L•s)} \times t + 5.0 \times 10^{-4}\,\text{M}$$

$$t = \frac{(5.0 \times 10^{-4}\ M) - (5.0 \times 10^{-5}\ M)}{3.7 \times 10^{-6}\ M/s} = 12\underline{1}.6 = 1.2 \times 10^2\ s$$

The half-life for a zero-order reaction is

$$t_{1/2} = \frac{[A]_o}{2k} = \frac{5.0 \times 10^{-4}\ M}{2(3.7 \times 10^{-6}\ M/s)} = 6\underline{7}.57 = 68\ s$$

13.113. Rearrange the two-temperature Arrhenius equation to solve for E_a in joules, using $k_1 = 0.498$ M/s at $T_1 = 592$ K (319°C) and $k_2 = 1.81$ M/s at 627 K (354°C). Assume $(1/T_1 - 1/T_2)$ has three significant figures.

$$E_a = \frac{(8.31\ \text{J/mol•K}) \ln\left(\dfrac{1.81}{0.498}\right)}{\left(\dfrac{1}{592\ K} - \dfrac{1}{627\ K}\right)} = 1.1\underline{3}7 \times 10^5\ \text{J/mol} = 114\ \text{kJ/mol}$$

To obtain A, rearrange the ln form of the one-temperature Arrhenius equation; substitute the value of E_a obtained above, and use $k_1 = 0.498$ M/s at $T_1 = 592$ K.

$$\ln A = \ln 0.498 + \frac{1.137 \times 10^5\ \text{J/mol}}{8.31\ \text{J/(mol•K)} \times 592\ K} = 22.4\underline{2}0$$

$$A = \underline{5}.46 \times 10^9 = 5 \times 10^9$$

To obtain k at 420°C (693 K), also use the ln form of the one-temperature Arrhenius equation:

$$\ln k = 22.420 - \frac{1.137 \times 10^5\ \text{J/mol}}{8.31\ \text{J/(mol•K)} \times 693\,K} = 2.\underline{6}71$$

$$k = e^{2.671} = 1\underline{4}.45 = 14\ M/s$$

13.115. If the reaction occurs in one step, the coefficients of NO_2 and CO in this elementary reaction are each one, so the rate law should be

$$\text{Rate} = k[NO_2][CO]$$

13.117. The slow step determines the observed rate, so the overall rate constant, k, should be equal to the rate constant for the first step, and the rate law should be

$$\text{Rate} = k[NO_2Br]$$

13.119. The slow step determines the observed rate; assuming k_2 is the rate constant for the second step, the rate law would appear to be

Rate = $k_2[NH_3][HOCN]$

However, this rate law includes two intermediate substances that are neither reactants nor products. The rate law cannot be used unless both are eliminated. This can be done only using an equation from Step 1. At equilibrium in Step 1, you can write the following equality, assuming k_1 and k_{-1} are the rate constants for the forward and back reactions, respectively:

$k_1[NH_4^+][OCN^-] = k_{-1}[NH_3][HOCN]$

Rearranging and then substituting for the $[NH_3][HOCN]$ product give

$[NH_3][HOCN] = (k_1/k_{-1})[NH_4^+][OCN^-]$

Rate = $k_2(k_1/k_{-1})[NH_4^+][OCN^-] = k[NH_4^+][OCN^-]$ (k = overall rate constant)

13.121. a. The reaction is first order in O_2 because the rate doubled with a doubling of the oxygen concentration (Exps. ½). The reaction is second order in NO because the rate increased by a factor of 8 when both the NO and O_2 concentrations were doubled (Exps. 2/3).

Rate = $k[NO]^2[O_2]$

b. The initial rate of the reaction for Experiment 4 can be determined by first calculating the value of the rate constant using Experiment 1 for the data.

$0.80 \times 10^{-2}\ M/s = k(4.5 \times 10^{-2}\ M)^2(2.2 \times 10^{-2}\ M)$

Solving for the rate constant gives

$k = 1.\underline{7}96 \times 10^2\ M^{-2}s^{-1}$

Now, use the data in Experiment 4 and the rate constant to determine the initial rate of the reaction.

Rate = $1.\underline{7}96 \times 10^2\ M^{-2}s^{-1}\ (3.8 \times 10^{-1}\ M)^2(4.6 \times 10^{-3}\ M)$

Rate = $0.1\underline{1}9 = 0.12$ mol/L•s

13.123. a. i) Rate will decrease because OH^- will react with H_3O^+ and lower its concentration.

ii) Rate will decrease because the dilution with water will decrease both the H_3O^+ and the CH_3CSNH_2 concentration.

b. i) The catalyst will provide another pathway, and k will increase because E_a will be smaller.

ii) The rate constant changes with temperature, and it will decrease with a decrease in temperature, because fewer molecules will have enough energy to react.

13.125. a.   The diagram:

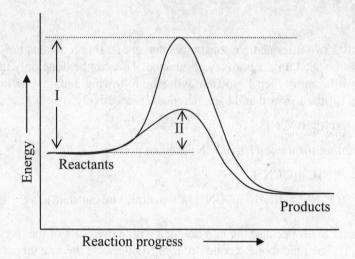

b.   In the diagram, I represents the activation energy for the uncatalyzed reaction, and II represents the activation energy for the catalyzed reaction. A catalyst provides another pathway for a chemical reaction, and with a lower activation energy, more molecules have enough energy to react, so the reaction will be faster.

13.127. a.   The rate of a chemical reaction is the change in the concentration of a reactant or product with time. For a reactant concentration given by [c],

$$-\Delta[c]/\Delta t \ or \ -d[c]/dt$$

b.   The rate changes because the concentration of the reactant has changed.

Rate = $k[A]^m$

c.   Rate = $k[A]^m[B]^n$

The rate will equal k when the reactants all have 1.00 M concentrations, or if the reaction is 0th order.

13.129.   The experiment involves using a laser, first to send a pump pulse to excite a reactant molecule to a higher energy state. Then, a weaker laser pulse or probe pulse of properly chosen wavelength is used to detect the molecule as it transforms to products. By varying the time between the pump pulse and the probe pulse, the experimenter can follow a molecule throughout the course of its reaction. The change of wavelength of the probe pulse tells the experimenter something about the change in character of the molecules as it reacts.

■   **SOLUTIONS TO STRATEGY PROBLEMS**

13.131. Use the Arrhenius equation.

$$\ln \frac{k_2}{1.4 \times 10^{-5} \ /M \cdot min} = \frac{2.11 \times 10^3 \ J/mol}{8.314 \ J/K \cdot mol} \left(\frac{1}{483 \ K} - \frac{1}{611 \ K} \right) = 0.1\underline{1}0$$

$$k_2 = (1.\underline{4} \times 10^{-5} \ /M \bullet min)e^{0.1\underline{1}0} = 1.\underline{5}6 \times 10^{-5} = 1.6 \times 10^{-5} \ /M \bullet min$$

13.133. $k = \dfrac{1}{t_{1/2}[A]_o} = \dfrac{1}{(287 \text{ s})(1.87 \times 10^{-2} \text{ M})} = 0.18\underline{6}3 = 0.186 \ /M\bullet s$

13.135. First write the rate law in terms of the slow step.

$$\text{Rate} = k_2[NOCl_2][NO]$$

Next, set the forward rate equal to the reverse rate for the fast equilibrium.

$$\text{Rate}_f = k_f[NO][Cl_2] = \text{Rate}_r = k_r[NOCl_2]$$

Rearrange this equation and solve for $[NOCl_2]$.

$$[NOCl_2] = \frac{k_f}{k_r}[NO][Cl_2]$$

Finally, substitute into the rate law above to eliminate $[NOCl_2]$. This gives the following rate equation.

$$\text{Rate} = k_2 \left\{ \frac{k_f}{k_r}[NO][Cl_2] \right\}[NO] = k[NO]^2[Cl_2]$$

13.137. You can set up an expression for the ratio of the two rates as follows. Use $[B]_2 = 2[B]_1$.

$$\frac{\text{Rate}_2}{\text{Rate}_1} = \frac{k[A]_2{}^2[B]_2{}^3}{k[A]_1{}^2[B]_1{}^3} = \left[\frac{[B]_2}{[B]_1} \right]^3 = \left[\frac{2[B]_1}{[B]_1} \right]^3 = 2^3 = 8$$

Therefore, the rate of the second run is eight times the rate of the first run.

13.139. a.   The overall reaction is

$$2H_2O_2 \rightarrow 2H_2O + O_2$$

     b.   The catalyst is I^-, and the intermediate is IO^-.

     c.   No, the rate law can not be specified until the rate-determining step is established.

13.141. a.   In the following potential energy diagram dotted lines indicate bonds which are about to form or break.

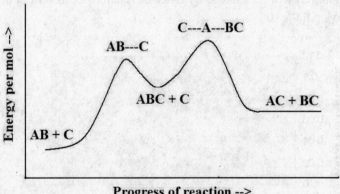

b.   Adding the two steps of the mechanism and eliminating the intermediate ABC gives the overall reaction:

$$AB + 2C \rightarrow AC + BC$$

c.   The second step is the rate limiting step because it has the highest overall activation energy.

d.   First write the rate law in terms of the second, slow step.

$$\text{Rate} = k_2[\text{ABC}][\text{C}]$$

Next, assume the first step quickly reaches equilibrium and set the forward rate equal to the reverse rate for this step.

$$\text{Rate}_f = k_f[\text{AB}][\text{C}] = \text{Rate}_r = k_r[\text{ABC}]$$

Rearrange this equation and solve for [ABC].

$$[\text{ABC}] = \frac{k_f}{k_r}[\text{AB}][\text{C}]$$

Finally, substitute into the rate law above to eliminate [ABC]. This gives the following rate equation.

$$\text{Rate} = k_2 \left\{ \frac{k_f}{k_r}[\text{AB}][\text{C}] \right\} [\text{C}] = k[\text{AB}][\text{C}]^2$$

e.   Since the energy per mole of products is higher than the energy per mole of reactants, the reaction is endothermic.

13.143. a.   The evidence presented in the problem statement indicate a rate law that is first-order in reactant A and second-order in reactant B, or rate = k[A][B]^2.

b.   You can set up an expression for the ratio of the two rates as follows. Use $[\text{A}]_2 = 0.5[\text{A}]_1$ and $[\text{B}]_2 = 2[\text{B}]_1$.

$$\frac{\text{Rate}_2}{\text{Rate}_1} = \frac{k[\text{A}]_2[\text{B}]_2^{\,2}}{k[\text{A}]_1[\text{B}]_1^{\,2}} = \frac{k(0.5[\text{A}]_1)(2[\text{B}]_1)^2}{k[\text{A}]_1[\text{B}]_1^{\,2}} = 0.5 \times 4 = 2$$

Therefore, the rate of the second run is twice the rate of the first run.

c.   By the overall reaction stoichiometry, when [A] is reduced to one half of its initial concentration, [B] will be reduced by twice as much. If both start at 0.10 M, B will be used up when $[\text{A}]_t = 0.05\ M$.

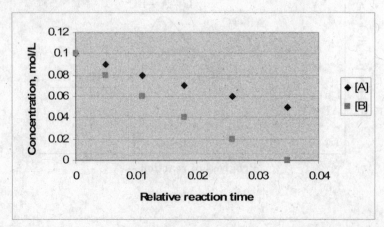

13.145. a.　　Rate = $k[N_2O_5]$ = 6.2 × 10^{-4} s^{-1} × $[N_2O_5]$

　　　b.　　Rate = 6.2 × 10^{-4} s^{-1} × $[N_2O_5]$ = 6.2 × 10^{-4} s^{-1} × (0.20 M) = 1.$\underline{2}$4 × 10^{-4} = 1.2 × 10^{-4} M/s

　　　c.　　The half-life equation for a first-order reaction is $t_{1/2} = 0.693/k$.

$$t_{1/2} = 0.693/(6.2 × 10^{-4}\ s^{-1}) = 1\underline{1}17\ s = 1.1 × 10^3\ s$$

　　　d.　　For $[N_2O_5]$ after 1.5 hours (5400 seconds), use the first-order rate law, and solve for the concentration at time t:

$$\ln \frac{[N_2O_5]_t}{(0.50\ M)} = -(6.2 × 10^{-4}\ /s)(5\underline{4}00\ s) = -3.\underline{3}48$$

Take the antilog of both sides to get

$$\frac{[N_2O_5]_t}{(0.50\ M)} = e^{-3.348} = 0.03\underline{5}1\ \text{and}\ [N_2O_5]_t = 0.50\ M × 0.03\underline{5}1 = 0.01\underline{7}6 = 0.018\ M$$

■ SOLUTIONS TO CUMULATIVE-SKILLS PROBLEMS

13.147. The balanced equation is

$$2N_2O_5 \quad \rightarrow \quad 4NO_2 + O_2.$$

Note that the number of moles of O_2 formed will be one-half the number of moles of N_2O_5 decomposed. Now use the integrated form of the first-order rate law to calculate the fraction of the 1.00 mol N_2O_5 decomposing in 20.0 hr, or 1200 min.

$$\ln \frac{[N_2O_5]_t}{[N_2O_5]_o} = -kt = -(6.2 × 10^{-4}/min)(1200\ min) = -0.7\underline{4}4$$

$$\frac{[N_2O_5]_t}{[N_2O_5]_o} = e^{-0.744} = 0.4\underline{7}52$$

Fraction of N_2O_5 decomposed = 1.000 − 0.4752 = 0.5$\underline{2}$48

Since there is 1.00 mol of N_2O_5 present at the start, the moles of N_2O_5 decomposed is 0.5$\underline{2}$48 mol. Thus,

$$\text{Moles of } O_2 \text{ formed} = 0.5248 \text{ mol } N_2O_5 × \frac{1 \text{ mol } O_2}{2 \text{ mol } N_2O_5} = 0.26\underline{2}37 \text{ mol } O_2$$

Now, use the ideal gas law to calculate the volume of this number of moles of O_2 gas at 45°C and 780 mmHg.

$$V = \frac{nRT}{P} = \frac{(0.26237 \text{ mol})(0.08206 \text{ L} \cdot \text{atm/ (K} \cdot \text{mol}))(318 \text{ K})}{(770/ 760) \text{ atm}} = 6.\underline{7}58 = 6.8 \text{ L}$$

13.149. Using the first-order rate law, the initial rate of decomposition is given by

$$\text{Rate} = k[H_2O_2] = (7.40 × 10^{-4}/s) × (1.50\ M\ H_2O_2) = 1.1\underline{1}0 × 10^{-3}\ M\ H_2O_2/s$$

The heat liberated per second per mol H_2O_2 can be found by first calculating the standard enthalpy of the decomposition of 1 mol H_2O_2:

$$H_2O_2(aq) \quad \rightarrow \quad H_2O(l) \quad + \quad 1/2\ O_2(g)$$

$$\Delta H_f° \quad = \quad \text{-191.2 kJ/mol} \qquad \text{-285.8 kJ/mol} \qquad \text{0 kJ/mol}$$

For the reaction, the standard enthalpy change is

$$\Delta H° = -285.8 \text{ kJ/mol} - (-191.2 \text{ kJ/mol}) = -94.\underline{6}0 \text{ kJ/mol } H_2O_2$$

The heat liberated per second is

$$\frac{-94.60 \text{ kJ}}{\text{mol } H_2O_2} \times \frac{1.110 \times 10^{-3} \text{ mol } H_2O_2}{L \bullet s} \times 2.00 \text{ L} = -0.21\underline{0}01 = -0.210 \text{ kJ/s}$$

13.151. Use the ideal gas law ($P/RT = n/V$) to calculate the mol/L of each gas:

$$[NO] = \frac{(155/760) \text{ atm}}{0.082057 \text{ L} \bullet \text{atm/(K} \bullet \text{mol) x 612 K}} = 0.00406\underline{1} \text{ mol NO/L}$$

$$[O_2] = \frac{(345/760) \text{ atm}}{0.082057 \text{ L} \bullet \text{atm/(K} \bullet \text{mol) x 612 K}} = 0.00903\underline{9} \text{ mol } O_2/L$$

The rate of decrease of NO is

$$\frac{1.16 \times 10^{-5} \text{ L}^2}{\text{mol}^2 \bullet s} \times \left(\frac{4.061 \times 10^{-3} \text{ mol}}{1 \text{ L}}\right)^2 \times \frac{9.039 \times 10^{-3} \text{ mol}}{1 \text{ L}} = 1.7\underline{2}9 \times 10^{-12} \text{ mol/(L}\bullet s)$$

The rate of decrease in atm/s is found by multiplying by RT:

$$\frac{1.729 \times 10^{-12} \text{ mol}}{\text{L} \bullet s} \times \frac{0.082057 \text{ L} \bullet \text{atm}}{\text{K} \bullet \text{mol}} \times 612 \text{ K} = 8.6\underline{8}2 \times 10^{-11} \text{ atm/s}$$

The rate of decrease of NO in mmHg/s is

$$8.682 \times 10^{-11} \text{ atm/s} \times \frac{760 \text{ mmHg}}{1 \text{ atm}} = 6.6\underline{0}0 \times 10^{-8} = 6.60 \times 10^{-8} \text{ mmHg/s}$$

CHAPTER 14

Chemical Equilibrium

■ SOLUTIONS TO EXERCISES

Note on significant figures: If the final answer to a solution needs to be rounded off, it is given first with one nonsignificant figure, and the last significant figure is underlined. The final answer is then rounded to the correct number of significant figures. In multistep problems, intermediate answers are given with at least one nonsignificant figure; however, only the final answer has been rounded off.

14.1. Use the table approach, and give the starting numbers, the change, and the equilibrium number of moles of each.

Amt. (mol)	$CO(g)$	+	$H_2O(g)$	$\rightleftharpoons$	$CO_2(g)$	+	$H_2(g)$
Starting	1.00		1.00		0		0
Change	$-x$		$-x$		$+x$		$+x$
Equilibrium	$(1.00 - x)$		$(1.00 - x)$		x		$x = 0.43$

Because we are given that $x = 0.43$ in the statement of the problem, we can use that to calculate the equilibrium amounts of the reactants and products:

Equilibrium amount CO = $1.00 - 0.43 = 0.57$ mol

Equilibrium amount $H_2O = 1.00 - 0.43 = 0.57$ mol

Equilibrium amount $CO_2 = x = 0.43$ mol

Equilibrium amount $H_2 = x = 0.43$ mol

14.2. For the equation $2NO_2 + 7H_2 \rightarrow 2NH_3 + 4H_2O$, the expression for the equilibrium constant, K_c, is

$$K_c = \frac{[NH_3]^2 [H_2O]^4}{[NO_2]^2 [H_2]^7}$$

Notice that each concentration term is raised to a power equal to its coefficient in the chemical equation.

For the equation $NO_2 + 7/2H_2 \rightarrow NH_3 + 2H_2O$, the expression for the equilibrium constant, K_c, is

$$K_c = \frac{[NH_3][H_2O]^2}{[NO_2][H_2]^{7/2}}$$

Note the correspondence between the power and coefficient for each molecule.

14.3.   The chemical equation for the reaction is

$$CO(g) + H_2O(g) \rightleftharpoons H_2(g) + CO_2(g)$$

The expression for the equilibrium constant for this reaction is

$$K_c = \frac{[CO_2][H_2]}{[CO][H_2O]}$$

We obtain the concentration of each substance by dividing the moles of substance by its volume. The equilibrium concentrations are as follows: $[CO] = 0.057\ M$, $[H_2O] = 0.057\ M$, $[CO_2] = 0.043\ M$, and $[H_2] = 0.043\ M$. Substituting these values into the equation for the equilibrium constant gives

$$K_c = \frac{(0.043)(0.043)}{(0.057)(0.057)} = 0.5\underline{6}9 = 0.57$$

14.4.   Use the table approach, and give the starting concentrations, the change, and the equilibrium concentration of each by dividing moles by volume in liters.

Conc. (M)	$2H_2S(g)$	$\rightleftharpoons$	$2H_2(g)$	+	$S_2(g)$
Starting	0.0100		0		0
Change	$-2x$		$+2x\ (= 0.00285)$		$+x$
Equilibrium	$0.0100 - 2x$		$2x$		x

Because the problem states that $0.00285\ M\ H_2$ was formed, we can use the $0.00285\ M$ to calculate the other concentrations. The S_2 molarity should be one-half that, or $0.0014\underline{2}5\ M$, and the H_2S molarity should be $0.0100 - 0.00285$, or $0.007\underline{1}5\ M$. Substituting into the equilibrium expression gives

$$K_c = \frac{[H_2]^2[S_2]}{[H_2S]^2} = \frac{(0.00285)^2\,(0.001425)}{(0.00715)^2} = 2.\underline{2}6 \times 10^{-4} = 2.3 \times 10^{-4}$$

14.5.   Use the expression that relates K_c to K_p:

$$K_p = K_c(RT)^{\Delta n}$$

The Δn term is the sum of the coefficients of the gaseous products minus the sum of the coefficients of the gaseous reactants. In this case, $\Delta n = (2 - 1) = 1$, and K_p is

$$K_p = (3.26 \times 10^{-2})\,(0.0821 \times 464)^1 = 1.2\underline{4}1 = 1.24$$

14.6.   For a heterogeneous equilibrium, the concentration terms for liquids and solids are omitted because such concentrations are constant at a given temperature and are incorporated into the measured value of K_c. For this case, K_c is defined as

$$K_c = \frac{[Ni(CO)_4]}{[CO]^4}$$

14.7.   Because the equilibrium constant is very large ($> 10^4$), the equilibrium mixture will contain mostly products. Rearrange the K_c expression to solve for $[NO_2]$.

$$[NO_2] = \sqrt{K_c[O_2][NO]^2} = \sqrt{(4.0\times10^{13})(2.0\times10^{-6})(2.0\times10^{-6})^2} = 1.\underline{7}8 \times 10^{-2} = 1.8 \times 10^{-2} = 0.018\ M$$

14.8. First, divide moles by volume in liters to convert to molar concentrations, giving 0.00015 M CO_2 and 0.010 M CO. Substitute these values into the reaction quotient and calculate Q.

$$Q = \frac{[CO]^2}{[CO_2]} = \frac{(0.010)^2}{(0.00015)} = 0.6\underline{6}6 = 0.67$$

Because $Q = 0.67$ and is less than K_c, the reaction will go to the right, forming more CO.

14.9. Rearrange the K_c expression, and substitute for K_c (= 0.0415) and the given moles per 1.00 L to solve for moles per 1.00 L of PCl_5.

$$[PCl_5] = \frac{[PCl_3][Cl_2]}{K_c} = \frac{(0.020)(0.020)}{0.0415} = 9.\underline{6}3 \times 10^{-3} = 9.6 \times 10^{-3}\ M$$

Because the volume is 1.00 L, the moles of PCl_5 = 0.0096 mol.

14.10. Use the table approach, and give the starting number, the change, and the equilibrium number of moles of each.

Amt. (mol)	$H_2(g)$	+	$I_2(g)$	$\rightleftharpoons$	$2HI(g)$
Starting	0.500		0.500		0
Change	$-x$		$-x$		$+2x$
Equilibrium	$0.500 - x$		$0.500 - x$		$2x$

Substitute the equilibrium concentrations into the expression for K_c (= 49.7).

$$K_c = \frac{[HI]^2}{[H_2][I_2]}; \quad 49.7 = \frac{(2x)^2}{(0.500 - x)(0.500 - x)} = \frac{(2x)^2}{(0.500 - x)^2}$$

Taking the square root of both sides of the right-hand equation and solving for x gives

$$\pm 7.05 = \frac{2x}{(0.500 - x)}, \text{ or } \pm 7.05(0.500 - x) = 2x$$

Using the positive root, $x = 0.3\underline{9}0$.

Using the negative root, $x = 0.6\underline{9}8$ (this must be rejected because 0.698 is greater than the 0.500 starting number of moles).

Substituting $x = 0.3\underline{9}0$ mol into the last line of the table to solve for equilibrium concentrations gives these amounts: 0.11 mol H_2, 0.11 mol I_2, and 0.78 mol HI.

14.11. Use the table approach for starting, change, and equilibrium concentrations of each species.

Conc. (M)	$PCl_5(g)$	$\rightleftharpoons$	$PCl_3(g)$	+	$Cl_2(g)$
Starting	1.00		0		0
Change	$-x$		$+x$		$+x$
Equilibrium	$1.00 - x$		x		x

Substitute the equilibrium-concentration expressions from the table into the equilibrium equation, and solve for x using the quadratic formula.

$$[PCl_3][Cl_2] = K_c \times [PCl_5] = 0.0211(1.00 - x) = x^2$$

$$x^2 + 0.0211x - 0.0211 = 0$$

$$x = \frac{-0.0211 \pm \sqrt{(0.0211)^2 - 4(-0.0211)}}{2} = \frac{-0.0211 \pm 0.2913}{2}$$

$x = -0.1562$ (impossible; reject), or $x = 0.13\underline{5}09 = 0.135\ M$ (logical)

Solve for the equilibrium concentrations using $x = 0.135\ M$: $[PCl_5] = 0.86\ M$, $[Cl_2] = 0.135\ M$, and $[PCl_3] = 0.135\ M$.

14.12. a.   Increasing the pressure will cause a net reaction to occur from right to left, and more $CaCO_3$ will form.

   b.   Increasing the concentration of hydrogen will cause a net reaction to occur from right to left, forming more Fe and H_2O.

14.13. a.   Because there are equal numbers of moles of gas on both sides of the equation, increasing the pressure will not increase the amount of product.

   b.   Because the reaction increases the number of moles of gas, increasing the pressure will decrease the amount of product.

   c.   Because the reaction decreases the number of moles of gas, increasing the pressure will increase the amount of product.

14.14. Because this is an endothermic reaction and absorbs heat, high temperatures will be more favorable to the production of carbon monoxide.

14.15. Because this is an endothermic reaction and absorbs heat, high temperatures will give the best yield of carbon monoxide. Because the reaction increases the number of moles of gas, decreasing the pressure will also increase the yield.

■ ANSWERS TO CONCEPT CHECKS

14.1. The statement that when reactant A decreases by an amount x, product C increases by amount x implies that A and C have the same coefficients. The statement that when reactant B decreases by an amount x, product C increases by amount $2x$ implies that the coefficient of C is twice that of B. Therefore, the coefficient of A is twice that of B. The simplest equation satisfying these conditions is $2A + B \rightarrow 2C$.

14.2. To answer this question, find the relationship between the two species present, using the equilibrium-constant expression and its value. For the first reaction, $A(g) \rightleftharpoons B(g)$, with $K = 2$, this becomes

$$K = 2 = \frac{[B]}{[A]}$$

This reduces to $[B] = 2[A]$. This corresponds to the container that has twice as many balls of one color than of the other color, namely container IV. Here, the blue molecules are B (eight of them), and the red molecules are A (four of them).

For the second reaction, $X(g) \rightleftharpoons 2Y(g)$, with $K = 6$, this becomes

$$K = 6 = \frac{[Y]^2}{[X]}$$

This reduces to $[Y]^2 = 6[X]$. This corresponds to container I, where there are six of each color molecule. Since there are the same numbers of each molecule, you cannot determine which color corresponds to which molecule.

For the third reaction, $2C(g) \rightleftharpoons D(g)$, with $K = 1$, this becomes

$$K = 1 = \frac{[D]}{[C]^2}$$

which reduces to $[C]^2 = [D]$. This corresponds to container II. The red balls (nine of them) correspond to molecule D, and the blue balls (three of them) correspond to molecule C.

14.3. The concentration of each substance initially doubles. This means that each concentration factor in the reaction quotient expression is double that in the initial equilibrium mixture. Because this expression contains $[CO][H_2]^2$ in the denominator, the denominator increases by a factor of 2^3. However, the numerator contains only $[CH_3OH]$, which merely doubles. Thus, the reaction quotient equals two divided by two cubed, or one-quarter, times the equilibrium constant. To approach the equilibrium constant, the numerator of the reaction quotient must increase, and the denominator must decrease. This means that more CH_3OH must be produced. The reaction goes from left to right.

14.4. The equilibrium-constant expression is $[C]/([A][B])$. A new equilibrium is attained in which the equilibrium-constant expression is $[C]'/([A]'[B]') = [C]'/(2[A]2[B])$, where primes indicate new equilibrium concentrations. The value of the equilibrium-constant expression, though, must remain fixed in value, so $[C]'/(2[A]2[B])$ equals $[C]/([A][B])$. This means that the new concentration of C, or $[C]'$, must be four times larger than the original equilibrium value. Thus, the concentration of C is quadrupled.

14.5. For an exothermic reaction, as the temperature is increased, the reaction shifts toward the reactant side to absorb the heat and counteract the temperature increase. This corresponds to the case where there are mostly reactant molecules and very few product molecules, namely container I. At lower temperatures, the reaction shifts toward the product side to release heat. This corresponds to the case where there is a larger ratio of product molecules to reactant molecules, namely container II.

■ ANSWERS TO SELF-ASSESSMENT AND REVIEW QUESTIONS

14.1. A reasonable graph showing the decrease in concentration of $N_2O_4(g)$ and the increase in concentration of $NO_2(g)$ is shown below.

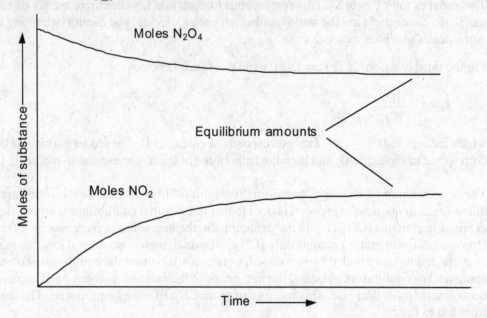

At first, the concentration of N_2O_4 is large, and the rate of the forward reaction is large, but then as the concentration of N_2O_4 decreases, the rate of the forward reaction decreases. In contrast, the concentration of NO_2 builds up from zero to a low concentration. Thus, the initial rate of the reverse reaction is zero, but it steadily increases as the concentration of NO_2 increases. Eventually, the two rates become equal when the reaction reaches equilibrium. This is a dynamic equilibrium because both the forward and reverse reactions are occurring at all times, even though there is no net change in concentration at equilibrium.

14.2. The 1.0 mol of $H_2(g)$ and 1.0 mol of $I_2(g)$ in the first mixture reach equilibrium when the amounts of reactants decrease to 0.50 mol each and when the amount of product increases to 1.0 mol. The total number of moles of the reactants at the start is 2.0 mol, which is the same number of moles as in the second mixture, the 2.0 mol of HI that is to be allowed to come to equilibrium. The second mixture should produce the same number of moles of H_2, I_2, and HI at equilibrium, because if the total number of moles is constant, it should not matter from which direction an equilibrium is approached.

14.3. The equilibrium constant for a gaseous reaction can be written using partial pressures instead of concentrations because all the reactants and products are in the same vessel. Therefore, at constant temperature, the pressure, P, is proportional to the concentration, n/V. (The ideal gas law says that $P = [n/V]RT$.)

14.4. The addition of reactions 1 and 2 yields reaction 3:

(Reaction 1)	HCN	+	OH^-	$\rightleftharpoons$	CN^-	+	H_2O
(Reaction 2)			H_2O	$\rightleftharpoons$	H^+	+	OH^-
(Reaction 3)			HCN	$\rightleftharpoons$	H^+	+	CN^-

The rule states that if a given equation can be obtained from the sum of other equations, the equilibrium constant for the given equation equals the product of the other equilibrium constants. Thus, K for reaction 3 is

$$K = K_1 \times K_2 = (4.9 \times 10^4) \times (1.0 \times 10^{-14}) = 4.9 \times 10^{-10}$$

14.5. a. Homogeneous equilibrium. All substances are gases and thus exist in one phase, a mixture of gases.

   b. Heterogeneous equilibrium. The two copper compounds are solids, but the other substances are gases. This fulfills the definition of a heterogeneous equilibrium.

   c. Homogeneous equilibrium. All substances are gases and thus exist in one phase, a mixture of gases.

   d. Heterogeneous equilibrium. The two copper-containing substances are solids, but the other substances are gases. This fulfills the definition of a heterogeneous equilibrium.

14.6. Pure liquids and solids can be ignored in an equilibrium-constant expression because their concentrations do not change. (If a solid is present, it has not dissolved in any gas or solution present.) In effect, concentrations of liquids and solids are incorporated into the value of K_c, as discussed in the chapter.

14.7. A qualitative interpretation of the equilibrium constant involves using the magnitude of the equilibrium constant to predict the relative amounts of reactants and products at equilibrium. If K_c is around 1, the equilibrium mixture contains appreciable amounts (same order of magnitude) of reactants and products. If K_c is large, the equilibrium mixture is mostly products. If K_c is small, the equilibrium mixture is mostly reactants. The type of reaction governs what "large" and "small" values are; but for some types of reactions, "large" might be no less than 10^2 to 10^4, whereas "small" might be no more than 10^{-4} to 10^{-2}.

14.8. The reaction quotient, Q_c, is an expression that has the same form as the equilibrium-constant expression but whose concentrations are not necessarily equilibrium concentrations. It is useful in determining whether a reaction mixture is at equilibrium or, if not, what direction the reaction will go as it approaches equilibrium.

14.9. The ways in which the equilibrium composition of a mixture can be altered are (1) changing concentrations by removing some of the products and/or some of the reactants, (2) changing the partial pressure of a gaseous reactant and/or a gaseous product, and (3) changing the temperature of the reaction mixture. (Adding a catalyst cannot alter the equilibrium concentration; it can affect only the rate of reaction.)

14.10. The role of the platinum is that of a catalyst; it provides conditions (a surface) suitable for speeding up the attainment of equilibrium. The platinum has no effect on the equilibrium composition of the mixture even though it greatly increases the rate of reaction.

14.11. In some cases, a catalyst can affect the product in a reaction because it affects only the rate of one reaction out of several reactions that are possible. If two reactions are possible, and the uncatalyzed rate of one is much slower but that is the only reaction that is catalyzed, then the products with and without a catalyst will be different. The Ostwald process is a good example. In the absence of a catalyst, NH_3 burns in O_2 to form only N_2 and H_2O, even though it is possible for NH_3 to react to form NO and H_2O. Ostwald found that adding a platinum catalyst favors the formation of the NO and H_2O almost to the exclusion of the N_2 and H_2O.

14.12. Four ways in which the yield of ammonia can be improved are (1) removing the gaseous NH_3 from the equilibrium by liquefying it, (2) increasing the nitrogen or hydrogen concentration, (3) increasing the total pressure on the mixture (the moles of gas decrease), and (4) lowering the temperature ($\Delta H°$ is negative, so heat is evolved). Each causes a shift to the right in accordance with Le Châtelier's principle.

14.13. The answer is d, 2.10 moles.

14.14. The answer is a, 1.24.

14.15. The answer is c, 0.157.

14.16. The answer is b, $Q_c = 6.33 \times 10^{-4}$; the concentration of NOBr increases.

■ ANSWERS TO CONCEPTUAL PROBLEMS

14.19. For each three moles of H_2 that react, two moles of ammonia form. The mole ratio is

$$\frac{2 \text{ mol } NH_3}{3 \text{ mol } H_2}$$

If x mol H_2 react, then the amount of ammonia that forms is

$$x \text{ mol } H_2 \times \frac{2 \text{ mol } NH_3}{3 \text{ mol } H_2} = \frac{2x}{3} \text{ mol } NH_3$$

14.21. Hydrogen, H_2, is the limiting reactant, so the maximum amount of CH_3OH that could form is 1 mol. However, because the reaction comes to equilibrium before it can go to completion, less than 1 mol of CH_3OH forms. The answer is a.

14.23. a. The equilibrium-constant expression for this reaction is

$$K = \frac{[H_2][I_2]}{[HI]^2} = 2.0$$

The equilibrium case is where the reaction quotient, Q, is equal to the equilibrium constant, K. This occurs in picture III, where

$$Q = \frac{(2)(4)}{(2)^2} = 2.0 = K$$

b. For picture I, the reaction quotient is

$$Q = \frac{(2)(2)}{(4)^2} = 0.25 < K$$

Since $Q < K$, the reaction shifts toward the product ($H_2 + I_2$) side.

For picture II, the reaction quotient is

$$Q = \frac{(4)(4)}{(4)^2} = 1.0 < K$$

Since $Q < K$, the reaction shifts toward the product ($H_2 + I_2$) side.

14.25. a.   When the volume is doubled, the pressure is reduced by one-half. A decrease in pressure results in the equilibrium shifting to the side of the reaction with the greater number of moles of gas. Note that in this reaction, there are 2 mol of gas reactants versus 1 mol of gas products. Since the pressure has been reduced, the reaction will shift to the left, toward the side of the reaction with the greater number of moles of gas.

   b.   Since the reaction has been shifted to the left, the concentrations of A and B will increase, while the concentration of C will decrease.

14.27.   The formation of SO_3 can be represented by the following reaction:

$$2SO_2(g) + O_2(g) \rightleftharpoons 2SO_3(g)$$

The first condition mentioned is the oxygen-enriched air. The higher concentration of O_2 drives the reaction to the right, increasing the yield of SO_3. Next, the reaction temperature is 420°C. Since the reaction is exothermic, the elevated temperature drives the reaction to the left, decreasing the yield of SO_3. The vanadium(V) oxide catalyst affects the rate of the reaction, but not the amount of SO_3 that forms at equilibrium. Finally, the SO_3 that forms in the reaction is absorbed by concentrated sulfuric acid and removed from the system. This causes the reaction to shift to the right, forming more SO_3.

Another condition that can be explored is a change in pressure. Since there are more moles of gas on the left side, an increase in pressure (or decrease in volume) should cause more SO_3 to form.

■ SOLUTIONS TO PRACTICE PROBLEMS

Note on significant figures: If the final answer to a solution needs to be rounded off, it is given first with one nonsignificant figure, and the last significant figure is underlined. The final answer is then rounded to the correct number of significant figures. In multistep problems, intermediate answers are given with at least one nonsignificant figure; however, only the final answer has been rounded off.

14.29.   Use the table approach, and give the starting, change, and equilibrium number of moles of each.

Amt. (mol)	$PCl_5(g)$	$\rightleftharpoons$	$PCl_3(g)$	+	$Cl_2(g)$
Starting	2.500		0		0
Change	$-x$		$+x$		$+x$
Equilibrium	$2.500 - x$		$x = 0.338$		x

Since the equilibrium amount of PCl_3 is given in the problem, this tells you $x = 0.338$. The equilibrium amounts for the other substances can now be determined.

Equilibrium amount $Cl_2 = \times = 0.338$ mol

Equilibrium amount $PCl_5 = 2.500 - \times = 2.500 - 0.338 = 2.162$ mol

Therefore, the amounts of the substances in the equilibrium mixture are 2.162 mol PCl_5, 0.338 mol PCl_3, and 0.338 mol Cl_2.

14.31. Use the table approach, and give the starting, change, and equilibrium number of moles of each.

Amt. (mol)	$N_2(g)$	+	$3H_2(g)$	$\rightleftharpoons$	$2NH_3(g)$
Starting	0.600		1.800		0
Change	$-x$		$-3x$		$+2x$
Equilibrium	$0.600 - x$		$1.800 - 3x$		$2x = 0.048$

Since the equilibrium amount of NH_3 is given in the problem, this tells you $\times = 0.024$. The equilibrium amounts for the other substances can now be determined.

Equilibrium amount $N_2 = 0.600 - 0.024 = 0.576$ mol

Equilibrium amount $H_2 = 1.800 - 3 \times (0.024) = 1.728$ mol

Therefore, the amounts of the substances in the equilibrium mixture are 0.576 mol N_2, 1.728 mol H_2, and 0.048 mol NH_3.

14.33. Use the table approach, and give the starting, change, and equilibrium number of moles of each.

Amt. (mol)	$2SO_2(g)$	+	$O_2(g)$	$\rightleftharpoons$	$2SO_3(g)$
Starting	0.0400		0.0200		0
Change	$-2x$		$-x$		$+2x$
Equilibrium	$0.0400 - 2x$		$0.0200 - x$		$2x (= 0.0296)$

Therefore, $x = 0.0148$, and the amounts of substances at equilibrium are 0.0104 mol SO_2, 0.0052 mol O_2, and 0.0296 mol SO_3.

14.35. a. $K_c = \dfrac{[NO_2][NO]}{[N_2O_3]}$

b. $K_c = \dfrac{[H_2]^2[S_2]}{[H_2S]^2}$

c. $K_c = \dfrac{[NO_2]^2}{[NO]^2[O_2]}$

d. $K_c = \dfrac{[P(NH_2)_3][HCl]^3}{[PCl_3][NH_3]^3}$

14.37. The reaction is $2H_2S(g) + 3O_2(g) \rightleftharpoons 2H_2O(g) + 2SO_2(g)$.

14.39. When the reaction is halved, the equilibrium-constant expression is

$$K_c = \frac{[NO_2]^2[O_2]^{1/2}}{[N_2O_5]}$$

When the reaction is then reversed, the equilibrium-constant expression becomes

$$K_c = \frac{[N_2O_5]}{[NO_2]^2[O_2]^{1/2}}$$

14.41. Because $K_c = 1.84$ for $2HI \rightleftharpoons H_2 + I_2$, the value of K_c for $H_2 + I_2 \rightleftharpoons 2HI$ must be the reciprocal of K_c for the first reaction. Mathematically, this can be shown as follows:

Forward: $K_c = \dfrac{[H_2][I_2]}{[HI]^2} = 1.84$

Reverse: $K_c = \dfrac{[HI]^2}{[H_2][I_2]} = \dfrac{1}{\dfrac{[H_2][I_2]}{[HI]^2}} = \dfrac{1}{K_c(f)}$

Thus, for the reverse reaction, K_c is calculated as follows:

$K_c = 1 \div 1.84 = 5.4\underline{3}4 \times 10^{-1} = 0.543$

14.43. First, calculate the molar concentration of each of the compounds in the equations:

$[H_2] = 0.488$ mol $H_2 \div 6.00$ L $= 0.081\underline{3}3$ M

$[I_2] = 0.206$ mol $I_2 \div 6.00$ L $= 0.034\underline{3}3$ M

$[HI] = 2.250$ mol HI $\div 6.00$ L $= 0.37\underline{5}0$ M

Now, substitute these into the K_c expression:

$K_c = \dfrac{(0.3750)^2}{(0.08133)(0.03433)} = 50.\underline{3}6 = 50.4$

14.45. Substitute the following concentrations into the K_c expression:

$[SO_3] = 0.0296$ mol $\div 2.000$ L $= 0.014\underline{8}0$ M

$[SO_2] = 0.0104$ mol $\div 2.000$ L $= 0.0052\underline{0}0$ M

$[O_2] = 0.0052$ mol $\div 2.000$ L $= 0.002\underline{6}0$ M

$K_c = \dfrac{(0.01480)^2}{(0.005200)^2(0.00260)} = 3.\underline{1}1 \times 10^3 = 3.1 \times 10^3$

14.47. For each mole of NOBr that reacts, $(1.000 - 0.094 = 0.906)$ mol remains. Starting with 2.00 mol NOBr, this means that 2×0.906 mol NOBr, or 1.812 mol NOBr, remains. Because the volume is 1.00 L, the concentration of NOBr at equilibrium is 1.812 M. Assemble a table of starting, change, and equilibrium concentrations:

Conc. (M)	2NOBr(g)	$\rightleftharpoons$	2NO(g)	+	Br$_2$(g)
Starting	2.00		0		0
Change	$-2x$		$+2x$		$+x$
Equilibrium	$2.00 - 2x\ (= 1.812)$		$2x$		x

Because $2.00 - 2x = 1.812$, $x = 0.094$ M. Therefore, the equilibrium concentrations are [NOBr] = 1.812 M, [NO] = 0.188 M, and [Br$_2$] = 0.094 M.

$K_c = \dfrac{[NO]^2[Br_2]}{[NOBr]^2} = \dfrac{(0.188)^2(0.094)}{(1.812)^2} = 1.\underline{0}1 \times 10^{-3} = 1.0 \times 10^{-3}$

14.49. a. $K_p = \dfrac{P_{HBr}^2}{P_{H_2}\,P_{Br_2}}$ 　　　　 b. $K_p = \dfrac{P_{CH_4}\,P_{H_2S}^2}{P_{CS_2}\,P_{H_2}^4}$

c. $K_p = \dfrac{P_{H_2O}^2\,P_{Cl_2}^2}{P_{HCl}^4\,P_{O_2}}$ 　　　 d. $K_p = \dfrac{P_{CH_3OH}}{P_{CO}\,P_{H_2}^2}$

14.51. There are 3 mol of gaseous product for every 5 mol of gaseous reactant, so $\Delta n = 3 - 5 = -2$. Using this, calculate K_p from K_c:

$$K_p = K_c(RT)^{\Delta n} = 0.28\,(0.0821 \times 1173)^{-2} = 3.\underline{0}19 \times 10^{-5} = 3.0 \times 10^{-5}$$

14.53. For each 1 mol of gaseous product, there are 1.5 mol of gaseous reactants; thus, $\Delta n = 1 - 1.5 = -0.5$. Using this, calculate K_c from K_p:

$$K_c = \frac{K_p}{(RT)^{\Delta n}} = \frac{6.55}{(0.0821 \times 900)^{-0.5}} = 6.55 \times (0.0821 \times 900)^{0.5} = 56.\underline{3}03 = 56.3$$

14.55. a. $K_c = \dfrac{[CO]^2}{[CO_2]}$ 　　　　 b. $K_c = \dfrac{[CO_2]}{[CO]}$

c. $K_c = \dfrac{[CO_2]}{[SO_2]\,[O_2]^{1/2}}$ 　　　 d. $K_c = [Pb^{2+}]\,[I^-]^2$

14.57. a. 　Not complete; K_c is very small (10^{-31}), indicating very little reaction.

b. 　Nearly complete; K_c is very large (10^{21}), indicating nearly complete reaction.

14.59. K_c is extremely small, indicating very little reaction at room temperature. Because the decomposition of HF yields equal amounts of H_2 and F_2, at equilibrium $[H_2] = [F_2]$. So, for the decomposition of HF,

$$K_c = \frac{[H_2]\,[F_2]}{[HF]^2} = \frac{[H_2]^2}{[HF]^2}$$

$$[H_2] = K_c^{1/2}\,[HF] = (1.0 \times 10^{-95})^{1/2}\,(1.0\ M) = 3.\underline{1}6 \times 10^{-48} = 3.2 \times 10^{-48}\ \text{mol/L}$$

This result does agree with what is expected from the very small magnitude of K_c.

14.61. Calculate Q, the reaction quotient, and compare it to the equilibrium constant ($K_c = 3.07 \times 10^{-4}$). If Q is larger, the reaction will go to the left; if Q is smaller, the reaction will go to the right; if they are equal, the reaction is at equilibrium. In all cases, Q is found by combining these terms:

$$Q = \frac{[NO]^2\,[Br_2]}{[NOBr]^2}$$

a. 　$Q = \dfrac{(0.0162)^2\,(0.0123)}{(0.0720)^2} = 6.2\underline{2}6 \times 10^{-4} = 6.23 \times 10^{-4}$

$Q > K_c$. The reaction should go to the left.

b. $Q = \dfrac{(0.0159)^2(0.0139)}{(0.121)^2} = 2.4\underline{0}0 \times 10^{-4} = 2.40 \times 10^{-4}$

$Q < K_c$. The reaction should go to the right.

c. $Q = \dfrac{(0.0134)^2(0.0181)}{(0.103)^2} = 3.0\underline{6}3 \times 10^{-4} = 3.06 \times 10^{-4}$

$Q = K_c$. The reaction should be at equilibrium.

d. $Q = \dfrac{(0.0121)^2(0.0105)}{(0.0472)^2} = 6.9\underline{0}0 \times 10^{-4} = 6.90 \times 10^{-4}$

$Q > K_c$. The reaction should go to the left.

14.63. Calculate Q, the reaction quotient, and compare it to the equilibrium constant. If Q is larger, the reaction will go to the left, and vice versa. Q is found by combining these terms:

$$Q = \frac{[CH_3OH]}{[CO][H_2]^2} = \frac{(0.020)}{(0.010)(0.010)^2} = 2\underline{0}.0 \; (>10.5)$$

The reaction goes to the left.

14.65. Substitute into the expression for K_c and solve for $[COCl_2]$:

$$K_c = 1.23 \times 10^3 = \frac{[COCl_2]}{[CO][Cl_2]} = \frac{[COCl_2]}{(0.012)(0.025)}$$

$[COCl_2] = (1.23 \times 10^3)(0.012)(0.025) = 0.3\underline{6}9 = 0.37 \; M$

14.67. Divide moles of substance by the volume 5.0 L to obtain concentration. The starting concentrations are $3.0 \times 10^{-4} \; M$ for both $[I_2]$ and $[Br_2]$. Assemble a table of starting, change, and equilibrium concentrations.

Conc. (M)	$I_2(g)$	+	$Br_2(g)$	$\rightleftharpoons$	2 IBr(g)
Starting	3.0×10^{-4}		3.0×10^{-4}		0
Change	$-x$		$-x$		$+2x$
Equilibrium	$(3.0 \times 10^{-4}) - x$		$(3.0 \times 10^{-4}) - x$		$2x$

Substituting into the equilibrium-constant expression gives

$$K_c = 1.2 \times 10^2 = \frac{[IBr]^2}{[I_2][Br_2]} = \frac{(2x)^2}{(3.0 \times 10^{-4} - x)(3.0 \times 10^{-4} - x)}$$

Taking the square root of both sides yields

$$1\underline{0}.95 = \frac{(2x)}{(3.0 \times 10^{-4} - x)}$$

Rearranging and simplifying the right side give

$$(3.0 \times 10^{-4} - x) = \frac{(2x)}{10.95} = (0.1\underline{8}2\,x)$$

$$x = 2.\underline{5}3 \times 10^{-4}\,M$$

Thus, $[I_2] = [Br_2] = \underline{4}.7 \times 10^{-5} = 5 \times 10^{-5}\,M$, and $[IBr] = 5.\underline{0}6 \times 10^{-4} = 5.1 \times 10^{-4}\,M$.

14.69.   Divide moles of substance by the volume 1.25 L to obtain concentration. The starting concentration is 1.00 M for $[CO_2]$, but the concentration of carbon, a solid, is omitted. Assemble a table of starting, change, and equilibrium concentrations.

Conc. (M)	$CO_2(g)$	+	$C(s)$	$\rightleftharpoons$	$2CO(g)$
Starting	1.00				0
Change	$-x$				$+2x$
Equilibrium	$1.00 - x$				$2x$

Substituting into the equilibrium expression for K_c gives

$$K_c = 14.0 = \frac{[CO]^2}{[CO_2]} = \frac{(2x)^2}{(1.00 - x)}$$

Rearranging and solving for x yields

$$14.0 - 14.0x = 4x^2$$

$$4x^2 + 14.0x - 14.0 = 0 \text{ (quadratic equation)}$$

Using the solution to the quadratic equation gives

$$x = \frac{-14.0 \pm \sqrt{(14.0)^2 - 4(4)(-14.0)}}{2(4)}$$

$x = -4.31$ (impossible; reject), or $x = 0.81\underline{1}7 = 0.812\,M$ (logical)

Thus, $[CO_2] = 0.19\,M$, and $[CO] = 1.62\,M$.

14.71.   Divide moles of substance by the volume 10.00 L to obtain concentration. The starting concentrations are 0.1000 M for $[CO]$ and 0.3000 M for $[H_2]$. Assemble a table of starting, change, and equilibrium concentrations.

Conc. (M)	$CO(g)$	+	$3H_2(g)$	$\rightleftharpoons$	$CH_4(g)$	+	$H_2O(g)$
Starting	0.1000		0.3000		0		0
Change	$-x$		$-3x$		$+x$		$+x$
Equilibrium	$0.1000 - x$		$0.3000 - 3x$		x		x

Substituting into the equilibrium expression for K_c gives

$$K_c = 3.92 = \frac{[CH_4][H_2O]}{[CO][H_2]^3} = \frac{x^2}{(0.1000 - x)[3(0.1000 - x)]^3} = \frac{x^2}{27(0.1000 - x)^4}$$

Multiplying both sides by 27 and taking the square root of both sides give

$$10.29 = \frac{x}{(0.1000 - x)^2}$$

Or,

$$10.29x^2 - 3.058x + 0.1029 = 0$$

Using the solution to the quadratic equation yields

$$x = \frac{3.058 \pm \sqrt{(-3.058)^2 - 4(10.29)(0.1029)}}{2(10.29)}$$

$x = 0.2585$ (can't be > 0.1000, so reject), or $x = 0.03868 = 0.0387$ M (use)

Thus, $[CO] = 0.0613$ M, $[H_2] = 0.1839$ M, $[CH_4] = 0.0387$ M, and $[H_2O] = 0.0387$ M.

14.73. Forward direction

14.75. a. A pressure increase has no effect because the number of moles of reactant gases equals that of product gases.

b. A pressure increase has no effect because the number of moles of reactant gases equals that of product gases.

c. A pressure increase causes the reaction to go to the left because the number of moles of reactant gases is less than that of product gases.

14.77. The fraction would not increase because an increase in temperature decreases the amounts of products of an exothermic reaction.

14.79. The value of $\Delta H°$ is calculated from the $\Delta H_f°$ values below each substance in the reaction:

$$2NO_2(g) \quad + \quad 7H_2(g) \quad \rightleftharpoons \quad 2NH_3(g) \quad + \quad 4H_2O(g)$$
$$2(33.10) \qquad\qquad 7(0) \qquad\qquad\qquad 2(-45.9) \qquad\quad 4(-241.8)$$

$\Delta H° = -967.2 + (-91.8) - 66.20 = -1125.2$ kJ/2 mol NO_2

The equilibrium constant will decrease with temperature because raising the temperature of an exothermic reaction causes the reaction to go farther to the left.

14.81. Because the reaction is exothermic, the formation of products will be favored by low temperatures. Because there are more molecules of gaseous products than of gaseous reactants, the formation of products will be favored by low pressures.

■ SOLUTIONS TO GENERAL PROBLEMS

14.83. Substitute the concentrations into the equilibrium expression to calculate K_c.

$$K_c = \frac{[CH_3OH]}{[CO][H_2]^2} = \frac{(0.015)}{(0.096)(0.191)^2} = 4.28 = 4.3$$

14.85.   Assume 100.00 g of gas: 90.55 g CO, and 9.45 g CO_2. The moles of each are

$$90.55 \text{ g CO} \times \frac{1 \text{ mol CO}}{28.01 \text{ g CO}} = 3.23\underline{2}8 \text{ mol CO}$$

$$9.45 \text{ g CO}_2 \times \frac{1 \text{ mol CO}_2}{44.01 \text{ g CO}_2} = 0.21\underline{4}7 \text{ mol CO}_2$$

Total moles of gas = (3.2328 + 0.2147) mol = 3.44$\underline{7}$5 mol. Use the ideal gas law to convert to the volume of gaseous solution:

$$V = \frac{nRT}{P} = \frac{(3.4475 \text{ mol})(0.082057 \text{ L} \cdot \text{atm/K} \cdot \text{mol})(850 + 273)\text{K}}{1.000 \text{ atm}} = 317.\underline{6}9 \text{ L}$$

The concentrations are

$$[CO] = \frac{3.2328 \text{ mol CO}}{317.69 \text{ L}} = 0.01017\underline{6} \, M$$

$$[CO_2] = \frac{0.2147 \text{ mol CO}_2}{317.69 \text{ L}} = 6.7\underline{5}8 \times 10^{-4} \, M$$

Find K_c by substituting into the equilibrium expression:

$$K_c = \frac{[CO]^2}{[CO_2]} = \frac{(0.01017\underline{6})^2}{(6.758 \times 10^{-4})} = 0.15\underline{3}2 = 0.153$$

14.87.   After calculating the concentrations after mixing, calculate Q, the reaction quotient, and compare it with K_c.

$[N_2] = [H_2] = 1.00 \text{ mol} \div 2.00 \text{ L} = 0.500 \, M$

$[NH_3] = 2.00 \text{ mol} \div 2.00 \text{ L} = 1.00 \, M$

$$Q = \frac{[NH_3]^2}{[N_2][H_2]^3} = \frac{(1.00)^2}{(0.500)(0.500)^3} = 16.\underline{0}0 = 16.0$$

Because Q is greater than K_c, the reaction will go in the reverse direction (to the left) to reach equilibrium.

14.89.   To calculate the concentrations after mixing, assume the volume to be 1.00 L, symbolized as V. Because the volumes in the numerator and denominator cancel each other, they do not matter. Assume a 1.00-L volume and calculate Q, the reaction quotient, and compare it with K_c.

$[CO] = [H_2O] = [CO_2] = [H_2] = 1.00 \text{ mol}/1.00 \text{ L}$

$$Q = \frac{[CO_2][H_2]}{[CO][H_2O]} = \frac{(1.00 \text{ mol}/1.00 \text{ L})(1.00 \text{ mol}/1.00 \text{ L})}{(1.000 \text{ mol}/1.00 \text{ L})(1.00 \text{ mol}/1.00 \text{ L})} = 1.\underline{0}0$$

Because Q is greater than K_c, the reaction will go in the reverse direction (left) to reach equilibrium.

14.91. Assemble a table of starting, change, and equilibrium concentrations, letting $2x$ = the change in [HBr].

Conc. (M)	2HBr(g) $\rightleftharpoons$	H$_2$(g) +	Br$_2$(g)
Starting	0.010	0	0
Change	$-2x$	$+x$	$+x$
Equilibrium	$0.010 - 2x$	x	x

$$K_c = 0.016 = \frac{[\text{H}_2][\text{Br}_2]}{[\text{HBr}]^2} = \frac{(x)(x)}{(0.010 - 2x)^2}$$

$$0.1\underline{2}6 = \frac{(x)}{(0.010 - 2x)}$$

$$1.26 \times 10^{-3} - (2.52 \times 10^{-1})x = x$$

$$x = (1.26 \times 10^{-3}) \div 1.252 = 1.\underline{0}06 \times 10^{-3} = 1.0 \times 10^{-3}\ M$$

Therefore, [HBr] = 0.008 M, or 0.008 mol; [H$_2$] = 0.0010 M, or 0.0010 mol; and [Br$_2$] = 0.0010 M, or 0.0010 mol.

14.93. The starting concentration of COCl$_2$ = 1.00 mol ÷ 25.00 L = 0.0400 M. Assemble a table of starting, change, and equilibrium concentrations.

Conc. (M)	COCl$_2$(g) $\rightleftharpoons$	Cl$_2$(g) +	CO(g)
Starting	0.0400	0	0
Change	$-x$	$+x$	$+x$
Equilibrium	$0.0400 - x$	x	x

Substituting into the equilibrium expression for K_c gives

$$K_c = 8.05 \times 10^{-4} = \frac{[\text{CO}][\text{Cl}_2]}{[\text{COCl}_2]} = \frac{(x)(x)}{(0.0400 - x)}$$

Rearranging and solving for × yield

$$3.22 \times 10^{-5} - (8.05 \times 10^{-4})x - x^2 = 0$$

$$x^2 + (8.05 \times 10^{-4})x - 3.22 \times 10^{-5} = 0 \text{ (quadratic equation)}$$

Using the solution to the quadratic equation gives

$$x = \frac{-(8.05 \times 10^{-4}) \pm \sqrt{(8.05 \times 10^{-4})^2 - 4(1)(-3.22 \times 10^{-5})}}{2(1)}$$

$$x = -6.09 \times 10^{-3} \text{ (impossible; reject), or } x = 5.2\underline{8}6 \times 10^{-3} \text{ (logical; use)}$$

Percent dissoc. = (change ÷ starting) × 100% = (0.005286 ÷ 0.0400) × 100% = 13.$\underline{2}$1 = 13.2%

14.95. Using 1.00 mol/10.00 L, or 0.100 M, and 4.00 mol/10.00 L, or 0.400 M, for the respective starting concentrations for CO and H_2, assemble a table of starting, change, and equilibrium concentrations.

Conc. (M)	$CO(g)$	+	$3H_2(g)$	$\rightleftharpoons$	$CH_2(g)$	+	$H_2O(g)$
Starting	0.100		0.400		0		0
Change	$-x$		$-3x$		$+x$		$+x$
Equilibrium	$0.100 - x$		$0.400 - 3x$		x		x

Substituting into the equilibrium expression for K_c gives

$$K_c = 3.92 = \frac{[CH_4][H_2O]}{[CO][H_2]^3} = \frac{x^2}{(0.100 - x)(0.400 - 3x)^3}$$

$$f(x) = \frac{x^2}{(0.100 - x)(0.400 - 3x)^3}$$

Because K_c is > 1 (> 50% reaction), choose $x = 0.05$ (about half of CO reacting), and use that for the first entry in the table of x, $f(x)$, and interpretations.

x	$f(x)$	Interpretation
0.05	3.20	$x > 0.05$
0.06	8.45	$x < 0.06$
0.055	5.18	$x < 0.055$
0.0525	4.07	$x < 0.0525$ (but close)
0.052	3.88	$f(x)$ of $3.88 \cong 3.92$

At equilibrium, concentrations and moles are CO: 0.048 M and 0.48 mol; H_2: 0.244 M and 2.44 mol; CH_4: 0.052 M and 0.52 mol; and H_2O: 0.052 M and 0.52 mol.

14.97. The dissociation is endothermic.

14.99. For $N_2 + 3H_2 \rightleftharpoons 2NH_3$, K_p is defined in terms of pressures as

$$K_p = \frac{P_{NH_3}^{\,2}}{P_{N_2} P_{H_2}^{\,3}}$$

But by the ideal gas law, where [i] = mol/L,

$$P_i = (n_i RT)/V, \text{ or } P_i = [\,i\,]RT$$

Substituting the right-hand equality into the K_p expression gives

$$K_p = \frac{[NH_3]^2 (RT)^2}{[N_2](RT)\,[H_2]^3 (RT)^3} = \frac{[NH_3]^2}{[N_2][H_2]^3}(RT)^{-2}$$

$$K_p = K_c(RT)^{-2}, \text{ or } K_c = K_p(RT)^2$$

14.101. a. The change in the number of moles of gas for the reaction is $\Delta n = 2 - 1 = 1$. Using this, calculate K_p from K_c:

$$K_p = K_c(RT)^{\Delta n} = 0.153\,(0.08206 \times 1123)^1 = 14.\underline{0}99 = 14.1$$

b.   Use the table approach, and give the starting, change, and equilibrium pressures in atm.

Press. (atm)	C(s)	+	$CO_2(g)$	$\rightleftharpoons$	2CO(g)
Starting			1.50		0
Change			$-x$		$+2x$
Equilibrium			$1.50 - x$		$2x$

Substituting into the equilibrium-constant expression gives

$$K_p = 14.\underline{1}0 = \frac{P_{CO}^2}{P_{CO_2}} = \frac{(2x)^2}{(1.50-x)}$$

Rearranging and solving for x give a quadratic equation.

$$4x^2 + 14.10x - 21.15 = 0$$

Using the quadratic formula gives

$$x = \frac{-14.10 \pm \sqrt{(14.10)^2 - (4)(4)(-21.15)}}{2(4)}$$

$$x = 1.\underline{1}35 \text{ (positive root)}$$

Thus, at equilibrium, the pressures of CO and CO_2 are

$$P_{CO_2} = 1.50 - 1.\underline{1}35 = 0.\underline{3}65 = 0.4 \text{ atm}$$

$$P_{CO} = 2x = 2(1.\underline{1}35) = 2.\underline{2}7 = 2.3 \text{ atm}$$

c.   Because the reaction is endothermic, the equilibrium will shift to the left, and the pressure of CO will decrease.

14.103. a.   The molar mass of PCl_5 is 208.22 g/mol. Thus, the initial concentration of PCl_5 is

$$\frac{35.8 \text{ g PCl}_5 \times \dfrac{1 \text{ mol PCl}_5}{208.22 \text{ g PCl}_5}}{5.0 \text{ L}} = 0.03\underline{4}4 \text{ } M$$

Use the table approach, and give the starting, change, and equilibrium concentrations.

Conc. (M)	$PCl_3(g)$	+	$Cl_2(g)$	$\rightleftharpoons$	$PCl_5(g)$
Starting	0		0		0.0344
Change	$+x$		$+x$		$-x$
Equilibrium	X		x		$0.03\underline{4}4 - x$

Substituting into the equilibrium-constant expression gives

$$K_c = 4.1 = \frac{[PCl_5]}{[PCl_3][Cl_2]} = \frac{0.0344 - x}{x^2}$$

Rearranging and solving for x gives a quadratic equation.

$$4.1x^2 + x - 0.0344 = 0$$

Using the quadratic formula gives

$$x = \frac{-1 \pm \sqrt{(1)^2 - (4)(4.1)(-0.0344)}}{2(4.1)}$$

$x = 0.03\underline{0}6$ (positive root)

Thus, at equilibrium, $[PCl_3] = [Cl_2] = x = 0.031\ M$. The concentration of PCl_5 is

$$[PCl_5] = .03\underline{4}4 - x = 0.0344 - 0.0306 = 0.00\underline{3}8 = 0.004\ M.$$

b. The fraction of PCl_5 decomposed is

$$\text{Fraction decomposed} = \frac{0.0306\ M}{0.0344\ M} = 0.8\underline{8}9 = 0.89$$

c. There would be a greater pressure, so, in order to minimize the increase in pressure, less PCl_5 would decompose.

14.105. The initial moles of $SbCl_5$ (molar mass 299.01 g/mol) are

$$65.4\ \text{g } SbCl_5 \times \frac{1\ \text{mol } SbCl_5}{299.01\ \text{g } SbCl_5} = 0.21\underline{8}7\ \text{mol}$$

The initial pressure of $SbCl_5$ is

$$P = \frac{nRT}{V} = \frac{(0.2187\ \text{mol})(0.08206\ \text{L} \cdot \text{atm} / \text{K} \cdot \text{mol})(468\ \text{K})}{5.00\ \text{L}} = 1.6\underline{8}0\ \text{atm}$$

Use the table approach, and give the starting, change, and equilibrium pressures in atm.

Press. (atm)	$SbCl_5(g)$	$\rightleftharpoons$	$SbCl_3(g)$	+	$Cl_2(g)$
Starting	1.680		0		0
Change	$-x$		$+x$		$+x$
Equilibrium	$(1.680)(0.642)$		$(1.680)(0.358)$		$(1.680)(0.358)$

At equilibrium, 35.8% of the $SbCl_5$ is decomposed, so $x = (1.680)(0.358)$ in this table. The equilibrium-constant expression is

$$K_p = \frac{P_{SbCl_3} \cdot P_{Cl_2}}{P_{SbCl_5}} = \frac{(1.680 \times 0.358)^2}{1.680 \times 0.642} = 0.33\underline{5}4 = 0.335$$

14.107. a. The initial concentration of SO_2Cl_2 (molar mass 134.97 g/mol) is

$$\frac{8.25\ \text{g } SO_2Cl_2 \times \dfrac{1\ \text{mol } SO_2Cl_2}{134.97\ \text{g } SO_2Cl_2}}{1.00\ \text{L}} = 0.061\underline{1}2\ M$$

Use the table approach, and give the starting, change, and equilibrium concentrations.

Conc. (M)	$SO_2Cl_2(g)$	$\rightleftharpoons$	$SO_2(g)$	+	$Cl_2(g)$
Starting	0.06112		0		0
Change	$-x$		$+x$		$+x$
Equilibrium	$0.06112 - x$		x		X

Substituting into the equilibrium-constant expression gives

$$K_c = \frac{[SO_2][Cl_2]}{[SO_2Cl_2]} = \frac{x^2}{(0.06112 - x)} = 0.045$$

Rearranging and solving for x give a quadratic equation.

$$x^2 + 0.045x - 0.0027506 = 0$$

Using the quadratic formula gives

$$x = \frac{-(0.045) \pm \sqrt{(0.045)^2 - (4)(1)(-0.0027506)}}{2(1)}$$

$x = 0.03\underline{4}56$ (positive root)

The concentrations at equilibrium are $[SO_2] = [Cl_2] = x = 0.035\ M$. For SO_2Cl_2,

$$[SO_2Cl_2] = 0.06112 - x = 0.06112 - 0.03\underline{4}56 = 0.02\underline{6}55 = 0.027\ M.$$

b. The fraction of SO_2Cl_2 decomposed is

$$\text{Fraction decomposed} = \frac{0.03456\ M}{0.06112\ M} = 0.5\underline{6}5 = 0.57$$

c. This would shift the equilibrium to the left and decrease the fraction of SO_2Cl_2 that has decomposed.

14.109. a. First, determine the initial concentration of the dimer assuming complete reaction. The reaction can be described as $2A \rightarrow D$. Therefore, the initial concentration of dimer is one-half of the concentration of monomer, or $2.0 \times 10^{-4}\ M$. Next, allow the dimer to dissociate into the monomer in equilibrium. Use the table approach, and give the starting, change, and equilibrium concentrations.

Conc. (M)	D(g)	$\rightleftharpoons$	2A(g)
Starting	2.0×10^{-4}		0
Change	$-x$		$+2x$
Equilibrium	$2.0 \times 10^{-4} - x$		$2x$

Substituting into the equilibrium-constant expression gives

$$K_c = \frac{[A]^2}{[D]} = \frac{(2x)^2}{(2.0 \times 10^{-4} - x)} = \frac{1}{3.2 \times 10^4} = 3.125 \times 10^{-5}$$

Rearranging and solving for x give a quadratic equation.

$$4x^2 + (3.125 \times 10^{-5})\,x - (6.250 \times 10^{-9}) = 0$$

Using the quadratic formula gives

$$x = \frac{-(3.125 \times 10^{-5}) \pm \sqrt{(3.125 \times 10^{-5})^2 - (4)(4)(-6.250 \times 10^{-9})}}{2(4)}$$

$x = 3.\underline{5}8 \times 10^{-5}$ (positive root)

Thus, the concentrations at equilibrium are

$$[CH_3COOH] = 2x = 2\ (3.\underline{58} \times 10^{-5}) = 7.\underline{16} \times 10^{-5} = 7.2 \times 10^{-5}\ M$$

$$[Dimer] = 2.0 \times 10^{-4} - 3.\underline{58} \times 10^{-5} = 1.\underline{64} \times 10^{-4} = 1.6 \times 10^{-4}\ M$$

b. Some hydrogen bonding can occur that results in a more stable system. The proposed structure of the dimer is

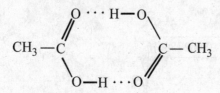

c. An increase in the temperature would facilitate bond breaking and would decrease the amount of dimer. We could also use a Le Châtelier-type argument.

14.111. The molar mass of Br_2 is 159.82 g/mol. Thus, the initial concentration of Br_2 is

$$\frac{18.22\ g\ Br_2 \times \dfrac{1\ mol\ Br_2}{159.82\ g\ Br_2}}{1.00\ L} = 0.11\underline{4}0\ M$$

Use the table approach, and give the starting, change, and equilibrium concentrations.

Conc. (*M*)	2NO(*g*)	+	Br$_2$(*g*)	⇌	2NOBr(*g*)
Starting	0.112		0.11$\underline{4}$0		0
Change	−2*x*		−*x*		+2*x*
Equilibrium	0.112 − 2*x* = 0.02$\underline{96}$0		= 0.1140 − × 0.07$\underline{28}$0		2*x* (= 0.0824 *M*) = 0.0824

Substituting into the equilibrium-constant expression gives

$$K_c = \frac{[NOBr]^2}{[NO]^2[Br_2]} = \frac{(0.0824)^2}{(0.02960)^2(0.07280)} = 1\underline{06}.4 = 1.1 \times 10^2$$

14.113. Chemists have shown that oscillation reactions occur by two different mechanisms, first by one, then by the other. These mechanisms are repeated in space or time, depending on the concentrations of intermediate substances. During the reaction, an indicator changes color depending on which mechanism is active. Although the complete set of elementary steps is complicated, the overall reaction occurs just as you would expect. The initial reactants continue to decrease over time, and the final products increase as the substances come to equilibrium.

■ SOLUTIONS TO STRATEGY PROBLEMS

14.115. First write out the equilibrium expression K_p. Then write each of the partial pressures in terms of its mole fraction, $P_i = X_i P_{tot}$.

$$K_p = \frac{P_{COF_2}{}^2}{P_{CO_2}\ P_{CF_4}} = \frac{(X_{COF_2}\ P_{tot})^2}{(X_{CO_2}\ P_{tot})\ (X_{CF_4}\ P_{tot})} = \frac{X_{COF_2}{}^2}{X_{CO_2}\ X_{CF_4}}$$

The mole fraction of CO_2 is $1 - 0.40 - 0.20 = 0.40$. Substitute the mole fractions and get

$$K_p = \frac{(0.20)^2}{(0.40)(0.40)} = 0.2\underline{5}0 = 0.25$$

14.117. Let n be the initial moles of each substance, and set up the usual table.

Amt. (mol)	$N_2(g)$	+	$O_2(g)$	$\rightleftharpoons$	$2NO(g)$
Starting	N		n		N
Change	$+x$		$+x$		$-2x$
Equilibrium	$n + x$		$n + x$		$n - 2x$

Substituting into the equilibrium-constant expression gives

$$K_p = 0.0123 = \frac{(n - 2x)^2}{(n + x)(n + x)}$$

Take the square root of each side.

$$0.11\underline{0}9 = \frac{(n - 2x)}{(n + x)}$$

Rearrange and solve for x.

$$0.1109(n + x) = n - 2x$$

$$x = \frac{1 - 0.1109}{2 + 0.1109} n = \frac{0.8890}{2.1109} n = 0.42\underline{1}19n = 0.421n$$

The equilibrium-composition mixture is

Moles of $N_2 = n + 0.4211n = 1.42\underline{1}1n$

Moles of $O_2 = n + 0.4211n = 1.42\underline{1}1n$

Moles of $NO = n - 2(0.4211n) = 0.15\underline{7}8n$

Total moles $= 1.421n + 1.421n + 0.1578n = 2.99\underline{9}6n$

The equilibrium-composition mixture is best expressed in terms of the mole fractions of the substances, since the equilibrium mixture is independent of the initial moles, as long as it is the same for all three substances.

$$X_{N_2} = \frac{1.4211n}{2.9996n} = 0.47\underline{3}8 = 0.474$$

$$X_{O_2} = \frac{1.4211n}{2.9996n} = 0.47\underline{3}8 = 0.474$$

$$X_{NO} = \frac{0.1578n}{2.9996n} = 0.052\underline{6}1 = 0.0526$$

14.119. This reaction requires the breaking of bonds, which requires energy and is an endothermic process. As you raise the temperature, the reaction shifts toward the formation of more $NO_2(g)$, so you would expect the reaction mixture to become more red-brown.

14.121. a. Removing some NH_3 from the flask would cause the reaction to shift from left to right, increasing the amount of H_2S produced.

 b. Adding some NH_3 to the flask would cause the reaction to shift from right to left, decreasing the amount of H_2S gas produced.

 c. Since NH_4HS is a solid, removing some of it would have no effect on the equilibrium, nor would it have any effect on the amount of H_2S produced.

 d. Increasing the pressure in the flask by adding helium gas would have no effect on the equilibrium, nor would it have any effect on the amount of H_2S produced. Adding helium has no effect on the partial pressures of the gasses in the flask.

14.123. The reaction involves breaking of bonds, which requires energy and is endothermic. This means that the equilibrium constant should be larger at higher temperatures. This allows you to assign K_p = 0.001745 at 700°C and K_p = 0.01106 at 800°C.

14.125. Use the table approach, and give the starting, change, and equilibrium concentrations.

Conc. (M)	2NO(g)	+	Br$_2$(g)	⇌	2NOBr(g)
Starting	0.01308		0.00559		0
Change	$-2x$		$-x$		$+2x$
Equilibrium	$0.01308 - 2x$		$0.00559 - x$		$2x$

Given the total pressure, volume, and temperature, calculate the total moles of gas at equilibrium with the ideal gas law and set this equal to the total moles of the gases at equilibrium derived from the table above:

$$n_{total} = \frac{PV}{RT} = \frac{(0.4027 \text{ atm})(1.000 \text{ L})}{(0.082057 \text{ L} \bullet \text{atm} / \text{K} \bullet \text{mol})(323.65 \text{ K})} = 0.0151\underline{6}37 \text{ mol}$$

$$n_{total} = n_{NO} + n_{Br_2} + n_{NOBr}$$

$$0.0151\underline{6}37 \text{ mol} = (0.01308 - 2x) + (0.00559 - x) + (2x) = 0.01867 - x \text{ mol}$$

$$x = 0.01867 \text{ mol} - 0.0151\underline{6}37 \text{ mol} = 0.003506 \text{ mol}$$

At equilibrium, the moles of each substance are as follows:

$$n_{NO} = 0.01308 - 2x = 0.01308 - 2(0.003506) = 0.006068 = 0.00607 \text{ mol NO}$$

$$n_{Br_2} = 0.00559 - x = 0.00559 - 0.003506 = 0.002084 = 0.00208 \text{ mol Br}_2$$

$$n_{NOBr} = 2x = 2(0.0035\underline{0}6) = 0.007012 = 0.00701 \text{ mol NOBr}$$

The partial pressures of the gases in the equilibrium are calculated with the ideal gas law:

$$P_{NO} = (n/V)RT = (0.0060\underline{6}8 \text{ mol}/1.000 \text{ L})[0.082057 \text{ L}\bullet\text{atm}/(\text{K}\bullet\text{mol})](323.65 \text{ K})$$

$$P_{NO} = 0.16\underline{1}15 = 0.161 \text{ atm}$$

$$P_{Br_2} = (n/V)RT = (0.0020\underline{8}4 \text{ mol}/1.000 \text{ L})[0.082057 \text{ L}\bullet\text{atm}/(\text{K}\bullet\text{mol})](323.65 \text{ K})$$

$$P_{Br_2} = 0.0553\underline{4}6 = 0.0553 \text{ atm}$$

$P_{NOBr} = (n/V)RT = (0.007012 \text{ mol}/1.000 \text{ L})[0.082057 \text{ L•atm}/(\text{K•mol})](323.65 \text{ K})$

$P_{NOBr} = 0.1862 = 0.186 \text{ atm}$

Substituting these partial pressures into the equilibrium constant expression for K_p gives

$$K_p = \frac{P^2_{NOBr}}{P^2_{NO}\, P_{Br_2}} = \frac{(0.1862)^2}{(0.16115)^2(0.055346)} = 24.12 = 24.1$$

14.127. For $2NOCl(g) \rightleftharpoons 2NO(g) + Cl_2(g)$:

$$K_p = \frac{P^2_{NO}\, P_{Cl_2}}{P^2_{NOCl}}$$

At equilibrium, the partial pressure of Cl_2 can be calculated from its mass (0.404 g).

$P_{Cl_2} = (n/V)RT = ((\text{mass}/M_{Cl_2})/V)\, RT$

$P_{Cl_2} = ((0.404 \text{ g} / 70.91 \text{ g/mol})/2.00 \text{ L})[0.082057 \text{ L•atm}/(\text{K•mol})](513 \text{ K})$

$P_{Cl_2} = 0.1199 \text{ atm}$

By the stoichiometry, the partial pressure of NO will be twice that of Cl_2, or 0.2398 atm. Furthermore, Dalton's law allows the partial pressure of NOCl to be calculated with knowledge of the total pressure (1.000 atm).

$P_{total} = P_{NOCl} + P_{NO} + P_{Cl_2}$

$1.000 \text{ atm} = P_{NOCl} + 0.2398 \text{ atm} + 0.1199 \text{ atm}$

$P_{NOCl} = 1.000 \text{ atm} - (0.2398 \text{ atm} + 0.1199 \text{ atm}) = 0.6403 \text{ atm}$

Substituting these partial pressures into the equilibrium constant expression for K_p gives

$$K_p = \frac{P^2_{NO}\, P_{Cl_2}}{P^2_{NOCl}} = \frac{(0.2398)^2 (0.1198)}{(0.6403)} = 0.01076 = 0.0108$$

14.129. For $I_2(g) + Br_2(g) \rightleftharpoons 2IBr(g)$:

Because volumes will cancel in the equilibrium-constant expression for a reaction having equal numbers of moles of product species and reactant species represented in the expression, use the table approach, and give the starting, change, and equilibrium molar amounts.

Amt. (*mol*)	$I_2(g)$	+	$Br_2(g)$	$\rightleftharpoons$	$2IBr(g)$
Starting	0.5000		0.5000		0
Change	$-x$		$-x$		$+2x\ (= 0.4221)$
Equilibrium	$0.5000 - 0.21105$		$0.5000 - 0.21105$		0.4221
	$= 0.28895$		$= 0.28895$		

Substituting into the equilibrium-constant expression gives

$$K_c = \frac{[IBr]^2}{[I_2][Br_2]} = \frac{(0.4221)^2}{(0.28895)(0.28895)} = 2.13\underline{3}9 = 2.134$$

Using this value for the equilibrium constant, use another table approach, and give the new values for the starting, change, and equilibrium molar amounts.

Amt. (*mol*)	$I_2(g)$	+	$Br_2(g)$	⇌	$2IBr(g)$
Starting	1.000		2.000		0
Change	$-x$		$-x$		$+2x$
Equilibrium	$1.000 - x$		$2.000 - x$		$2x$

Substituting into the equilibrium-constant expression gives

$$K_c = 2.134 = \frac{[IBr]^2}{[I_2][Br_2]} = \frac{(2x)^2}{(1.000 - x)(2.000 - x)}$$

Rearrange this expression into a quadratic equation in standard form.

$$1.866x^2 + 6.402x - 4.268 = 0 \text{ (quadratic)}$$

Solving the quadratic equation gives $x = -4.002$ (impossible) and $x = 0.5715$ mol (use). The equilibrium composition of the mixture is readily calculated.

mol $I_2 = 1.000 - x = 1.000 - 0.5715 = 0.42\underline{8}54 = 0.429$ mol I_2

mol $Br_2 = 2.000 - x = 2.000 - 0.5715 = 1.42\underline{8}54 = 1.429$ mol Br_2

mol $IBr = 2x = 2(0.571\underline{5}) = 1.143$ mol IBr

14.131. For $Br_2(g) \rightleftharpoons 2Br(g)$:

$$K_p = \frac{P^2_{Br}}{P_{Br_2}}$$

Given the total pressure (1.000 atm), volume (3.000 L), and temperature (1600 K), calculate the total moles of gas at equilibrium with the ideal gas law.

$$n_{total} = \frac{PV}{RT} = \frac{(1.000 \text{ atm})(3.000 \text{ L})}{(0.082057 \text{ L} \bullet \text{atm} / \text{K} \bullet \text{mol})(1600 \text{ K})} = 0.02285\underline{0} = 0.02285 \text{ moles}$$

The partial pressure of Br is calculated by using its mass and the ideal gas law with the same volume and temperature.

$$P_{Br} = (n/V)RT = ((\text{mass}/ M_{Br})/ V) RT$$

$$P_{Br} = ((1.395 \text{ g} / 79.904 \text{ g/mol})/3.000 \text{ L})[0.082057 \text{ L} \bullet \text{atm}/(\text{K} \bullet \text{mol})](1600 \text{ K})$$

$$P_{Br} = 0.764\underline{0}4 = 0.7640 \text{ atm}$$

The total equilibrium pressure (1.000 atm) and the equilibrium partial pressure for one of the two gases involved in the equilibrium are now known. Use Dalton's law to determine the partial pressure of the remaining gas.

$$P_{total} = P_{Br} + P_{Br_2}$$

$$1.000 \text{ atm} = 0.7640 \text{ atm} + P_{Br_2}$$

$$P_{Br_2} = 1.000 - 0.7640 = 0.236 \text{ atm}$$

Substituting into the equilibrium-constant expression gives

$$K_p = \frac{P^2_{Br}}{P_{Br_2}} = \frac{(0.7640)^2}{(0.236)} = 2.4\underline{7}3 = 2.47$$

14.133. For $PCl_5(g) \rightleftharpoons PCl_3(g) + Cl_2(g)$: $\qquad K_p = \dfrac{P_{PCl_3} P_{Cl_2}}{P_{PCl_5}}$

Initially the reaction mixture contains only PCl_5 and the inert noble gas He. The initial partial pressures of these gases are calculated using the ideal gas law. Being inert, the pressure calculated here for He will also be the partial pressure of He in the equilibrium mixture.

$$P_{He} = (n/V)RT = (0.0800 \text{ mol}/1.000 \text{ L})[0.082057 \text{ L}\bullet\text{atm}/(\text{K}\bullet\text{mol})](523.15 \text{ K})$$

$$P_{He} = 3.4\underline{3}4 = 3.43 \text{ atm}$$

$$P_{PCl_5, \text{initial}} = (n/V)RT = (0.0565 \text{ mol}/1.000 \text{ L})[0.082057 \text{ L}\bullet\text{atm}/(\text{K}\bullet\text{mol})](523.15 \text{ K})$$

$$P_{PCl_5, \text{initial}} = 2.4\underline{2}54 = 2.43 \text{ atm}$$

Assemble a table of starting, change, and equilibrium partial pressures.

Pressure (*atm*)	$PCl_5(g)$	$\rightleftharpoons$	$PCl_3(g)$	+	$Cl_2(g)$
Starting	2.4254		0		0
Change	$-x$		$+x$		$+x$
Equilibrium	$2.4254 - x$		x		x

The total pressure at equilibrium (6.505 atm) can be used with Dalton's law to determine the value of x as follows:

$$P_{total} = P_{PCl_5} + P_{PCl_3} + P_{Cl_2} + P_{He}$$

$$6.505 \text{ atm} = (2.4254 - x) + x + x + 3.4\underline{3}4 \text{ atm}$$

$$x = 6.505 - 2.4254 - 3.434 = 0.64\underline{5}6 = 0.646 \text{ atm}$$

Substituting into the equilibrium expression for K_p gives

$$K_p = \frac{P_{PCl_3} P_{Cl_2}}{P_{PCl_5}} = \frac{(x)(x)}{2.4254 - x} = \frac{(0.64\underline{5}6)^2}{2.4254 - 0.64\underline{5}6} = 0.234\underline{1} = 0.234$$

To find K_c, use the relationship $K_p = K_c(RT)^{\Delta n}$, where Δn is the difference between the number of moles of gas products and moles of gas reactants (i.e., $\Delta n = 2 - 1 = 1$).

$$K_c = K_p/(RT)^{+1} = 0.2341/(0.082057 \times 523.15) = 5.4\underline{5}3 \times 10^{-3} = 5.45 \times 10^{-3}$$

■ SOLUTIONS TO CUMULATIVE-SKILLS PROBLEMS

14.135. For $Sb_2S_3(s) + 3H_2(g) \rightleftharpoons 2Sb(s) + 3H_2S(g)$ [+$3Pb^{2+} \rightarrow 3PbS(s) + 6H^+$]:

Starting M of $H_2(g) = 0.0100$ mol ÷ 2.50 L = 0.00400 M H_2

1.029 g PbS ÷ 239.26 g PbS/mol H_2S = 4.30$\underline{0}$7 × 10^{-3} mol H_2S

4.3007 × 10^{-3} mol H_2S ÷ 2.50 L = 1.7$\underline{2}$03 × 10^{-3} M of H_2S

Conc. (M)	$3H_2(g)$	+	$Sb_2S_3(s)$	$\rightleftharpoons$	$3H_2S(g)$	+	$2Sb(s)$
Starting	0.00400				0		
Change	−0.0017203				+0.0017203		
Equilibrium	0.0022$\underline{7}$97				0.0017$\underline{2}$03		

Substituting into the equilibrium expression for K_c gives

$$K_c = \frac{[H_2S]^3}{[H_2]^3} = \frac{(0.0017\underline{2}03)^3}{(0.0022\underline{7}97)^3} = 0.42\underline{9}7 = 0.430$$

14.137. For $PCl_5(g) \rightleftharpoons PCl_3(g) + Cl_2(g)$:

Starting M of $PCl_5 = 0.0100$ mol ÷ 2.00 L = 0.00500 M

Conc. (M)	$PCl_5(g)$	$\rightleftharpoons$	$PCl_3(g)$	+	$Cl_2(g)$
Starting	0.00500		0		0
Change	−x		+x		+x
Equilibrium	0.00500 − x		x		X

Substituting into the equilibrium expression for K_c gives

$$K_c = 4.15 \times 10^{-2} = \frac{[PCl_3][Cl_2]}{[PCl_5]} = \frac{(x)(x)}{(0.00500 - x)}$$

$$x^2 + (4.15 \times 10^{-2})x - 2.075 \times 10^{-4} = 0 \text{ (quadratic)}$$

Solving the quadratic equation gives × = −4.60 × 10^{-2} (impossible) and × = 4.$\underline{5}$1 × 10^{-3} M (use).

Total M of gas = 0.004$\underline{5}$1 + 0.004$\underline{5}$1 + 0.000$\underline{4}$9 = 0.009$\underline{5}$10 M

$$P = (n/V)RT = (0.009\underline{5}10 \ M)[0.082057 \ L\bullet atm/(K\bullet mol)](523 \ K) = 0.4\underline{0}8 = 0.41 \text{ atm}$$

CHAPTER 15

Acids and Bases

■ SOLUTIONS TO EXERCISES

Note on significant figures: If the final answer to a solution needs to be rounded off, it is given first with one nonsignificant figure, and the last significant figure is underlined. The final answer is then rounded to the correct number of significant figures. In multistep problems, intermediate answers are given with at least one nonsignificant figure; however, only the final answer has been rounded off.

15.1.   See labels below reaction:

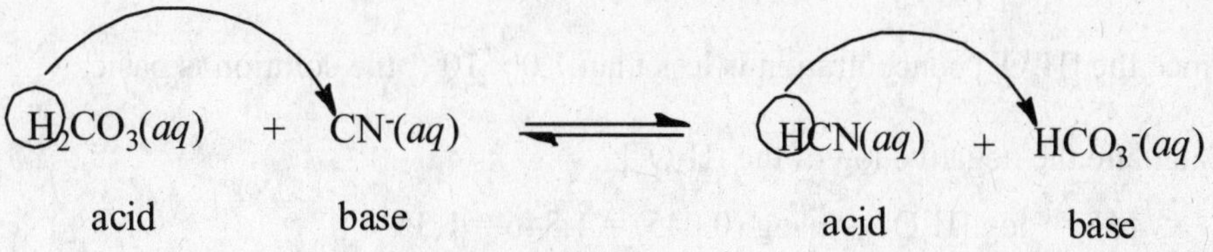

$$H_2CO_3(aq) \quad + \quad CN^-(aq) \quad \rightleftharpoons \quad HCN(aq) \quad + \quad HCO_3^-(aq)$$

acid   base   acid   base

H_2CO_3 is the proton donor (Brønsted-Lowry acid) on the left, and HCN is the proton donor (Brønsted-Lowry acid) on the right. The CN^- and HCO_3^- ions are proton acceptors (Brønsted-Lowry bases). HCN is the conjugate acid of CN^-.

15.2.   Part a involves molecules with all single bonds; part b does not, so bonds are drawn in.

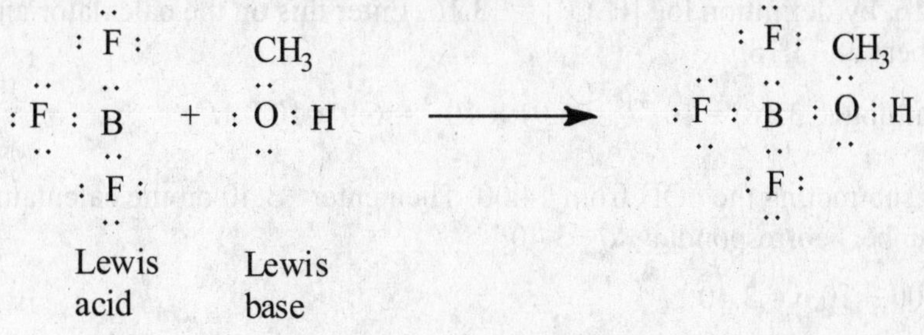

a.   (Lewis structures of BF_3 as Lewis acid + CH_3OH as Lewis base forming adduct)

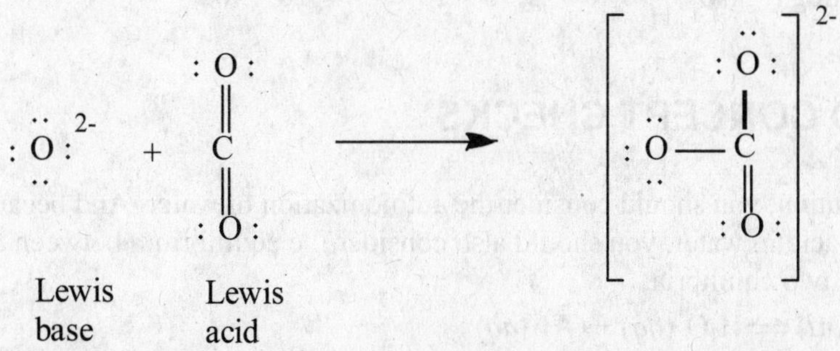

b.   (Lewis structures of O^{2-} as Lewis base + CO_2 as Lewis acid forming CO_3^{2-})

15.3.   The $HC_2H_3O_2$ is a stronger acid than H_2S, and HS^- is a stronger base than the $C_2H_3O_2^-$ ion. The equilibrium favors the weaker acid and weaker base; therefore, the reactants are favored.

15.4.   a. PH_3

      b.   HI

      c. H_2SO_3

      d. H_3AsO_4

      e. HSO_4^-

15.5.   A 0.125 M solution of $Ba(OH)_2$, a strong base, ionizes completely to yield 0.125 M Ba^{2+} ion and 2 × 0.125 M, or 0.250 M, OH^- ion. Use the K_w equation to calculate the $[H_3O^+]$.

$$[H_3O^+] = \frac{K_w}{[OH^-]} = \frac{1.0 \times 10^{-14}}{(0.250)} = 4.00 \times 10^{-14} = 4.0 \times 10^{-14}\ M$$

15.6.   Use the K_w equation to calculate the $[H_3O^+]$.

$$[H_3O^+] = \frac{K_w}{[OH^-]} = \frac{1.0 \times 10^{-14}}{1.0 \times 10^{-5}} = 1.00 \times 10^{-9} = 1.0 \times 10^{-9}\ M$$

Since the $[H_3O^+]$ concentration is less than 1.0×10^{-7}, the solution is basic.

15.7.   Calculate the negative log of the $[H_3O^+]$:

pH = $-\log[H_3O^+] = -\log(0.045) = 1.3\underline{4}6 = 1.35$

15.8.   Calculate the pOH of 0.025 M OH^-, and then subtract from 14.00 to find pH:

pOH = $-\log[OH^-] = -\log(0.025) = 1.6\underline{0}2$

pH = $14.00 - 1.602 = 12.3\underline{9}7 = 12.40$

15.9.   Because pH = 3.16, by definition $\log[H_3O^+] = -3.16$. Enter this on the calculator and convert to the antilog (number) of -3.16.

$[H_3O^+]$ = antilog $(-3.16) = 10^{-3.16} = 6.\underline{9}1 \times 10^{-4} = 6.9 \times 10^{-4}\ M$

15.10.   Find the pOH by subtracting the pOH from 14.00. Then enter -3.40 on the calculator to convert to the antilog (number) corresponding to -3.40.

pOH = $14.00 - 10.6 = 3.\underline{4}0$

$[H_3O^+]$ = antilog $(-3.40) = 10^{-3.40} = \underline{3}.98 \times 10^{-4} = 4 \times 10^{-4}\ M$

■ ANSWERS TO CONCEPT CHECKS

15.1.   In any aqueous solution, you should consider the autoionization of water. And because we have a solution of a weak acid in water, you should also consider the equilibrium between this acid and water. Here are the two equilibria:

$H_2O(l) + H_2O(l) \rightleftharpoons H_3O^+(aq) + OH^-(aq)$

$HCHO_2(aq) + H_2O(l) \rightleftharpoons CHO_2^-(aq) + H_3O^+(aq)$

The species present in these equilibria are $H_2O(l)$, $H_3O^+(aq)$, $OH^-(aq)$, $HCHO_2(aq)$, and $CHO_2^-(aq)$.

15.2. The stronger acid gives up its proton more readily, and therefore, its conjugate base ion holds on to a proton less strongly. In other words, the stronger acid has the weaker conjugate base. Because formic acid is the stronger acid, the formate ion is the weaker base. Acetate ion is the stronger base.

15.3. Look at each solution, and determine whether it is acidic, basic, or neutral. In solution A, the numbers of H_3O^+ and OH^- ions are equal, so the solution is neutral. For solution B, the number of H_3O^+ ions is greater than the number of OH^- ions, so the solution is acidic. In solution C, the number of H_3O^+ ions is less than the number of OH^- ions, so the solution is basic. Therefore, the ranking from most acidic to least acidic (most basic) is B > A > C.

15.4. In order to answer this problem qualitatively, it is essential that all the solutions have the same solute concentrations. Bases produce solutions of pH greater than 7, whereas acids produce solutions of pH less than 7. NH_3 and $NaOH$ are bases, and HCl and $HC_2H_3O_2$ are acids. $NaOH$ is a stronger base than NH_3, so the $NaOH$ solution would have the highest pH, followed by the NH_3 solution. $HC_2H_3O_2$ is a much weaker acid than HCl, so the $HC_2H_3O_2$ solution would have a higher pH than the HCl solution. Therefore, the ranking from highest to lowest pH for solutions with the same solute concentrations is $NaOH > NH_3 > HC_2H_3O_2 > HCl$.

■ ANSWERS TO SELF-ASSESSMENT AND REVIEW QUESTIONS

15.1. You can classify these acids using the information in Section 15.1. Also recall that all diatomic acids of Group VIIA halides are strong except for HF.

a. Weak

b. Weak

c. Strong

d. Strong

e. Weak

f. Weak

15.2. In Section 15.1, we are told that all neutralizations involving strong acids and bases evolve 55.90 kJ of heat per mole of H_3O^+. Thus, the thermochemical evidence for the Arrhenius concept is based on the fact that when 1 mol of any strong acid (1 mol H_3O^+) is neutralized by 1 mole of any strong base (1 mol OH^-), the heat of neutralization is always the same ($\Delta H° = -55.90$ kJ/mol).

15.3. A Brønsted-Lowry acid is a molecule or ion that donates an H^+ ion (proton donor) to a base in a proton-transfer reaction. A Brønsted-Lowry base is a molecule or ion that accepts an H^+ ion (proton acceptor) from an acid in a proton-transfer reaction. An example of an acid-base equation:

$$HF(aq) \; + \; NH_3(aq) \quad \rightarrow \quad NH_4^+(aq) \; + \; F^-(aq)$$

　　　acid　　　　　base　　　　　　　acid　　　　　base

15.4. The conjugate acid of a base is a species that differs from the base by only one H^+. Consider the base, HSO_3^-. Its conjugate acid would be H_2SO_3 but not H_2SO_4. H_2SO_4 differs from HSO_3^- by one H and one O.

15.5. You can write the equations by considering that $H_2PO_3^-$ is both a Brønsted-Lowry acid and a Brønsted-Lowry base. The $H_2PO_3^-$ acts as a Brønsted-Lowry acid when it reacts with a base such as OH^-:

$$H_2PO_3^-(aq) + OH^-(aq) \rightarrow HPO_3^{2-}(aq) + H_2O(l)$$

The $H_2PO_3^-$ acts as a Brønsted-Lowry base when it reacts with an acid such as HCl:

$$H_2PO_3^-(aq) + HCl(aq) \rightarrow H_3PO_3(aq) + Cl^-(aq)$$

15.6. The Brønsted-Lowry concept enlarges on the Arrhenius concept in the following ways: (1) It expands the concept of a base to include any species that accepts protons, not just the OH^- ion or compounds containing the OH^- ion. (2) It enlarges the concepts of acids and bases to include ions as well as molecules. (3) It enables us to write acid-base reactions in nonaqueous solutions as well as in aqueous solutions, whereas the Arrhenius concept applies only to aqueous solutions. (4) It allows some species to be considered as acids or bases, depending on the other reactant with which they are mixed.

15.7. According to the Lewis concept, an acid is an electron-pair acceptor and a base is an electron-pair donor. An example is

$$Ag^+(aq) \; + \; 2(:NH_3) \quad \rightarrow \quad Ag(NH_3)_2^+(aq)$$

acid   base

15.8. Recall that the weaker the acid, the stronger it holds on to its proton(s). Thus, if a reaction mixture consists of a stronger acid and base and a weaker acid and base, the weaker-acid side will always be favored because the proton(s) will bond more strongly to the weaker acid.

15.9. The two factors that determine the strength of an acid are (1) the polarity of the bond to which the H atom is attached, and (2) the strength of the bond, or how tightly the proton is held by the atom to which it is bonded. An increase in the polarity of the bond makes it easier to remove the proton, increasing the strength of the acid. An increase in the strength of the bond makes it more difficult to remove the proton, decreasing the strength of the acid. The strength of the bond depends in turn on the size of the atom, so larger atoms have weaker bonds, whereas smaller atoms have stronger bonds.

15.10. The autoionization of water is the reaction of two water molecules in which a proton is transferred from one molecule to the other to form H_3O^+ and OH^- ions. At 25°C, the K_w expression is $K_w = [H_3O^+][OH^-] = 1.0 \times 10^{-14}$.

15.11. The pH $= -\log [H_3O^+]$ of an aqueous solution. Measure pH by using electrodes and a pH meter or by interpolating the pH from the color changes of a series of acid-base indicators.

15.12. A solution of pH 4 has a $[H_3O^+] = 1 \times 10^{-4}$ M and is more acidic than a solution of pH 5, which has a $[H_3O^+] = 1 \times 10^{-5}$ M.

15.13. For a neutral solution, $[H_3O^+] = [OH^-]$; thus, the $[H_3O^+]$ of a neutral solution at 37°C is the square root of K_w at 37°C:

$$[H_3O^+] = \sqrt{2.5 \times 10^{-14}} = 1.\underline{5}8 \times 10^{-7} \, M$$

$$pH = -\log(1.58 \times 10^{-7}) = 6.8\underline{0}1 = 6.80$$

15.14. Because $pH + pOH = pK_w$ at any temperature,

$$pH + pOH = -\log(2.5 \times 10^{-14}) = 13.60$$

15.15. The answer is a, F^-.

15.16. The answer is d, Fe^{3+}.

15.17. The answer is d, $3.8 \times 10^{-13} \, M$.

15.18. The answer is b, $3.5 \times 10^{-5} \, M$.

■ ANSWERS TO CONCEPTUAL PROBLEMS

15.21. It is not necessary to have the species NH_4OH in order to have OH^- in the solution. When ammonia reacts with water, hydroxide ion forms in the reaction.

$$NH_3(aq) + H_2O(l) \rightleftharpoons NH_4^+(aq) \quad + OH^-(aq)$$

15.23. The hydroxide ion acts as a base and donates a pair of electrons on the O atom, forming a bond with CO_2 to give HCO_3^-.

15.25. When you lower the temperature of pure water, the value of K_w decreases. In pure water, the hydronium-ion concentration equals the hydroxide-ion concentration, so $K_w = [H_3O^+]^2$. When K_w decreases, the hydronium-ion concentration decreases, and the corresponding pH increases.

15.27. A strong monoprotic acid will dissolve completely in water to form hydronium ions (H_3O^+) and anions in equal number. None of the original monoprotic acid molecules will remain. This is represented by the picture in the middle. The picture on the left represents an undissociated acid. No ions are present in the solution. The picture on the right represents a weak acid where only some of the acid molecules have dissociated to form ions.

■ SOLUTIONS TO PRACTICE PROBLEMS

Note on significant figures: If the final answer to a solution needs to be rounded off, it is given first with one nonsignificant figure, and the last significant figure is underlined. The final answer is then rounded to the correct number of significant figures. In multistep problems, intermediate answers are given with at least one nonsignificant figure; however, only the final answer has been rounded off.

15.29. The reaction with labels of "acid" and "base" written below is as follows:

$$OH^-(aq) + HF(aq) \rightleftharpoons F^-(aq) + H_2O(l)$$
$$\text{base} \qquad \text{acid} \qquad\qquad \text{base} \qquad \text{acid}$$

15.31. a. PO_4^{3-}

b. HS^-

c. NO_2^-

d. $HAsO_4^{2-}$

15.33. a. $HClO$

b. AsH_4^+

c. H_3PO_4

d. $HTeO_3^-$

15.35. Each equation is given below with the labels for acid and base:

$$HSO_4^-(aq) + NH_3(aq) \rightleftharpoons SO_4^{2-}(aq) + NH_4^+(aq)$$
$$\text{acid} \qquad\quad \text{base} \qquad\qquad\quad \text{acid} \qquad\quad \text{base}$$

a.

The conjugate acid-base pairs are (HSO_4^-, SO_4^{2-}) and (NH_4^+, NH_3).

$$HPO_4^{2-}(aq) + NH_4^+(aq) \rightleftharpoons H_2PO_4^-(aq) + NH_3(aq)$$
$$\text{base} \qquad\quad \text{acid} \qquad\qquad \text{base} \qquad\quad \text{acid}$$

b.

The conjugate acid-base pairs are ($H_2PO_4^-$, HPO_4^{2-}) and (NH_4^+, NH_3)

$$Al(H_2O)_6^{3+}(aq) + H_2O(l) \rightleftharpoons Al(H_2O)_5(OH)^{2+}(aq) + H_3O^+(aq)$$
$$\text{acid} \qquad\qquad \text{base} \qquad\qquad\qquad \text{acid} \qquad\qquad\qquad \text{base}$$

c.

The conjugate acid-base pairs are ($Al(H_2O)_6^{3+}$, $Al(H_2O)_5(OH)^{2+}$) and (H_3O^+, H_2O).

$$SO_3^{2-}(aq) + NH_4^+(aq) \rightleftharpoons HSO_3^-(aq) + NH_3(aq)$$
$$\text{base} \qquad\quad \text{acid} \qquad\qquad \text{base} \qquad\qquad \text{acid}$$

d.

The conjugate acid-base pairs are (HSO_3^-, SO_3^{2-}) and (NH_4^+, NH_3).

15.37. The reaction is

$$\underset{\substack{\text{Lewis}\\\text{base}}}{:\!\overset{\cdot\cdot}{F}\!:\!\overset{\cdot\cdot}{As}\!:} \quad + \quad \underset{\substack{\text{Lewis}\\\text{acid}}}{\overset{\cdot\cdot}{B}\!:\!\overset{\cdot\cdot}{F}\!:} \quad \longrightarrow \quad :\!\overset{\cdot\cdot}{F}\!:\!\overset{\cdot\cdot}{As}\!:\!\overset{\cdot\cdot}{B}\!:\!\overset{\cdot\cdot}{F}$$

15.39. **a.** The completed equation is

$$AlCl_3 + Cl^- \rightleftharpoons AlCl_4^-$$

The Lewis formula representation is

$AlCl_3$ is the electron-pair acceptor and is the acid. Cl^- is the electron-pair donor and is the base.

b. The completed equation is

$$^- + I_2 \rightleftharpoons I_3^-$$

The Lewis formula representation is

I_2 is the electron-pair acceptor and is the acid. The I^- ion is the electron-pair donor and is the base.

15.41. **a.** Each water molecule donates a pair of electrons to copper(II), making the water molecule a Lewis base and the Cu^{2+} ion a Lewis acid.

b. The AsH_3 donates a pair of electrons to the boron atom in BBr_3, making AsH_3 a Lewis base and the BBr_3 molecule a Lewis acid.

15.43. The equation is $H_2S + HOCH_2CH_2NH_2 \rightarrow HOCH_2CH_2NH_3^+ + HS^-$. The H_2S is a Lewis acid, and $HOCH_2CH_2NH_2$ is a Lewis base. The hydrogen ion from H_2S accepts a pair of electrons from the N atom in $HOCH_2CH_2NH_2$.

15.45. The reaction is $HSO_4^- + ClO^- \rightarrow HClO + SO_4^{2-}$. According to Table 15.2, HClO is a weaker acid than HSO_4^-. Because the equilibrium for this type of reaction favors formation of the weaker acid (or weaker base), the reaction occurs to a significant extent.

15.47. a. NH_4^+ is a weaker acid than H_3PO_4, so the left-hand species are favored at equilibrium.

b.   HCN is a weaker acid than H_2S, so the left-hand species are favored at equilibrium.

c. H_2O is a weaker acid than HCO_3^-, so the right-hand species are favored at equilibrium.

d. H_2O is a weaker acid than $Al(H_2O)_6^{3+}$, so the right-hand species are favored at equilibrium.

15.49. Trichloroacetic acid is the stronger acid because, in general, the equilibrium favors the formation of the weaker acid, which is formic acid in this case.

15.51. a. H_2S is stronger because acid strength decreases with increasing anion charge for polyprotic acid species.

b. H_2SO_3 is stronger because, for a series of oxoacids, acid strength increases with increasing electronegativity.

c.   HBr is stronger because Br is more electronegative than Se. Within a period, acid strength increases as electronegativity increases.

d. HIO_4 is stronger because acid strength increases with the number of oxygen atoms bonded to the central atom.

e. H_2S is stronger because, within a group, acid strength increases with the increasing size of the central atom in binary acids.

15.53. a. $[H_3O^+] = 1.2\ M$

$$[OH^-] = \frac{K_w}{[H_3O^+]} = \frac{1.0 \times 10^{-14}}{1.2} = 8.\underline{3}3 \times 10^{-15} = 8.3 \times 10^{-15}\ M$$

b. $[OH^-] = 0.32\ M$

$$[H_3O^+] = \frac{K_w}{[OH^-]} = \frac{1.0 \times 10^{-14}}{0.32} = 3.\underline{1}2 \times 10^{-14} = 3.1 \times 10^{-14}\ M$$

c. $[OH^-] = 2 \times (0.085\ M) = 0.170\ M$

$$[H_3O^+] = \frac{K_w}{[OH^-]} = \frac{1.0 \times 10^{-14}}{0.170} = 5.\underline{8}8 \times 10^{-14} = 5.9 \times 10^{-14}\ M$$

d. $[H_3O^+] = 0.38\ M$

$$[OH^-] = \frac{K_w}{[H_3O^+]} = \frac{1.0 \times 10^{-14}}{0.38} = 2.\underline{6}3 \times 10^{-14} = 2.6 \times 10^{-14}\ M$$

15.55. The $[H_3O^+] = 0.050\ M$ (HCl is a strong acid); using K_w, the $[OH^-] = 2.0 \times 10^{-13}\ M$.

15.57. Because the $Ba(OH)_2$ forms two OH^- per formula unit, the $[OH^-] = 2 \times 0.0085 = 0.017\ M$.

$$[H_3O^+] = \frac{K_w}{[OH^-]} = \frac{1.0 \times 10^{-14}}{0.017} = 5.\underline{8}8 \times 10^{-13} = 5.9 \times 10^{-13}\ M$$

15.59   a. $5 \times 10^{-6}\ M\ H_3O^+ > 1.0 \times 10^{-7}$, so the solution is acidic.

b.   Use K_w to determine $[H_3O^+]$.

$$[H_3O^+] = \frac{K_w}{[OH^-]} = \frac{1.00 \times 10^{-14}}{5 \times 10^{-9}} = \underline{2}.0 \times 10^{-6} = 2 \times 10^{-6}\ M$$

Since $2 \times 10^{-6}\ M > 1.0 \times 10^{-7}$, the solution is acidic.

c.   When $[OH^-] = 1.0 \times 10^{-7}\ M$, $[H_3O^+] = 1.0 \times 10^{-7}\ M$, and the solution is neutral.

d. $2 \times 10^{-9}\ M\ H_3O^+ < 1.0 \times 10^{-7}$, so the solution is basic.

15.61.   The $[H_3O^+]$ calculated below is $> 1.0 \times 10^{-7}\ M$, so the solution is acidic.

$$[H_3O^+] = \frac{K_w}{[OH^-]} = \frac{1.00 \times 10^{-14}}{1.5 \times 10^{-9}} = 6.\underline{6}6 \times 10^{-6} = 6.7 \times 10^{-6}\ M$$

15.63.   a.   pH 4.6, acidic solution   b.   pH 7.0, neutral solution

c.   pH 1.6, acidic solution   d.   pH 10.5, basic solution

15.65.   a.   Acidic (3.5 < 7.0)   b.   Neutral (7.0 = 7.0)

c.   Basic (9.0 > 7.0)   d.   Acidic (5.5 < 7.0)

15.67.   Record the same number of places after the decimal point in the pH as the number of significant figures in the $[H_3O^+]$.

a. $-\log (1.0 \times 10^{-8}) = 8.0\underline{00} = 8.00$

b. $-\log (5.0 \times 10^{-12}) = 11.3\underline{01} = 11.30$

c. $-\log (7.5 \times 10^{-3}) = 2.1\underline{24} = 2.12$

d. $-\log (6.35 \times 10^{-9}) = 8.19\underline{72} = 8.197$

15.69.   Record the same number of places after the decimal point in the pH as the number of significant figures in the $[H_3O^+]$.

$$-\log (7.5 \times 10^{-3}) = 2.1\underline{2}49 = 2.12$$

15.71.   a. $pOH = -\log (5.25 \times 10^{-9}) = 8.27\underline{98}$; pH $= 14.00 - 8.27\underline{98} = 5.7\underline{2}02 = 5.72$

b. $pOH = -\log (8.3 \times 10^{-3}) = 2.0\underline{809}$; pH $= 14.00 - 2.0\underline{809} = 11.9\underline{1}908 = 11.92$

c. $pOH = -\log (3.6 \times 10^{-12}) = 11.4\underline{44}$; pH $= 14.00 - 11.4\underline{44} = 2.5\underline{56} = 2.56$

d. $pOH = -\log (2.1 \times 10^{-8}) = 7.6\underline{78}$; pH $= 14.00 - 7.6\underline{78} = 6.3\underline{22} = 6.32$

15.73.   First, convert the $[OH^-]$ to $[H_3O^+]$ using the K_w equation. Then find the pH, recording the same number of places after the decimal point in the pH as the number of significant figures in the $[H_3O^+]$.

$$[H_3O^+] = K_w \div [OH^-] = (1.0 \times 10^{-14}) \div (0.0040) = 2.\underline{5}0 \times 10^{-12}\ M$$

$$pH = -\log (2.50 \times 10^{-12}) = 11.6\underline{0}2 = 11.60$$

15.75.   From the definition, pH = $-\log$ [H_3O^+] and $-$pH = log [H_3O^+], so enter the negative value of the pH on the calculator, and use the inverse and log keys (or 10^x) key to find the antilog of $-$pH.

$$\log \text{[H}_3\text{O}^+] = -\text{pH} = -5.12$$

$$\text{[H}_3\text{O}^+] = \text{antilog } (-5.12) = 10^{-5.12} = 7.\underline{58} \times 10^{-6} = 7.6 \times 10^{-6} \ M$$

15.77.   From the definition, pH = $-\log$ [H_3O^+] and $-$pH = log [H_3O^+], so enter the negative value of the pH on the calculator, and use the inverse and log keys (or 10^x) key to find the antilog of $-$pH. Then use the K_w equation to calculate [OH^-] from [H_3O^+].

$$\log \text{[H}_3\text{O}^+] = -\text{pH} = -11.63$$

$$\text{[H}_3\text{O}^+] = \text{antilog } (-11.63) = 10^{-11.63} = 2.\underline{34} \times 10^{-12} \ M$$

$$\text{[OH}^-] = K_w \div \text{[H}_3\text{O}^+] = (1.0 \times 10^{-14}) \div (2.34 \times 10^{-12}) = 4.\underline{27} \times 10^{-3} = 4.3 \times 10^{-3} \ M$$

15.79.   First, calculate the molarity of the OH^- ion from the mass of NaOH. Next, convert the [OH^-] to [H_3O^+] using the K_w equation. Then find the pH, recording the same number of places after the decimal point in the pH as the number of significant figures in the [H_3O^+].

$$\frac{5.80 \text{ g NaOH}}{1.00 \text{ L}} \times \frac{1 \text{ mol NaOH}}{40.00 \text{ g NaOH}} = \frac{0.1450 \text{ mol NaOH}}{1.00 \text{ L}} = 0.14\underline{50} \ M \text{ OH}^-$$

$$\text{[H}_3\text{O}^+] = K_w \div \text{[OH}^-] = (1.0 \times 10^{-14}) \div (0.1450) = 6.\underline{896} \times 10^{-14} \ M$$

$$\text{pH} = -\log \text{[H}_3\text{O}^+] = -\log (6.896 \times 10^{-14}) = 13.1\underline{6}14 = 13.16$$

15.81.   Figure 15.10 shows that the methyl-red indicator is yellow at pH values above about 5.5 (slightly past the midpoint of the range for methyl red). Bromthymol blue is yellow at pH values up to about 6.5 (slightly below the midpoint of the range for bromthymol blue). Therefore, the pH of the solution is between 5.5 and 6.5, and the solution is acidic.

■ SOLUTIONS TO GENERAL PROBLEMS

15.83.   a.   BaO is a base; $BaO + H_2O \rightarrow Ba^{2+} + 2OH^-$

b. H_2S is an acid; $H_2S + H_2O \rightarrow H_3O^+ + HS^-$

c. CH_3NH_2 is a base; $CH_3NH_2 + H_2O \rightarrow CH_3NH_3^+ + OH^-$

d. SO_2 is an acid; $SO_2 + 2H_2O \rightarrow H_3O^+ + HSO_3^-$

15.85.   a. $H_2O_2(aq) + S^{2-}(aq) \rightarrow HO_2^-(aq) + HS^-(aq)$

b. $HCO_3^-(aq) + OH^-(aq) \rightarrow CO_3^{2-}(aq) + H_2O(l)$

c. $NH_4^+(aq) + CN^-(aq) \rightarrow NH_3(aq) + HCN(aq)$

d. $H_2PO_4^-(aq) + OH^-(aq) \rightarrow HPO_4^{2-}(aq) + H_2O(l)$

15.87.   a.   The ClO^- ion is a Brønsted base, and water is a Brønsted acid. The complete chemical equation is $ClO^-(aq) + H_2O(l) \rightleftharpoons HClO(aq) + OH^-(aq)$. The equilibrium does not favor the products because ClO^- is a weaker base than OH^-. In Lewis language, a proton from H_2O acts as a Lewis acid by accepting a pair of electrons on the oxygen of ClO^-.

$$H^+ \;+\; \left[\ddot{\underset{\cdot\cdot}{Cl}} : \ddot{\underset{\cdot\cdot}{O}} : \right]^- \;\longrightarrow\; \ddot{\underset{\cdot\cdot}{Cl}} : \ddot{\underset{\cdot\cdot}{O}} : H$$

   b.   The NH_2^- ion is a Brønsted base, and NH_4^+ is a Brønsted acid. The complete chemical equation is $NH_4^+ + NH_2^- \rightleftharpoons 2NH_3$. The equilibrium favors the products because the reactants form the solvent, a weakly ionized molecule. In Lewis language, the proton from NH_4^+ acts as a Lewis acid by accepting a pair of electrons on the nitrogen of NH_2^-.

$$\left[\begin{array}{c} H \\ \cdot\cdot \\ H : N : H \\ \cdot\cdot \\ H \end{array} \right]^+ \;+\; \left[\begin{array}{c} \cdot\cdot \\ : N : H \\ \cdot\cdot \\ H \end{array} \right]^- \;\longrightarrow\; 2\; \begin{array}{c} \cdot\cdot \\ H : N : H \\ \cdot\cdot \\ H \end{array}$$

15.89.   Table 15.2 shows that HNO_2 is a stronger acid than HF. Because an acid-base reaction normally goes in the direction of the weaker acid, the reaction is more likely to go in the direction written:

$$HNO_2 + F^- \rightleftharpoons HF + NO_2^-$$

15.91.   The order is $H_2S < H_2Se < HBr$. H_2Se is stronger than H_2S because, within a group, acid strength increases with increasing size of the central atom in binary acids. HBr is a strong acid, whereas the others are weak acids.

15.93.   The KOH is a strong base and is fully ionized in solution, so you can use its formula and molar concentration to determine the $[OH^-]$ of the solution. Therefore, the 0.25 M KOH contains 0.25 M OH^-. The $[H_3O^+]$ is obtained from the K_w expression:

$$K_w = 1.0 \times 10^{-14} = [H_3O^+] \times 0.25 \; M \; OH^-$$

$$[H_3O^+] = \frac{1.0 \times 10^{-14}}{0.25} = 4.\underline{00} \times 10^{-14} = 4.0 \times 10^{-14} \; M$$

15.95.   Enter the H_3O^+ concentration of 1.5×10^{-3} into the calculator, press the log key, and press the sign key to change the negative log to a positive log. This follows the negative-log definition of pH. The number of decimal places of the pH should equal the significant figures in the H_3O^+.

$$pH = -\log[H_3O^+] = -\log(1.5 \times 10^{-3}) = 2.8\underline{23} = 2.82$$

15.97.   Find the pOH from the pH using pH + pOH = 14.00. Then calculate the [OH⁻] from the pOH by entering the pOH into the calculator, pressing the sign key to change the positive log to a negative log, and finding the antilog. On some calculators, the antilog is found by using the inverse of the log; on other calculators, the antilog is found using the 10^x key. The number of significant figures in the [OH⁻] should equal the number of decimal places in the pOH.

pOH = 14.00 − 3.15 = 10.85

[OH⁻] = antilog (−10.85) = $10^{-10.85}$ = 1.$\underline{4}$12 × 10^{-11} = 1.4 × 10^{-11} M

15.99.   a. $H_2SO_4(aq) + 2NaHCO_3(aq) \rightarrow Na_2SO_4(aq) + 2CO_2(g) + 2H_2O(l)$ (molecular)

$H_3O^+(aq) + HCO_3^-(aq) \rightarrow CO_2(g) + 2H_2O(l)$ (net ionic)

b.   The total moles of H_3O^+ from the H_2SO_4 is

$$\text{Moles of } H_3O^+ = \frac{0.437 \text{ mol } H_2SO_4}{1 \text{ L}} \times 0.02500 \text{ L} \times \frac{2 \text{ mol } H_3O^+}{1 \text{ mol } H_2SO_4} = 0.021\underline{8}5 \text{ mol } H_3O^+$$

The moles of H_3O^+ that reacted with the NaOH is given by

$$\text{Moles of } H_3O^+ = \frac{0.108 \text{ mol NaOH}}{1 \text{ L}} \times 0.0354 \text{ L} = 0.003\underline{8}23 \text{ mol}$$

The moles of $NaHCO_3$ present in the original sample is equal to the moles of H_3O^+ that reacted with the HCO_3^-, which is given by

Total moles H_3O^+ − moles H_3O^+ reacted with the NaOH = moles HCO_3^-

0.021$\underline{8}$5 mol − 0.003$\underline{8}$23 mol = 0.018$\underline{0}$3 = 0.0180 mol $NaHCO_3$

c.   The mass of $NaHCO_3$ (molar mass 84.01 g/mol) present in the original sample is

$$0.018\underline{0}3 \text{ mol } NaHCO_3 \times \frac{84.01 \text{ g } NaHCO_3}{1 \text{ mol } NaHCO_3} = 1.5\underline{1}4 \text{ g}$$

Thus, the percent $NaHCO_3$ in the original sample is given by

$$\text{Percent } NaHCO_3 = \frac{1.514 \text{ g}}{2.500 \text{ g}} \times 100\% = 60.\underline{5}6 = 60.6\%$$

The percent KCl in the original sample is

Percent KCl = 100 − 60.56 = 39.$\underline{4}$4 = 39.4%

15.101. $HCO_3^-(aq) + H_2O(l) \rightleftharpoons H_3O^+(aq) + CO_3^{2-}(aq)$

$HCO_3^-(aq) + H_2O(l) \rightleftharpoons H_2CO_3(aq) + OH^-(aq)$

$HCO_3^-(aq) + Na^+(aq) + OH^-(aq) \rightleftharpoons Na^+(aq) + CO_3^{2-}(aq) + H_2O(l)$

$HCO_3^-(aq) + H^+(aq) + Cl^-(aq) \rightleftharpoons H_2O(l) + CO_2(g) + Cl^-(aq)$

15.103. $CaH_2(s) + 2H_2O(l) \rightarrow Ca(OH)_2(s) + 2H_2(g)$

The hydride ion is a stronger base because it took an H^+ from water, leaving the OH^- ion. Every time a strong base is added to water, it will react with the water, leaving the OH^- as the product, so a base stronger than hydroxide ion cannot exist in water.

15.105. A bitter taste seems to be a common feature of a base. It is a fact that many medicinal substances are nitrogen bases, substances that organic chemists call amines, which are bases.

15.107. Such solutions work by chemically reacting with fat and with hair, the usual ingredients of a stopped drain. When fat reacts with a strong base such as sodium hydroxide, it forms a salt of a fatty acid, a product otherwise known as soap. Hair is a protein material, and in the presence of a strong base, the protein breaks up into the salts of its constituent amino acid salts. That solution washes easily down the drain.

■ SOLUTIONS TO STRATEGY PROBLEMS

15.109. a. $[Al(H_2O)_6]^{3+} + NH_3 \rightarrow [Al(H_2O)_5OH]^{2+} + NH_4^+$

  acid   base   base   acid

The conjugate acid-base pairs are ($[Al(H_2O)_6]^{3+}$, $[Al(H_2O)_5OH]^{2+}$) and (NH_4^+, NH_3).

  b. $CH_3CH_2SH + H_2SO_4 \rightarrow CH_3CH_2SH_2^+ + HSO_4^-$

  base   acid   acid   base

The conjugate acid-base pairs are ($CH_3CH_2SH_2^+$, CH_3CH_2SH) and (H_2SO_4, HSO_4^-).

15.111. The electronegative chlorine atom withdraws electron density from the acidic end of the molecule thereby weakening the O−H bond and making the acidic proton more readily available for ionization. Another way of viewing this is to recognize that the Cl stabilizes the negatively-charged conjugate base produced when the proton leaves. This effect is enhanced when there are multiple chlorine atoms and when the chlorine atoms are closer to the acidic end of the molecule.

Ordered from weakest acid to strongest acid:

  1-chloropropanoic acid < 2-chloropropanoic acid < 2,2-dichloropropanoic acid

15.113. The equations for arsine (AsH_3) and phosphine (PH_3) acting as bases in water are

  $AsH_3(aq) + H_2O(l) \rightarrow AsH_4^+(aq) + OH^-(aq)$

  $PH_3(aq) + H_2O(l) \rightarrow PH_4^+(aq) + OH^-(aq)$

The ions (conjugate acids) formed by NH_3, AsH_3, and PH_3 with H^+ are NH_4^+, AsH_4^+, and PH_4^+, respectively. Because acid strength for binary acids increases with the size of the central atom, the acid strengths of these ions increases as $NH_4^+ < PH_4^+ < AsH_4^+$. Accordingly, because stronger acids produce weaker conjugate bases, the base strengths of the associated bases increases as $AsH_3 < PH_3 < NH_3$.

15.115. Ethanol reacting as a Brønsted-Lowry acid with OH^- is

$$CH_3CH_2OH + OH^- \rightleftharpoons CH_3CH_2O^- + H_2O$$

Ethanol reacting as a Brønsted-Lowry base with H_3O^+ is

$$CH_3CH_2OH + H_3O^+ \rightleftharpoons CH_3CH_2OH_2^+ + H_2O$$

In both of these reactions, a proton is transferred from the acid to the base, which is in agreement with the Brønsted-Lowry definitions of an acid and a base. These reactions can also be considered Lewis acid-base reactions. In the first reaction, the oxygen atom of OH^- can act as an electron-pair donor, and the hydrogen of CH_3CH_2OH can act as an electron-pair acceptor. In the second reaction, the oxygen of CH_3CH_2OH acts as the electron-pair donor and the hydrogen of H_3O^+ as the electron-pair acceptor.

15.117. This is a Lewis acid-base reaction with $N(CH_3)_3$ the electron-pair donor (Lewis base) and $AlCl_3$ the electron-pair acceptor (Lewis acid). The product is $AlCl_3–N(CH_3)_3$.

15.119. a. $HBrO < HBrO_2 < HBrO_3$. For a series of oxoacids with the same central atom, acid strength increases with increasing number of oxygen atoms bonded to the central atom.

b. $H_2TeO_3 < H_2SeO_3 < H_2SO_3$. For a series of oxoacids having the same structure but different central atoms, acid strength increases with increasing electronegativity of the central atom. For elements in the same column on the periodic table, electronegativity decreases as you go down the column, so acid strength decreases as you go down the column.

c. $SbH_3 < H_2Te < HI$. For acids with the structure HX, acid strength increases with increasing electronegativity of atom X. Going across a row of elements on the periodic table, the electronegativity increases, the bond polarity increases, and the acid strength increases.

d. $H_2S < H_2Se < HBr$. For acids with the structure HX, acid strength increases with increasing electronegativity of atom X. In going down a column of the periodic table, the size of atom × increases, the bond strength decreases, and the acid strength increases. H_2S and H_2Se are in the same column, and Se has bigger atoms, so H_2Se is a stronger acid than H_2S. Also, going across a row of elements on the periodic table, the electronegativity increases, the bond polarity increases, and the acid strength increases. Se and Br are in the same row, and Br is more electronegative, so HBr is a stronger acid than H_2Se.

e. $HBrO_2 < HClO_2 < HClO_3$. For a series of oxoacids having the same structure but different central atoms, acid strength increases with increasing electronegativity of the central atom. For elements in the same column on the periodic table, electronegativity decreases as you go down the column, so acid strength decreases as you go down the column. Thus, $HClO_2$ is a stronger acid than $HBrO_2$. Also, for a series of oxoacids with the same central atom, acid strength increases with increasing number of oxygen atoms bonded to the central atom. Thus, $HClO_3$ is a stronger acid than $HClO_2$.

15.121. First, determine the H_3O^+ concentration in the solution with pH 1.831.

$$[H_3O^+] = 10^{-pH} = 10^{-1.831} = 0.014\underline{7}57 \ M$$

Now, use the dilution formula, $M_1V_1 = M_2V_2$, to solve for the final volume.

$$V_2 = \frac{M_1V_1}{M_2} = \frac{(557 \text{ mL})(0.0300 \ M)}{(0.014757 \ M)} = 113\underline{2}.3 \text{ mL} = 1.1\underline{3}2 \text{ L} = 1.13 \text{ L}$$

15.123. In a solution with pH 2.00, the H_3O^+ ion concentration is $1.00 \times 10^{-2} = 0.0100 \ M$. Since HCl is a strong acid, this would also be the concentration of HCl. The mass of HCl required is

$$3.00 \text{ L} \times \frac{0.0100 \text{ mol}}{1 \text{ L}} \times \frac{36.458 \text{ g}}{1 \text{ mol HCl}} = 1.0\underline{9}37 \text{ g HCl}$$

The solution is 37.2 mass percent HCl, so the mass of concentrated hydrochloric acid solution required is

$$\frac{1.097 \text{ g}}{0.372} = 2.9\underline{4}0 = 2.94 \text{ g concentrated HCl}$$

15.125. a. $2HF(l) \rightleftharpoons H_2F^+ + F^-$

   b.   NaF will be a base because F^- is a conjugate base of HF.

   c. $HClO_4 + HF \rightarrow H_2F^+ + ClO_4^-$

   The conjugate acid is H_2F^+.

15.127. The reaction of ammonia with water is given by

$$NH_3(aq) + H_2O(l) \rightleftharpoons NH_4^+(aq) + OH^-(aq)$$

The initial concentration of NH_3 (molar mass 17.03 g/mol) is

$$\text{Molarity} = \frac{4.25 \text{ g NH}_3 \times \dfrac{1 \text{ mol NH}_3}{17.03 \text{ g NH}_3}}{0.2500 \text{ L}} = 0.99\underline{8}2 \ M$$

Since the NH_3 is 0.42% reacted, the concentration of OH^- is

$$[OH^-] = 0.9982 \ M \times 0.0042 = 0.004\underline{1}9 \ M$$

$$pOH = -\log [OH^-] = -\log (0.004\underline{1}9) = 2.3\underline{7}8$$

$$pH = 14.00 - pOH = 14.00 - 2.3\underline{7}8 = 11.6\underline{2}2 = 11.62$$

■ SOLUTIONS TO CUMULATIVE-SKILLS PROBLEMS

15.129. For $(HO)_m YO_n$ acids, acid strength increases with n regardless of the number of OH's. The structure of H_3PO_4 is $(HO)_3PO$; because H_3PO_3 and H_3PO_4 have about the same acidity, H_3PO_3 must also have $n = 1$; thus, $m = 2$. This leaves one H, which must bond to phosphorus, giving a structure of $(HO)_2(O)PH$. Assuming that only two H's react with NaOH, the mass of NaOH that reacts with 1.00 g of H_3PO_3 (PA) is calculated as follows:

$$1.00 \text{ g PA} \times \frac{1 \text{ mol PA}}{81.994 \text{ g PA}} \times \frac{2 \text{ mol NaOH}}{1 \text{ mol PA}} \times \frac{40.00 \text{ g NaOH}}{1 \text{ mol NaOH}} = 0.97\underline{5}6 = 0.976 \text{ g NaOH}$$

15.131. BF_3 acts as a Lewis acid, accepting an electron pair from NH_3:

$$BF_3 + :NH_3 \rightarrow F_3B:NH_3$$

The NH_3 acts as a Lewis base in donating an electron pair to BF_3. When 10.0 g of each are mixed, the BF_3 is the limiting reagent because it has the higher formula mass. The mass of $BF_3:NH_3$ formed is

$$10.0 \text{ g BF}_3 \times \frac{1 \text{ mol BF}_3}{67.81 \text{ g BF}_3} \times \frac{1 \text{ mol BF}_3:NH_3}{1 \text{ mol BF}_3} \times \frac{84.84 \text{ g BF}_3:NH_3}{1 \text{ mol BF}_3:NH_3} = 12.\underline{5}1 = 12.5 \text{ g BF}_3:NH_3$$

CHAPTER 16

Acid-Base Equilibria

■ SOLUTIONS TO EXERCISES

Note on significant figures: If the final answer to a solution needs to be rounded off, it is given first with one nonsignificant figure, and the last significant figure is underlined. The final answer is then rounded to the correct number of significant figures. In multistep problems, intermediate answers are given with at least one nonsignificant figure; however, only the final answer has been rounded off.

16.1. Abbreviate the formula of lactic acid as HL. To solve, assemble a table of starting, change, and equilibrium concentrations.

Conc. (M)	HL + H_2O $\rightleftharpoons$	H_3O^+ +	L^-
Starting	0.025	0	0
Change	$-x$	$+x$	$+x$
Equilibrium	$0.025 - x$	x	x

Substituting into the equilibrium-constant equation gives

$$K_a = \frac{[H_3O^+]\,[L^-]}{[HL]} = \frac{(x)^2}{(0.025-x)}$$

The value of x equals the value of the molarity of the H_3O^+ ion, which can be obtained from the pH:

$$[H_3O^+] = \text{antilog}\,(-pH) = \text{antilog}\,(-2.75) = 0.001\underline{7}8\ M$$

Substitute this value for x into the equation to get

$$K_a = \frac{(x)^2}{(0.025-x)} = \frac{(0.00178)^2}{(0.025-0.00178)} = 1.\underline{3}6 \times 10^{-4} = 1.4 \times 10^{-4}$$

The degree of ionization is

$$\text{Degree of ionization} = \frac{0.00178}{0.025} = 0.071$$

16.2. To solve, assemble a table of starting, change, and equilibrium concentrations. Use HAc as the symbol for acetic acid.

Conc. (M)	HAc + H_2O $\rightleftharpoons$	H_3O^+ +	Ac^-
Starting	0.10	0	0
Change	$-x$	$+x$	$+x$
Equilibrium	$0.10 - x$	x	x

Now, substitute these concentrations and the value of K_a into the equilibrium-constant equation for acid ionization:

$$K_a = \frac{[H_3O^+][Ac^-]}{[HAc]} = \frac{(x)^2}{(0.10-x)} = 1.7 \times 10^{-5}$$

Solve the equation for x, assuming x is much smaller than 0.10, so $(0.10 - x) \cong 0.10$.

$$\frac{(x)^2}{(0.10)} \cong 1.7 \times 10^{-5}$$

$$x^2 = 1.7 \times 10^{-5} \times 0.10 = 1.7 \times 10^{-6}$$

$$x = 0.001\underline{3}0 \ M$$

Check to make sure the assumption that $(0.10 - x) \cong 0.10$ is valid:

$$0.10 - 0.001\underline{3}0 = 0.0\underline{9}87, = 0.10 \text{ (to two significant figures)}$$

The concentrations of hydronium ion and acetate ion are

$$[H_3O^+] = [Ac^-] = x = 0.0013 = 1.3 \times 10^{-3} \ M$$

The pH of the solution is

$$pH = -\log[H_3O^+] = -\log(0.001\underline{3}0) = 2.8\underline{8}4 = 2.88$$

The degree of ionization is

$$\text{Degree of ionization} = \frac{0.00130}{0.10} = 0.01\underline{3}0 = 0.013$$

16.3.   Abbreviate the formula for pyruvic acid as HPy. To solve, assemble a table of starting, change, and equilibrium concentrations:

Conc. (M)	HPy + H$_2$O $\rightleftharpoons$		H$_3$O$^+$ +	Py$^-$
Starting	0.0030		0	0
Change	$-x$		$+x$	$+x$
Equilibrium	$0.0030 - x$		x	x

Substitute the equilibrium concentrations and the value of K_a into the equilibrium-constant expression to get

$$K_a = \frac{[H_3O^+][Py^-]}{[HPy]} = \frac{(x)^2}{(0.0030-x)} = 1.4 \times 10^{-4}$$

Note that the concentration of acid divided by K_a is $0.0030/1.4 \times 10^{-4} = 21$, which is considerably smaller than 100. Thus, you can expect that x cannot be ignored compared with 0.0030. The quadratic formula must be used. Rearrange the preceding equation to put it into the form $ax^2 + bx + c = 0$.

$$x^2 + 1.4 \times 10^{-4} x - 4.20 \times 10^{-7} = 0$$

Substitute into the quadratic formula to get

$$x = \frac{-1.4 \times 10^{-4} \pm \sqrt{(1.4 \times 10^{-4})^2 - 4(-4.20 \times 10^{-7})}}{2} = \frac{-1.4 \times 10^{-4} \pm 1.303 \times 10^{-3}}{2}$$

Using the positive root, $x = [H_3O^+] = 5.\underline{8}1 \times 10^{-4}$ M. Now you can calculate the pH.

$$pH = -\log [H_3O^+] = -\log (5.81 \times 10^{-4}) = 3.2\underline{3}50 = 3.24$$

16.4.   To solve, note that $K_{a_1} = 1.3 \times 10^{-2} \gg K_{a_2} = 6.3 \times 10^{-8}$, and hence the second ionization and K_{a_2} can be ignored. Assemble a table of starting, change, and equilibrium concentrations.

Conc. (M)	$H_2SO_3 + H_2O$	$\rightleftharpoons$	H_3O^+	+	HSO_3^-
Starting	0.25		0		0
Change	$-x$		$+x$		$+x$
Equilibrium	$0.25 - x$		x		x

Substitute into the equilibrium-constant expression for the first ionization.

$$K_{a_1} = \frac{[H_3O^+][HSO_3^-]}{[H_2SO_3]} = \frac{(x)^2}{(0.25 - x)} = 1.3 \times 10^{-2} = 0.013$$

This gives $x^2 + 0.013x - 0.00325 = 0$.

Note that the concentration of acid divided by K_a is $0.25/0.013 = 19$, which is considerably smaller than 100. Thus, you can expect that x cannot be ignored compared with 0.25. Reorganize the above equilibrium-constant expression into the form $ax^2 + bx + c = 0$, and substitute for a, b, and c in the quadratic formula.

$$x = \frac{-0.013 \pm \sqrt{(0.013)^2 - 4(-0.00325)}}{2} = \frac{-0.013 \pm 0.1147}{2}$$

Using the positive root, $x = [H_3O^+] = 0.05\underline{0}87$ M.

$$pH = -\log (0.05\underline{0}87) = 1.2\underline{9}3 = 1.29$$

To calculate $[SO_3^{2-}]$, which will be represented by y, use the second ionization. Assume the starting concentrations of H_3O^+ and HSO_3^- are those from the first equilibrium.

Conc. (M)	$HSO_3^- + H_2O$	$\rightleftharpoons$	H_3O^+	+	SO_3^{2-}
Starting	0.05\underline{0}8		0.05\underline{0}8		0
Change	$-y$		$+y$		$+y$
Equilibrium	$0.05\underline{0}8 - y$		$0.05\underline{0}8 - y$		y

Now, substitute into the K_{a_2} expression for the second ionization.

$$K_{a_2} = \frac{[H_3O^+][SO_3^{2-}]}{[HSO_3^-]} = \frac{(0.0508 + y)(y)}{(0.0508 - y)} = 6.3 \times 10^{-8}$$

Assuming y is much smaller than 0.0508, note that the $(0.0508 + y)$ cancels the $(0.0508 - y)$ term, leaving $y \cong K_{a_2}$, or

$$y = [SO_3^{2-}] \cong 6.3 \times 10^{-8} \ M \text{ (note the assumption that } y \ll 0.0508 \text{ is valid)}$$

16.5.   Convert the pH first to pOH and then to $[OH^-]$:

$$pOH = 14.00 - pH = 14.00 - 9.84 = 4.16$$

$$[OH^-] = \text{antilog}(-4.16) = 6.\underline{9}2 \times 10^{-5} \, M$$

Using the symbol Qu for quinine, assemble a table of starting, change, and equilibrium concentrations.

Conc. (M)	$Qu + H_2O \rightleftharpoons$		HQu^+	+	OH^-
Starting	0.0015		0		0
Change	$-x$		$+x$		$+x$
Equilibrium	$0.0015 - x$		x		x

Note that $x = 6.\underline{9}2 \times 10^{-5}$. Substitute into the equilibrium-constant expression to get

$$K_b = \frac{[HQ^+][OH^-]}{[Qu]} = \frac{(x)^2}{(0.0015 - x)} = \frac{(6.92 \times 10^{-5})^2}{(0.0015 - 6.92 \times 10^{-5})} = 3.\underline{3}46 \times 10^{-6} = 3.3 \times 10^{-6}$$

16.6.   Assemble a table of starting, change, and equilibrium concentrations.

Conc. (M)	$NH_3 + H_2O \rightleftharpoons$		NH_4^+	+	OH^-
Starting	0.20		0		0
Change	$-x$		$+x$		$+x$
Equilibrium	$0.20 - x$		x		x

Assume x is small enough to ignore compared with 0.20. Substitute into the equilibrium-constant expression to get

$$K_b = \frac{[NH_4^+][OH^-]}{[NH_3]} = \frac{(x)^2}{(0.20 - x)} \cong \frac{(x)^2}{(0.20)} = 1.8 \times 10^{-5}$$

Solving for x gives

$$x^2 = (0.20) \times 1.8 \times 10^{-5} = 3.6 \times 10^{-6}$$

$$x = [OH^-] \cong 1.\underline{8}9 \times 10^{-3} \, M \text{ (Note that } x \text{ is negligible compared to 0.20.)}$$

Now calculate the hydronium-ion concentration.

$$[H_3O^+] = \frac{K_w}{[OH^-]} = \frac{1.0 \times 10^{-14}}{1.89 \times 10^{-3}} = 5.\underline{2}9 \times 10^{-12} = 5.3 \times 10^{-12} \, M$$

16.7.   a.   Acidic. NH_4NO_3 is the salt of a weak base (NH_3) and a strong acid (HNO_3), so a solution of NH_4NO_3 is acidic because of the hydrolysis of NH_4^+.

b.   Neutral. KNO_3 is the salt of a strong base (KOH) and a strong acid (HNO_3), so a solution of NH_4NO_3 is neutral because none of the ions hydrolyze.

c.   Acidic. $Al(NO_3)_3$ is the salt of a weak base [$Al(OH)_3$] and a strong acid (HNO_3), so a solution of $Al(NO_3)_3$ is acidic because of the hydrolysis of Al^{3+}.

16.8. a. Calculate K_b of the F^- ion from the K_a of its conjugate acid, HF:

$$K_b = \frac{K_w}{K_a} = \frac{1.0 \times 10^{-14}}{6.8 \times 10^{-4}} = 1.\underline{4}7 \times 10^{-11} = 1.5 \times 10^{-11}$$

b. Calculate K_a of $C_6H_5NH_3^+$ from the K_b of its conjugate base, $C_6H_5NH_2$:

$$K_a = \frac{K_w}{K_b} = \frac{1.0 \times 10^{-14}}{4.2 \times 10^{-10}} = 2.\underline{3}8 \times 10^{-5} = 2.4 \times 10^{-5}$$

16.9. Assemble the usual table, writing HBen for benzoic acid and Ben$^-$ for the benzoate ion. Let 0.015 $- x$ equal the equilibrium concentration of the benzoate anion.

Conc. (M)	Ben$^-$ + H$_2$O $\rightleftharpoons$	HBen +	OH$^-$
Starting	0.015	0	0
Change	$-x$	$+x$	$+x$
Equilibrium	$0.015 - x$	x	x

Calculate K_b for the benzoate ion from K_a for HBen

$$K_b = \frac{K_w}{K_a} = \frac{1.0 \times 10^{-14}}{6.3 \times 10^{-5}} = 1.\underline{5}8 \times 10^{-10}$$

Substitute into the equilibrium-constant expression. Assume x is much smaller than 0.015.

$$K_b = \frac{[\text{HBen}][\text{OH}^-]}{[\text{Ben}^-]} = \frac{(x)^2}{(0.015 - x)} \cong \frac{(x)^2}{(0.015)} = 1.\underline{5}8 \times 10^{-10}$$

$x = [\text{HBen}] = [\text{OH}^-] \cong 1.\underline{5}39 \times 10^{-6} \, M$ (x is negligible compared to 0.015.)

Thus, the concentration of benzoic acid in the solution is $1.5 \times 10^{-6} \, M$. The pH is

$$\text{pOH} = -\log[\text{OH}^-] = -\log(1.539 \times 10^{-6}) = 5.8\underline{1}2$$

$$\text{pH} = 14.00 - 5.812 = 8.1\underline{8}8 = 8.19$$

It is noteworthy to point out that the hydroxide ion provided by the autoionization of water has been ignored here. Pure water provides $10^{-7} \, M$ hydroxide ion. This is ~6% of the amount calculated in the problem. If $[\text{OH}^-]_{starting}$ is set at $10^{-7} \, M$ a more precise value of $\times$ results, i.e., $x = 1.\underline{4}9 \times 10^{-6} \, M$. This results in the same reported concentration for benzoic acid but a slightly higher pH value of 8.20.

16.10. Assemble the usual table, using starting $[\text{H}_3\text{O}^+] = 0.20 \, M$ from $0.20 \, M$ HCl and letting HFo symbolize HCHO$_2$.

Conc. (M)	HFo + H$_2$O $\rightleftharpoons$	H$_3$O$^+$ +	Fo$^-$
Starting	0.10	0.20	0
Change	$-x$	$+x$	$+x$
Equilibrium	$0.10 - x$	$0.20 + x$	x

Assume x is negligible compared to 0.10 M and 0.20 M, and substitute into the equilibrium-constant expression to get

$$K_a = \frac{[\text{H}_3\text{O}^+][\text{Fo}^-]}{[\text{HFo}]} = \frac{(0.20 + x)(x)}{(0.10 - x)} \cong \frac{(0.20)(x)}{(0.10)} = 1.7 \times 10^{-4}$$

$$x = [\text{Fo}^-] = 8.\underline{50} \times 10^{-5} = 8.5 \times 10^{-5} \ M$$

The degree of ionization is

$$\text{Degree of ionization} = \frac{8.50 \times 10^{-5}}{0.10} = 8.\underline{50} \times 10^{-4} = 8.5 \times 10^{-4}$$

16.11. Assemble the usual table, using a starting $[\text{CHO}_2^-]$ of 0.018 M from 0.018 M NaCHO_2 and symbolizing HCHO_2 as HFo and the CHO_2^- anion as Fo$^-$.

Conc. (M)	HFo + H$_2$O	$\rightleftharpoons$	H$_3$O$^+$ +	Fo$^-$
Starting	0.025		0	0.018
Change	$-x$		$+x$	$+x$
Equilibrium	$0.025 - x$		x	$0.018 + x$

Substitute into the equilibrium-constant expression. Assume x is negligible compared to 0.025 M and 0.018 M.

$$K_a = \frac{[\text{H}_3\text{O}^+][\text{Fo}^-]}{[\text{HFo}]} = \frac{(0.018 + x)(x)}{(0.025 - x)} \cong \frac{(0.018)(x)}{(0.025)} = 1.7 \times 10^{-4}$$

$$x = [\text{H}_3\text{O}^+] \cong 2.\underline{36} \times 10^{-4} \ M \ \text{(note the validity of the assumptions)}$$

The pH can now be calculated.

$$\text{pH} = -\log[\text{H}_3\text{O}^+] = -\log(2.36 \times 10^{-4}) = 3.6\underline{27} = 3.63$$

16.12. Let HOAc represent $\text{HC}_2\text{H}_3\text{O}_2$ and OAc$^-$ represent $\text{C}_2\text{H}_3\text{O}_2^-$. The total volume of the buffer is

$$\text{Total volume} = 30.0 \ \text{mL} + 70.0 \ \text{mL} = 100.0 \ \text{mL} = 0.1000 \ \text{L}$$

The moles of HOAc and OAc$^-$ in the buffer are

$$\text{mol HOAc} = 0.15 \ M \times 0.0300 \ \text{L} = 0.00450 \ \text{mol}$$

$$\text{mol OAc}^- = 0.20 \ M \times 0.0700 \ \text{L} = 0.0140 \ \text{mol}$$

The concentrations of HOAc and OAc$^-$ in the buffer are

$$[\text{HOAc}] = \frac{0.00450 \ \text{mol}}{0.1000 \ \text{L}} = 0.04\underline{50} \ M$$

$$[\text{OAc}^-] = \frac{0.0140 \ \text{mol}}{0.1000 \ \text{L}} = 0.1\underline{40} \ M$$

Now, assemble these starting concentrations into a table.

Conc. (M)	HOAc + H$_2$O	$\rightleftharpoons$	H$_3$O+ +	OAc$^-$
Starting	0.0450		0	0.140
Change	$-x$		$+x$	$+x$
Equilibrium	$0.0450 - x$		x	$0.140 + x$

Substitute the equilibrium concentrations into the equilibrium-constant expression; then assume x is negligible compared to the starting concentrations of both HOAc and OAc⁻.

$$K_a = \frac{[H_3O^+][OAc^-]}{[HOAc]} = \frac{(0.140 + x)(x)}{(0.0450 - x)} \cong \frac{(0.140)(x)}{(0.0450)} = 1.7 \times 10^{-5}$$

$$x = [H_3O^+] \cong 5.\underline{4}6 \times 10^{-6}\ M$$

You can now calculate the pH.

$$pH = -\log[H_3O^+] = -\log(5.46 \times 10^{-6}) = 5.2\underline{6}2 = 5.26$$

16.13. First, do the stoichiometric calculation. From Exercise 16.11, [HFo] = 0.025 M and [Fo⁻] = 0.018 M. In 1 L of buffer, there are 0.025 mol HFo and 0.018 mol Fo⁻. The moles of OH⁻ (equal to moles of NaOH) added are

(0.10 M) × 0.0500 L = 0.00500 mol OH⁻

The total volume of solution is

Total volume = 1 L + 0.0500 L = 1.0500 L

After reaction with the OH⁻, the moles of HFo and Fo⁻ remaining in the solution are

mol HFo = (0.025 − 0.00500) mol = 0.0200 mol

mol Fo⁻ = (0.018 + 0.00500) mol = 0.0230 mol

The concentrations are

$$[HFo] = \frac{0.0200\ mol}{1.0500\ L} = 0.01\underline{9}0\ M$$

$$[Fo^-] = \frac{0.0230\ mol}{1.0500\ L} = 0.02\underline{1}9\ M$$

Now account for the ionization of HFo to Fo⁻ at equilibrium by assembling the usual table.

Conc. (M)	HFo + H₂O ⇌	H₃O⁺ +	OAc⁻
Starting	0.0190	0	0.0219
Change	−x	+x	+x
Equilibrium	0.0190 − x	x	0.0219 + x

Assume x is negligible compared to 0.0190 M and 0.0219 M, and substitute into the equilibrium-constant expression to get

$$K_a = \frac{[H_3O^+][Fo^-]}{[HFo]} = \frac{(0.0219 + x)(x)}{(0.0190 - x)} \cong \frac{(0.0219)(x)}{(0.0190)} = 1.7 \times 10^{-4}$$

$$x = [H_3O^+] = 1.\underline{4}7 \times 10^{-4}\ M$$

Now, calculate the pH.

$$pH = -\log[H_3O^+] = -\log(1.47 \times 10^{-4}) = 3.8\underline{3}1 = 3.83 \text{ (as expected, the pH increases)}$$

16.14. All the OH^- reacts with the H_3O^+ from HCl. Calculate the stoichiometric amounts of OH^- and H_3O^+.

$$mol\ H_3O^+ = (0.10\ mol/L) \times 0.025\ L = 0.0025\ mol$$

$$mol\ OH^- = (0.10\ mol\ NaOH/L) \times 0.015\ L = 0.0015\ mol$$

The total volume of solution is

$$Total\ volume = 0.025\ L + 0.015\ L = 0.040\ L$$

Subtract the moles of OH^- from the moles of H_3O^+, and divide by the total volume to get the concentration of H_3O^+.

$$mol\ H_3O^+\ left = (0.0025 - 0.0015)\ mol = 0.0010\ mol$$

$$[H_3O^+] = \frac{0.0010\ mol}{0.040\ L} = 0.02\underline{5}0\ M$$

Now calculate the pH.

$$pH = -\log[H_3O^+] = -\log(0.0250) = 1.6\underline{0}2 = 1.60$$

16.15. At the equivalence point, the solution will contain NaF. The molar amount of F^- is equal to the molar amount of HF and is calculated as follows:

$$(0.10\ mol\ HF/L) \times 0.025\ L = 0.0025\ mol\ F^-$$

The volume of 0.15 M NaOH added and the total volume of solution are calculated next.

$$Volume\ NaOH = \frac{M_{acid}V_{acid}}{M_{base}} = \frac{(0.10\ M)(25\ mL)}{0.15\ M} = 1\underline{6}.6\ mL$$

$$Total\ volume = 25\ mL + 16.6\ mL = 4\underline{1}.6\ mL = 0.04\underline{1}6\ L$$

The concentration of F^- at the equivalence point can now be calculated.

$$[F^-] = \frac{0.0025\ mol}{0.0416\ L} = 0.06\underline{0}0\ M$$

Next, consider the hydrolysis of F^-. Start by calculating the hydrolysis constant of F^- from the K_a of its conjugate acid, HF.

$$K_b = \frac{K_w}{K_a} = \frac{1.0 \times 10^{-14}}{6.8 \times 10^{-4}} = 1.\underline{4}7 \times 10^{-11}$$

Now, assemble the usual table of concentrations, assume x is negligible compared to 0.0600, and calculate $[OH^-]$.

Conc. (M)	F + H$_2$O	$\rightleftharpoons$	HF	+	OH$^-$
Starting	0.0600		0		0
Change	$-x$		$+x$		$+x$
Equilibrium	$0.0600 - x$		x		x

Substitute into the equilibrium-constant expression to get

$$K_b = \frac{[HF][OH^-]}{[F^-]} = \frac{(x)^2}{(0.0600-x)} \cong \frac{(x)^2}{(0.0600)} = 1.\underline{4}7 \times 10^{-11}$$

$$x = [OH^-] = 9.\underline{3}9 \times 10^{-7}\ M$$

Finally, calculate the pOH and then the pH.

$$pOH = -\log [OH^-] = -\log (9.\underline{3}9 \times 10^{-7}) = 6.0\underline{2}6$$

$$pH = 14.00 - 6.0\underline{2}6 = 7.9\underline{7}4 = 7.97$$

It is noteworthy to point out that the hydroxide ion provided by the autoionization of water has been ignored here. Pure water provides 10^{-7} M hydroxide ion. This is ~11% of the amount calculated above, i.e., water provides a significant contribution to hydroxide concentration. If $[OH^-]_{starting}$ is set at 10^{-7} M a more precise value of $\times$ results, i.e., $x = 8.\underline{9}0 \times 10^{-7}$ M. This results in $[OH^-] = x + 10^{-7} = 9.90 \times 10^{-7}$ and a slightly higher pH of 8.00.

16.16.   a.   Assemble the usual table of concentrations.

Conc. (M)	$NH_3 + H_2O$	$\rightleftharpoons$	NH_4^+	$+$	OH^-
Starting	0.200		0		0
Change	$-x$		$+x$		$+x$
Equilibrium	$0.200 - x$		x		x

Now substitute into the equilibrium-constant expression, assume x is negligible compared to 0.200 M, and calculate $[OH^-]$.

$$K_b = \frac{(x)^2}{(0.200 - x)} = \frac{(x)^2}{(0.200)} = 1.8 \times 10^{-5}$$

$$x = [OH^-] = 1.\underline{8}97 \times 10^{-3} \ M$$

Finally, calculate the pOH and then the pH.

$$pOH = -\log [OH^-] = -\log (1.\underline{8}97 \times 10^{-3}) = 2.7\underline{2}1$$

$$pH = 14.00 - 2.7\underline{2}1 = 11.2\underline{7}8 = 11.28$$

b.   At the half-way point in the titration of a weak base with a strong acid, $pOH = pK_b$.

$$pOH = -\log (1.8 \times 10^{-5}) = 4.7\underline{4}4$$

$$pH = 14.00 - pOH = 14.00 - 4.744 = 9.2\underline{5}5 = 9.26$$

c.   At the equivalence point, the solution will contain NH_4Cl. The molar amount of NH_4^+ is equal to the molar amount of NH_3 and is calculated as follows:

$$(0.200 \ M) \times 0.0800 \ L = 0.016\underline{0}0 \ mol \ NH_4^+$$

The volume of 0.100 M HCl added and the total volume of solution are calculated next.

$$\text{Volume HCl} = \frac{M_{base}V_{base}}{M_{acid}} = \frac{(0.200 \ M)(80.0 \ mL)}{0.100 \ M} = 16\underline{0}.0 \ mL$$

Total volume = 80.0 mL + 160.0 mL = 24\underline{0}.0 mL = 0.24\underline{0}0 L

The concentration of NH_4^+ at the equivalence point can now be calculated.

$$[NH_4^+] = \frac{0.01600 \ mol}{0.2400 \ L} = 0.066\underline{6}6 \ M$$

Next, consider the hydrolysis of NH_4^+. Start by calculating the hydrolysis constant of NH_4^+ from the K_b of its conjugate base, NH_3.

$$K_a = \frac{K_w}{K_b} = \frac{1.0 \times 10^{-14}}{1.8 \times 10^{-5}} = 5.\underline{5}6 \times 10^{-10}$$

Now, assemble the usual table of concentrations, assume x is negligible compared to 0.06666, and calculate $[H_3O^+]$.

Conc. (M)	$NH_4^+ + H_2O$	$\rightleftharpoons$	NH_3	$+$	H_3O^+
Starting	0.06666		0		0
Change	$-x$		$+x$		$+x$
Equilibrium	$0.06666 - x$		x		x

Substitute into the equilibrium-constant expression to get

$$K_a = \frac{[NH_3][H_3O^+]}{[NH_4^+]} = \frac{(x)^2}{(0.06666 - x)} \cong \frac{(x)^2}{(0.06666)} = 5.\underline{5}6 \times 10^{-10}$$

$$x = [H_3O^+] = 6.\underline{0}8 \times 10^{-6}\ M$$

Finally, calculate the pH.

$$pH = -\log[H_3O^+] = -\log(6.08 \times 10^{-6}) = 5.2\underline{1}5 = 5.22$$

d. Calculate the moles of acid added.

$$(0.100\ M) \times 0.175\ L = 0.017\underline{5}0\ mol$$

The moles of base added are the same as for part c, 0.016\underline{0}0 mol. The excess moles of acid and the total volume are

Moles of acid remaining $= 0.01750\ mol - 0.01600\ mol = 0.001\underline{5}0\ mol$

$$V = 80.0\ mL + 175\ mL = 25\underline{5}.0\ mL = 0.25\underline{5}0\ L$$

The $[H_3O^+]$ concentration and the pH are

$$[H_3O^+] = \frac{0.00150\ mol}{0.2550\ L} = 5.\underline{8}82 \times 10^{-3}\ M$$

$$pH = -\log(5.882 \times 10^{-3}) = 2.2\underline{3}0 = 2.23$$

■ ANSWERS TO CONCEPT CHECKS

16.1. You would probably guess that the pH's of the acid solutions depend on their respective K_a's; the larger the K_a, the greater the acidity, or the lower the pH. We can put this on a firm basis by looking at the acid-ionization equilibrium. An acid, HA, ionizes in water as follows:

$$HA(aq) + H_2O(l) \rightleftharpoons H_3O^+(aq) + A^-(aq)$$

The corresponding equilibrium constant, K_a, equals $[H_3O^+][A^-]/[HA]$. When you start with the same concentration of HA, the concentration of HA in solution is essentially the same for each acid. Also, $[H_3O^+] = [A^-]$. This means K_a is proportional to $[H_3O^+]^2$, or $pH = -\log[H_3O^+]$ is proportional to $-\log K_a$. Therefore, the larger the K_a, the lower the pH. As an example, compare two acids, one with K_a equal to 10^{-5} and the other with K_a equal to 10^{-4}. The corresponding $-\log K_a$ values are 5 and 4, respectively. The second acid (the one with the greater K_a) would have the lower pH. If you look at Table 16.1, the acid with the largest K_a of those listed in the problem statement is HF. So the ranking from highest to lowest pH is HCN > $HC_2H_3O_2$ > HNO_2 > HF.

16.2. By examining the contents of the beaker, you see there are three different species present: the ions BH^+ and OH^- and unreacted B molecules. This represents a weak base. The ionization reaction for this base is

$$B(aq) + H_2O(l) \rightleftharpoons BH^+(aq) + OH^-(aq)$$

16.3. Ammonia, NH_3, is a weak base; the other compounds are salts. You can decide the acidity or basicity of salt solutions by noting whether the corresponding acid and base are strong or weak. For example, NH_4Br is the salt of a weak base (NH_3) and a strong acid (HBr), so the salt is acidic. Similarly, NaF is basic (it is the salt of a strong base, NaOH, and a weak acid, HF). NaCl is neutral. This means two of the solutions are basic (NH_3 and NaF), one solution is neutral (NaCl), and the other is acidic (NH_4Br). Although a salt might be as basic as NH_3, this occurs only when the acid from which the salt formed is quite weak (for example, NaCN is quite basic). Thus, the solution with highest pH is 0.1 M NH_3 (a), and the solution of lowest pH is 0.1 M NH_4Br (b).

16.4. Addition of $NaNO_3$ or NaCl do not add any common ions nor do the added ions react with any of the species in the given equation. Therefore these salt solutions will not affect the degree of ionization. On the other hand, KNO_2 provides the NO_2^- and HNO_3 provides the H_3O^+ ion. Both of these situations involve the addition of a product ion in the given equation. Therefore, by LeChâtelier's principle, addition of either KNO_2 or HNO_3 will suppress the ionization and reduce the degree of ionization of HNO_2.

16.5. The amount of any substance in a solution is proportional to the volume times molarity. Let's look at each solution

   a. The 1.5 mL of 1 M HCl just neutralizes 15 mL of 0.1 M NaOH, giving a solution of NaCl. Thus, the pH of the original solution changes from very basic to neutral (pH = 7) after the addition of HCl.

   b. The solution of acetic acid changes from weakly acidic to strongly acidic with the addition of HCl.

   c. Equal amounts of NaOH and $HC_2H_3O_2$ in the original solution exactly neutralize each other to produce the salt $NaC_2H_3O_2$, which is slightly basic. The addition of the strong acid HCl gives an acidic solution.

   d. The 30 mL of NaOH reacts with 30 mL of $HC_2H_3O_2$ to give the salt $NaC_2H_3O_2$, leaving an equal amount of the corresponding acid, $HC_2H_3O_2$. The result is a buffer solution. The addition of HCl to the buffer does not change the pH appreciably. (This is true as long as the amount of added acid does not overwhelm the capacity of the buffer. In this case, it does not. The amount of acid and base conjugates in the buffer is twice the amount of added acid.)

   Only d does not change appreciably in pH.

16.6. a. When two formula units of NaOH are added to the beaker on the left, a reaction occurs consuming two HA molecules and forming two A^- ions. This results in a solution with two HA molecules and five A^- ions, which is depicted in beaker Y.

   b. Since the original buffer contains three A^- ions, three HCl molecules could be added before the buffer capacity would be exceeded.

c.   The beaker would contain seven HA molecules. In addition, the extra HCl molecules would dissociate into H_3O^+ and Cl^- ions. This could be represented as follows:

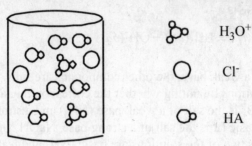

H_3O^+

Cl^-

HA

■ ANSWERS TO SELF-ASSESSMENT AND REVIEW QUESTIONS

16.1.   The equation is

$$HCN(aq) + H_2O(l) \rightleftharpoons H_3O^+(aq) + CN^-(aq)$$

The equilibrium-constant expression is

$$K_a = \frac{[H_3O^+][CN^-]}{[HCN]}$$

16.2.   HCN is the weakest acid. Its K_a of 4.9×10^{-10} is less than the K_a of 1.7×10^{-5} of $HC_2H_3O_2$; $HClO_4$ is a strong acid, of course.

16.3.   Both methods involve direct measurement of the concentrations of the hydronium ion and the anion of the weak acid and calculation of the concentration of the un-ionized acid. All concentrations are substituted into the K_a expression to obtain a value for K_a. In the first method, the electrical conductivity of a solution of the weak acid is measured. The conductivity is proportional to the concentration of the hydronium ion and anion. In the second method, the pH of a known starting concentration of weak acid is measured. The pH is converted to $[H_3O^+]$, which will be equal to [anion].

16.4.   The degree of ionization of a weak acid decreases as the concentration of the acid added to the solution increases. Compared to low concentrations, at high concentrations, there is less water for each weak acid molecule to react with as the weak acid ionizes:

$$HA(aq) + H_2O(l) \rightleftharpoons H_3O^+(aq) + A^-(aq)$$

16.5.   You can neglect x if $C_a/K_a \geq 100$. In this case, $C_a/K_a = [(0.0010\ M \div 6.8 \times 10^{-4}) = 1.47]$, which is significantly less than 100, and x cannot be neglected in the $(0.0010 - x)$ term. This says the degree of ionization is significant.

16.6.   The ionization of the first H_3O^+ is

$$H_2PHO_3(aq) + H_2O(l) \rightleftharpoons H_3O^+(aq) + HPHO_3^-(aq)$$

The equilibrium-constant expression is

$$K_{a_1} = \frac{[H_3O^+][HPHO_3^-]}{[H_2PHO_3]}$$

The ionization of the second H_3O^+ is

$$HPHO_3^-(aq) + H_2O(l) \rightleftharpoons H_3O^+(aq) + PHO_3^{2-}(aq)$$

The equilibrium-constant expression is

$$K_{a_2} = \frac{[H_3O^+][PHO_3^{2-}]}{[HPHO_3^-]}$$

16.7.   As shown in Example 16.4, the concentration of a 2– anion of a polyprotic acid in a solution of the diprotic acid alone is approximately equal to the value of K_{a_2}. For oxalic acid, begin by noting that $[H_3O^+] \cong [HC_2O_4^-]$. Then, substitute $[H_3O^+]$ for the $[HC_2O_4^-]$ term in the equilibrium-constant expression for K_{a_2}:

$$K_{a_2} = \frac{[H_3O^+][C_2O_4^{2-}]}{[HC_2O_4^-]} \cong \frac{[H_3O^+][C_2O_4^{2-}]}{[H_3O^+]} = [C_2O_4^{2-}]$$

16.8.   The balanced chemical equation for the ionization of aniline is

$$C_6H_5NH_2(aq) + H_2O(l) \rightleftharpoons C_6H_5NH_3^+(aq) + OH^-(aq)$$

The equilibrium-constant equation, or expression for K_b, is defined without an $[H_2O]$ term; this term is included in the value for K_b, as discussed in Section 16.3. The expression is

$$K_b = \frac{[C_6H_5NH_3^+][OH^-]}{[C_6H_5NH_2]}$$

16.9.   First, decide whether any of the three is a strong base. Because all the molecules are among the nitrogen-containing weak bases listed in Table 16.2, none is a strong base. Next, recognize that the greater the $[OH^-]$, the stronger the weak base. Because $[OH^-]$ can be calculated from the square root of the product of K_b and concentration, the larger the K_b, the greater the $[OH^-]$ and the stronger the weak base. Thus, CH_3NH_2 is the strongest of these three weak bases because its K_b is the largest.

16.10. The solution of anilinium chloride is acidic. Anilinium chloride is a salt that contains the anilinium ion, $C_6H_5NH_3^+$, and the Cl^- ion. The chloride ion does not hydrolyze because it could form only HCl, a strong acid. The anilinium ion does hydrolyze as follows:

$$C_6H_5NH_3^+ + H_2O(l) \rightleftharpoons C_6H_5NH_2 + H_3O^+$$

The equilibrium-constant expression for this reaction is

$$K_a = \frac{[C_6H_5NH_2]\,[H_3O^+]}{[C_6H_5NH_3^+]}$$

Obtain the value for K_a by calculating the value of K_w/K_b, where K_b is the ionization constant for aniline, $C_6H_5NH_2$.

16.11. The common-ion effect is the shift in an ionic equilibrium caused by the addition of a solute that furnishes an ion that is common to, or takes part in, the equilibrium. If the equilibrium involves the ionization of a weak acid, then the common ion is usually the anion formed by the ionization of the weak acid. If the equilibrium involves the ionization of a weak base, then the common ion is usually the cation formed by the ionization of the weak base. An example is the addition of F^- ion (as NaF) to a solution of the weak acid HF, which ionizes as shown below:

$$HF(aq) + H_2O(l) \rightleftharpoons H_3O^+(aq) + F^-(aq)$$

The effect of adding F^- to this equilibrium is that it causes a shift in the equilibrium composition to the left. The additional F^- reacts with H_3O^+, lowering its concentration and raising the concentration of HF.

16.12. The addition of CH_3NH_3Cl to 0.10 M CH_3NH_2 exerts a common-ion effect that causes the equilibrium below to exhibit a shift in composition to the left:

$$CH_3NH_2\,(aq) + H_2O(l) \rightleftharpoons CH_3NH_3^+(aq) + OH^-(aq)$$

This shift lowers the equilibrium concentration of the OH^- ion, which increases the $[H_3O^+]$. An increase in $[H_3O^+]$ lowers the pH below 11.8. The shift in composition to the left occurs according to Le Châtelier's principle, which states that a system shifts to counteract any change in composition.

16.13. A buffer is most often a solution of a mixture of two substances that is able to resist pH changes when limited amounts of acid or base are added to it. A buffer must contain a weak acid and its conjugate (weak) base. Strong acids and/or bases cannot form effective buffers because a buffer acts by converting H_3O^+ (strong acid) to the un-ionized (weak) buffer acid and by converting OH^- (strong base) to the un-ionized (weak) buffer base. An example of a buffer pair is a mixture of H_2CO_3 and HCO_3^-, the principal buffer in the blood.

16.14. The capacity of a buffer is the amount of acid or base with which the buffer can react before exhibiting a significant pH change. (A significant change in blood pH might mean 0.01−0.02 pH unit; for other systems a significant change might mean 0.5 pH unit.) A high-capacity buffer might be of the type discussed for Figure 16.11: 1 mol of buffer acid and 1 mol of buffer base. A low-capacity buffer might involve quite a bit less than these amounts: 0.01−0.05 mol of buffer acid and buffer base.

16.15. The pH of a weak base before titration is relatively high, around pH 10 for a 0.1 M solution of a typical weak base. As a strong acid titrant is added, the $[OH^-]$ decreases, and the pH decreases. At 50% neutralization, a buffer of equal amounts of acid and base is formed. The $[OH^-]$ equals the K_b, or the pOH equals the pK_b. The equivalence point is the point in a titration when a stoichiometric amount of reactant has been added. At the equivalence point, the pH is governed by the hydrolysis of the salt of the weak base formed and is usually in the pH 4−6 region. After the equivalence point, the pH decreases to a level just greater than the pH of the strong acid titrant.

16.16. If the pH is 8.0, an indicator that changes color in the basic region would be needed. Of the indicators mentioned in the text, phenolphthalein (pH 8.2–10.0) and thymol blue would work. In actual practice, cresol red (pH 7.2–8.8) would be the best choice because the pH should be closer to the middle of the range than to one end.

16.17. The answer is a, NaF.

16.18. The answer is d, slightly acidic.

16.19. The answer is a, H_2S.

16.20. The answer is d, 5.05.

■ ANSWERS TO CONCEPTUAL PROBLEMS

16.23. A solution of the weak acid, HA, will contain hydronium ions (H_3O^+) and anions (A^-) in equal amounts, as well as some undissociated acid (HA) molecules. This is represented by the solution in container A, which contains six HA molecules, two H_3O^+ ions, and two A^- ions. The solution in container B contains eight HA molecules and represents an undissociated acid. In container C, all of the HA molecules have dissociated, so this represents a strong acid.

16.25. a.   When HF is dissolved in water, the F^- hydrolyzes. The reaction is

$$HF(aq) + H_2O(l) \rightleftharpoons H_3O^+(aq) + F^-(aq)$$

b.   When NaF is dissolved in water, F^- hydrolyzes. The reaction is

$$F^-(aq) + H_2O(l) \rightleftharpoons HF(aq) + OH^-(aq)$$

c.   When $C_6H_5NH_2$ is dissolved in water, the following reaction occurs:

$$C_6H_5NH_2(aq) + H_2O(l) \rightleftharpoons C_6H_5NH_3^+(aq) + OH^-(aq)$$

d.   When $C_6H_5NH_3Cl$ is dissolved in water, $C_6H_5NH_3^+$ hydrolyzes. The reaction is

$$C_6H_5NH_3^+(aq) + H_2O(l) \rightleftharpoons C_6H_5NH_2(aq) + H_3O^+(aq)$$

16.27. A solution of rantidine hydrochloride should be acidic. Let Ran represent rantidine. Then RanHCl is the chloride salt, rantidinium chloride. The cation rantidinium, $RanH^+$, should hydrolyze according to the equation

$$RanH^+(aq) + H_2O(l) \rightleftharpoons Ran(aq) + H_3O^+(aq)$$

16.29. To prepare a buffer solution that has a pH equal to the pK_a value of the acid, you need equal amounts of acid and conjugate base in the solution. The easiest way to make the buffer is to mix equal volumes of equal molar solutions of HA and NaA. Thus, mix 100 mL of 0.10 M NaA with the 100 mL of 0.10 M HA to prepare the buffer.

16.31. a.   First, since the pH of the solution is less than 7 at the beginning of the titration and rises slightly before leveling off a bit midway to the equivalence point, you can conclude that a weak acid is being titrated with a base.

b.   The pH of the equivalence point is about 8.5. This is due to the hydrolysis of the weak conjugate base generated from the weak acid.

c.   You need to pick an indicator that changes color in the pH range of about 7 to 10. Therefore, thymol blue or phenolphthalein would work fine for this titration.

■ SOLUTIONS TO PRACTICE PROBLEMS

Note on significant figures: If the final answer to a solution needs to be rounded off, it is given first with one nonsignificant figure, and the last significant figure is underlined. The final answer is then rounded to the correct number of significant figures. In multistep problems, intermediate answers are given with at least one nonsignificant figure; however, only the final answer has been rounded off.

16.33. a. $HBrO(aq) + H_2O(l) \rightleftharpoons H_3O^+(aq) + BrO^-(aq)$

b. $HClO_2(aq) + H_2O(l) \rightleftharpoons H_3O^+(aq) + ClO_2^-(aq)$

c. $HNO_2(aq) + H_2O(l) \rightleftharpoons H_3O^+(aq) + NO_2^-(aq)$

d. $HCN(aq) + H_2O(l) \rightleftharpoons H_3O^+(aq) + CN^-(aq)$

16.35.   HAc will be used throughout as an abbreviation for acrylic acid and Ac$^-$ for the acrylate ion. At the start, the H_3O^+ from the self-ionization of water is so small it is approximately zero. Once the acrylic acid solution is prepared, some of the 0.10 M HAc ionizes to H_3O^+ and Ac$^-$. Then, let x equal the mol/L of HAc that ionize, forming x mol/L of H_3O^+ and x mol/L of Ac$^-$ and leaving $(0.10 - x)$ M HAc in solution. We can summarize the situation in tabular form:

Conc. (M)	$HAc + H_2O$	$\rightleftharpoons$	H_3O^+	+	Ac^-
Starting	0.10		0		0
Change	$-x$		$+x$		$+x$
Equilibrium	$0.10 - x$		x		x

The equilibrium-constant expression is

$$K_a = \frac{[H_3O^+][Ac^-]}{[HAc]} = \frac{x^2}{(0.10 - x)}$$

The value of x can be obtained from the pH of the solution:

$$x = [H_3O^+] = \text{antilog} (-pH) = \text{antilog} (-2.63) = 2.3\underline{4} \times 10^{-3} = 0.0023\underline{4} \ M$$

Note that $(0.10 - x) = (0.10 - 0.00234) = 0.09766$, which is significantly different from 0.10, so x cannot be ignored in the calculation.

Thus, we substitute for x in both the numerator and the denominator to obtain the value of K_a:

$$K_a = \frac{x^2}{(0.10 - x)} = \frac{(0.00234)^2}{(0.10 - 0.00234)} = 5.\underline{6}27 \times 10^{-5} = 5.6 \times 10^{-5}$$

16.37. To solve, assemble a table of starting, change, and equilibrium concentrations. Use HBo as the symbol for boric acid and Bo⁻ as the symbol for $B(OH)_4^-$.

Conc. (M)	HBo + H_2O	$\rightleftharpoons$	H_3O^+	+	Bo⁻
Starting	0.015		0		0
Change	$-x$		$+x$		$+x$
Equilibrium	$0.015 - x$		x		x

The value of x equals the value of the molarity of the H_3O^+ ion, which can be obtained from the equilibrium-constant expression.

Substitute into the equilibrium-constant expression, and solve for x.

$$K_a = \frac{[H_3O^+][Bo^-]}{[HBo]} = \frac{(x)^2}{(0.015-x)} = 5.9 \times 10^{-10}$$

Solve the equation for x, assuming x is much smaller than 0.015.

$$\frac{(x)^2}{(0.015-x)} \cong \frac{(x)^2}{(0.015)} = 5.9 \times 10^{-10}$$

$$x^2 = 5.9 \times 10^{-10} \times (0.015) = 8.85 \times 10^{-12}$$

$$x = [H_3O^+] = 2.97 \times 10^{-6}\,M$$

Check to make sure the assumption that $(0.015 - x) \cong 0.015$ is valid:

$$0.015 - (2.97 \times 10^{-6}) = 0.014997, \text{ or } \cong 0.015 \text{ to two sig. figs.}$$

$$pH = -\log[H_3O^+] = -\log(2.97 \times 10^{-6}) = 5.527 = 5.53$$

The degree of ionization is

$$\text{Degree of ionization} = \frac{2.97 \times 10^{-6}}{(0.015)} = 0.000198 = 0.00020 = 2.0 \times 10^{-4}$$

16.39. To solve, assemble a table of starting, change, and equilibrium concentrations. Use HPaba as a symbol for p-aminobenzoic acid (PABA), and use Paba⁻ as the symbol for the 1− anion.

Conc. (M)	HPaba + H_2O	$\rightleftharpoons$	H_3O^+	+	Paba⁻
Starting	0.055		0		0
Change	$-x$		$+x$		$+x$
Equilibrium	$0.055 - x$		x		x

Write the equilibrium-constant expression in terms of chemical symbols, and then substitute the terms x and $(0.055 - x)$:

$$K_a = \frac{[H_3O^+][Paba^-]}{[HPaba]} = \frac{(x)^2}{(0.055-x)} = 2.2 \times 10^{-5}$$

Solve the equation for x, assuming x is much smaller than 0.055.

$$x^2 = (2.2 \times 10^{-5}) \times 0.055 = 1.21 \times 10^{-6}$$

$$x = [H_3O^+] = [Paba^-] \cong 1.10 \times 10^{-3} = 0.0011 = 1.1 \times 10^{-3}\,M$$

Check to make sure the assumption that $(0.055 - x) \cong 0.055$ is valid.

$$0.055 - 0.00110 = 0.0539, \text{ or } 0.054$$

16.41. To solve, first convert the pH to $[H_3O^+]$, which also equals $[C_2H_3O_2^-]$, here symbolized as $[Ac^-]$. Then assemble the usual table, and substitute into the equilibrium-constant expression to solve for $[HC_2H_3O_2]$, here symbolized as $[HAc]$.

$$[H_3O^+] = \text{antilog} (-2.68) = 2.\underline{0}89 \times 10^{-3} \ M$$

Conc. (M)	HAc + H^{2}O	$\rightleftharpoons$	H^{3}O$^+$	+	Ac$^-$
Starting	x		0		0
Change	-2.089×10^{-3}		$+2.089 \times 10^{-3}$		$+2.089 \times 10^{-3}$
Equilibrium	$x - (2.089 \times 10^{-3})$		2.089×10^{-3}		2.089×10^{-3}

Write the equilibrium-constant expression in terms of chemical symbols, and then substitute the x and the $x - (2.089 \times 10^{-3})$ terms into the expression:

$$K_a = \frac{[H_3O^+][Ac^-]}{[HAc]} = \frac{(2.089 \times 10^{-3})^2}{(x - 2.089 \times 10^{-3})} = 1.7 \times 10^{-5}$$

Solve the equation for x, assuming 0.002089 is much smaller than x.

$$x = [HAc] \cong \frac{(2.089 \times 10^{-3})^2}{(1.7 \times 10^{-5})} = 0.2\underline{5}6 = 0.26 \ M$$

16.43. To solve, assemble the usual table of starting, change, and equilibrium concentrations of HF and F$^-$ ions.

Conc. (M)	HF + H$_2$O	$\rightleftharpoons$	H$_3$O$^+$	+	F$^-$
Starting	0.040		0		0
Change	$-x$		$+x$		$+x$
Equilibrium	$0.040 - x$		x		x

Write the equilibrium-constant expression in terms of chemical symbols, and then substitute the terms x and $(0.040 - x)$:

$$K_a = \frac{[H_3O^+][F^-]}{[HF]} = \frac{(x)^2}{(0.040 - x)} = 6.8 \times 10^{-4}$$

In this case, x cannot be ignored compared to 0.040 M. (If it is ignored, subtracting the calculated $[H_3O^+]$ from 0.040 yields a significant change.) The quadratic formula must be used. Reorganize the equilibrium-constant expression into the form $ax^2 + bx + c = 0$, and substitute for a, b, and c in the quadratic formula.

$$x^2 + (6.8 \times 10^{-4}) \times - (2.72 \times 10^{-5}) = 0$$

$$x = \frac{-6.8 \times 10^{-4} \pm \sqrt{(6.8 \times 10^{-4})^2 + 4(2.72 \times 10^5)}}{2}$$

$$x = \frac{-6.8 \times 10^{-4} \pm 0.01045}{2}$$

Use the positive root.

$$x = [H_3O^+] = 4.\underline{88} \times 10^{-3} = 0.0049 = 4.9 \times 10^{-3}\ M$$

$$pH = -\log(4.88 \times 10^{-3}) = 2.3\underline{11} = 2.31$$

16.45. To solve, assemble the usual table of starting, change, and equilibrium concentrations of $(NO_2)_2C_6H_3CO_2H$, symbolized as HDin, and the $(NO_2)_2C_6H_3CO_2^-$ ion, symbolized as Din$^-$.

Conc. (M)	HDin + H$_2$O $\rightleftharpoons$	H$_3$O$^+$ +	Din$^-$
Starting	2.00	0	0
Change	$-x$	$+x$	$+x$
Equilibrium	$2.00 - x$	x	x

Write the equilibrium-constant expression in terms of chemical symbols, and then substitute the terms x and $(2.00 - x)$:

$$K_a = \frac{[H_3O^+][Din^-]}{[HDin]} = \frac{(x)^2}{(2.00 - x)} = 7.94 \times 10^{-2} = 0.0794$$

In this case, x cannot be ignored compared to 2.00 M. (If it is ignored, subtracting the calculated $[H_3O^+]$ from 2.00 yields a significant change.) The quadratic formula must be used. Reorganize the equilibrium-constant expression into the form $ax^2 + bx + c = 0$, and substitute for a, b, and c in the quadratic formula.

$$x^2 + (0.0794)\,x - 0.1588 = 0$$

$$x = \frac{-0.0794 \pm \sqrt{(0.0794)^2 + 4(0.1588)}}{2}$$

$$x = \frac{-0.0794 \pm 0.8009}{2}$$

Use the positive root.

$$x = [H_3O^+] = 0.36\underline{07} = 0.361\ M$$

16.47. a. To solve, note that $K_{a_1} = 1.2 \times 10^{-3} \gg K_{a_2} = 3.9 \times 10^{-6}$, and hence the second ionization and K_{a_2} can be neglected. Assemble a table of starting, change, and equilibrium concentrations. Let $H_2Ph = H_2C_8H_4O_4$ and $HPh^- = H\,C_8H_4O_4^-$.

Conc. (M)	H$_2$Ph + H$_2$O $\rightleftharpoons$	H$_3$O$^+$ +	HPh$^-$
Starting	0.015	0	0
Change	$-x$	$+x$	$+x$
Equilibrium	$0.015 - x$	x	x

Write the equilibrium-constant expression in terms of chemical symbols, and then substitute x and $(0.015 - x)$:

$$K_{a_1} = \frac{[H_3O^+][HPh^-]}{[H_2Ph]} = \frac{(x)^2}{(0.015 - x)} = 1.2 \times 10^{-3} = 0.0012$$

In this case, x cannot be ignored in the $(0.015\ M - x)$ term. (If it is ignored, the calculated $[H_3O^+]$ when subtracted from 0.0015 M yields a significant change.) The quadratic formula must be used. Reorganize the equilibrium-constant expression into the form $ax^2 + bx + c = 0$, and substitute for a, b, and c in the quadratic formula.

$$x^2 + (0.0012)\,x - 1.80 \times 10^{-5} = 0$$

$$x = \frac{-0.0012 \pm \sqrt{(0.0012)^2 - 4(-1.80 \times 10^{-5})}}{2}$$

$$x = \frac{-0.0012 \pm 0.008569}{2}$$

Use the positive root.

$$x = [H_3O^+] \cong 3.\underline{6}84 \times 10^{-3} = 0.0037 = 3.7 \times 10^{-3}\ M$$

b.   Because $[HPh^-] \cong [H_3O^+]$, these terms cancel in the K_{a_2} expression. This reduces to

$$[Ph^{2-}] = K_{a_2} = 3.9 \times 10^{-6}\ M.$$

16.49.   The equation is

$$CH_3NH_2(aq) + H_2O(l) \rightleftharpoons CH_3NH_3^+(aq) + OH^-(aq)$$

The K_b expression is

$$K_b = \frac{[CH_3NH_3^+]\,[OH^-]}{[CH_3NH_2]}$$

16.51.   To solve, convert the pH to $[OH^-]$:

$$pOH = 14.00 - pH = 14.00 - 11.34 = 2.66$$

$$[OH^-] = \text{antilog}\ (-2.66) = 2.\underline{1}88 \times 10^{-3}\ M$$

Using the symbol EtN for ethanolamine, assemble a table of starting, change, and equilibrium concentrations.

Conc. (M)	EtN + H$_2$O	$\rightleftharpoons$	HEtN$^+$	+	OH$^-$
Starting	0.15		0		0
Change	$-x$		$+x$		$+x$
Equilibrium	$0.15 - (2.188 \times 10^{-3})$		2.188×10^{-3}		2.188×10^{-3}

Write the equilibrium-constant expression in terms of chemical symbols, and then substitute the terms, and solve for K_b:

$$K_b = \frac{[HEtN^+]\,[OH^-]}{[EtN]} = \frac{(2.188 \times 10^{-3})^2}{(0.15 - 2.188 \times 10^{-3})} = 3.\underline{2}3 \times 10^{-5} = 3.2 \times 10^{-5}$$

16.53. To solve, assemble a table of starting, change, and equilibrium concentrations:

Conc. (M)	$CH_3NH_2 + H_2O$	$\rightleftharpoons$	$CH_3NH_3^+$ +	OH^-
Starting	0.060		0	0
Change	$-x$		$+x$	$+x$
Equilibrium	$0.060 - x$		x	x

Write the equilibrium-constant expression in terms of chemical symbols, and then substitute the terms and the value of K_b:

$$K_b = \frac{[CH_3NH_3^+][OH^-]}{[CH_3NH_2]} = \frac{(x)^2}{(0.060 - x)} = 4.4 \times 10^{-4}$$

In this case, x cannot be ignored compared to 0.060 M. (If it is ignored, subtracting the calculated [OH$^-$] from 0.060 yields a significant change.) The quadratic formula must be used. Reorganize the equilibrium-constant expression into the form $ax^2 + bx + c = 0$, and substitute for a, b, and c in the quadratic formula.

$$x^2 + (4.4 \times 10^{-4})x - 2.64 \times 10^{-5} = 0$$

$$x = \frac{-4.4 \times 10^{-4} \pm \sqrt{(4.4 \times 10^{-4})^2 + 4(2.64 \times 10^{-5})}}{2}$$

$$x = \frac{-4.4 \times 10^{-4} \pm 0.01028}{2}$$

Use the positive root.

$$x = [OH^-] = 4.\underline{9}2 \times 10^{-3} = 0.0049 = 4.9 \times 10^{-3} \, M$$

$$pOH = -\log(4.92 \times 10^{-3}) = 2.3\underline{0}7$$

$$pH = 14.00 - 2.307 = 11.6\underline{9}2 = 11.69$$

16.55. **a.** No hydrolysis occurs because the nitrate ion (NO_3^-) is the anion of a strong acid.

b. Hydrolysis occurs. Equation:

$$OCl^- + H_2O \rightleftharpoons HOCl + OH^-$$

Equilibrium-constant expression:

$$K_b = \frac{K_w}{K_a} = \frac{[HOCl][OH^-]}{[OCl^-]}$$

c. Hydrolysis occurs. Equation:

$$NH_2NH_3^+ + H_2O \rightleftharpoons H_3O^+ + NH_2NH_2$$

Equilibrium-constant expression:

$$K_a = \frac{K_w}{K_b} = \frac{[H_3O^+][NH_2NH_2]}{[NH_2NH_3^+]}$$

d. No hydrolysis occurs because the bromide ion (Br^-) is the anion of a strong acid.

16.57. Acid ionization is

$$Zn(H_2O)_6^{2+}(aq) + H_2O(l) \rightleftharpoons Zn(H_2O)_5(OH)^+(aq) + H_3O^+(aq)$$

16.59. a. $Fe(NO_3)_3$ is a salt of a weak base, $Fe(OH)_3$, and a strong acid, HNO_3, so it would be expected to be acidic. Fe^{3+} is not in Group IA or IIA, so it would be expected to form a metal hydrate ion that would hydrolyze to form an acidic solution.

b. Na_2CO_3 is a salt of a strong base, NaOH, and the anion of a weak acid, HCO_3^-, so it would be expected to be basic.

c. $Ca(CN)_2$ is a salt of a strong base, $Ca(OH)_2$, and a weak acid, HCN, so it would be expected to be basic.

d. NH_4ClO_4 is a salt of a weak base, NH_3, and a strong acid, $HClO_4$, so it would be expected to be acidic.

16.61. a. Both ions hydrolyze:

$$NH_4^+ + H_2O \rightleftharpoons NH_3 + H_3O^+$$

$$C_2H_3O_2^- + H_2O \rightleftharpoons HC_2H_3O_2 + OH^-$$

Calculate the K_a and K_b constants of the two to compare them:

$$NH_4^+ \text{ as an acid: } K_a = \frac{K_w}{K_b} = \frac{1.0 \times 10^{-14}}{1.8 \times 10^{-5}} = 5.\underline{55} \times 10^{-10}$$

$$C_2H_3O_2^- \text{ as a base: } K_b = \frac{K_w}{K_a} = \frac{1.0 \times 10^{-14}}{1.7 \times 10^{-5}} = 5.\underline{88} \times 10^{-10}$$

Because the K_b for the hydrolysis of $C_2H_3O_2^-$ is slightly larger than the constant, K_a, for the hydrolysis of NH_4^+, the solution will be slightly basic but close to pH 7.0.

b. Both ions hydrolyze:

$$C_6H_5NH_3^+ + H_2O \rightleftharpoons C_6H_5NH_2 + H_3O^+$$

$$C_2H_3O_2^- + H_2O \rightleftharpoons HC_2H_3O_2 + OH^-$$

Calculate the K_a and K_b constants of the two to compare them:

$$C_6H_5NH_3^+ \text{ as an acid: } K_a = \frac{K_w}{K_b} = \frac{1.0 \times 10^{-14}}{4.2 \times 10^{-10}} = 2.\underline{38} \times 10^{-5}$$

$$C_2H_3O_2^- \text{ as a base: } K_b = \frac{K_w}{K_a} = \frac{1.0 \times 10^{-14}}{1.7 \times 10^{-5}} = 5.\underline{88} \times 10^{-10}$$

Because the constant, K_a, for the hydrolysis of $C_6H_5NH_3^+$ is larger than the hydrolysis constant, K_b, for the hydrolysis of $C_2H_3O_2^-$, the solution will be acidic and significantly less than pH 7.0.

16.63. a. The reaction is

$$NO_2^- + H_2O \rightleftharpoons HNO_2 + OH^-$$

The constant, K_b, is obtained by dividing K_w by the K_a of the conjugate acid, HNO_2:

$$K_b = \frac{K_w}{K_a} = \frac{1.0 \times 10^{-14}}{4.5 \times 10^{-4}} = 2.\underline{2}2 \times 10^{-11} = 2.2 \times 10^{-11}$$

b. The reaction is

$$C_5H_5NH^+ + H_2O \rightleftharpoons C_5H_5N + H_3O^+$$

The constant, K_a, is obtained by dividing K_w by the K_b of the conjugate base, C_5H_5N:

$$K_a = \frac{K_w}{K_b} = \frac{1.0 \times 10^{-14}}{1.4 \times 10^{-9}} = 7.\underline{1}4 \times 10^{-6} = 7.1 \times 10^{-6}$$

16.65. Assemble the usual table, letting $[Pr^-]$ equal the equilibrium concentration of the propionate anion (the only ion that hydrolyzes). Then calculate the K_b of the Pr^- ion from the K_a of its conjugate acid, HPr. Assume x is much smaller than the 0.025 M concentration in the denominator, and solve for x in the numerator of the equilibrium-constant expression. Finally, calculate pOH from the $[OH^-]$ and pH from the pOH.

Conc. (M)	$Pr^- + H_2O$	$\rightleftharpoons$	HPr	+	OH^-
Starting	0.025		0		0
Change	$-x$		$+x$		$+x$
Equilibrium	$0.025 - x$		x		x

$$K_b = \frac{K_w}{K_a} = \frac{1.0 \times 10^{-14}}{1.3 \times 10^{-5}} = 7.\underline{6}9 \times 10^{-10}$$

Substitute into the equilibrium-constant expression.

$$K_b = \frac{[HPr][OH^-]}{[Pr^-]} = \frac{(x)^2}{(0.025-x)} \cong \frac{(x)^2}{(0.025)} = 7.\underline{6}9 \times 10^{-10}$$

$$x = [OH^-] = [HPr] \cong 4.\underline{3}8 \times 10^{-6} = 4.4 \times 10^{-6}\ M$$

$$pOH = -\log[OH^-] = -\log(4.38 \times 10^{-6}) = 5.3\underline{5}8$$

$$pH = 14.00 - 5.358 = 8.6\underline{4}2 = 8.64$$

16.67. Assemble the usual table, letting $[PyNH^+]$ equal the equilibrium concentration of the pryridinium cation (the only ion that hydrolyzes). Then calculate the K_a of the $PyNH^+$ ion from the K_b of its conjugate base, PyN. Assume x is much smaller than the 0.15 M concentration in the denominator, and solve for x in the numerator of the equilibrium-constant expression. Finally, calculate pH from the $[H_3O^+]$.

Conc. (M)	$PyNH^+ + H_2O$	$\rightleftharpoons$	H_3O^+	+	PyN
Starting	0.15		0		0
Change	$-x$		$+x$		$+x$
Equilibrium	$0.15 - x$		x		x

$$K_a = \frac{K_w}{K_b} = \frac{1.0 \times 10^{-14}}{1.4 \times 10^{-9}} = 7.\underline{1}4 \times 10^{-6}$$

Write the equilibrium-constant expression in terms of chemical symbols and then substitute the terms and solve for K_a:

$$K_a = \frac{[PyN][H_3O^+]}{[PyNH^+]} = \frac{(x)^2}{(0.15-x)} \cong \frac{(x)^2}{(0.15)} = 7.\underline{1}4 \times 10^{-6}$$

$$x = [H_3O^+] = [PyN] \cong 1.\underline{0}3 \times 10^{-3} = 0.0010 = 1.0 \times 10^{-3} \ M$$

$$pH = -\log[H^+] = -\log(1.03 \times 10^{-3}) = 2.9\underline{8}7 = 2.99$$

16.69. To solve, assemble a table of starting, change, and equilibrium concentrations for each part. For each part, assume x is much smaller than the 0.75 M starting concentration of HF. Then solve for x in the numerator of each equilibrium-constant expression by using the product of 6.8×10^{-4} and other terms.

a.   0.75 M Hydrofluoric acid, HF:

Conc. (M)	HF + H$_2$O $\rightleftharpoons$		H$_3$O$^+$ +	F$^-$
Starting	0.75		0	0
Change	$-x$		$+x$	$+x$
Equilibrium	$0.75-x$		x	X

$$K_a = \frac{[H_3O^+][F^-]}{[HF]} = \frac{(x)^2}{(0.75-x)} \cong \frac{(x)^2}{(0.75)} = 6.8 \times 10^{-4}$$

$$x^2 = 6.8 \times 10^{-4} \times (0.75)$$

$$x = [H_3O^+] = 0.02\underline{2}58 \ M$$

Check to see whether the assumption is valid.

$$0.75 - (0.02258) = 0.7\underline{2}7 = 0.73$$

This is a borderline case; the quadratic equation gives $[H_3O^+] = 0.02224 \ M$, not much different. The degree of ionization is

$$\text{Degree of ionization} = \frac{0.02258}{0.75} = 0.03\underline{0}1 = 0.030$$

b.   0.75 M HF with 0.12 M HCl:

Conc. (M)	HF + H$_2$O $\rightleftharpoons$		H$_3$O$^+$ +	F$^-$
Starting	0.75		0.12	0
Change	$-x$		$+x$	$+x$
Equilibrium	$0.75-x$		$0.12+x$	x

Assuming x is negligible compared to 0.12 and to 0.75, substitute into the equilibrium-constant expression 0.12 for $[H_3O^+]$ from 0.12 M HCl and 0.75 from the HF:

$$K_a = \frac{[H_3O^+][F^-]}{[HF]} = \frac{(0.12+x)(x)}{(0.75-x)} \cong \frac{(0.12)(x)}{(0.75)} = 6.8 \times 10^{-4}$$

$$x = [F^-] = \frac{(0.75)(6.8 \times 10^{-4})}{(0.12)} \cong 4.\underline{2}50 \times 10^{-3}\, M$$

Check to see whether the assumptions are valid:

$$0.75 - (4.250 \times 10^{-3}) = 0.7\underline{4}57 = 0.75$$

$$0.12 + (4.250 \times 10^{-3}) = 0.1\underline{2}42 = 0.12$$

$$\text{Degree of ionization} = \frac{4.25 \times 10^{-3}}{0.75} = 0.005\underline{6}6 = 0.0057$$

16.71. Assemble the usual table, using a starting NO_2^- of 0.10 M, from 0.10 M KNO_2, and a starting HNO_2 of 0.15 M. Assume x is negligible compared to 0.10 M and 0.15 M, and solve for the x in the numerator.

Conc. (M)	$HNO_2 + H_2O$	$\rightleftharpoons$	H_3O^+	+	NO_2^-
Starting	0.15		0		0.10
Change	$-x$		$+x$		$+x$
Equilibrium	$0.15 - x$		x		$0.10 + x$

$$K_a = \frac{[H_3O^+][NO_2^-]}{[HNO_2]} = \frac{(0.10 + x)(x)}{(0.15 - x)} \cong \frac{(0.10)(x)}{(0.15)} = 4.5 \times 10^{-4}$$

$$x = [H_3O^+] = 6.\underline{7}5 \times 10^{-4}\, M$$

$$pH = -\log[H_3O^+] = -\log(6.75 \times 10^{-4}) = 3.1\underline{7}0 = 3.17$$

16.73. Assemble the usual table, using a starting $CH_3NH_3^+$ of 0.15 M, from 0.15 M CH_3NH_3Cl, and a starting CH_3NH_2 of 0.10 M. Assume x is negligible compared to 0.15 M and 0.10 M, and solve for the x in the numerator.

Conc. (M)	$CH_3NH_2 + H_2O$	$\rightleftharpoons$	OH^-	+	$CH_3NH_3^+$
Starting	0.10		0		0.15
Change	$-x$		$+x$		$+x$
Equilibrium	$0.10 - x$		x		$0.15 + x$

$$K_b = \frac{[CH_3NH_3^+][OH^-]}{[CH_3NH_2]} = \frac{(0.15 + x)(x)}{(0.10 - x)} \cong \frac{(0.15)(x)}{(0.10)} = 4.4 \times 10^{-4}$$

$$x = [OH^-] = 2.\underline{9}3 \times 10^{-4}\, M$$

$$pOH = -\log[OH^-] = -\log(2.93 \times 10^{-4}) = 3.5\underline{3}2$$

$$pH = 14.00 - pOH = 14.00 - 3.532 = 10.4\underline{6}8 = 10.47$$

16.75. Find the mol/L of HF and the mol/L of F^-, and assemble the usual table. Substitute the equilibrium concentrations into the equilibrium-constant expression; then, assume x is negligible compared to the starting concentrations of both HF and F^-. Solve for x in the numerator of the equilibrium-constant expression, and calculate the pH from this value.

Total volume = 0.045 L + 0.035 L = 0.080 L

$(0.10 \text{ mol HF/L}) \times 0.035 \text{ L} = 0.0035 \text{ mol HF } (\div 0.080 \text{ L total volume} = 0.04375\, M)$

$(0.15 \text{ mol } F^-/L) \times 0.045 \text{ L} = 0.00675 \text{ mol } F^- (\div 0.080 \text{ L total volume} = 0.084375\, M)$

Now, substitute these starting concentrations into the usual table:

Conc. (M)	HF + H_2O $\rightleftharpoons$	H_3O^+ +	F^-
Starting	0.04375	0	0.084375
Change	$-x$	$+x$	$+x$
Equilibrium	$0.04375 - x$	x	$0.084375 + x$

$$K_a = \frac{[H_3O^+][F^-]}{[HF]} = \frac{(x)(0.084375 + x)}{(0.04375 - x)} \cong \frac{(x)(0.084375)}{(0.04375)} = 6.8 \times 10^{-4}$$

$$x = [H_3O^+] = 3.\underline{5}2 \times 10^{-4}\ M$$

$$pH = -\log[H_3O^+] = -\log(3.52 \times 10^{-4}) = 3.4\underline{5}3 = 3.45$$

16.77. First, use the 0.10 M NH_3 and 0.10 M NH_4^+ to calculate the $[OH^-]$ and pH before HCl is added. Assemble a table of starting, change, and equilibrium concentrations. Assume x is negligible compared to 0.10 M, and substitute the approximate concentrations into the equilibrium-constant expression.

Conc. (M)	NH_3 + H_2O $\rightleftharpoons$	NH_4^+ +	OH^-
Starting	0.10	0.10	0
Change	$-x$	$+x$	$+x$
Equilibrium	$0.10 - x$	$0.10 + x$	x

$$K_b = \frac{[NH_4^+][OH^-]}{[NH_3]} = \frac{(0.10 + x)(x)}{(0.10 - x)} \cong \frac{(0.10)(x)}{(0.10)} = 1.8 \times 10^{-5}$$

$$x = [OH^-] = 1.8 \times 10^{-5}\ M$$

$$pOH = -\log[OH^-] = -\log(1.8 \times 10^{-5}) = 4.7\underline{4}4$$

$$pH = 14.00 - pOH = 14.00 - 4.744 = 9.2\underline{5}52 = 9.26\ \text{(before HCl added)}$$

Now, calculate the pH after the 0.012 L (12 mL) of 0.20 M HCl is added by noting that the H_3O^+ ion reacts with the NH_3 to form additional NH_4^+. Calculate the stoichiometric amount of HCl; then subtract the moles of HCl from the moles of NH_3. Add the resulting moles of NH_4^+ to the 0.0125 starting moles of NH_4^+ in the 0.125 L of buffer.

(0.20 mol HCl/L) × 0.012 L = 0.0024 mol HCl (reacts with 0.0024 mol NH_3)

mol NH_3 left = (0.01$\underline{2}$5 − 0.0024) mol = 0.010$\underline{1}$ mol

mol NH_4^+ present = (0.0125 + 0.0024) mol = 0.014$\underline{9}$ mol

The concentrations of NH_3 and NH_4^+ are

$$[NH_3] = \frac{0.0101\ \text{mol}\ NH_3}{0.137\ L} = 0.07\underline{3}7\ M$$

$$[NH_4^+] = \frac{0.0149\ \text{mol}\ NH_3}{0.137\ L} = 0.1\underline{0}8\ M$$

Now, account for the ionization of NH_3 to NH_4^+ and OH^- at equilibrium by assembling the usual table. Assume x is negligible compared to $0.0737\ M$ and $0.108\ M$, and solve the equilibrium-constant expression for x in the numerator. Calculate the pH from x, the $[OH^-]$.

Conc. (M)	$NH_3 + H_2O$	$\rightleftharpoons$	NH_4^+	$+$	OH^-
Starting	0.0737		0.108		0
Change	$-x$		$+x$		$+x$
Equilibrium	$0.0737 - x$		$0.108 + x$		x

$$K_b = \frac{[NH_4^+][OH^-]}{[NH_3]} = \frac{(0.108 + x)(x)}{(0.0737 - x)} \cong \frac{(0.108)(x)}{(0.0737)} = 1.8 \times 10^{-5}$$

$$x = [OH^-] \cong 1.\underline{2}2 \times 10^{-5}\ M$$

$$pOH = -\log[OH^-] = -\log(1.22 \times 10^{-5}) = 4.9\underline{1}3$$

$$pH = 14.00 - pOH = 14.00 - 4.913 = 9.0\underline{8}6 = 9.09 \text{ (after HCl added)}$$

16.79. Use the Henderson-Hasselbalch equation, where $pK_a = -\log K_a$.

$$pH = -\log K_a + \log\frac{[\text{buff. base}]}{[\text{buff. acid}]} = -\log(1.3 \times 10^{-3}) + \log\frac{(0.10\ M)}{(0.15\ M)} = 2.7\underline{1}0 = 2.71$$

16.81. Calculate the K_a of the pyridinium ion from the K_b of pyridine, and then use the Henderson-Hasselbalch equation, where $pK_a = -\log K_a$.

$$K_a = \frac{K_w}{K_b} = \frac{1.0 \times 10^{-14}}{1.4 \times 10^{-9}} = 7.\underline{1}4 \times 10^{-6}$$

$$pH = -\log K_a + \log\frac{[\text{buff. base}]}{[\text{buff. acid}]} = -\log(7.14 \times 10^{-6}) + \log\frac{(0.15\ M)}{(0.10\ M)} = 5.3\underline{2}2 = 5.32$$

16.83. Symbolize acetic acid as HOAc and sodium acetate as Na^+OAc^-. Use the Henderson-Hasselbalch equation to find the log of $[OAc^-]/[HOAc]$. Then solve for $[OAc^-]$ and for moles of NaOAc in the 2.0 L of solution.

$$pH = -\log K_a + \log\frac{[OAc^-]}{[HOAc]} = 5.00$$

$$5.00 = -\log(1.7 \times 10^{-5}) + \log\frac{[OAc^-]}{(0.10\ M)}$$

$$5.00 = 4.7\underline{7}0 + \log[OAc^-] - \log(0.10)$$

$$\log[OAc^-] = 5.00 - 4.770 - 1.00 = -0.770$$

$$[OAc^-] = 0.1\underline{6}98\ M$$

$$\text{mol NaOAc} = 0.1698\ \text{mol/L} \times 2.0\ \text{L} = 0.3\underline{3}96 = 0.34\ \text{mol}$$

16.85. All the OH⁻ (from the NaOH) reacts with the H_3O^+ from HCl. Calculate the stoichiometric amounts of OH⁻ and H_3O^+, and subtract the moles of OH⁻ from the moles of H_3O^+. Next, divide the remaining H_3O^+ by the total·volume of 0.015 L + 0.025 L, or 0.040 L, to find the [H_3O^+]. Then calculate the pH.

$$\text{mol } H_3O^+ = (0.10 \text{ mol HCl/L}) \times 0.025 \text{ L HCl} = 0.0025 \text{ mol } H_3O^+$$

$$\text{mol OH}^- = (0.10 \text{ mol NaOH/L}) \times 0.015 \text{ L NaOH} = 0.0015 \text{ mol OH}^-$$

$$\text{mol } H_3O^+ \text{ left} = (0.0025 - 0.0015) \text{ mol } H_3O^+ = 0.0010 \text{ mol } H_3O^+$$

$$[H_3O^+] = 0.0010 \text{ mol } H_3O^+ \div 0.040 \text{ L total volume} = 0.02\underline{5}0 \text{ } M$$

$$\text{pH} = -\log [H_3O^+] = -\log (0.0250) = 1.6\underline{0}2 = 1.60$$

16.87. Use HBen to symbolize benzoic acid and Ben⁻ to symbolize the benzoate anion. At the equivalence point, equal molar amounts of HBen and NaOH react to form a solution of NaBen. Start by calculating the moles of HBen. Use this to calculate the volume of NaOH needed to neutralize all of the HBen (and use the moles of HBen as the moles of Ben⁻ formed at the equivalence point). Add the volume of NaOH to the original 0.0500 L to find the total volume of solution.

$$\text{mol HBen} = 1.24 \text{ g HBen} \div (122.1 \text{ g HBen/mol HBen}) = 0.010\underline{1}5 \text{ mol HBen}$$

$$\text{Volume NaOH} = 0.010\underline{1}5 \text{ mol NaOH} \div (0.180 \text{ mol NaOH/L}) = 0.056\underline{4}1 \text{ L}$$

$$\text{Total volume} = 0.05641 \text{ L} + 0.0500 \text{ L HBen soln} = 0.106\underline{4}1 \text{ L}$$

$$[\text{Ben}^-] = (0.010\underline{1}5 \text{ mol Ben}^- \text{ from HBen}) \div 0.106\underline{4}1 \text{ L} = 0.095\underline{3}8 \text{ } M$$

Because the Ben⁻ hydrolyzes to OH⁻ and HBen, use this to calculate the [OH⁻]. Start by calculating the K_b constant of Ben⁻ from the K_a of its conjugate acid, HBen. Then, assemble the usual table of concentrations, assume x is negligible, and calculate [OH⁻] and pH.

$$K_b = \frac{K_w}{K_a} = \frac{1.0 \times 10^{-14}}{6.3 \times 10^{-5}} = 1.\underline{5}9 \times 10^{-10}$$

Conc. (M)	Ben⁻ + H₂O	$\rightleftharpoons$	HBen	+	OH⁻
Starting	0.09538		0		0
Change	$-x$		$+x$		$+x$
Equilibrium	$0.09538 - x$		x		x

$$K_b = \frac{[\text{HBen}][\text{OH}^-]}{[\text{Ben}^-]} = \frac{(x)^2}{(0.09538 - x)} \cong \frac{(x)^2}{(0.09538)} = 1.59 \times 10^{-10}$$

$$x = [\text{OH}^-] = 3.\underline{8}91 \times 10^{-6} \text{ } M; \text{pOH} = -\log [\text{OH}^-] = -\log (3.891 \times 10^{-6}) = 5.4\underline{0}99$$

$$\text{pH} = 14.00 - 5.4099 = 8.5\underline{9}01 = 8.59$$

16.89. Use EtN to symbolize ethylamine and EtNH⁺ to symbolize the ethylammonium cation. At the equivalence point, equal molar amounts of EtN and HCl react to form a solution of EtNHCl. Start by calculating the moles of EtN. Use this to calculate the volume of HCl needed to neutralize all of the EtN (and use the moles of EtN as the moles of EtNH⁺ formed at the equivalence point). Add the volume of HCl to the original 0.032 L to find the total volume of solution.

$$(0.087 \text{ mol EtN/L}) \times 0.032 \text{ L} = 0.002\underline{7}8 \text{ mol EtN}$$

$$\text{Volume HCl} = 0.002\underline{7}8 \text{ mol HCl} \div (0.15 \text{ mol HCl/L}) = 0.01\underline{8}56 \text{ L}$$

Total volume = 0.018̲56 L + 0.032 L EtN soln = 0.050̲56 L

$$[EtNH^+] = (0.00278 \text{ mol } EtNH^+ \text{ from } EtN) \div 0.05056 \text{ L} = 0.055̲0 \ M$$

Because the $EtNH^+$ hydrolyzes to H_3O^+ and EtN, use this to calculate the $[H_3O^+]$. Start by calculating the K_a constant of $EtNH^+$ from the K_b of its conjugate base, EtN. Then assemble the usual table of concentrations, assume x is negligible, and calculate $[H_3O^+]$ and pH.

$$K_a = \frac{K_w}{K_b} = \frac{1.0 \times 10^{-14}}{4.7 \times 10^{-4}} = 2.1̲3 \times 10^{-11}$$

Conc. (M)	$EtNH^+ + H_2O \rightleftharpoons$		EtN +	H_3O^+
Starting	0.0550		0	0
Change	$-x$		$+x$	$+x$
Equilibrium	$0.0550 - x$		x	x

$$K_a = \frac{[EtN][H_3O^+]}{[EtNH^+]} = \frac{(x)^2}{(0.0550 - x)} \cong \frac{(x)^2}{(0.0550)} = 2.1̲3 \times 10^{-11}$$

$$x = [H_3O^+] = 1.0̲8 \times 10^{-6} \ M$$

$$pH = -\log [H_3O^+] = -\log (1.08 \times 10^{-6}) = 5.96̲56 = 5.97$$

16.91. a. Assemble the usual table of concentrations.

Conc. (M)	$CN^- + H_2O \rightleftharpoons$		HCN +	OH^-
Starting	0.100		0	0
Change	$-x$		$+x$	$+x$
Equilibrium	$0.100 - x$		x	x

Now substitute into the equilibrium expression, assume x is negligible compared to 0.100 M, and calculate $[OH^-]$.

$$K_b = \frac{(x)^2}{(0.100 - x)} = \frac{(x)^2}{(0.100)} = 2.0 \times 10^{-5}$$

$$x = [OH^-] = 1.4̲14 \times 10^{-3} \ M$$

Finally, calculate the pOH and then the pH.

$$pOH = -\log [OH^-] = -\log (1.414 \times 10^{-3}) = 2.84̲9$$

$$pH = 14.00 - 2.84̲9 = 11.1̲50 = 11.15$$

b. After 15.0 mL of 0.200 M HCl is added. The reaction is

$$CN^- + H_3O^+ \rightarrow HCN + H_2O$$

The total volume at this point is 50.0 mL + 15.0 mL = 65.0 mL.

The moles of CN^- present at the start and the moles of HCl added are

$$\text{mol } CN^- = M \times V = 0.100 \ M \times 50.0 \times 10^{-3} \text{ L} = 5.0̲00 \times 10^{-3} \text{ mol}$$

$$\text{mol } HCl = M \times V = 0.200 \ M \times 15.0 \times 10^{-3} \text{ L} = 3.0̲00 \times 10^{-3} \text{ mol}$$

After reaction the moles of HCN equal the moles of added HCl. The moles of CN^- present are

$$\text{mol } CN^- = 5.000 \times 10^{-3} \text{ mol} - 3.000 \times 10^{-3} = 2.0\underline{0}0 \times 10^{-3} \text{ mol}$$

Now calculate the concentrations.

$$[CN^-] = \frac{2.000 \times 10^{-3} \text{ mol } CN^-}{65.0 \times 10^{-3} \text{ L}} = 0.030\underline{7}6 \ M$$

$$[HCN] = \frac{3.000 \times 10^{-3} \text{ mol } HCN}{65.0 \times 10^{-3} \text{ L}} = 0.046\underline{1}5 \ M$$

Substitute into the K_b expression and solve for $x = [OH^-]$.

$$K_b = 2.0 \times 10^{-5} = \frac{[HCN][OH^-]}{[CN^-]} = \frac{(0.04615 + x)(x)}{(0.03076 - x)} \cong \frac{(0.04615)(x)}{(0.03076)}$$

$$x = [OH^-] = \frac{(0.03076)(2.0 \times 10^{-5})}{(0.04615)} = 1.\underline{3}3 \times 10^{-5} \ M$$

Now calculate the pOH and finally the pH.

$$pOH = -\log(1.33 \times 10^{-5}) = 4.8\underline{7}5$$

$$pH = 14.00 - pOH = 14.00 - 4.875 = 9.1\underline{2}4 = 9.12$$

c.   First calculate the volume of HCl added to reach the equivalence point.

$$V_2 = \frac{M_1 V_1}{M_2} = \frac{(0.100 \ M)(50.0 \text{ mL})}{(0.200 \ M)} = 25.\underline{0}0 \text{ mL}$$

The total volume at this point is 50.0 mL + 25.0 mL = 75.0 mL. The equilibrium is now

$$HCN + H_2O \rightleftharpoons H_3O^+ + CN^-$$

The moles of HCN present are the same as the moles of CN^- present initially, 5.00×10^{-3} mol. The concentration is

$$[HCN] = \frac{5.000 \times 10^{-3} \text{ mol } HCN}{75.0 \times 10^{-3} \text{ L}} = 0.06\underline{6}6 \ M$$

Calculate the value of K_a from K_b, set up the equilibrium expression, and solve.

$$K_a = \frac{K_w}{K_b} = \frac{1.00 \times 10^{-14}}{2.0 \times 10^{-5}} = 5.\underline{0}0 \times 10^{-10}$$

$$K_a = 5.00 \times 10^{-10} = \frac{[CN^-][H_3O^+]}{[HCN]} = \frac{x^2}{(0.0666 - x)}$$

$$x = [H_3O^+] = 5.\underline{7}73 \times 10^{-6} \ M$$

$$pH = -\log(5.773 \times 10^{-6}) = 5.2\underline{3}8 = 5.24$$

d.   After the addition of 30.0 mL HCl. The volume at this point is 50.0 mL + 30.0 mL = 80.0 mL. Now calculate the molarity of the excess H_3O^+.

$$\text{mol HCl added} = M \times V = (0.200 \; M)(30.0 \times 10^{-3} \; L) = 6.0\underline{0}0 \times 10^{-3} \; \text{mol}$$

$$\text{Excess mol HCl} = 6.000 \times 10^{-3} \; \text{mol} - 5.000 \times 10^{-3} \; \text{mol} = 1.0\underline{0}0 \times 10^{-3} \; \text{mol}$$

$$[H_3O^+] = \frac{1.000 \times 10^{-3} \; \text{mol HCl}}{80.0 \times 10^{-3} \; L} = 0.012\underline{5}0 \; M$$

Finally, calculate the pH

$$pH = -\log(0.012\underline{5}0) = 1.90\underline{3}1 = 1.903$$

16.93.   Calculate the stoichiometric amounts of NH_3 and HCl, which forms NH_4^+. Then divide NH_3 and NH_4^+ by the total volume of 0.500 L + 0.200 L = 0.700 L to find the starting concentrations. Calculate the $[OH^-]$, the pOH, and the pH.

$$\text{mol } NH_3 = (0.10 \; \text{mol } NH_3/L) \times 0.500 \; L = 0.05\underline{0}0 \; \text{mol } NH_3$$

$$\text{mol HCl} = (0.15 \; \text{mol HCl}/L) \times 0.200 \; L = 0.03\underline{0}0 \; \text{mol HCl} \; (\rightarrow 0.0300 \; \text{mol } NH_4^+)$$

$$\text{mol } NH_3 \text{ left} = 0.05\underline{0}0 \; \text{mol} - 0.03\underline{0}0 \; \text{mol HCl} = 0.02\underline{0}0 \; \text{mol } NH_3$$

$$0.02\underline{0}0 \; \text{mol } NH_3 \div 0.700 \; L = 0.028\underline{6} \; M \; NH_3$$

$$0.03\underline{0}0 \; \text{mol } NH_4^+ \div 0.700 \; L = 0.04\underline{2}9 \; M \; NH_4^+$$

Conc. (M)	$NH_3 + H_2O$	$\rightleftharpoons$	NH_4^+	+	OH^-
Starting	0.0286		0.0429		0
Change	$-x$		$+x$		$+x$
Equilibrium	$0.0286 - x$		$0.0429 + x$		x

$$K_b = \frac{[NH_4^+][OH^-]}{[NH_3]} = \frac{(0.0429 + x)(x)}{(0.0286 - x)} \cong \frac{(0.0429)(x)}{(0.0286)} = 1.8 \times 10^{-5}$$

$$x = [OH^-] = 1.2\underline{0} \times 10^{-5} \; M$$

$$pOH = -\log[OH^-] = -\log(1.20 \times 10^{-5}) = 4.9\underline{2}0$$

$$pH = 14.00 - pOH = 14.00 - 4.920 = 9.0\underline{7}9 = 9.08$$

■ SOLUTIONS TO GENERAL PROBLEMS

16.95.   To solve, assemble a table of starting, change, and equilibrium concentrations. Use HSal to symbolize salicylic acid, and use Sal^- for the anion. Begin by converting pH to $[H_3O^+]$:

$$[H_3O^+] = \text{antilog}(-pH) = \text{antilog}(-2.43) = 3.\underline{7}2 \times 10^{-3} \; M$$

$$\text{Starting } M \text{ of HSal} = (2.2 \; g \div 138 \; g/mol) \div 1.00 \; L = 0.01\underline{5}9 \; M$$

Conc. (M)	$HSal + H_2O$	$\rightleftharpoons$	H_3O^+	+	Sal^-
Starting	0.0159		0		0
Change	$-x$		$+x$		$+x$
Equilibrium	$0.0159 - x$		X		x

The value of x equals the value of the molarity of the H_3O^+ ion, which is $3.\underline{7}2 \times 10^{-3}$ M. Substitute into the equilibrium-constant expression to find K_a:

$$K_a = \frac{(x)^2}{(0.0159-x)} = \frac{(3.\underline{7}2 \times 10^{-3})^2}{(0.0159-3.\underline{7}2 \times 10^{-3})} = 1.\underline{1}3 \times 10^{-3} = 1.1 \times 10^{-3}$$

16.97. To solve, assemble a table of starting, change, and equilibrium concentrations. Begin by converting pH to $[H_3O^+]$:

$$[H_3O^+] = \text{antilog}\,(-pH) = \text{antilog}\,(-1.73) = 1.\underline{8}6 \times 10^{-2}\ M$$

Starting M of $HSO_4^- = 0.050$ M

Conc. (M)	$HSO_4^- + H_2O$	$\rightleftharpoons$	H_3O^+	$+$	SO_4^{2-}
Starting	0.050		0		0
Change	$-x$		$+x$		$+x$
Equilibrium	$0.050 - x$		x		x

The value of x equals the value of the molarity of the H_3O^+ ion, which is $1.\underline{8}6 \times 10^{-2}$ M. Substitute into the equilibrium-constant expression to find K_{a_2}:

$$K_{a_2} = \frac{(x)^2}{(0.050-x)} = \frac{(1.86 \times 10^{-2})^2}{(0.050-1.86 \times 10^{-2})} = 1.\underline{1}0 \times 10^{-2} = 1.1 \times 10^{-2}$$

16.99. For the base ionization (hydrolysis) of CN^- to $HCN + OH^-$, the base-ionization constant is

$$K_b = \frac{K_w}{K_a} = \frac{1.0 \times 10^{-14}}{4.9 \times 10^{-10}} = 2.\underline{0}4 \times 10^{-5} = 2.0 \times 10^{-5}$$

For the base ionization (hydrolysis) of CO_3^{2-} to $HCO_3^- + OH^-$, the base-ionization constant is calculated from the ionization constant (K_{a_2}) of HCO_3^-, the conjugate acid of CO_3^{2-}.

$$K_b = \frac{K_w}{K_a} = \frac{1.0 \times 10^{-14}}{4.8 \times 10^{-11}} = 2.\underline{0}8 \times 10^{-4} = 2.1 \times 10^{-4}$$

Because the constant of CO_3^{2-} is larger, it is the stronger base.

16.101. Assume Al^{3+} is $Al(H_2O)_6^{3+}$. Assemble the usual table to calculate the $[H_3O^+]$ and pH. Use the usual equilibrium-constant expression.

Conc. (M)	$Al(H_2O)_6^{3+} + H_2O$	$\rightleftharpoons$	H_3O^+	$+$	$Al(H_2O)_5(OH)^{2+}$
Starting	0.15		0		0
Change	$-x$		$+x$		$+x$
Equilibrium	$0.15 - x$		x		x

$$K_a = \frac{[Al(H_2O)_5(OH)^{2+}][H_3O^+]}{[Al(H_2O)_6^{3+}]} = \frac{(x)^2}{(0.15-x)} \cong \frac{(x)^2}{(0.15)} = 1.4 \times 10^{-5}$$

$$x = [H_3O^+] = 1.\underline{4}49 \times 10^{-3}\ M$$

$$pH = -\log [H_3O^+] = -\log (1.449 \times 10^{-3}) = 2.8\underline{3}8 = 2.84$$

16.103. Calculate the concentrations of the tartaric acid (H_2Tar) and the hydrogen tartrate ion ($HTar^-$).

$$(11.0 \text{ g } H_2Tar \div 150.1 \text{ g/mol}) \div 1.00 \text{ L} = 0.07328 \ M \ H_2Tar$$

$$(20.0 \text{ g } KHTar^- \div 188.2 \text{ g/mol}) \div 1.00 \text{ L} = 0.1063 \ M \ [HTar^-]$$

Conc. (M)	$H_2Tar + H_2O$	$\rightleftharpoons$	H_3O^+	$+$	$HTar^-$
Starting	0.07328		0		0.1063
Change	$-x$		$+x$		$+x$
Equilibrium	$0.07328 - x$		x		$0.1063 + x$

Ignoring x compared to 0.07328 and 0.1063 and substituting into the K_{a_1} expression give

$$K_{a_1} = \frac{[H_3O^+][HTar^-]}{[H_2Tar]} = \frac{(0.1063 + x)(x)}{(0.07328 - x)} \cong \frac{(0.1063)(x)}{(0.07328)} = 1.0 \times 10^{-3}$$

$$x = [H_3O^+] = 6.89 \times 10^{-4} \ M$$

$$pH = -\log[H_3O^+] = -\log(6.89 \times 10^{-4}) = 3.161 = 3.16$$

16.105. Use the Henderson-Hasselbalch equation, where $[H_2CO_3]$ = the buffer acid, $[HCO_3^-]$ = the buffer base, and K_{a_1} of carbonic acid is the ionization constant.

$$pH = -\log K_a + \log \frac{[HCO_3^-]}{[H_2CO_3]} = 7.40$$

$$7.40 = -\log(4.3 \times 10^{-7}) + \log \frac{[HCO_3^-]}{[H_2CO_3]}$$

$$\log \frac{[HCO_3^-]}{[H_2CO_3]} = 7.40 - 6.366 = 1.034$$

$$\frac{[HCO_3^-]}{[H_2CO_3]} = \frac{10.8}{1} = \frac{11}{1}$$

16.107. All the OH^- (from the NaOH) reacts with the H_3O^+ from HCl. Calculate the stoichiometric amounts of OH^- and H_3O^+, and subtract the moles of OH^- from the moles of H_3O^+. Next, divide the remaining H_3O^+ by the total volume of 0.456 L + 0.285 L, or 0.741 L, to find the $[H_3O^+]$. Then calculate the pH.

$$\text{mol } H_3O^+ = (0.10 \text{ mol HCl/L}) \times 0.456 \text{ L HCl} = 0.0456 \text{ mol } H_3O^+$$

$$\text{mol } OH^- = (0.15 \text{ mol NaOH/L}) \times 0.285 \text{ L NaOH} = 0.0428 \text{ mol } OH^-$$

$$\text{mol } H_3O^+ \text{ left} = (0.0456 - 0.0428) \text{ mol } H_3O^+ = 0.0028 \text{ mol } H_3O^+$$

$$[H_3O^+] = 0.0028 \text{ mol } H_3O^+ \div 0.741 \text{ L total volume} = 0.0038 \ M$$

$$pH = -\log[H_3O^+] = -\log(0.0038) = 2.42 = 2.4$$

16.109. Use BzN to symbolize benzylamine and BzNH$^+$ to symbolize the benzylammonium cation. At the equivalence point, equal molar amounts of BzN and HCl react to form a solution of BzNHCl. Start by calculating the moles of BzN. Use this number to calculate the volume of HCl needed to neutralize all the BzN (and use the moles of BzN as the moles of BzNH$^+$ formed at the equivalence point). Add the volume of HCl to the original 0.025 L to find the total volume of solution.

$$(0.065 \text{ mol BzN/L}) \times 0.025 \text{ L} = 0.00162 \text{ mol BzN}$$

Volume HCl = 0.00162 mol HCl ÷ (0.050 mol HCl/L) = 0.03$\underline{2}$4 L

Total volume = 0.025 L + 0.0324 L = 0.05$\underline{7}$4 L

$$[\text{BzNH}^+] = (0.00162 \text{ mol BzNH}^+ \text{ from BzN}) \div 0.0574 \text{ L} = 0.02\underline{8}2 \ M$$

Because the BzNH$^+$ hydrolyzes to H$_3$O$^+$ and BzN, use this to calculate the [H$_3$O$^+$]. Start by calculating the K_a constant of BzNH$^+$ from the K_b of its conjugate base, BzN. Then assemble the usual table of concentrations, assume x is negligible, and calculate [H$_3$O$^+$] and pH.

$$K_a = \frac{K_w}{K_b} = \frac{1.0 \times 10^{-14}}{4.7 \times 10^{-10}} = 2.\underline{1}3 \times 10^{-5}$$

Conc. (M)	BzNH^{+-} + H$_2$O $\rightleftharpoons$	H$_3$O$^+$ +	BzN
Starting	0.0282	0	0
Change	$-x$	$+x$	$+x$
Equilibrium	0.0282 $- x$	X	x

Substitute into the equilibrium-constant equation.

$$K_a = \frac{[\text{H}_3\text{O}^+][\text{BzN}]}{[\text{BzNH}^+]} = \frac{(x)^2}{(0.0282 - x)} \cong \frac{(x)^2}{(0.0282)} = 2.\underline{1}3 \times 10^{-5}$$

$$x = [\text{H}_3\text{O}^+] = 7.\underline{7}5 \times 10^{-4} \ M$$

$$\text{pH} = -\log [\text{H}_3\text{O}^+] = -\log (7.\underline{7}5 \times 10^{-4}) = 3.1\underline{1}1 = 3.11$$

16.111. a. $[\text{H}_3\text{O}^+] \cong 0.100 \ M$

b. The 0.100 M H$_2$SO$_4$ ionizes to 0.100 M H$_3$O$^+$ and 0.100 M HSO$_4^-$. Assemble the usual table, and substitute into the K_{a_2} equilibrium-constant expression for H$_2$SO$_4$. Solve the resulting quadratic equation.

Conc. (M)	HSO$_4^-$ + H$_2$O $\rightleftharpoons$	H$_3$O$^+$ +	SO$_4^{2-}$
Starting	0.100	0.100	0
Change	$-x$	$+x$	$+x$
Equilibrium	0.100 $- x$	0.100 $+ x$	x

$$x^2 + 0.111 \, x - (1.10 \times 10^{-3}) = 0$$

$$x = \frac{-0.111 \pm \sqrt{(0.111)^2 + 4(1.10 \times 10^{-3})}}{2}$$

$$x = \frac{-0.111 \pm 0.1293}{2}$$

$$x = 9.1\underline{5}4 \times 10^{-3} \ M$$

$$[H_3O^+] = 0.100 + x = 0.10\underline{0} + 0.0091\underline{5}4 = 0.10\underline{9} = 0.11 \ M$$

16.113. a. From the pH, calculate the H_3O^+ ion concentration:

$$[H_3O^+] = 10^{-pH} = 10^{-5.82} = 1.\underline{5}1 \times 10^{-6} \ M$$

Use the table approach, giving the starting, change, and equilibrium concentrations.

Conc. (M)	$CH_3NH_3^+ + H_2O$	$\rightleftharpoons$	CH_3NH_2	$+$	H_3O^+
Starting	0.10		0		0
Change	$-x$		$+x$		$+x$
Equilibrium	$0.10 - x$		x		0

From the hydronium-ion concentration, $x = 1.51 \times 10^{-6}$. Substituting into the equilibrium-constant expression gives

$$K_a = \frac{[CH_3NH_2][H_3O^+]}{[CH_3NH_3^+]} = \frac{(x)^2}{(0.10-x)} \cong \frac{(1.51 \times 10^{-6})^2}{(0.10)} = 2.\underline{2}8 \times 10^{-11} = 2.3 \times 10^{-11}$$

b. Now, use K_w to calculate the value of K_b:

$$K_b = \frac{K_w}{K_a} = \frac{1.0 \times 10^{-14}}{2.28 \times 10^{-11}} = 4.\underline{3}8 \times 10^{-4} = 4.4 \times 10^{-4}$$

c. The equilibrium concentration of $CH_3NH_3^+$ is approximately 0.450 mol/1.00 L = 0.450 M. Use $[CH_3NH_2] \cong 0.250 \ M$. For K_a, we get

$$K_a = \frac{[CH_3NH_2][H_3O^+]}{[CH_3NH_3^+]} \cong \frac{(0.250) \ [H_3O^+]}{(0.450)} = 2.\underline{2}8 \times 10^{-11}$$

Solving for $[H_3O^+]$ gives

$$[H_3O^+] \cong \frac{(2.28 \times 10^{-11})(0.450)}{(0.250)} = 4.\underline{1}0 \times 10^{-11} \ M$$

Thus, the pH is

$$pH = -\log(4.10 \times 10^{-11}) = 10.3\underline{8}7 = 10.39$$

16.115. a. True. Weak acids have small K_a values, so most of the solute is present as undissociated molecules.

b. True. Weak acids have small K_a values, so most of the solute is present as the molecule.

c. False. The hydroxide concentration equals the hydronium concentration only in neutral solutions.

d. False. If HA were a strong acid, the pH would be equal to 2.

e. False. The H_3O^+ would be 0.010 M if HA were a strong acid.

f. True. For every HA molecule that dissociates, one H_3O^+ is generated along with one A^-.

16.117. **a.** At the equivalence point, moles of acid equal moles of base. Thus,

$$\text{Moles of acid} = 0.115 \text{ mol/L} \times 0.03383 \text{ L} = 3.8\underline{9}0 \times 10^{-3}$$

The molar mass is

$$\text{Molar mass} = \frac{0.288 \text{ g}}{3.890 \times 10^{-3} \text{ mol}} = 74.\underline{0}4 = 74.0 \text{ g/mol}$$

b. At the 50% titration point, pH = pK_a. Since the pH measurement wasn't made, it is necessary to obtain the $[A^-]/[HA]$ ratio. The ratio can be in terms of moles, percent, mL, or M because the units end up canceling out. First, use the pH to obtain the H_3O^+ ion concentration. Express the other concentrations in milliliters for convenience.

$$[H_3O^+] = 10^{-4.92} = 1.\underline{2}0 \times 10^{-5} \text{ } M$$

$$HA_0 \cong 33.83 \text{ mL}$$

$$[HA] \cong 33.83 - 17.54 = 16.29 \text{ mL}$$

$$[A^-] \cong [OH^-] = 17.54 \text{ mL}$$

$$K_a = [H_3O^+] \times \frac{[A^-]}{[HA]} = 1.20 \times 10^{-5} \text{ } M \times \frac{17.54 \text{ mL}}{16.29 \text{ mL}} = 1.\underline{2}9 \times 10^{-5} = 1.3 \times 10^{-5}$$

16.119. **a.** Initial pH: Use the table approach, and give the starting, change, and equilibrium concentrations.

Conc. (M)	$NH_3 + H_2O$	$\rightleftharpoons$	NH_4^+	$+$	OH^-
Starting	0.10		0		0
Change	$-x$		$+x$		$+x$
Equilibrium	$0.10 - x$		x		0

Substituting into the equilibrium-constant expression gives

$$K_b = \frac{[NH_4^+][OH^-]}{[OH^-]} = \frac{(x)^2}{(0.10-x)} \cong \frac{(x)^2}{(0.10)} = 1.8 \times 10^{-5}$$

Rearranging and solving for x give

$$x = [OH^-] = \sqrt{(0.10)(1.8 \times 10^{-5})} = 1.\underline{3}4 \times 10^{-3} \text{ } M$$

$$pOH = -\log(1.34 \times 10^{-3}) = 2.8\underline{7}3$$

$$pH = 14 - pOH = 14 - 2.873 = 11.1\underline{2}7 = 11.13$$

30% titration point: Express the concentrations as percents for convenience.

$$[NH_3] \approx 70\% \text{ and } [NH_4^+] \approx 30\%$$

Plug into the equilibrium-constant expression.

$$K_b = \frac{[NH_4^+][OH^-]}{[NH_3]} = \frac{(30\%)(x)}{(70\%)} = 1.8 \times 10^{-5}$$

Solving for x gives

$$x = [OH^-] = 1.8 \times 10^{-5} \times \frac{70\%}{30\%} = 4.\underline{2}0 \times 10^{-5} \, M$$

$$pOH = -\log(4.20 \times 10^{-5}) = 4.3\underline{77}$$

$$pH = 14 - pOH = 14 - 4.377 = 9.6\underline{2}3 = 9.62$$

50% titration point:

$$[NH_4^+] = [NH_3]$$

$$K_b = [OH^-] = 1.8 \times 10^{-5} \, M$$

$$pOH = -\log(1.8 \times 10^{-5}) = 4.7\underline{44}$$

$$pH = 14 - pOH = 14 - 4.744 = 9.2\underline{5}6 = 9.26$$

100% titration point:

The NH_4Cl that is produced has undergone a twofold dilution.

$$[NH_4^+] = 0.05\underline{0}0 \, M$$

Use the table approach, and give the starting, change, and equilibrium concentrations.

Conc. (M)	$NH_3 + H_2O$	$\rightleftharpoons$	NH_3	+	H_3O^+
Starting	0.0500		0		0
Change	$-x$		$+x$		$+x$
Equilibrium	$0.0500 - x$		x		x

Now, use K_w to calculate the value of K_a:

$$K_a = \frac{K_w}{K_b} = \frac{1.0 \times 10^{-14}}{1.8 \times 10^{-5}} = 5.\underline{5}5 \times 10^{-10}$$

Plug into the equilibrium-constant expression.

$$K_a = \frac{[NH_3][H_3O^+]}{[NH_4^+]} = \frac{(x)^2}{(0.0500 - x)} \cong \frac{(x)^2}{(0.0500)} = 5.55 \times 10^{-10}$$

Solving for x gives

$$x = [H_3O^+] = \sqrt{0.0500 \times \frac{1.0 \times 10^{-14}}{1.8 \times 10^{-5}}} = 5.\underline{2}7 \times 10^{-6} \, M$$

$$pH = -\log(5.27 \times 10^{-6}) = 5.2\underline{7}8 = 5.28$$

b.   The solution is acidic because the NH_4^+ ion reacts with water to produce acid. Ammonium chloride is the salt of a weak base and a strong acid.

16.121. a.   Select the conjugate pair that has a pK_a value closest to a pH of 2.88.

$$pK_a \, (H_2C_2O_4) = 1.25$$

$$pK_a \, (H_3PO_4) = 2.16$$

$$pK_a \, (HCOOH) = 3.77$$

Therefore, the best pair is H_3PO_4 and $H_2PO_4^-$.

b.   Using the Henderson-Hasselbalch equation,

$$pH = pK_a + \log \frac{[A^-]}{[HA]} ;$$

$$2.88 = 2.16 + \log \frac{[A^-]}{[HA]} ; \quad \log \frac{[A^-]}{[HA]} = 0.72$$

$$\frac{[A^-]}{[HA]} = 10^{0.72} = 5.2\underline{4}$$

Therefore, 5.24 times more conjugate base is needed than acid. Since the starting concentrations of H_3PO_4 (HA) and $H_2PO_4^-$ (A^-) are the same, the volume of A^- needed is 5.24 times the volume of HA needed. For 50 mL of buffer, this is

50 mL = vol HA + vol A^- = vol HA + 5.24 vol HA = 6.24 vol HA

Therefore, the volume of 0.10 M H_3PO_4 required is

$$\text{Volume of } H_3PO_4 = \frac{50 \text{ mL}}{6.24} = \underline{8}.01 \text{ mL} = 8 \text{ mL}$$

The volume of 0.10 M $H_2PO_4^-$ required is

50 mL − 8.01 mL = 4$\underline{2}$.0 mL = 42 mL

16.123. a.   At the equivalence point, moles of base equal moles of acid. Therefore,

$$M_{NH_2OH} \times 25.0 \text{ mL} = 0.150 \, M \times 35.8 \text{ mL}$$

$$M_{NH_2OH} = \frac{0.150 \, M \times 35.8 \text{ mL}}{25.0 \text{ mL}} = 0.214\underline{8} = 0.215 \, M$$

b.   Concentration of NH_3OH^+ at the equivalence point is

$$[NH_3OH^+] = \frac{(25.0 \text{ mL})(0.215 \, M)}{25.0 \text{ mL} + 35.8 \text{ mL}} = 0.088\underline{4}0 \, M$$

$$K_a = \frac{K_w}{K_b} = \frac{1.0 \times 10^{-14}}{1.1 \times 10^{-8}} = 9.\underline{0}9 \times 10^{-7}$$

Use the table approach, and give the starting, change, and equilibrium concentrations.

Conc. (M)	$NH_3OH^+ + H_2O$	$\rightleftharpoons$	NH_2OH	+	H_3O^+
Starting	0.088$\underline{4}$0		0		0
Change	$-x$		$+x$		$+x$
Equilibrium	0.088$\underline{4}$0 $- x$		x		x

Substituting into the equilibrium-constant expression gives

$$K_a = \frac{[NH_2OH][H_3O^+]}{[NH_3OH^+]} = \frac{(x)^2}{(0.08840 - x)} \cong \frac{(x)^2}{(0.08840)} = 9.\underline{0}9 \times 10^{-7}$$

Rearranging and solving for x give

$$x = [H_3O^+] = \sqrt{(0.08840)(9.\underline{0}9 \times 10^{-7})} = 2.\underline{8}3 \times 10^{-4} \ M$$

$$pH = -\log(2.\underline{8}4 \times 10^{-4}) = 3.5\underline{4}7 = 3.55$$

c. You need an indicator to change color around a pH of 3 to 4. Therefore, the appropriate indicator is bromophenol blue. Select an indicator that changes color around the equivalence point.

16.125. a. $H_3O^+(aq) + NH_3(aq) \rightarrow NH_4^+(aq) + H_2O(l)$

b. $NH_4^+(aq) + OH^-(aq) \rightarrow NH_3(aq) + H_2O(l)$

c. Initial:

$$\text{mol } NH_3 = 1.0 \text{ mol/L} \times 0.100 \text{ L} = 0.1\underline{0}0 = 0.10 \text{ mol}$$

$$\text{mol } NH_4^+ = 0.50 \text{ mol/L} \times 0.100 \text{ L} \times \frac{2 \text{ mol } NH_4^+}{1 \text{ mol } (NH_4)_2SO_4} = 0.1\underline{0}0 = 0.10 \text{ mol}$$

After addition of HCl: The HCl is completely consumed by producing 0.0100\underline{0} mol of NH_4^+. The amount of NH_3 is decreased by 0.0100\underline{0} mol.

$$\text{mol HCl added} = 1.00 \text{ mol/L} \times 0.0100 \text{ L} = 0.0100\underline{0} \text{ mol}$$

$$\text{mol } NH_3 = 0.1\underline{0}0 - 0.0100\underline{0} = 0.0\underline{9}0 = 0.09 \text{ mol}$$

$$\text{mol } NH_4^+ = 0.1\underline{0}0 + 0.0100\underline{0} = 0.1\underline{1}0 = 0.11 \text{ mol}$$

The reaction is

$$NH_3 + H_2O \rightleftharpoons NH_4^+ + OH^-$$

Substituting into the equilibrium-constant expression gives

$$K_b = \frac{[NH_4^+][OH^-]}{[NH_3]} = \frac{(0.11)[OH^-]}{(0.09)} = 1.8 \times 10^{-5}$$

Rearranging and solving for $[OH^-]$ give

$$[OH^-] = 1.8 \times 10^{-5} \times \frac{0.090}{0.110} = \underline{1}.47 \times 10^{-5} \ M$$

$$pOH = -\log(\underline{1}.47 \times 10^{-5}) = 4.\underline{8}3$$

$$pH = 14 - pOH = 14 - 4.83 = 9.\underline{1}7 = 9.2$$

d. This is a buffer system, so the ratio of NH_4^+/NH_3 has not changed very much.

16.127. a. From the pH, $[H_3O^+] = 10^{-7.44} = 3.\underline{6}3 \times 10^{-8} \ M$. The reaction is

$$H_2PO_4^-(aq) + H_2O \rightleftharpoons H_3O^+(aq) + HPO_4^{2-}(aq) \quad K_{a_2} = 6.2 \times 10^{-8}$$

$$K_{a_2} = \frac{[HPO_4^{2-}][H_3O^+]}{[H_2PO_4^-]}$$

Rearranging gives

$$\frac{[H_2PO_4^-]}{[HPO_4^{2-}]} = \frac{[H_3O^+]}{K_{a_2}} = \frac{3.63 \times 10^{-8}}{6.2 \times 10^{-8}} = \frac{0.5855}{1} = 0.59 \text{ to } 1$$

Or, using the Henderson-Hasselbalch equation,

$$\text{pH} = \text{p}K_a + \log\frac{[\text{base}]}{[\text{acid}]};\qquad\qquad 7.44 = 7.21 + \log\frac{[\text{base}]}{[\text{acid}]}$$

$$\log\frac{[\text{base}]}{[\text{acid}]} = 0.23;\qquad\qquad \frac{[\text{base}]}{[\text{acid}]} = 10^{0.23} = 1.\underline{7}1$$

You must invert each side. The result is

$$\frac{[\text{acid}]}{[\text{base}]} = \frac{1}{1.71} = \frac{0.5857}{1} = 0.59 \text{ to } 1$$

b. $$[H_3O^+] = K_{a_2} \times \frac{[H_2PO_4^-]}{[HPO_4^{2-}]}$$

If $HPO_4^{2-} = 1.00$ mol, then when 25% of it is converted into $H_2PO_4^-$, 0.75 mol remains, and $H_2PO_4^-$ becomes $0.5\underline{8}6 + 0.25 = 0.8\underline{3}6$ mol. Therefore,

$$[H_3O^+] = 6.2 \times 10^{-8} \times \frac{0.836}{0.75} = 6.\underline{9}1 \times 10^{-8}$$

$$\text{pH} = -\log(6.\underline{9}1 \times 10^{-8}) = 7.1\underline{6}1 = 7.16$$

c. Assume $H_2PO_4^- = 0.5\underline{8}6$ mol. Then, the numbers of moles of $H_2PO_4^-$ remaining is

$$0.5\underline{8}6 - (0.15 \times 0.5\underline{8}6) = 0.85 \times 0.5\underline{8}6 = 0.4\underline{9}8 \text{ mol left}$$

The moles of $HPO_4^{2-} = 1.00 + (0.15 \times 0.5\underline{8}6) = 1.0\underline{8}8$ mol

$$[H_3O^+] = 6.2 \times 10^{-8} \times \frac{0.498}{1.088} = 2.\underline{8}4 \times 10^{-8}\ M$$

$$\text{pH} = -\log(2.84 \times 10^{-8}) = 7.5\underline{4}7 = 7.55$$

16.129. a. $$H_2A + H_2O \rightleftharpoons H_3O^+ + HA^-\quad K_{a_1}$$

$$HA^- + H_2O \rightleftharpoons H_3O^+ + A^{2-}\quad K_{a_2}$$

$$H_2A + 2\,H_2O \rightleftharpoons 2\,H_3O^+ + A^{2-},\ K = K_{a_1} \times K_{a_2}$$

b. $H_2A \gg H_3O^+ = HA^- \gg A^{2-}$

c.

$$H_2A\ +\ H_2O\ \rightleftharpoons\ H_3O^+\ +\ HA^-\qquad K_{a_1} = 1.0 \times 10^{-3}$$

$$0.0250 - x \qquad\qquad\qquad x \qquad\quad x$$

$$K_{a_1} = \frac{[HA^-][H_3O^+]}{[H_2A]} = \frac{(x)^2}{(0.0250 - x)} = 1.0 \times 10^{-3}$$

Rearranging into a quadratic equation and solving for x gives

$$x^2 + (1.0 \times 10^{-3})\, x + (-2.50 \times 10^{-5}) = 0$$

$$x = \frac{-(1.0 \times 10^{-3}) \pm \sqrt{(1.0 \times 10^{-3})^2 - (4)(1)(-2.50 \times 10^{-5})}}{2}$$

$$x = [H_3O^+] = [HA^-] = 4.\underline{5}2 \times 10^{-3} = 4.5 \times 10^{-3}\ M$$

$$pH = -\log(4.\underline{5}2 \times 10^{-3}) = 2.3\underline{4}4 = 2.34$$

$$[H_2A] = 0.0250 - x = 0.0250 - 4.52 \times 10^{-3} = 0.020\underline{4}8 = 0.0205\ M$$

d.

$$HA^- \ + \ H_2O \ \rightleftharpoons \ H_3O^+ \ + \ A^{2-} \qquad Ka_2 = 4.6 \times 10^{-5}$$

$$4.52 \times 10^{-3} + y \qquad\qquad 4.52 \times 10^{-3} + y \quad y$$

Assume y is small compared to $4.52 \times 10^{-3}\ M$. Substitute into the rearranged equilibrium-constant equation to get

$$[A^{2-}] = \frac{[HA^-]K_{a_2}}{[H_3O^+]} = \frac{(4.52 \times 10^{-3})(4.6 \times 10^{-5})}{(4.52 \times 10^{-3})} = 4.6 \times 10^{-5}\ M$$

16.131. a.   From the pH, $[H_3O^+] = 10^{-4.45} = 3.\underline{5}5 \times 10^{-5}\ M$. The $NaCH_3COO$ is generated by the acid-base reaction, resulting in the formation of a buffer solution. The reaction is

$$CH_3COOH \ + \ H_2O \ \rightleftharpoons \ H_3O^+ \ + \ CH_3COO^- \qquad K_a = 1.7 \times 10^{-5}$$

$$0.15 - x \qquad\qquad\qquad x \qquad\quad x$$

$$K_a = \frac{[H_3O^+][CH_3COO^-]}{[CH_3COOH]}$$

Rearranging gives

$$\frac{[CH_3COO^-]}{[CH_3COOH]} = \frac{K_a}{[H_3O^+]}$$

$$\frac{x}{0.15 - x} = \frac{1.7 \times 10^{-5}}{3.55 \times 10^{-5}}$$

Solving for x gives $x = 0.04\underline{8}6$ mol. Therefore, the molar concentration is

$$[CH_3COO^-] = 0.04\underline{8}6\ \text{mol}/0.375\ L = 0.1\underline{2}96 = 0.13\ M$$

b.   mol $OH^- =$ mol CH_3COO^-

$$0.04\underline{8}6\ \text{mol} = 0.25\ M \times V_{NaOH}$$

$$V_{NaOH} = 0.0486\ \text{mol}/0.25\ M = 0.1\underline{9}4 = 0.19\ L\ (1.9 \times 10^2\ mL)$$

c.   The volume of the original acid is $V = 0.375\ L - 0.1\underline{9}4\ L = 0.1\underline{8}1\ L$. Therefore, the concentration of the original acid is

$$[CH_3COOH] = 0.15\ \text{mol}/0.181\ L = 0.8\underline{2}9 = 0.83\ M$$

16.133. Natural rain dissolves carbon dioxide from the atmosphere to give a slightly acidic solution.

■ SOLUTIONS TO STRATEGY PROBLEMS

16.135. a.   Assemble the usual table of concentrations.

Conc. (M)	HClO + H$_2$O $\rightleftharpoons$	H$_3$O$^+$ +	ClO$^-$
Starting	0.05	0	0
Change	$-x$	$+x$	$+x$
Equilibrium	$0.05 - x$	x	x

Now substitute into the equilibrium expression, assume x is negligible compared to 0.05 M, and calculate [H$_3$O$^+$].

$$K_a = \frac{(x)^2}{(0.05-x)} \cong \frac{(x)^2}{(0.05)} = 3.5 \times 10^{-8}$$

$$x = [\text{H}_3\text{O}^+] = \underline{4}.18 \times 10^{-5} \, M$$

Finally, calculate the pH.

$$\text{pH} = -\log [\text{H}_3\text{O}^+] = -\log (4.18 \times 10^{-5}) = 4.\underline{37} = 4.4$$

b.   After 30.00 mL of 0.0250 M KOH is added, the reaction is

$$\text{HClO} + \text{OH}^- \rightarrow \text{ClO}^- + \text{H}_2\text{O}$$

The total volume at this point is 30.0 mL + 30.00 mL = 60.$\underline{00}$ mL.

The moles of HClO present at the start and the moles of OH$^-$ added are

$$\text{mol HClO} = M \times V = 0.05 \, M \times 30.0 \times 10^{-3} \, \text{L} = \underline{1}.50 \times 10^{-3} \, \text{mol}$$

$$\text{mol OH}^- = M \times V = 0.0250 \, M \times 30.0 \times 10^{-3} \, \text{L} = 0.75\underline{00} \times 10^{-3} \, \text{mol}$$

After reaction the moles of ClO$^-$ equal the moles of added OH$^-$. The moles of HClO present are

$$\text{mol HClO} = 1.50 \times 10^{-3} \, \text{mol} - 0.7500 \times 10^{-3} = \underline{0}.7500 \times 10^{-3} \, \text{mol}$$

Now calculate the concentrations.

$$[\text{HClO}] = \frac{0.7500 \times 10^{-3} \, \text{mol}}{60.00 \times 10^{-3} \, \text{L}} = 0.0\underline{1}25 \, M$$

$$[\text{ClO}^-] = \frac{0.7500 \times 10^{-3} \, \text{mol}}{60.00 \times 10^{-3} \, \text{L}} = 0.0\underline{1}25 \, M$$

Substitute into the K_a expression and solve for x = [H$_3$O$^+$].

$$K_a = 3.5 \times 10^{-8} = \frac{[\text{H}_3\text{O}^+][\text{ClO}^-]}{[\text{HClO}]} = \frac{(x)(0.0125 + x)}{(0.00125 - x)} \cong x$$

$$x = [\text{H}_3\text{O}^+] = 3.5 \times 10^{-8} \, M$$

$$\text{pH} = -\log (3.5 \times 10^{-8}) = 7.4\underline{55} = 7.46 \text{ (however, with the significant uncertainty in the canceled quantities, a pH of 7.5 is a better value to report)}$$

c. First calculate the volume of KOH added to reach the equivalence point.

$$V_2 = \frac{M_1 V_1}{M_2} = \frac{(0.05\ M)(30.0\ mL)}{(0.0250\ M)} = \underline{6}0.0\ mL$$

The total volume at this point is 30.0 mL + 60.0 mL = $\underline{9}$0.0 mL. The equilibrium is now

$$ClO^- + H_2O \rightleftharpoons HClO + OH^-$$

The moles of ClO^- present are the same as the moles of HClO present initially, $\underline{1}.50 \times 10^{-3}$ mol. The concentration is

$$[ClO^-] = \frac{1.50 \times 10^{-3}\ mol}{90.0 \times 10^{-3}\ L} = 0.0\underline{1}66\ M$$

Calculate the value of K_b from K_a, set up the equilibrium expression, and solve.

$$K_b = \frac{K_w}{K_a} = \frac{1.00 \times 10^{-14}}{3.5 \times 10^{-8}} = 2.\underline{8}5 \times 10^{-7}$$

$$K_b = 2.85 \times 10^{-7} = \frac{[HClO]\,[OH^-]}{[ClO^-]} = \frac{x^2}{(0.0166 - x)}$$

$$x = [OH^-] = \underline{6}.90 \times 10^{-5}\ M$$

$$pOH = -\log(6.90 \times 10^{-5}) = 4.\underline{1}61$$

$$pH = 14.00 - pOH = 14.00 - 4.161 = 9.\underline{8}4 = 9.8$$

d. The volume at this point is 90.0 mL + 4.0 mL = 94.0 mL. Now calculate the molarity of the excess KOH.

$$mol\ KOH\ added = M \times V = (0.0250\ M)(64.0 \times 10^{-3}\ L) = 1.\underline{6}0 \times 10^{-3}\ mol$$

$$Excess\ mol\ KOH = 1.60 \times 10^{-3}\ mol - \underline{1}.5 \times 10^{-3}\ mol = \underline{0}.10 \times 10^{-3}\ mol$$

$$[OH^-] = \frac{0.10 \times 10^{-3}\ mol}{94.0 \times 10^{-3}\ L} = 0.00\underline{1}06\ M$$

Finally, calculate the pOH and pH.

$$pOH = -\log(0.00106) = 2.\underline{9}73$$

$$pH = 14.00 - pOH = 14.00 - 2.973 = 11.\underline{0}2 = 11.0$$

16.137. The reaction is

$$B^- + H_2O \rightleftharpoons HB + OH^-$$

Calculate K_b from K_a and $[OH^-]$ from the pH 10.10.

$$K_b = \frac{K_w}{K_a} = \frac{1.00 \times 10^{-14}}{1.99 \times 10^{-9}} = 5.0\underline{2}5 \times 10^{-6}$$

$$pOH = 14.00 - pH = 14.00 - 10.10 = 3.90$$

$$[OH^-] = 10^{-pOH} = 10^{-3.90} = 1.\underline{2}58 \times 10^{-4}\ M$$

Now set up the equilibrium expression with $x = [OH^-]$ and solve for the initial concentration.

$$K_b = 5.0\underline{2}5 \times 10^{-6} = \frac{x^2}{[B^-]_0 - x} = \frac{(1.258 \times 10^{-4})^2}{[B^-]_0 - 1.258 \times 10^{-4}}$$

$$[B^-]_0 = 1.258 \times 10^{-4} + \frac{(1.258 \times 10^{-4})^2}{5.025 \times 10^{-6}} = 0.003\underline{2}7 = 0.0033 \ M$$

16.139. The equilibrium is

$$HOCN + H_2O \rightleftharpoons H_3O^+ + OCN^-$$

Set up the equilibrium expression and solve for $x = [H_3O^+]$.

$$K_a = 3.5 \times 10^{-4} = \frac{(x)(0.0419 + x)}{(0.293 - x)}$$

$$x = [H_3O^+] = \frac{(3.5 \times 10^{-4})(0.293 - x)}{(0.0419 + x)} \cong \frac{(3.5 \times 10^{-4})(0.293)}{(0.0419)} = 2.\underline{4}47 \times 10^{-3}$$

Finally, calculate the degree of ionization.

$$\text{Degree of ionization} = \frac{[H_3O^+]}{[HOCN]_o} = \frac{2.447 \times 10^{-3}}{0.293} = 8.\underline{3}5 \times 10^{-3} = 8.4 \times 10^{-3}$$

16.141. Before any HCl is added:

The total volume at this point is 529 mL + 494 mL = 1023 mL. Calculate the concentration of $HCHO_2$ and CHO_2^- after mixing together.

$$[HCHO_2] = \frac{M_1 V_1}{V_2} = \frac{(0.465 \ M)(529 \ \text{mL})}{(1023 \ \text{mL})} = 0.240\underline{4}5 \ M$$

$$[CHO_2^-] = \frac{M_1 V_1}{V_2} = \frac{(0.524 \ M)(494 \ \text{mL})}{(1023 \ \text{mL})} = 0.253\underline{0}3 \ M$$

The equilibrium is

$$HCHO_2 + H_2O \rightleftharpoons H_3O^+ + CHO_2^-$$

Now use the Hendersen-Hasselbalch equation to calculate the pH.

$$pH = pK_a + \log \frac{[\text{base}]}{[\text{acid}]} = -\log(1.7 \times 10^{-4}) + \log\left(\frac{0.25303}{0.24045}\right)$$

$$= 3.7\underline{6}95 + 0.022\underline{1}4 = 3.7\underline{9}1 = 3.79$$

After adding 110. mL of 0.152 M HCl:

The total volume is 1023 mL + 110. mL = 1123 mL. The concentration of $HCHO_2$ at this point is

$$[HCHO_2] = \frac{(\text{mol } HCHO_2 \text{ at start}) + (\text{mol HCl added})}{\text{total volume}}$$

$$[HCHO_2] = \frac{(0.465 \ M)(529 \ \text{mL}) + (0.152 \ M)(110. \ \text{mL})}{1133 \ \text{mL}} = 0.23\underline{1}86 \ M$$

The concentration of CHO_2^- at this point is

$$[CHO_2^-] = \frac{(\text{mol } CHO_2^- \text{ at start}) - (\text{mol HCl added})}{\text{total volume}}$$

$$[CHO_2^-] = \frac{(0.524\ M)(494\ \text{mL}) - (0.152\ M)(110.\ \text{mL})}{1133\ \text{mL}} = 0.21371\ M$$

Now use the Hendersen-Hasselbalch equation to calculate the pH.

$$pH = pK_a + \log \frac{[\text{base}]}{[\text{acid}]} = -\log (1.7 \times 10^{-4}) + \log \left(\frac{0.21371}{0.23186} \right)$$

$$= 3.7695 - 0.03540 = 3.734 = 3.73$$

16.143. In this system, HCl is in excess. The reaction is

$$Ca(OH)_2 + 2HCl \rightarrow CaCl_2 + 2H_2O$$

The total volume after mixing is 7.52 mL + 22.5 mL = 30.02 mL. Note that for each mole of $Ca(OH)_2$, two moles of HCl are reacted. Thus, the concentration of H_3O^+ after mixing is

$$[H_3O^+] = \frac{(\text{mol HCl at start}) - (2)(\text{mol } Ca(OH)_2 \text{ added})}{\text{total volume}}$$

$$[H_3O^+] = \frac{(0.11\ M)(22.5\ \text{mL}) - (2)(0.049\ M)(7.52\ \text{mL})}{30.02\ \text{mL}} = 0.05789\ M$$

Now, calculate the pH.

$$pH = -\log (0.05789) = 1.237 = 1.24$$

16.145. The dissolution equation is as follows:

$$NH_4NO_2(s) \rightarrow NH_4^+(aq) + NO_2^-(aq)$$

Both of the ions produced have properties that affect the pH of aqueous solutions. The NH_4^+ ion is the weak conjugate acid of NH_3 and the NO_2^- ion is the weak conjugate base of HNO_2. Their corresponding hydrolysis reactions in water are

$$NH_4^+ + H_2O \rightleftharpoons NH_3 + H_3O^+,\ K_a = \frac{K_w}{K_{b,NH_3}} = \frac{1.00 \times 10^{-14}}{1.8 \times 10^{-5}} = 5.6 \times 10^{-10}$$

$$NO_2^- + H_2O \rightleftharpoons HNO_2 + OH^-,\ K_b = \frac{K_w}{K_{a,HNO_2}} = \frac{1.00 \times 10^{-14}}{4.5 \times 10^{-4}} = 2.2 \times 10^{-11}$$

Since the K_a for NH_4^+ is greater than the K_b for NO_2^-, the solution will be slightly acidic. To make an aqueous solution of NH_4NO_2 neutral, a base would therefore have to be added. The only choice available is KOH. Adding HCl would make the solution more acidic and adding NaCl would produce no changes in the pH other than that observed through dilution.

16.147. a. The only solution capable of providing a weak base component to a buffer having a pH greater than 7 is the 50.0 mL of 0.10 M NH_3. If a strong acid is added to this weak base solution, NH_4^+, the weak acid component of the buffer, will be produced. If 50.0 mL of 0.10 M HCl is added, all of the NH_3 will be converted to NH_4^+. This would be a solution having zero buffer capacity. On the other hand, if 20.0 mL of 0.10 HNO_3 is added, only a portion of the NH_3 would be converted to NH_4^+. This would result in a buffer solution having pH > 7 with significant quantities of both NH_3 and NH_4^+ being present.

b. Initially 5.00×10^{-3} moles of NH_3 is present with very little NH_4^+ being produced via ionization. When the 2.00×10^{-3} moles of HNO_3 is added, the following reaction shifts to the right to convert 2.00×10^{-3} moles of NH_3 to 2.00×10^{-3} moles of NH_4^+:

$$NH_3 + H_3O^+ \rightleftharpoons NH_4^+ + H_2O$$

The total solution volume is 50.0 mL + 20.0 mL = 70.0 mL.

Calculate the concentrations of NH_3 and NH_4^+ after mixing the two solutions.

$$[NH_3] = \frac{3.0 \times 10^{-3}\,\text{moles}}{0.0700\,\text{L}} = 0.0428\,M$$

$$[NH_4^+] = \frac{2.0 \times 10^{-3}\,\text{moles}}{0.0700\,\text{L}} = 0.0286\,M$$

The equilibrium is

$$NH_3 + H_2O \rightleftharpoons NH_4^+ + OH^-$$

Calculate K_a from K_b.

$$K_a = \frac{K_w}{K_b} = \frac{1.00 \times 10^{-14}}{1.8 \times 10^{-5}} = 5.\underline{5}55 \times 10^{-10}$$

Now use the Hendersen-Hasselbalch equation to calculate the pH.

$$pH = pK_a + \log \frac{[\text{base}]}{[\text{acid}]} = -\log(5.55 \times 10^{-10}) + \log\left(\frac{0.0428}{0.0286}\right)$$

$$pH = 9.2\underline{5}5 + 0.1\underline{7}6 = 9.4\underline{3}0 = 9.43$$

16.149. a. (d) is the correct selection. The pH of the solution at the equivalence point is between 2.0 and 7.0.

b. (c) is the correct selection. Because the solution contains the conjugate acid of the weak base at the equivalence point, the solution will be acidic. An example would be the titration of NH_3 with HCl where all of the NH_3 has been converted to NH_4^+ at the equivalence point.

■ SOLUTIONS TO CUMULATIVE-SKILLS PROBLEMS

16.151. Use the pH to calculate $[H_3O^+]$, and then use the K_a of 1.7×10^{-5} and the K_a expression to calculate the molarity of acetic acid (HAc), assuming ionization is negligible. Convert molarity to mass percentage using the formula mass of 60.05 g/mol of HAc.

$$[H_3O^+] = \text{antilog}\,(-2.45) = 3.\underline{5}48 \times 10^{-3}\,M$$

Write the equilibrium-constant expression in terms of chemical symbols, and then substitute the x and the (0.003548 M) terms into the expression:

$$K_a \doteq \frac{[H_3O^+][Ac^-]}{[HAc]} \cong \frac{(0.003548)^2}{(x)}$$

Solve the equation for x, assuming 0.003548 is much smaller than x.

$$x = (0.003548)^2 \div (1.7 \times 10^{-5}) \cong [HAc] \cong 0.7\underline{4}04 \ M$$

$$(0.7\underline{4}04 \text{ mol HAc/L}) \times (60.05 \text{ g/mol}) \times (1 \text{ L/1090 g})(100\%) = 4.\underline{0}79 = 4.1\% \text{ HAc}$$

16.153. Find $[H_3O^+]$ and $[C_2H_3O_2^-]$ by solving for the approximate $[H_3O^+]$, noting that x is much smaller than the starting 0.92 M of acetic acid. The usual table is used but is not shown; only the final setup for $[H_3O^+]$ is shown. Use $K_f = 1.858$ °C/m for the constant for water.

$$[H_3O^+] = [C_2H_3O_2^-] = (1.7 \times 10^{-5} \times 0.92)^{1/2} = 0.003\underline{9}54 \ M$$

Total molarity of acid + ions = 0.92 + 0.003954 = 0.9\underline{2}39

The mass of water in 1 L of solution is

$$1000 \text{ mL} \times 1.008 \text{ g/mL} - 0.92 \text{ mol} \times 60.05 \text{ g/mol} = 95\underline{2}.8 \text{ g} = 0.95\underline{2}8 \text{ kg}$$

Molality = m = 0.9\underline{2}39 mol ÷ (1.000 L × 0.9528 kg H_2O/L) = 0.9\underline{6}97 m

Freezing point = $-\Delta T_f = -K_f c_m = (-1.858 \text{ °C}/m) \times 0.9\underline{6}97 \ m = -1.\underline{8}02 = -1.8$°C

16.155. The $[H_3O^+] = -$antilog $(-4.35) = 4.\underline{4}6 \times 10^{-5} \ M$. Note that 0.465 L of 0.0941 M NaOH will produce 0.0437\underline{5}6 mol of acetate, Ac^-, ion. Rearranging the K_a expression for acetic acid (HAc) and Ac^- and canceling the volume in the mol/L of each, you obtain

$$\frac{[HAc]}{[Ac^-]} = \frac{[H^+]}{K_a} = \frac{4.46 \times 10^{-5}}{1.7 \times 10^{-5}} = \frac{2.63}{1.00} \cong \frac{x \text{ mol HAc}}{0.043756 \text{ mol Ac}^-}$$

$$x = 0.1\underline{1}48 \text{ mol HAc}$$

Total moles of HAc added = 0.1148 + 0.0437\underline{5}6 = 0.1\underline{5}86 mol HAc

$$\text{mol/L of pure HAc} = 1049 \text{ g HAc/L} \times (1 \text{ mol HAc/60.05 g}) = 17.4\underline{6}7 \text{ mol/L}$$

L of pure HAc needed = 0.1\underline{5}86 mol HAc × (L/17.467 mol) = 0.009\underline{0}8 L (9.1 mL)

CHAPTER 17

Solubility and Complex-Ion Equilibria

■ SOLUTIONS TO EXERCISES

Note on significant figures If the final answer to a solution needs to be rounded off, it is given first with one nonsignificant figure, and the last significant figure is underlined. The final answer is then rounded to the correct number of significant figures. In multistep problems, intermediate answers are given with at least one nonsignificant figure; however, only the final answer has been rounded off.

17.1. a. $BaSO_4(s) \rightleftharpoons Ba^{2+}(aq) + SO_4^{2-}(aq)$ $K_{sp} = [Ba^{2+}][SO_4^{2-}]$

 b. $Fe(OH)_3(s) \rightleftharpoons Fe^{3+}(aq) + 3OH^-(aq)$ $K_{sp} = [Fe^{3+}][OH^-]^3$

 c. $Ca_3(PO_4)_2(s) \rightleftharpoons 3Ca^{2+}(aq) + 2PO_4^{3-}(aq)$ $K_{sp} = [Ca^{2+}]^3[PO_4^{3-}]^2$

17.2. Calculate the molar solubility. Then assemble the usual concentration table, and substitute the equilibrium concentrations from it into the equilibrium-constant expression. (Because no concentrations can be given for solid AgCl, dashes are written. In later problems, similar spaces will be left blank.)

$$\frac{1.9 \times 10^{-3} \text{ g}}{1 \text{ L}} \times \frac{1 \text{ mol}}{143 \text{ g}} = 1.\underline{3}3 \times 10^{-5} \ M$$

Set up the table as usual.

Conc. (M)	AgCl(s) $\rightleftharpoons$	Ag$^+$	+ Cl$^-$
Starting	—	0	0
Change	—	$+1.33 \times 10^{-5}$	$+1.33 \times 10^{-5}$
Equilibrium	—	1.33×10^{-5}	1.33×10^{-5}

$$K_{sp} = [Ag^+][Cl^-] = (1.33 \times 10^{-5})(1.33 \times 10^{-5}) = 1.\underline{7}68 \times 10^{-10} = 1.8 \times 10^{-10}$$

17.3. Calculate the molar solubility. Then assemble the usual concentration table, and substitute from it into the equilibrium-constant expression. (Because no concentrations can be given for solid $Pb_3(AsO_4)_2$, spaces are left blank.)

$$\frac{3.0 \times 10^{-5} \text{ g}}{1 \text{ L}} \times \frac{1 \text{ mol}}{899 \text{ g}} = 3.\underline{3}4 \times 10^{-8} \ M$$

Conc. (M)	$Pb_3(AsO_4)_2(s)$	$\rightleftharpoons$	$3Pb^{2+}$	+	$2AsO_4^{3-}$
Starting			0		0
Change			$+3(3.34 \times 10^{-8})$		$+2(3.34 \times 10^{-8})$
Equilibrium			$3(3.34 \times 10^{-8})$		$2(3.34 \times 10^{-8})$

$$K_{sp} = [Pb^{2+}]^3[AsO_4^{3-}]^2 = [3 \times (3.34 \times 10^{-8})]^3(2 \times 3.34 \times 10^{-8})^2 = 4.\underline{4}89 \times 10^{-36} = 4.5 \times 10^{-36}$$

17.4. Assemble the usual concentration table. Let x equal the molar solubility of $CaSO_4$. When x mol $CaSO_4$ dissolves in 1 L of solution, x mol Ca^{2+} and x mol SO_4^{2-} form.

Conc. (M)	$CaSO_4(s)$	$\rightleftharpoons$	Ca^{2+}	+	SO_4^{2-}
Starting			0		0
Change			$+x$		$+x$
Equilibrium			x		x

Substitute the equilibrium concentrations into the equilibrium-constant expression, and solve for x. Then convert to g $CaSO_4$ per liter.

$$[Ca^{2+}][SO_4^{2-}] = K_{sp}$$

$$(x)(x) = x^2 = 2.4 \times 10^{-5}$$

$$x = \sqrt{(2.4 \times 10^{-5})} = 4.\underline{8}9 \times 10^{-3}\ M$$

$$\frac{4.89 \times 10^{-3}\ \text{mol}}{L} \times \frac{136\ g}{1\ \text{mol}} = 0.6\underline{6}64 = 0.67\ \text{g/L}$$

17.5. a. Let x equal the molar solubility of BaF_2. Assemble the usual concentration table, and substitute from the table into the equilibrium-constant expression.

Conc. (M)	$BaF_2(s)$	$\rightleftharpoons$	Ba^{2+}	+	$2F^-$
Starting			0		0
Change			$+x$		$+2x$
Equilibrium			x		$2x$

$$[Ba^{2+}][F^-]^2 = K_{sp}$$

$$(x)(2x)^2 = 4x^3 = 1.0 \times 10^{-6}$$

$$x = \sqrt[3]{\frac{1.0 \times 10^{-6}}{4}} = 6.\underline{2}99 \times 10^{-3} = 6.3 \times 10^{-3}\ M$$

b. At the start, before any BaF_2 dissolves, the solution contains 0.15 M F^-. At equilibrium, x mol of solid BaF_2 dissolves to yield x mol Ba^{2+} and $2x$ mol F^-. Assemble the usual concentration table, and substitute the equilibrium concentrations into the equilibrium-constant expression. As an approximation, assume x is negligible compared to 0.15 M F^-.

Conc. (M)	$BaF_2(s)$	$\rightleftharpoons$	Ba^{2+}	+	$2F^-$
Starting			0		0.15
Change			$+x$		$+2x$
Equilibrium			x		$0.15 + 2x$

$$[Ba^{2+}][F^-]^2 = K_{sp}$$

$$(x)(0.15 + 2x)^2 \cong (x)(0.15)^2 \cong 1.0 \times 10^{-6}$$

$$x \cong \frac{1.0 \times 10^{-6}}{(0.15)^2} = 4.\underline{4}44 \times 10^{-5} = 4.4 \times 10^{-5} \, M$$

Note that adding $2x$ to 0.15 M will not change it (to two significant figures), so $2x$ is negligible compared to 0.15 M. The solubility of 4.4×10^{-5} M in 0.15 M NaF is lower than the solubility of 6.3×10^{-3} M in pure water.

17.6. Calculate the ion product, Q_c, after evaporation, assuming no precipitation has occurred. Compare it with the K_{sp}.

$$Q_c = [Ca^{2+}][SO_4^{2-}] = (2 \times 0.0052)(2 \times 0.0041) = 8.528 \times 10^{-5}$$

Since $Q_c > K_{sp}$ (2.4×10^{-5}), precipitation occurs.

17.7. Calculate the concentrations of Pb^{2+} and SO_4^{2-}, assuming no precipitation. Use a total volume of 0.456 L + 0.255 L, or 0.711 L.

$$[Pb^{2+}] = \frac{\dfrac{0.00016 \text{ mol}}{L} \times 0.255 \text{ L}}{0.711 \text{ L}} = 5.\underline{7}4 \times 10^{-5} \, M$$

$$[SO_4^{2-}] = \frac{\dfrac{0.00023 \text{ mol}}{L} \times 0.456 \text{ L}}{0.711 \text{ L}} = 1.\underline{4}8 \times 10^{-4} \, M$$

Calculate the ion product, and compare it to K_{sp}.

$$Q_c = [Pb^{2+}][SO_4^{2-}] = (5.74 \times 10^{-5})(1.48 \times 10^{-4}) = 8.\underline{4}9 \times 10^{-9}$$

Since Q_c is less than the K_{sp} of 1.7×10^{-8}, no precipitation occurs, and the solution is unsaturated.

17.8. The solubility of AgCN would increase as the pH decreases, because the increasing concentration of H_3O^+ would react with the CN^- to form the weakly ionized acid HCN. As CN^- is removed, more AgCN dissolves to replace the cyanide:

$$AgCN(s) \rightleftharpoons Ag^+(aq) + CN^-(aq) \; [+ \, H_3O^+ \rightarrow HCN + H_2O]$$

In the case of AgCl, the chloride ion is the conjugate base of a strong acid and would, therefore, not be affected by any amount of hydrogen ion.

17.9. Because $K_f = 4.8 \times 10^{12}$ and because the starting concentration of NH_3 is much larger than that of the Cu^{2+} ion, you can make a rough assumption that most of the copper(II) is converted to $Cu(NH_3)_4^{2+}$ ion. This ion then dissociates slightly to give a small concentration of Cu^{2+} and additional NH_3. The amount of NH_3 remaining at the start after reacting with 0.015 M Cu^{2+} is

$$[0.100 \, M - (4 \times 0.015 \, M)] = 0.040 \, M \text{ starting } NH_3$$

Assemble the usual concentration table using this starting concentration for NH_3 and assuming the starting concentration of Cu^{2+} is zero.

Conc. (M)	$Cu(NH_3)_4^{2+}$	$\rightleftharpoons$	Cu^{2+}	+	$4NH_3$
Starting	0.015		0		0.040
Change	$-x$		$+x$		$+4x$
Equilibrium	$0.015 - x$		$+x$		$0.040 + 4x$

Even though this reaction is the opposite of the equation for the formation constant, the formation-constant expression can be used. Simply substitute all exact equilibrium concentrations into the formation-constant expression; then simplify the exact equation by assuming x is negligible compared to 0.015 and $4x$ is negligible compared to 0.040.

$$K_f = \frac{[Cu(NH_3)_4^{2+}]}{[Cu^{2+}][NH_3]^4} = \frac{(0.015 - x)}{(x)(0.040 + 4x)^4} \cong \frac{(0.015)}{(x)(0.040)^4} \cong 4.8 \times 10^{12}$$

Rearrange and solve for x:

$$x = [Cu^{2+}] \cong (0.015) \div [(4.8 \times 10^{12})(0.040)^4] \cong 1.\underline{2}2 \times 10^{-9} = 1.2 \times 10^{-9} \ M$$

17.10. Start by calculating the $[Ag^+]$ in equilibrium with the $Ag(CN)_2^-$ formed from Ag^+ and CN^-. Then use the $[Ag^+]$ to decide whether or not AgI will precipitate by calculating the ion product and comparing it with the K_{sp} of 8.3×10^{-17} for AgI. Assume all the $0.0045 \ M \ Ag^+$ reacts with CN^- to form $0.0045 \ M \ Ag(CN)_2^-$, and calculate the remaining CN^-. Use these as starting concentrations for the usual concentration table.

$$[0.20 \ M \ KCN - (2 \times 0.0045 \ M)] = 0.1\underline{9}1 \ M \ \text{starting} \ CN^-$$

Conc. (M)	$Ag(CN)_2^-$	$\rightleftharpoons$	Ag^+	+	$2CN^-$
Starting	0.0045		0		0.191
Change	$-x$		$+x$		$+2x$
Equilibrium	$0.0045 - x$		x		$0.191 + 2x$

Even though this reaction is the opposite of the equation for the formation constant, the formation-constant expression can be used. Simply substitute all exact equilibrium concentrations into the formation-constant expression; then simplify the exact equation by assuming $\times$ is negligible compared to 0.0045 and $2x$ is negligible compared to 0.191.

$$K_f = \frac{[Ag(CN)_2^-]}{[Ag^+][CN^-]^2} = \frac{(0.0045 - x)}{(x)(0.191 + 2x)^2} \cong \frac{(0.0045)}{(x)(0.191)^2} \cong 5.6 \times 10^{18}$$

Rearrange and solve for x:

$$x = [Ag^+] \cong (0.0045) \div [(5.6 \times 10^{18})(0.191)^2] \cong 2.\underline{2}02 \times 10^{-20} \ M$$

Now, calculate the ion product for AgI:

$$Q_c = [Ag^+][I^-] = (2.20 \times 10^{-20})(0.15) = 3.\underline{3}0 \times 10^{-21} = 3.3 \times 10^{-21}$$

Because Q_c is less than the K_{sp} of 8.3×10^{-17}, no precipitate will form, and the solution is unsaturated.

17.11. Obtain the overall equilibrium constant for this reaction from the product of the individual equilibrium constants of the two individual equations whose sum gives this equation:

$AgBr(s)$	$\rightleftharpoons$	$Ag^+(aq) + Br^-(aq)$	$K_{sp} = 5.0 \times 10^{-13}$
$Ag^+(aq) + 2S_2O_3^{2-}(aq)$	$\rightleftharpoons$	$Ag(S_2O_3)_2^{3-}(aq)$	$K_f = 2.9 \times 10^{13}$
$AgBr(s) + 2S_2O_3^{2-}(aq)$	$\rightleftharpoons$	$Ag(S_2O_3)_2^{3-}(aq) + Br^-(aq)$	$K_c = K_{sp} \times K_f = 14.5$

Assemble the usual table using 1.0 M as the starting concentration of $S_2O_3^{2-}$ and x as the unknown concentration of $Ag(S_2O_3)_2^{3-}$ formed.

Conc. (M)	$AgBr(s)$	+	$2S_2O_3^{2-}$	$\rightleftharpoons$	$Ag(S_2O_3)_2^{3-}$	+	Br^-
Starting			1.0		0		0
Change			$-2x$		$+x$		$+x$
Equilibrium			$1.0 - 2x$		x		x

The equilibrium-constant expression can now be used. Simply substitute all exact equilibrium concentrations into the equilibrium-constant expression. The solution can be obtained without using the quadratic equation.

$$K_c = \frac{[Ag(S_2O_3)_2^{3-}][Br^-]}{[S_2O_3^{2-}]^2} = \frac{(x)^2}{(1.0-2x)^2} = 14.5$$

Take the square root of both sides of the two right-hand terms, and solve for x:

$$\frac{x}{(1.0-2x)} = 3.\underline{8}08$$

$$x = 3.808\,(1.0 - 2x)$$

$$7.62x + x = 3.808$$

$$x = 0.4\underline{4}17 = 0.44\ M \text{ (molar solubility of AgBr in 1.0 } M\ Na_2S_2O_3)$$

■ ANSWERS TO CONCEPT CHECKS

17.1. Solubility and K_{sp} are related, although not directly. You can compare K_{sp}'s for a series of salts, however, if they have the same number of cations and anions in each of their formulas. (In that case, K_{sp} and solubility are related in the same way for each salt.) In this problem, each of the lead(II) compounds has one Pb^{2+} cation and one anion, so you can compare the K_{sp}'s directly. Lead(II) sulfate has the largest K_{sp} and, therefore, is the most soluble of these lead(II) compounds.

17.2. Let's look at each compound in turn. $NaNO_3$ has no ion in common with $PbSO_4$, so it should have little effect on its solubility. Na_2SO_4 is a soluble compound and provides the common ion SO_4^{2-}, which would suppress the solubility of $PbSO_4$. PbS has an ion in common with $PbSO_4$ (Pb^{2+}), but the compound is so insoluble that very little of the Pb^{2+} ion is available. Because of this, the solubility of $PbSO_4$ is little affected by the PbS. Therefore, the $NaNO_3$ solution will dissolve the most $PbSO_4$.

17.3. If NaCl were added to a saturated AgCl solution, the equilibrium would shift to consume the added chloride ion, and some AgCl would precipitate. After the addition of two Cl^- ions, there would be six Cl^- ions, four Ag^+ ions, and one AgCl formula unit. The solution would look like the following (For clarity, Na^+ is not shown).

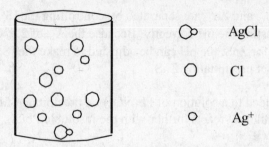

17.4. If you compare K_{sp}'s for magnesium oxalate (8.5×10^{-5}) and calcium oxalate (2.3×10^{-9}), you can see magnesium oxalate is much more soluble in water solution than the calcium salt (the K_{sp} is larger). This means it provides a greater concentration of oxalate ion. In water solution, some of the magnesium oxalate dissolves, giving an oxalate ion concentration that tends to suppress the dissolution of calcium oxalate (common-ion effect). The addition of acid tends to remove oxalate ion, but this is replenished by the dissolution of more magnesium oxalate. Therefore, you would expect the magnesium oxalate to be more likely to dissolve.

■ ANSWERS TO SELF-ASSESSMENT AND REVIEW QUESTIONS

17.1. The solubility equation is $Ni(OH)_2(s) \rightleftharpoons Ni^{2+}(aq) + 2OH^-(aq)$. If the molar solubility of $Ni(OH)_2$ = x molar, the concentrations of the ions in the solution must be x M Ni^{2+} and $2x$ M OH^-. Substituting into the equilibrium-constant expression gives

$$K_{sp} = [Ni^{2+}][OH^-]^2 = (x)(2x)^2 = 4x^3$$

17.2. Calcium sulfate is less soluble in a solution containing sodium sulfate because the increase in sulfate from the sodium sulfate causes the equilibrium composition in the equation below to shift to the left:

$$CaSO_4(s) \rightleftharpoons Ca^{2+}(aq) + SO_4^{2-}(aq)$$

The result is a decrease in the calcium ion concentration and a decrease in the solubility of calcium sulfate.

17.3. Substitute the 0.10 M concentration of chloride into the solubility product expression and solve for $[Ag^+]$:

$$[Ag^+] = \frac{K_{sp}}{[Cl^-]} = \frac{1.8 \times 10^{-10}}{0.10} = 1.\underline{8}0 \times 10^{-9} = 1.8 \times 10^{-9} \ M$$

17.4. In order to predict whether or not PbI_2 will precipitate when lead nitrate and potassium iodide are mixed, the concentrations of Pb^{2+} and I^- after mixing would have to be calculated first (if the concentrations are not known or are not given). Then, the value of Q_c, the ion product, would have to be calculated for PbI_2. Finally, Q_c would have to be compared with the value of K_{sp}. If $Q_c > K_{sp}$, then a precipitate will form at equilibrium. If $Q_c \leq K_{sp}$, no precipitate will form.

17.5. Barium fluoride, normally insoluble in water, dissolves in dilute hydrochloric acid because the fluoride ion, once it forms, reacts with the hydronium ion to form weakly ionized HF:

$$BaF_2(s) \rightleftharpoons Ba^{2+}(aq) + 2F^-(aq) \ [+ 2H_3O^+ \rightarrow 2HF + 2H_2O]$$

17.6. Metal ions such as Pb^{2+} and Zn^{2+} are separated by controlling the $[S^{2-}]$ in a solution of saturated H_2S by means of adjusting the pH correctly. Because the K_{sp} of 2.5×10^{-27} for PbS is smaller than the K_{sp} of 1.1×10^{-21} for ZnS, the pH can be adjusted to make the $[S^{2-}]$ just high enough to precipitate PbS without precipitating ZnS.

17.7. When NaCl is first added to a solution of $Pb(NO_3)_2$, a precipitate of $PbCl_2$ forms. As more NaCl is added, the excess chloride reacts further with the insoluble $PbCl_2$, forming soluble complex ions of $PbCl_3^-$ and $PbCl_4^{2-}$:

$$Pb^{2+}(aq) + 2Cl^-(aq) \rightleftharpoons PbCl_2(s)$$

$$PbCl_2(s) + Cl^-(aq) \rightleftharpoons PbCl_3^-(aq)$$

$$PbCl_3^-(aq) + Cl^-(aq) \rightleftharpoons PbCl_4^{2-}(aq)$$

17.8. When a small amount of NaOH is added to a solution of $Al_2(SO_4)_3$, a precipitate of $Al(OH)_3$ forms at first. As more NaOH is added, the excess hydroxide ion reacts further with the insoluble $Al(OH)_3$, forming a soluble complex ion of $Al(OH)_4^-$.

17.9. The Ag^+, Cu^{2+}, and Ni^{2+} ions can be separated in two steps: (1) Add HCl to precipitate just the Ag^+ as AgCl, leaving the others in solution. (2) After pouring the solution away from the precipitate, add 0.3 M HCl and H_2S to precipitate only the CuS away from the Ni^{2+} ion, whose sulfide is soluble under these conditions.

17.10. By controlling the pH through the appropriate buffer, one can control the $[CO_3^{2-}]$ using the equilibrium reaction:

$$H_3O^+(aq) + CO_3^{2-}(aq) \rightleftharpoons HCO_3^-(aq) + H_2O(l)$$

Calcium carbonate is much less soluble than magnesium carbonate and thus will precipitate in weakly basic solution, whereas magnesium carbonate will not. Magnesium carbonate will precipitate only in highly basic solution. (There is the possibility that $Mg(OH)_2$ might precipitate, but the $[OH^-]$ is too low for this to occur.)

17.11. The answer is c, 9.1×10^{-40}.

17.12. The answer is e, $K_{sp} = [Ag^+]^3[PO_4^{3-}]$.

17.13. The answer is d, $1.1 \times 10^{-8} M$.

17.14. The answer is a, AX.

■ ANSWERS TO CONCEPTUAL PROBLEMS

17.17. a. Since both compounds contain the same number of ions, the salt with the larger K_{sp} value will be more soluble. The K_{sp} for AgCl is 1.8×10^{-10} and for AgI is 8.3×10^{-17}. Therefore, silver chloride (AgCl) is more soluble.

b. Since both compounds contain the same number of ions, the salt with the larger K_{sp} value will be more soluble. The K_{sp} for $Mg(OH)_2$ is 1.8×10^{-11} and for $Cu(OH)_2$ is 2.6×10^{-19}. Therefore, magnesium hydroxide ($Mg(OH)_2$) is more soluble.

17.19. Let's consider each possibility. (a) In adding 0.1 M NaCl to saturated $PbCl_2$, almost all of the $PbCl_2$ would be precipitated from the solution, since the NaCl is soluble and is a solution of the common ion, Cl^-. (b) PbS is the least soluble of the two compounds, $PbCl_2$ and PbS. Thus, PbS would be nearly all precipitated by the Pb^{2+} provided by the $PbCl_2$ solution. (c) The 0.1 M $NaClO_4$ should give no precipitate; $Pb(ClO_4)_2$ is expected to be soluble. Comparing (a) with (b), since $PbCl_2$ is much more soluble than PbS, it is expected to form the most precipitate, given similar volumes of solution. Therefore, the answer is (a).

17.21. The beaker on the left depicts all the NaCl as individual formula units in solution. This implies NaCl is a soluble nonelectrolye, which is not the case since NaCl is a very soluble ionic compound that produces ions in solution. The center beaker depicts NaCl as a soluble ionic compound that completely dissolves in solution, producing only $Na^+(aq)$ and $Cl^-(aq)$. This must be correct since NaCl is a very soluble ionic compound. The beaker on the right indicates that there are ions of Na^+ and Cl^- present in the solution, along with solid NaCl. The presence of solid is not consistent with NaCl being an unsaturated solution as stated in the problem.

17.23. Add just enough Na_2SO_4 to precipitate all the Ba^{2+}; filter off the $BaSO_4$; add more Na_2SO_4 to precipitate all the Ca^{2+}; filter off the $CaSO_4$; Mg^{2+} remains in the solution.

■ SOLUTIONS TO PRACTICE PROBLEMS

Note on significant figures If the final answer to a solution needs to be rounded off, it is given first with one nonsignificant figure, and the last significant figure is underlined. The final answer is then rounded to the correct number of significant figures. In multistep problems, intermediate answers are given with at least one nonsignificant figure; however, only the final answer has been rounded off.

17.25. a. NaBr is soluble (Group IA salts are soluble).

b. PbI_2 is insoluble (PbI_2 is an insoluble iodide).

c. $BaCO_3$ is insoluble (carbonates are generally insoluble).

d. $(NH_4)_2SO_4$ is soluble (all ammonium salts are soluble).

17.27. a. $K_{sp} = [Mg^{2+}][OH^-]^2$ b. $K_{sp} = [Sr^{2+}][CO_3^{2-}]$

c. $K_{sp} = [Ca^{2+}]^3[AsO_4^{3-}]^2$ d. $K_{sp} = [Fe^{3+}][OH^-]^3$

17.29. Calculate molar solubility, assemble the usual table, and substitute the equilibrium concentrations from it into the equilibrium-constant expression. (Dashes are given for $AgBrO_3(s)$. They simply imply that some of the solid is present. In later problems, the dashes may be omitted.)

$$\frac{7.2 \times 10^{-3}\ g}{L} \times \frac{1\ mol}{236\ g} = 3.0\underline{5} \times 10^{-5}\ M$$

Conc. (M)	$AgBrO_3(s)$	$\rightleftharpoons$	Ag^+	$+$	BrO_3^-
Starting	—		0		0
Change	—		$+3.05 \times 10^{-5}$		$+3.05 \times 10^{-5}$
Equilibrium	—		3.05×10^{-5}		3.05×10^{-5}

$$K_{sp} = [Ag^+][BrO_3^-] = (3.05 \times 10^{-5})(3.05 \times 10^{-5}) = 9.\underline{3}02 \times 10^{-10} = 9.3 \times 10^{-10}$$

17.31. Calculate the molar solubility. Then assemble the usual concentration table, and substitute the equilibrium concentrations from it into the equilibrium-constant expression.

$$\frac{0.13 \text{ g}}{0.100 \text{ L}} \times \frac{1 \text{ mol}}{413 \text{ g}} = 3.\underline{1}47 \times 10^{-3} \text{ } M$$

Conc. (M)	$Cu(IO_3)_2(s)$	$\rightleftharpoons$	Cu^{2+}	$+$	$2IO_3^-$
Starting			0		0
Change			$+3.147 \times 10^{-3}$		$+2 \times 3.147 \times 10^{-3}$
Equilibrium			3.147×10^{-3}		$2 \times 3.147 \times 10^{-3}$

$$K_{sp} = [Cu^{2+}][IO_3^-]^2 = (3.147 \times 10^{-3})[2(3.147 \times 10^{-3})]^2 = 1.\underline{2}47 \times 10^{-7} = 1.2 \times 10^{-7}$$

17.33. Calculate the pOH from the pH, and then convert pOH to $[OH^-]$. Then assemble the usual concentration table, and substitute the equilibrium concentrations from it into the equilibrium-constant expression.

$$pOH = 14.00 - 10.52 = 3.48$$

$$[OH^-] = \text{antilog}(-pOH) = \text{antilog}(-3.48) = 3.\underline{3}11 \times 10^{-4} \text{ } M$$

$$[Mg^{2+}] = [OH^-] \div 2 = (3.311 \times 10^{-4}) \div 2 = 1.\underline{6}55 \times 10^{-4} \text{ } M$$

Conc. (M)	$Mg(OH)_2(s)$	$\rightleftharpoons$	Mg^{2+}	$+$	$2OH^-$
Starting			0		0
Change			$+1.\underline{6}55 \times 10^{-4}$		$+3.\underline{3}11 \times 10^{-4}$
Equilibrium			$1.\underline{6}55 \times 10^{-4}$		$3.\underline{3}11 \times 10^{-4}$

$$K_{sp} = [Mg^{2+}][OH^-]^2 = (1.\underline{6}55 \times 10^{-4})(3.\underline{3}11 \times 10^{-4})^2 = 1.\underline{8}1 \times 10^{-11} = 1.8 \times 10^{-11}$$

17.35. Assemble the usual concentration table. Let x equal the molar solubility of $SrCO_3$. When x mol $SrCO_3$ dissolves in 1 L of solution, x mol Sr^{2+} and x mol CO_3^{2-} form.

Conc. (M)	$SrCO_3(s)$	$\rightleftharpoons$	Sr^{2+}	$+$	CO_3^{2-}
Starting			0		0
Change			$+x$		$+x$
Equilibrium			x		x

Substitute the equilibrium concentrations into the equilibrium-constant expression and solve for x. Then convert to grams $SrCO_3$ per liter.

$$[Sr^{2+}][CO_3^{2-}] = K_{sp}$$

$$(x)(x) = x^2 = 9.3 \times 10^{-10}$$

$$x = \sqrt{(9.3 \times 10^{-10})} = 3.\underline{0}4 \times 10^{-5} \text{ } M$$

$$\frac{3.04 \times 10^{-5} \text{ mol}}{L} \times \frac{147.63 \text{ g}}{1 \text{ mol SrCO}_3} = 4.\underline{5}0 \times 10^{-3} = 0.0045 \text{ g/L}$$

17.37. Let x equal the molar solubility of PbF_2. Assemble the usual concentration table, and substitute from the table into the equilibrium-constant expression.

Conc. (M)	$PbF_2(s)$ $\rightleftharpoons$	Pb^{2+} +	$2F^-$
Starting		0	0
Change		+x	+2x
Equilibrium		x	2x

$$[Pb^{2+}][F^-]^2 = K_{sp} ; \qquad (x)(2x)^2 = 4x^3 = 2.7 \times 10^{-8}$$

$$x = \sqrt[3]{\frac{2.7 \times 10^{-8}}{4}} = 1.\underline{8}9 \times 10^{-3} = 1.9 \times 10^{-3} \text{ M}$$

17.39. At the start, before any $SrSO_4$ dissolves, the solution contains 0.23 M SO_4^{2-}. At equilibrium, x mol of solid $SrSO_4$ dissolves to yield x mol Sr^{2+} and x mol SO_4^{2-}. Assemble the usual concentration table, and substitute the equilibrium concentrations into the equilibrium-constant expression. As an approximation, assume x is negligible compared to 0.23 M SO_4^{2-}.

Conc. (M)	$SrSO_4(s)$ $\rightleftharpoons$	Sr^{2+} +	SO_4^{2-}
Starting		0	0.23
Change		+x	+x
Equilibrium		X	0.23 + x

$$[Sr^{2+}][SO_4^{2-}] = K_{sp}$$

$$(x)(0.23 + x) \cong (x)(0.23) \cong 2.5 \times 10^{-7}$$

$$x \cong \frac{2.5 \times 10^{-7}}{0.23} = 1.\underline{0}86 \times 10^{-6} \text{ M}$$

$$\frac{1.086 \times 10^{-6} \text{ mol}}{L} \times \frac{183.69 \text{ g}}{1 \text{ mol SrSO}_4} = 1.\underline{9}9 \times 10^{-4} = 2.0 \times 10^{-4} \text{ g/L}$$

Note that adding x to 0.23 M will not change it (to two significant figures), so x is negligible compared to 0.23 M.

17.41. Calculate the value of K_{sp} from the solubility using the concentration table. Then, using the common-ion calculation, assemble another concentration table. Use 0.020 M NaF as the starting concentration of F^- ion. Substitute the equilibrium concentrations from the table into the equilibrium-constant expression. As an approximation, assume 2x is negligible compared to 0.020 M F^- ion.

$$\frac{0.016 \text{ g}}{L} \times \frac{1 \text{ mol MgF}_2}{62.30 \text{ g}} = 2.\underline{5}68 \times 10^{-4} \text{ M}$$

Conc. (M)	$MgF_2(s)$ $\rightleftharpoons$	Mg^{2+}	+ $2F^-$
Starting		0	0
Change		$+2.\underline{5}68 \times 10^{-4}$	$+2 \times 2.\underline{5}68 \times 10^{-4}$
Equilibrium		$2.\underline{5}68 \times 10^{-4}$	$2 \times 2.\underline{5}68 \times 10^{-4}$

$$K_{sp} = [Mg^{2+}][F^-]^2 = (2.\underline{5}68 \times 10^{-4})[2(2.\underline{5}68 \times 10^{-4})]^2 = 6.\underline{7}76 \times 10^{-11}$$

Now, use K_{sp} to calculate the molar solubility of MgF_2 in 0.020 M NaF.

Conc. (M)	$MgF_2(s)$ $\rightleftharpoons$	Mg^{2+} +	$2F^-$
Starting		0	0.020
Change		+x	+2x
Equilibrium		x	0.020 + 2x

$$[Mg^{2+}][F^-]^2 = K_{sp}$$

$$(x)(0.020 + 2x)^2 \cong (x)(0.020)^2 = 6.\underline{7}72 \times 10^{-11}$$

$$x \cong \frac{6.772 \times 10^{-11}}{(0.020)^2} = 1.\underline{6}93 \times 10^{-7} M$$

$$\frac{1.693 \times 10^{-7} \text{ mol}}{L} \times \frac{62.30 \text{ g}}{1 \text{ mol } MgF_2} = 1.\underline{0}55 \times 10^{-5} = 1.1 \times 10^{-5} \text{ g/L}$$

17.43. The concentration table follows.

Conc. (M)	$MgC_2O_4(s)$ $\rightleftharpoons$	Mg^{2+} +	$C_2O_4^{2-}$
Starting		0	0.020
Change		+x	+x
Equilibrium		x	0.020 + x

The equilibrium-constant expression is

$$K_{sp} = [Mg^{2+}][C_2O_4^{2-}]$$

$$8.5 \times 10^{-5} = (x)(0.020 + x)$$

$$x^2 + 0.020x - (8.5 \times 10^{-5}) = 0$$

Solving the quadratic equation gives

$$x = \frac{-0.020 \pm \sqrt{(0.020)^2 + 4(8.5 \times 10^{-5})}}{2} = 0.00\underline{3}6 M$$

The solubility in grams per liter is

$$\frac{0.0036 \text{ mol}}{L} \times \frac{112 \text{ g}}{1 \text{ mol}} = 0.\underline{4}03 = 0.4 \text{ g/L}$$

17.45. a.   Calculate Q_c, the ion product of the solution, using the concentrations in the problem as the concentrations present after mixing and assuming no precipitation. Then compare Q_c with K_{sp} to determine whether precipitation has occurred. Start by defining the ion product with brackets as used for the definition of K_{sp}; then use parentheses for the concentrations.

$$Q_c = [Ba^{2+}][F^-]^2$$

$$Q_c = (0.020)(0.015)^2 = 4.\underline{5}0 \times 10^{-6}$$

Since $Q_c > K_{sp}$ (1.0×10^{-6}), precipitation will occur.

b.　Calculate Q_c, the ion product of the solution, using the concentrations in the problem as the concentrations present after mixing and assuming no precipitation. Then compare Q_c with K_{sp} to determine whether precipitation has occurred. Start by defining the ion product with brackets as used for the definition of K_{sp}; then use parentheses for the concentrations.

$$Q_c = [Pb^{2+}][Cl^-]^2$$

$$Q_c = (0.035)(0.15)^2 = 7.\underline{8}7 \times 10^{-4}$$

Since $Q_c > K_{sp}$ (1.6×10^{-5}), precipitation will occur.

17.47.　Calculate the ion product, Q_c, after preparation of the solution, assuming no precipitation has occurred. Compare it with the K_{sp}.

$$Q_c = [Pb^{2+}][CrO_4^{2-}]$$

$$Q_c = (5.0 \times 10^{-4})(5.0 \times 10^{-5}) = 2.\underline{5}0 \times 10^{-8} \; (> K_{sp} \text{ of } 1.8 \times 10^{-14})$$

The solution is supersaturated before equilibrium is reached. At equilibrium, precipitation occurs, and the solution is saturated.

17.49.　Calculate the concentrations of Mg^{2+} and OH^-, assuming no precipitation. Use a total volume of $1.0 \text{ L} + 1.0 \text{ L}$, or 2.0 L. (Note that the concentrations are halved when the volume is doubled.)

$$[Mg^{2+}] = \frac{\dfrac{0.0020 \text{ mol}}{L} \times 1.0 \text{ L}}{2.0 \text{ L}} = 1.\underline{0}0 \times 10^{-3} \, M$$

$$[OH^-] = \frac{\dfrac{0.00010 \text{ mol}}{L} \times 1.0 \text{ L}}{2.0 \text{ L}} = 5.\underline{0}0 \times 10^{-5} \, M$$

Calculate the ion product, and compare it to K_{sp}.

$$Q_c = [Mg^{2+}][OH^-]^2 = (1.00 \times 10^{-3})(5.00 \times 10^{-5})^2 = 2.\underline{5}0 \times 10^{-12}$$

Because Q_c is less than the K_{sp} of 1.8×10^{-11}, no precipitation occurs, and the solution is unsaturated.

17.51.　Calculate the concentrations of Ba^{2+} and F^-, assuming no precipitation. Use a total volume of $0.045 \text{ L} + 0.075 \text{ L}$, or 0.120 L.

$$[Ba^{2+}] = \frac{\dfrac{0.0015 \text{ mol}}{L} \times 0.045 \text{ L}}{0.120 \text{ L}} = 5.\underline{6}25 \times 10^{-4} \, M$$

$$[F^-] = \frac{\dfrac{0.0025 \text{ mol}}{L} \times 0.075 \text{ L}}{0.120 \text{ L}} = 1.\underline{5}6 \times 10^{-3} \, M$$

Calculate the ion product and compare it to K_{sp}.

$$Q_c = [Ba^{2+}][F^-]^2 = (5.625 \times 10^{-4})(1.56 \times 10^{-3})^2 = 1.\underline{3}6 \times 10^{-9}$$

Because $Q_c < K_{sp}$ (1.0×10^{-6}), no precipitation occurs, and the solution is unsaturated.

17.53. A mixture of $CaCl_2$ and K_2SO_4 can precipitate only $CaSO_4$ because KCl is soluble. Use the K_{sp} expression to calculate the $[Ca^{2+}]$ needed to just begin precipitating the 0.020 M SO_4^{2-} (in essentially a saturated solution). Then convert to moles.

$$[Ca^{2+}][SO_4^{2-}] = K_{sp} = 2.4 \times 10^{-5}$$

$$[Ca^{2+}] = \frac{K_{sp}}{[SO_4^{2-}]} = \frac{2.4 \times 10^{-5}}{2.0 \times 10^{-2}} = 1.\underline{2}0 \times 10^{-3} \ M$$

The number of moles in 1.5 L of this calcium-containing solution is (mol $CaCl_2$ = mol Ca^{2+}):

$$1.5 \ L \times (1.\underline{2}0 \times 10^{-3}) \ mol/L = 1.\underline{8}0 \times 10^{-3} = 0.0018 \ mol \ CaCl_2$$

17.55. Because the $AgNO_3$ solution is relatively concentrated, ignore the dilution of the solution of Cl^- and I^- from the addition of $AgNO_3$. The $[Ag^+]$ just as the AgCl begins to precipitate can be calculated from the K_{sp} expression for AgCl using $[Cl^-] = 0.015 \ M$. Therefore, for AgCl,

$$[Ag^+][Cl^-] = K_{sp}$$

$$[Ag^+][0.015] = 1.8 \times 10^{-10}$$

$$[Ag^+] = \frac{1.8 \times 10^{-10}}{0.015} = 1.\underline{2}0 \times 10^{-8} \ M$$

The $[I^-]$ at this point can be obtained by substituting the $[Ag^+]$ into the K_{sp} expression for AgI. Therefore, for AgI,

$$[Ag^+][I^-] = K_{sp}$$

$$[1.20 \times 10^{-8}][I^-] = 8.3 \times 10^{-17}$$

$$[I^-] = \frac{8.3 \times 10^{-17}}{1.2 \times 10^{-8}} = 6.\underline{9}1 \times 10^{-9} = 6.9 \times 10^{-9} \ M$$

Because this I^- concentration is very small compared to the initial 0.015 M concentration, you can also deduce that essentially all the iodide ion precipitates before the AgCl begins to precipitate.

17.57. The net ionic equation is $BaF_2(s) + 2H_3O^+(aq) \rightleftharpoons Ba^{2+}(aq) + 2HF(aq) + 2H_2O(l)$

17.59. Calculate the value of K for the reaction of H_3O^+ with both the SO_4^{2-} and F^- anions as they form by the slight dissolving of the insoluble salts. These constants are the reciprocals of the K_a values of the conjugate acids of these anions.

$$F^-(aq) + H_3O^+(aq) \rightleftharpoons HF(aq) + H_2O(l)$$

$$K = \frac{1}{K_a} = \frac{1}{6.8 \times 10^{-4}} = 1.\underline{4}7 \times 10^3$$

$$SO_4^{2-}(aq) + H_3O^+(aq) \rightleftharpoons HSO_4^-(aq) + H_2O(l)$$

$$K = \frac{1}{K_{a_2}} = \frac{1}{1.1 \times 10^{-2}} = 9\underline{0}.9$$

Because K for the fluoride ion is larger, BaF_2 will dissolve more readily in acid than $BaSO_4$.

17.61. The equation is $\qquad Cu^+(aq) + 2\,CN^-(aq) \rightleftharpoons Cu(CN)_2^-(aq)$

The K_f expression is

$$K_f = \frac{[Cu(CN)_2^-]}{[Cu^+][CN^-]^2} = 1.0 \times 10^{16}$$

17.63. Assume the only $[Ag^+]$ is that in equilibrium with the $Ag(CN)_2^-$ formed from Ag^+ and CN^-. (In other words, assume all the $0.015\,M\;Ag^+$ reacts with CN^- to form $0.015\,M\;Ag(CN)_2^-$.) Subtract the CN^- that forms the $0.015\,M\;Ag(CN)_2^-$ from the initial $0.100\,M\;CN^-$. Use this as the starting concentration of CN^- for the usual concentration table.

$$[0.100\,M\;NaCN - (2 \times 0.015\,M)] = 0.070\,M \text{ starting } CN^-$$

Conc. (M)	$Ag(CN)_2^-$	$\rightleftharpoons$	Ag^+	+	$2CN^-$
Starting	0.015		0		0.070
Change	$-x$		$+x$		$+2x$
Equilibrium	$0.015 - x$		x		$0.070 + 2x$

Even though this reaction is the opposite of the equation for the formation constant, the formation-constant expression can be used. Simply substitute all the exact equilibrium concentrations into the formation-constant expression; then simplify the exact equation by assuming x is negligible compared to 0.015 and $2x$ is negligible compared to 0.070.

$$K_f = \frac{[Ag(CN)_2^-]}{[Ag^+][CN^-]^2} = \frac{(0.015 - x)}{(x)(0.070 + 2x)^2} \cong \frac{(0.015)}{(x)(0.070)^2} \cong 5.6 \times 10^{18}$$

Rearrange and solve for $x = [Ag^+]$:

$$x \cong (0.015) \div [(5.6 \times 10^{18})(0.070)^2] \cong 5.\underline{4}6 \times 10^{-19} = 5.5 \times 10^{-19}\,M$$

17.65. Start by calculating the $[Cd^{2+}]$ in equilibrium with the $Cd(NH_3)_4^{2+}$ formed from Cd^{2+} and NH_3. Then use the $[Cd^{2+}]$ to decide whether or not CdC_2O_4 will precipitate by calculating the ion product and comparing it with the K_{sp} of 1.5×10^{-8} for CdC_2O_4. Assume all the $0.0020\,M\;Cd^{2+}$ reacts with NH_3 to form $0.0020\,M\;Cd(NH_3)_4^{2+}$, and calculate the remaining NH_3. Use these as the starting concentrations for the usual concentration table.

$$[0.10\,M\;NH_3 - (4 \times 0.0020\,M)] = 0.0\underline{9}2\,M \text{ starting } NH_3$$

Conc. (M)	$Cd(NH_3)_4^{2+}$	$\rightleftharpoons$	Cd^{2+}	+	$4NH_3$
Starting	0.0020		0		0.092
Change	$-x$		$+x$		$+4x$
Equilibrium	$0.0020 - x$		x		$0.092 + 4x$

Even though this reaction is the opposite of the equation for the formation constant, the formation-constant expression can be used. Simply substitute all the exact equilibrium concentrations into the formation-constant expression; then simplify the exact equation by assuming x is negligible compared to 0.0020 and $4x$ is negligible compared to 0.092.

$$K_f = \frac{[Cd(NH_3)_4^{2+}]}{[Cd^{2+}][NH_3]^4} = \frac{(0.0020 - x)}{(x)(0.092 + 4x)^4} \cong \frac{(0.0020)}{(x)(0.092)^4} \cong 1.0 \times 10^7$$

Rearrange and solve for x:

$$x \cong (0.0020) \div [(1.0 \times 10^7)(0.092)^4] \cong \underline{2.79} \times 10^{-6} \, M \cong [Cd^{2+}]$$

Now, calculate the ion product for CdC_2O_4:

$$Q_c = [Cd^{2+}][C_2O_4^{2-}] = (2.79 \times 10^{-6})(0.010) = 2.\underline{79} \times 10^{-8}$$

Because Q_c is greater than the K_{sp} of 1.5×10^{-8}, the solution is supersaturated before equilibrium. At equilibrium, a precipitate will form, and the solution will be saturated.

17.67. Using the rule from Chapter 14, obtain the overall equilibrium constant for this reaction from the product of the individual equilibrium constants of the two individual equations whose sum gives this equation.

$CdC_2O_4(s)$	$\rightleftharpoons$	$Cd^{2+}(aq) + C_2O_4^{2-}(aq)$	$K_{sp} = 1.5 \times 10^{-8}$
$Cd^{2+}(aq) + 4NH_3(aq)$	$\rightleftharpoons$	$Cd(NH_3)_4^{2+}(aq)$	$K_f = 1.0 \times 10^7$
$CdC_2O_4(s) + 4NH_3(aq)$	$\rightleftharpoons$	$Cd(NH_3)_4^{2+}(aq) + C_2O_4^{2-}(aq)$	$K_c = K_{sp} \times K_f = 0.15$

Assemble the usual table using $0.10 \, M$ as the starting concentration of NH_3 and x as the unknown concentration of $Cd(NH_3)_4^{2+}$ formed.

Conc. (M)	$CdC_2O_4(s)$ +	$4NH_3$	$\rightleftharpoons$	$Cd(NH_3)_4^{2+}$ +	$C_2O_4^{2-}$
Starting		0.10		0	0
Change		$-4x$		$+x$	$+x$
Equilibrium		$0.10 - 4x$		x	x

The equilibrium-constant expression can now be used. Simply substitute all the exact equilibrium concentrations into the equilibrium-constant expression.

$$K_c = \frac{[Cd(NH_3)_4^{2+}][C_2O_4^{2-}]}{[NH_3]^4} = \frac{(x)^2}{(0.10 - 4x)^4} = 0.15$$

Take the square root of both sides of the two right-hand terms, rearrange into a quadratic equation, and solve for x:

$$\frac{x}{(0.10 - 4x)^2} = 0.3\underline{87}$$

$$16x^2 - 3.38x + 0.010 = 0$$

$$x = \frac{3.38 \pm \sqrt{(-3.38)^2 - 4(16)(0.010)}}{2(16)} = 0.208 \, (\text{too large}) \text{ and } 3.\underline{001} \times 10^{-3}$$

Using the smaller root, $x = 3.\underline{001} \times 10^{-3} = 3.0 \times 10^{-3} \, M$ (molar solubility of CdC_2O_4).

17.69. The Pb^{2+}, Cd^{2+}, and Sr^{2+} ions can be separated in two steps: (1) Add HCl to precipitate only the Pb^{2+} as $PbCl_2$, leaving the others in solution. (2) After decanting or filtering the solution away from the precipitate, add $0.3 \, M$ HCl and H_2S to precipitate only the CdS away from the Sr^{2+} ion, whose sulfide is soluble under these conditions.

17.71.   a. Ag^+ is not possible because no precipitate formed with HCl.

   b. Ca^{2+} is not possible if the compound contains only one cation because Mn^{2+} is indicated by the evidence. However, if the compound consists of two or more cations, Ca^{2+} is possible because no reactions were described involving Ca^{2+}.

   c. Mn^{2+} is possible because a precipitate was obtained with basic sulfide ion.

   d. Cd^{2+} is not possible because no precipitate was obtained with acidic sulfide solution.

■ SOLUTIONS TO GENERAL PROBLEMS

17.73.   Assemble the usual concentration table. Let x equal the molar solubility of $PbSO_4$. When x mol $PbSO_4$ dissolves in 1 L of solution, x mol Pb^{2+} and x mol SO_4^{2-} form.

Conc. (M)	$PbSO_4(s) \rightleftharpoons$	Pb^{2+} +	SO_4^{2-}
Starting		0	0
Change		+x	+x
Equilibrium		x	X

Substitute the equilibrium concentrations into the equilibrium-constant expression and solve for x.

$$[Pb^{2+}][SO_4^{2-}] = K_{sp}$$

$$(x)(x) = x^2 = 1.7 \times 10^{-8}$$

$$x = \sqrt{(1.7 \times 10^{-8})} = 1.\underline{3}03 \times 10^{-4} = 1.3 \times 10^{-4}\ M$$

17.75.   Let x equal the molar solubility of Hg_2Cl_2. Assemble the usual concentration table, and substitute from the table into the equilibrium-constant expression.

Conc. (M)	$Hg_2Cl_2(s) \rightleftharpoons$	Hg_2^{2+} +	$2Cl^-$
Starting		0	0
Change		+x	+2x
Equilibrium		x	2x

$$[Hg_2^{2+}][Cl^-]^2 = K_{sp}$$

$$(x)(2x)^2 = 4x^3 = 1.3 \times 10^{-18}$$

$$x = \sqrt[3]{\frac{1.3 \times 10^{-18}}{4}} = 6.\underline{8}7 \times 10^{-7}\ M$$

   a.   Molar solubility = $6.\underline{8}7 \times 10^{-7} = 6.9 \times 10^{-7}\ M$

   b. $\dfrac{6.87 \times 10^{-7}\ \text{mol}}{L} \times \dfrac{472.1\ \text{g}\ Hg_2Cl_2}{1\ \text{mol}} = 3.\underline{2}4 \times 10^{-4} = 3.2 \times 10^{-4}\ \text{g/L}$

17.77. Let x equal the molar solubility of $Ce(OH)_3$. Assemble the usual concentration table, and substitute from the table into the equilibrium-constant expression.

Conc. (M)	$Ce(OH)_3(s)$ $\rightleftharpoons$	Ce^{3+}	$+$	$3OH^-$
Starting		0		0
Change		$+x$		$+3x$
Equilibrium		x		$3x$

$$[Ce^{3+}][OH^-]^3 = K_{sp}$$

$$(x)(3x)^3 = 27x^4 = 2.0 \times 10^{-20}$$

$$x = \sqrt[4]{\frac{2.0 \times 10^{-20}}{27}} = 5.\underline{2}16 \times 10^{-6}\ M$$

a. Molar solubility $= 5.\underline{2}16 \times 10^{-6} = 5.2 \times 10^{-6}\ M$

b. $[OH^-] = 3x = 1.\underline{5}6 \times 10^{-5}\ M$

$pOH = 4.8\underline{0}54 = 4.81$

17.79. Calculate the pOH from the pH, and then convert pOH to $[OH^-]$. Next, assemble the usual concentration table, and substitute the equilibrium concentrations from it into the equilibrium-constant expression.

$$pOH = 14.00 - 8.80 = 5.20$$

$$[OH^-] = \text{antilog}\ (-pOH) = \text{antilog}\ (-5.20) = 6.\underline{3}09 \times 10^{-6}\ M$$

Conc. (M)	$Mg(OH)_2(s)$ $\rightleftharpoons$	Mg^{2+}	$+$	$2OH^-$
Starting		0		0
Change		$+x$		0
Equilibrium		x		6.309×10^{-6}

$$K_{sp} = [Mg^{2+}][OH^-]^2 = (x)(6.309 \times 10^{-6})^2 = 1.8 \times 10^{-11}$$

$$x = \frac{1.8 \times 10^{-11}}{(6.309 \times 10^{-6})^2} = 0.4\underline{5}2 = 0.45\ M$$

$$\frac{0.452\ \text{mol}}{\text{L}} \times \frac{58.3\ \text{g}\ Mg(OH)_2}{1\ \text{mol}} = 2\underline{6}.3 = 26\ \text{g/L}$$

17.81. Let x equal the change in M of Mg^{2+} and 0.10 M equal the starting OH^- concentration. Then assemble the usual concentration table, and substitute the equilibrium concentrations from it into the equilibrium-constant expression. Assume $2x$ is negligible compared to 0.10 M, and perform an approximate calculation.

Conc. (M)	$Mg(OH)_2(s)$ $\rightleftharpoons$	Mg^{2+}	$+$	$2OH^-$
Starting		0		0.10
Change		$+x$		$+2x$
Equilibrium		x		$0.10 + 2x$

$$K_{sp} = [Mg^{2+}][OH^-]^2 = (x)(0.10 + 2x)^2 \cong (x)(0.10)^2 \cong 1.8 \times 10^{-11}$$

$$x = \frac{1.8 \times 10^{-11}}{(0.10)^2} = 1.\underline{8}0 \times 10^{-9} = 1.8 \times 10^{-9}\ M$$

17.83. To begin precipitation, you must add just slightly more sulfate ion than that required to give a saturated solution. Use the K_{sp} expression to calculate the $[SO_4^{2-}]$ needed to just begin precipitating the $0.0030\ M\ Ca^{2+}$.

$$[Ca^{2+}][SO_4^{2-}] = K_{sp} = 2.4 \times 10^{-5}$$

$$[SO_4^{2-}] = \frac{K_{sp}}{[Ca^{2+}]} = \frac{2.4 \times 10^{-5}}{3.0 \times 10^{-3}} = 8.\underline{0}0 \times 10^{-3}\ M$$

When the sulfate ion concentration slightly exceeds $8.0 \times 10^{-3}\ M$, precipitation begins.

17.85. Calculate the concentrations of Pb^{2+} and Cl^-. Use a total volume of $3.20\ L + 0.80\ L$, or $4.00\ L$.

$$[Pb^{2+}] = \frac{\dfrac{1.25 \times 10^{-3}\ mol}{L} \times 3.20\ L}{4.00\ L} = 1.0\underline{0} \times 10^{-3}\ M$$

$$[Cl^-] = \frac{\dfrac{5.0 \times 10^{-1}\ mol}{L} \times 0.80\ L}{4.00\ L} = 1.\underline{0}0 \times 10^{-1}\ M$$

Calculate the ion product, and compare it to K_{sp}.

$$Q_c = [Pb^{2+}][Cl^-]^2 = (1.00 \times 10^{-3})(1.00 \times 10^{-1})^2 = 1.\underline{0}0 \times 10^{-5}\ M^3$$

Because the Q_c is less than the K_{sp} of 1.6×10^{-5}, no precipitation occurs, and the solution is not saturated.

17.87. A mixture of $AgNO_3$ and $NaCl$ can precipitate only $AgCl$ because $NaNO_3$ is soluble. Use the K_{sp} expression to calculate the $[Cl^-]$ needed to prepare a saturated solution (just before precipitating the $0.0015\ M\ Ag^+$). Then convert to moles and finally to grams.

$$[Ag^+][Cl^-] = K_{sp} = 1.8 \times 10^{-10}$$

$$[Cl^-] = \frac{K_{sp}}{[Ag^+]} = \frac{1.8 \times 10^{-10}}{1.5 \times 10^{-3}} = 1.\underline{2}0 \times 10^{-7}\ M$$

The numbers of moles and grams in $0.785\ L$ ($785\ mL$) of this chloride-containing solution are

$$0.785\ L \times (1.20 \times 10^{-7}\ mol/L) = 9.\underline{4}2 \times 10^{-8}\ mol\ Cl^- = 9.\underline{4}2 \times 10^{-8}\ mol\ NaCl$$

$$(9.42 \times 10^{-8}\ mol\ NaCl) \times (58.5\ g\ NaCl/1mol) = 5.\underline{5}1 \times 10^{-6} = 5.5 \times 10^{-6}\ g\ NaCl$$

This amount of $NaCl$ is too small to weigh on a balance.

17.89. From the magnitude of K_f, assume Fe^{3+} and SCN^- react essentially completely to form $2.00\ M$ $Fe(SCN)^{2+}$ at equilibrium. Use $2.00\ M$ as the starting concentration of $Fe(SCN)^{2+}$ for the usual concentration table.

Conc. (M)	Fe^{3+}	+	SCN^-	$\rightleftharpoons$	$Fe(SCN)^{2+}$
Starting	0		0		2.00
Change	$+x$		$+x$		$-x$
Equilibrium	x		x		$2.00 - x$

Substitute all the exact equilibrium concentrations into the formation-constant expression; then simplify the exact equation by assuming $\times$ is negligible compared to 2.00 M.

$$K_f = \frac{[\text{Fe(SCN)}^{2+}]}{[\text{Fe}^{3+}][\text{SCN}^-]} = \frac{(2.00 - x)}{(x)(x)} \cong \frac{(2.00)}{x^2} \cong 9.0 \times 10^2$$

Rearrange and solve for x:

$$x = \sqrt{\frac{2.00}{9.0 \times 10^2}} = 4.\underline{7}1 \times 10^{-2} = 4.7 \times 10^{-2} \ M$$

Fraction dissociated = $[(4.\underline{7}1 \times 10^{-2}) \div (2.00)] \times 100\% = 0.02\underline{3}5$ (< 0.03, so acceptable)

17.91. Obtain the overall equilibrium constant for this reaction from the product of the individual equilibrium constants of the two individual equations whose sum gives this equation:

$\text{AgBr}(s)$	$\rightleftharpoons$	$\text{Ag}^+(aq) + \text{Br}^-(aq)$	$K_{sp} = 5.0 \times 10^{-13}$
$\text{Ag}^+(aq) + 2\text{NH}_3(aq)$	$\rightleftharpoons$	$\text{Ag(NH}_3)_2{}^+(aq)$	$K_f = 1.7 \times 10^7$
$\text{AgBr}(s) + 2\text{NH}_3(aq)$	$\rightleftharpoons$	$\text{Ag(NH}_3)_2{}^+(aq) + \text{Br}^-(aq)$	$K_c = K_{sp} \times K_f = 8.\underline{5}0 \times 10^{-6}$

Assemble the usual table using 5.0 M as the starting concentration of NH_3 and x as the unknown concentration of $\text{Ag(NH}_3)_2{}^+$ formed.

Conc. (M)	$\text{AgBr}(s)$ +	2NH_3	$\rightleftharpoons$	$\text{Ag(NH}_3)_2{}^+$ +	Br^-
Starting		5.0		0	0
Change		$-2x$		$+x$	$+x$
Equilibrium		$5.0 - 2x$		x	x

The equilibrium-constant expression can now be used. Simply substitute all the exact equilibrium concentrations into the equilibrium-constant expression; it will not be necessary to simplify the equation, because taking the square root of both sides removes the x^2 term.

$$K_c = \frac{[\text{Ag(NH}_3)_2{}^+][\text{Br}^-]}{[\text{NH}_3]^2} = \frac{x^2}{(5.0 - 2x)^2} = 8.\underline{5}0 \times 10^{-6}$$

Take the square root of both sides of the two right-hand terms and solve for x.

$$\frac{x}{(5.0 - 2x)} = 2.\underline{9}15 \times 10^{-3}$$

$$x + (5.8 \times 10^{-3}) x = 1.\underline{4}575 \times 10^{-2}$$

$$x = 1.\underline{4}49 \times 10^{-2} = 1.4 \times 10^{-2} \ M \text{ (the molar solubility of AgBr in 5.0 } M \text{ NH}_3)$$

17.93. Start by recognizing that because each zinc oxalate produces one oxalate ion, the solubility of zinc oxalate equals the oxalate concentration:

$$\text{ZnC}_2\text{O}_4(s) + 4\text{NH}_3 \rightleftharpoons \text{Zn(NH}_3)_4{}^{2+} + \text{C}_2\text{O}_4{}^{2-}$$

Thus, the $[\text{C}_2\text{O}_4{}^{2-}] = 3.6 \times 10^{-4} \ M$. Now, calculate the $[\text{Zn}^{2+}]$ in equilibrium with the oxalate ion using the K_{sp} expression for zinc oxalate.

$$K_{sp} = [\text{Zn}^{2+}][\text{C}_2\text{O}_4{}^{2-}] = 1.5 \times 10^{-9}$$

$$[Zn^{2+}] = \frac{1.5 \times 10^{-9}}{3.6 \times 10^{-4}} = 4.\underline{1}6 \times 10^{-6} = 4.2 \times 10^{-6} \, M$$

To calculate K_f, the $[Zn(NH_3)_4^{2+}]$ term must be calculated. This can be done by recognizing that the molar solubility of ZnC_2O_4 is the sum of the concentration of Zn^{2+} and $Zn(NH_3)_4^{2+}$ ions:

Molar solubility of $ZnC_2O_4 = [Zn^{2+}] + [Zn(NH_3)_4^{2+}]$

$$3.6 \times 10^{-4} = (4.16 \times 10^{-6}) + [Zn(NH_3)_4^{2+}]$$

$$[Zn(NH_3)_4^{2+}] = (3.6 \times 10^{-4}) - (4.16 \times 10^{-6}) = 3.\underline{5}58 \times 10^{-4} \, M$$

Now, the $[NH_3]$ term must be calculated by subtracting the ammonia in $[Zn(NH_3)_4^{2+}]$ from the starting NH_3 of 0.0150 M.

$$[NH_3] = 0.0150 - 4\,[Zn(NH_3)_4^{2+}] = 0.0150 - 4(3.558 \times 10^{-4}) = 0.013\underline{5}7 \, M$$

Solve for K_f by substituting the known concentrations into the K_f expression:

$$K_f = \frac{[Zn(NH_3)_4^{2+}]}{[Zn^{2+}][NH_3]^4} = \frac{3.558 \times 10^{-4}}{(4.16 \times 10^{-6})(0.01357)^4} = 2.\underline{5}2 \times 10^{9} = 2.5 \times 10^{9}$$

17.95. The OH^- formed by ionization of NH_3 (to NH_4^+ and OH^-) is a common ion that will precipitate Mg^{2+} as the slightly soluble $Mg(OH)_2$ salt. The simplest way to treat the problem is to calculate the $[OH^-]$ of 0.10 M NH_3 before the soluble Mg^{2+} salt is added. As the soluble Mg^{2+} salt is added, the $[Mg^{2+}]$ will increase until the solution is saturated with respect to $Mg(OH)_2$ (any more added Mg^{2+} ions will precipitate). Calculate the $[Mg^{2+}]$ at the point at which precipitation begins.

To calculate the $[OH^-]$ of 0.10 M NH_3, let x equal the moles per liter of NH_3 that ionize, forming x mol/L of NH_4^+ and x mol/L of OH^- and leaving $(0.10 - x)$ M NH_3 in solution. We can summarize the situation in tabular form:

Conc. (M)	NH_3	+	H_2O	$\rightleftharpoons$	NH_4^+	+	OH^-
Starting	0.10				~0		0
Change	$-x$				$+x$		$+x$
Equilibrium	$0.10 - x$				X		x

The equilibrium-constant equation is:

$$K_b = \frac{[NH_4^+][OH^-]}{[NH_3]} = \frac{x^2}{(0.10 - x)} \cong \frac{x^2}{(0.10)}$$

The value of x can be obtained by rearranging and taking the square root:

$$[OH^-] \cong \sqrt{1.8 \times 10^{-5} \times 0.10} = 1.\underline{3}4 \times 10^{-3} \, M$$

Note that $(0.10 - x)$ is not significantly different from 0.10, so x can be ignored in the $(0.10 - x)$ term. Now, use the K_{sp} of $Mg(OH)_2$ to calculate the $[Mg^{2+}]$ of a saturated solution of $Mg(OH)_2$, which essentially will be the Mg^{2+} ion concentration when $Mg(OH)_2$ begins to precipitate.

$$[Mg^{2+}] = \frac{K_{sp}}{[OH^-]^2} = \frac{1.8 \times 10^{-11}}{(1.34 \times 10^{-3})^2} = 1.\underline{0}0 \times 10^{-5} = 1.0 \times 10^{-5} \, M$$

17.97. a.   Use the solubility information to calculate K_{sp}. The reaction is

$$Cu(IO_3)_2(s) \rightleftharpoons Cu^{2+}(aq) + 2IO_3^-(aq)$$
$$ 2.7 \times 10^{-3} 2 \times (2.7 \times 10^{-3})$$

$$K_{sp} = [Cu^{2+}][IO_3^-]^2 = [2.7 \times 10^{-3}][2 \times (2.7 \times 10^{-3})]^2 = 7.\underline{8}7 \times 10^{-8}$$

Set up an equilibrium. The reaction is

$$Cu(IO_3)_2(s) \rightleftharpoons Cu^{2+}(aq) + 2IO_3^-(aq)$$
$$ y 0.35 + 2y \approx 0.35$$

$$K_{sp} = [y][0.35]^2 = 7.87 \times 10^{-8}$$

Molar solubility $= y = 6.\underline{4}2 \times 10^{-7} = 6.4 \times 10^{-7} \ M$

b.   Set up an equilibrium. The reaction is

$$Cu(IO_3)_2(s) \rightleftharpoons Cu^{2+}(aq) + 2IO_3^-(aq)$$
$$ y + 0.35 \approx 0.35 2y$$

$$K_{sp} = [0.35][2y]^2 = 7.87 \times 10^{-8}$$

Molar solubility $= y = 2.\underline{3}7 \times 10^{-4} = 2.4 \times 10^{-4} \ M$

c.   Yes, $Cu(IO_3)_2$ is a 1:2 electrolyte. It takes two IO_3^- ions to combine with one Cu^{2+} ion. The IO_3^- ion is involved as a square term in the K_{sp} expression.

17.99. a.   Set up an equilibrium. The reaction and equilibrium-constant expression are

$$PbI_2(s) \rightleftharpoons Pb^{2+}(aq) + 2I^-(aq) K_{sp} = [Pb^{2+}][I^-]^2 = 6.5 \times 10^{-9}$$

The Pb^{2+} ion concentration is 0.0150 M. Plug this in, and solve for the iodide ion concentration.

$$[I^-] = \sqrt{\frac{6.5 \times 10^{-9}}{0.0150}} = 6.\underline{5}8 \times 10^{-4} = 6.6 \times 10^{-4} \ M$$

b.   Solve the equilibrium-constant expression for the lead-ion concentration.

$$[Pb^{2+}] = \frac{6.5 \times 10^{-9}}{(2.0 \times 10^{-3})^2} = 1.\underline{6}3 \times 10^{-3} = 1.6 \times 10^{-3} \ M$$

The percent of the lead(II) ion remaining in solution is

$$\text{Percent } Pb^{2+} \text{ remaining} = \frac{1.63 \times 10^{-3}}{0.0150} \times 100\% = 1\underline{0}.8 = 11\%$$

17.101. a.   The reaction and equilibrium-constant expression are

$$Co(OH)_2(s) \rightleftharpoons Co^{2+}(aq) + 2OH^-(aq) K_{sp} = [Co^{2+}][OH^-]^2$$

From the molar solubility, $[Co^{2+}] = 5.4 \times 10^{-6} \ M$ and $[OH^-] = 2 \times (5.4 \times 10^{-6}) \ M$. Therefore,

$$K_{sp} = [5.4 \times 10^{-6}][2 \times (5.4 \times 10^{-6})]^2 = 6.\underline{3}0 \times 10^{-16} = 6.3 \times 10^{-16}$$

b. From the pOH $(14 - \text{pH})$, the $[\text{OH}^-] = 10^{-3.57} = 2.\underline{6}9 \times 10^{-4}\ M$. The molar solubility is equal to the cobalt-ion concentration at equilibrium.

$$[\text{Co}^{2+}] = \frac{K_{sp}}{[\text{OH}^-]^2} = \frac{6.3 \times 10^{-16}}{(2.69 \times 10^{-4})^2} = 8.\underline{6}9 \times 10^{-9} = 8.7 \times 10^{-9}\ M$$

c. The common-ion effect (OH^-) in part b decreases the solubility of Co(OH)_2.

17.103. a.

$\text{AgCl}(s)$	$\rightleftharpoons$	$\text{Ag}^+(aq) + \text{Cl}^-(aq)$	$K_{sp} = 1.8 \times 10^{-10}$
$\text{Ag}^+(aq) + 2\text{NH}_3(aq)$	$\rightleftharpoons$	$\text{Ag(NH}_3)_2^+(aq)$	$K_f = 1.7 \times 10^7$
$\text{AgCl}(s) + 2\text{NH}_3(aq)$	$\rightleftharpoons$	$\text{Ag(NH}_3)_2^+(aq) + \text{Cl}^-(aq)$	

$$K = K_{sp} \times K_f = (1.8 \times 10^{-10})(1.7 \times 10^7) = 3.\underline{0}6 \times 10^{-3} = 3.1 \times 10^{-3}$$

b. The equilibrium-constant expression is

$$\frac{[\text{Ag(NH}_3)_2^+][\text{Cl}^-]}{[\text{NH}_3]^2} = \frac{y^2}{(0.80)^2} = 3.06 \times 10^{-3}$$

$$y = [\text{Ag(NH}_3)_2^+] = 0.04\underline{4}3 = 0.044\ M$$

$\text{mol AgCl dissolved} = \text{mol Ag(NH}_3)_2^+ = 0.044\ \text{mol/L} \times 1.00\ \text{L} = 0.044\ \text{mol}$

$$\text{mol NH}_3\ \text{reacted} = 0.0443\ \text{mol Ag(NH}_3)_2^+ \times \frac{2\ \text{mol NH}_3}{1\ \text{mol Ag(NH}_3)_2^+} = 0.088\underline{5}\ \text{mol}$$

Total moles of NH_3 added $= 0.80\ M \times 1.00\ \text{L} + 0.0885 = 0.8\underline{8}9 = 0.89\ \text{mol}$

17.105. a. The moles of NH_4Cl (molar mass 53.49 g/mol) are given by

$$\text{mol NH}_4\text{Cl} = 26.7\ \text{g} \times \frac{1\ \text{mol NH}_4\text{Cl}}{53.49\ \text{g NH}_4\text{Cl}} = 0.49\underline{9}2\ \text{mol}$$

The reaction and equilibrium-constant expression are

$$\text{NH}_3 + \text{H}_2\text{O} \rightleftharpoons \text{NH}_4^+ + \text{OH}^- \quad K_b = \frac{[\text{NH}_4^+][\text{OH}^-]}{[\text{NH}_3]} = 1.8 \times 10^{-5}$$

Solve the equilibrium-constant expression for $[\text{OH}^-]$. The molarity of the NH_4Cl is 0.49$\underline{9}$2 mol/1.0 L = 0.49$\underline{9}$2 M.

$$[\text{OH}^-] = \frac{(1.8 \times 10^{-5})(4.2)}{(0.4992)} = 1.\underline{5}1 \times 10^{-4} = 1.5 \times 10^{-4}\ M$$

b.   The reaction and equilibrium-constant expression are

$$Mg(OH)_2 \rightleftharpoons Mg^{2+} + 2OH^- \quad K_{sp} = [Mg^{2+}][OH^-]^2 = 1.8 \times 10^{-11}$$

Solving for $[Mg^{2+}]$ gives

$$[Mg^{2+}] = \frac{(1.8 \times 10^{-11})}{(1.51 \times 10^{-4})^2} = 7.\underline{8}47 \times 10^{-4} = 7.8 \times 10^{-4} \; M$$

The percent Mg^{2+} that has been removed is given by

$$\text{Percent } Mg^{2+} \text{ removed} = \frac{0.075 - 7.89 \times 10^{-4}}{0.075} \times 100\% = 9\underline{8}.9 = 99\%$$

17.107. Water that has filtered through decomposing vegetation contains carbonic acid, as well as other acids. When such an acidic solution comes in contact with limestone, it carves out caverns. The water is now a solution of calcium hydrogen carbonate.

$$CaCO_3(s) + H_2O(l) + CO_2(g) \rightarrow Ca^{2+}(aq) + 2HCO_3^-(aq)$$

■ SOLUTIONS TO STRATEGY PROBLEMS

17.109. When the solutions are mixed together, the combined volume is 100.0 mL. Since the volume doubled, the concentrations are reduced by one-half. Thus, after mixing, the solution is initially 0.0500 M HCl and 0.0500 M AgNO$_3$. HCl is a strong acid, so the concentration of H_3O^+ is also 0.0500 M. Silver chloride precipitates. The solubility product constant is

$$K_{sp} = 1.8 \times 10^{-10} = [Ag^+][Cl^-] = (0.0500 - x)^2$$

where x is the concentration of ion precipitated. Solve for the chloride-ion concentration.

$$[Cl^-] = (0.0500 - x) = \sqrt{1.8 \times 10^{-10}} = 1.\underline{3}4 \times 10^{-5} = 1.3 \times 10^{-5} \; M$$

17.111. First, convert the solubility to molarity using the molar mass of PbBr$_2$.

$$\frac{1.31 \text{ g}}{1 \text{ L}} \times \frac{1 \text{ mol PbBr}_2}{367.01 \text{ g}} = 3.5\underline{6}9 \times 10^{-3} \; M$$

In a solution of 0.100 M NaBr, the concentrations of Pb^{2+} and Br^- are

$$[Pb^{2+}] = 3.569 \times 10^{-3} \; M$$

$$[Br^-] = 0.100 \; M + 2(3.569 \times 10^{-3} \; M) = 0.10\underline{7}1 \; M$$

Now calculate the solubility product constant for PbBr$_2$.

$$K_{sp} = [Pb^{2+}][Br^-]^2 = (3.569 \times 10^{-3})(0.1071)^2 = 4.0\underline{9}7 \times 10^{-5} = 4.10 \times 10^{-5}$$

17.113. Assume all the chloride-ion reacts when the AgNO$_3$ is added. The initial moles of chloride present are equal to the moles of added silver-ion. From the titration, the volume of silver nitrate added is 60.3 mL − 50.0 mL = 10.3 mL.

$$\text{mol } Cl^- = \text{mol } Ag^+ = (0.100 \; M) \times (10.3 \times 10^{-3} \text{ L}) = 1.0\underline{3}0 \times 10^{-3} = 1.03 \times 10^{-3} \text{ mol}$$

Next, determine the silver ion concentration when Ag_2CrO_4 begins to precipitate. The concentration of CrO_4^{2-} at this point is

$$[CrO_4^{2-}] = 1.00 \text{ g} \times \frac{1 \text{ mol } K_2CrO_4}{194.190 \text{ g}} \times \frac{1}{0.0603 \text{ L}} = 0.08539 \ M$$

$$[Ag^+] = \sqrt{\frac{K_{sp}}{[CrO_4^{2-}]}} = \sqrt{\frac{1.1 \times 10^{-12}}{0.08539}} = 3.588 \times 10^{-6} \ M$$

Next, use K_{sp} for AgCl to determine the chloride-ion concentration.

$$[Cl^-] = \frac{K_{sp}}{[Ag^+]} = \frac{1.8 \times 10^{-10}}{3.588 \times 10^{-6}} = 5.015 \times 10^{-5} \ M$$

The final volume in the titration is 60.3 mL, so the moles of chloride-ion at this point are

$$5.015 \times 10^{-5} \ M \times 60.3 \times 10^{-3} \ L = 3.029 \times 10^{-6} = 3.0 \times 10^{-6} \text{ mol}$$

17.115. First calculate the OH^- ion concentration using the pOH, which is $14.00 - 4.50 = 9.50$.

$$[OH^-] = 10^{-pOH} = 10^{-9.50} = 3.16 \times 10^{-10} \ M$$

Now calculate the solubility of $Fe(OH)_3$ in the solution using K_{sp}. Because the solution is a buffer, the OH^- concentration remains around $3.16 \times 10^{-10} \ M$.

$$K_{sp} = 2.5 \times 10^{-39} = [Fe^{3+}][OH^-]^3 = (x)(3.16 \times 10^{-10})^3$$

$$[Fe^{3+}] = x = \frac{2.5 \times 10^{-39}}{(3.162 \times 10^{-10})^3} = 7.90 \times 10^{-11} \ M$$

The nanograms of iron in 1.00 L can now be calculated.

$$\frac{7.905 \times 10^{-11} \text{ mol}}{1 \text{ L}} \times \frac{55.845 \text{ g}}{1 \text{ mol Fe}} \times \frac{10^9 \text{ ng}}{1 \text{ g}} = 4.41 = 4.4 \text{ ng}$$

17.117. The HF comes from the reaction of the conjugate base F^- with water. Its formation should increase the solubility of CaF_2 slightly. To determine the concentration of HF in the solution, consider the hydrolysis of the fluoride ion and calculate the value of K_b for the base using K_w.

$$F^-(aq) + H_2O(l) \rightarrow HF(aq) + OH^-(aq)$$

$$K_b = \frac{K_w}{K_a} = \frac{1.00 \times 10^{-14}}{6.8 \times 10^{-4}} = 1.47 \times 10^{-11}$$

Now write out the expression for the equilibrium constant. From Example 17.4, the initial fluoride-ion concentration is $4.0 \times 10^{-4} \ M$.

$$K_b = \frac{[HF][OH^-]}{[F^-]} = \frac{x^2}{4.0 \times 10^{-4} - x} = 1.47 \times 10^{-11}$$

Assume x is negligible with respect to 4.0×10^{-4} and solve for the concentration of HF in the solution.

$$[HF] = x = \sqrt{(1.47 \times 10^{-11})(4.0 \times 10^{-4})} = 7.67 \times 10^{-8} = 7.7 \times 10^{-8} \ M$$

Therefore, the fluoride-ion concentration did not change significantly, and the formation of HF has a negligible effect on the solubility of calcium fluoride.

For $CaCO_3$, the acid-dissociation constant for HCO_3^- is 4.8×10^{-11}. This gives 2.08×10^{-4} for the value of K_b for CO_3^{2-}. Since K_b is much larger, the concentration of HCO_3^- is significant, and the reaction of CO_3^{2-} with water is important in determining the solubility of calcium carbonate.

17.119. When equal volumes of the two solutions are mixed together, the volume is doubled and the concentrations before any reaction are reduced by one-half. Thus, after mixing, the solution is initially $0.050\ M\ Ca^{2+}$, $0.10\ M\ Cl^-$, $0.075\ M\ Na^+$, and $0.075\ M\ F^-$. Na^+ and Cl^- are spectator ions so their concentrations will remain at these values. Calcium fluoride precipitates. The net ionic equation is $Ca^{2+}(aq) + 2F^-(aq) \rightleftharpoons CaF_2(s)$

Assemble a table showing the precipitation of CaF_2.

Conc. (M)	Ca^{2+}	+	$2F^-$	$\rightleftharpoons$	$CaF_2(s)$
Starting	0.050		0.075		
Change	−0.075/2		−0.075		
Equilibrium	0.0125		0.000		

To calculate $[F^-]$, use the K_{sp} expression for CaF_2.

$$[F^-] = \sqrt{\frac{K_{sp}}{[Ca^{2+}]}} = \sqrt{\frac{3.4 \times 10^{-11}}{0.0125\ M}} = 5.21 \times 10^{-5} = 5.2 \times 10^{-5}\ M$$

$$[Ca^{2+}] = 0.1090 = 0.109\ M$$

17.121. First note that only the first proton of H_2SO_4 acts as a strong acid. The net ionic equation is

$$Ba^{2+}(aq) + 2OH^-(aq) + H^+(aq) + HSO_4^-(aq) \rightleftharpoons BaSO_4(s) + 2H_2O(l)$$

Start by calculating the moles per liter of each ion after mixing and before precipitation. Use a total volume of $0.0356 + 0.0556\ L = 0.0912\ L$.

M of $Ba^{2+} = (0.578\ mol/L \times 0.0356\ L) \div 0.0912\ L = 0.2256\ M$

M of $OH^- = (2 \times 0.578\ mol/L \times 0.0356\ L) \div 0.0912\ L = 0.4512\ M$

M of $H^+ = (0.491\ mol/L \times 0.0556\ L) \div 0.0912\ L = 0.2993\ M$

M of $HSO_4^- = (0.491\ mol/L \times 0.0556\ L) \div 0.0912\ L = 0.2993\ M$

Assemble a table showing the precipitation of $BaSO_4$.

Conc. (M)	Ba^{2+}	+	HSO_4^-	+	H^+	+ $2OH^-$ $\rightleftharpoons$ $BaSO_4(s)$ + $2H_2O(l)$
Starting	0.2256		0.2993		0.2993	0.4512
Change	−0.2256		−0.2256		−0.4512/2	−0.4512
Equilibrium	0.0000		0.0737		0.0737	0.0000

With an excess of $0.0737\ M\ H_2SO_4$, the $[SO_4^{2-}]$ and pH are calculated by using the K_{a2} expression for HSO_4^- with $0.0737\ M$ as the initial concentrations for HSO_4^- and H^+. The reaction and equilibrium-constant expression are

$$HSO_4^- + H_2O \rightleftharpoons H_3O^+ + SO_4^{2-} \qquad K_{a2} = \frac{[H_3O^+][SO_4^{2-}]}{[HSO_4^-]} = 1.1 \times 10^{-2}$$

Let x equal the amount of HSO_4^- that ionizes. Assemble the usual concentration table, and substitute from the table into the equilibrium-constant expression.

Conc. (M)	HSO_4^-	$+ H_2O \rightleftharpoons$	H_3O^+	$+$	SO_4^{2-}
Starting	0.073̲7		0.073̲7		0
Change	$-x$		$+x$		$+x$
Equilibrium	$0.073̲7 - x$		$0.073̲7 + x$		X

The equilibrium-constant expression is

$$1.1 \times 10^{-2} = \frac{[H_3O^+][SO_4^{2-}]}{[HSO_4^-]} = \frac{(0.0737 + x)x}{(0.0737 - x)}$$

Rearrange into a quadratic equation and solve for x.

$$1.1 \times 10^{-2}(0.0737 - x) = (x)(0.0737 + x)$$

$$8.10 \times 10^{-4} - 1.1 \times 10^{-2}x = 0.0737x + x^2$$

$$x^2 + 0.0847x - (8.10 \times 10^{-4}) = 0$$

$$x = \frac{-0.0847 \pm \sqrt{(-0.0847)^2 + 4(8.10 \times 10^{-4})}}{2} = 0.008̲68 \, M$$

Thus, $[SO_4^{2-}] = 0.009 \, M$.

To calculate $[Ba^{2+}]$, use the K_{sp} expression for $BaSO_4$.

$$[Ba^{2+}] = \frac{1.1 \times 10^{-10}}{0.00868 \, M \, SO_4^{2-}} = 1̲.27 \times 10^{-8} = 1 \times 10^{-8} \, M$$

Calculate the pH from the $[H_3O^+]$: $\quad pH = -\log [H_3O^+]$

$$pH = -\log(0.073̲7 + x) = -\log(0.073̲7 + 0.008̲68) = -\log(0.082̲4) = 1.08̲4 = 1.08$$

17.123. The molecular and net ionic equations for the reaction between an aqueous solution of calcium hydrogen carbonate and calcium hydroxide are as follows:

$$Ca(HCO_3)_2(aq) + Ca(OH)_2(aq) \rightleftharpoons 2CaCO_3(s) + 2H_2O(l)$$

$$2Ca^{2+}(aq) + 2HCO_3^-(aq) + 2OH^-(aq) \rightleftharpoons 2CaCO_3(s) + 2H_2O(l)$$

If a spectator cation such as Na^+ were present, the acid-base reaction between HCO_3^- and OH^- would take the following form:

$$HCO_3^- + OH^- \rightleftharpoons CO_3^{2-} + H_2O$$

However, in the present scenario the cation is Ca^{2+} and it forms a precipitate with CO_3^{2-}. As such, "free" CO_3^{2-} ions do not appear in the net ionic equation.

In summary, when the pH of a calcium hydrogen carbonate solution is raised by the addition of the Ca-containing strong base, the bicarbonate ions are converted to carbonate ions which immediately precipitate the calcium ions originally present as well as those added with the strong base. The implied paradox is thus solved.

17.125. Start by calculating the molarity of magnesium ion ($[Mg^{2+}]$) in seawater.

$$[Mg^{2+}] = \frac{1.35 \text{ mg } Mg^{2+}}{L} \times \frac{1 \text{ g}}{10^3 \text{ mg}} \times \frac{1 \text{ mol } Mg^{2+}}{24.305 \text{ g } Mg^{2+}} = 5.554 \times 10^{-5} M$$

90.0% precipitation of Mg^{2+} means its concentration will decrease to 10.0% of its original value, or $5.554 \times 10^{-6} M$. The concentration of OH^- at this point is calculated using the solubility product for $Mg(OH)_2$:

$$K_{sp} = 1.8 \times 10^{-11} = [Mg^{2+}][OH^-]^2 = (5.554 \times 10^{-6})[OH^-]^2$$

$$[OH^-] = \sqrt{\frac{1.8 \times 10^{-11}}{5.554 \times 10^{-6}}} = 1.80 \times 10^{-3} M \; OH^-$$

The pH of the equilibrium solution is calculated from the pOH of the solution.

$$pOH = -\log([OH^-]) = -\log(1.80 \times 10^{-3}) = 2.744$$

$$pH = 14.00 - pOH = 14.00 - 2.744 = 11.2553 = 11.26$$

To calculate the mass of $Ca(OH)_2$ added per liter of seawater to cause precipitation of Mg^{2+}, consider the stoichiometry of the relevant reaction and the change in Mg^{2+} concentration.

$$Mg^{2+}(aq) + Ca(OH)_2(aq) \rightarrow Mg(OH)_2(s) + Ca^{2+}(aq)$$

90.0% precipitation of Mg^{2+} means $0.900 (5.554 \times 10^{-5})$ moles of Mg^{2+} per liter will precipitate. Use this to calculate the required mass of $Ca(OH)_2$ as follows:

$$\text{mass Ca}(OH)_2 = \frac{0.900(5.554 \times 10^{-5} \text{ mol } Mg^{2+})}{L} \times \frac{1 \text{ mol Ca}(OH)_2}{1 \text{ mol } Mg^{2+}} \times \frac{74.09 \text{ g Ca}(OH)_2}{1 \text{ mol Ca}(OH)_2}$$

$$\text{mass Ca}(OH)_2 = 3.703 \times 10^{-3} = 3.70 \times 10^{-3} \text{ g Ca}(OH)_2$$

17.127. Using the rule from Chapter 14, combine the solubility equilibrium for $Mg(OH)_2$ with (twice) the reverse reaction for the base ionization equilibrium for NH_3 and obtain the overall equilibrium constant for the combination of reactions from the product of the individual equilibrium constants of the two individual equations whose sum gives this equation.

$$Mg(OH)_2(s) \rightleftharpoons Mg^{2+}(aq) + 2OH^-(aq) \qquad K_{sp} = 1.8 \times 10^{-11}$$

$$2NH_4^+(aq) + 2OH^-(aq) \rightleftharpoons 2NH_3(aq) + 2H_2O(l) \qquad (1/K_b)^2 = 3.09 \times 10^9$$

$$Mg(OH)_2(s) + 2NH_4^+(aq) \rightleftharpoons Mg^{2+}(aq) + 2NH_3(aq) + 2H_2O(l) \qquad K_c = K_{sp} \times (1/K_b)^2 = 0.556$$

Assemble the usual table using $1.00 \, M$ as the starting concentration of NH_4^+ and x as the unknown concentration of $Zn(OH)_4^{2-}$ formed, or the requested solubility of $Zn(OH)_2$.

Conc. (M)	$Mg(OH)_2(s)$	+	$2NH_4^+(aq)$	$\rightleftharpoons$	$Mg^{2+}(aq)$	+	$2NH_3(aq)$	+	$2H_2O(l)$
Starting			1.00		0		0		
Change			$-2x$		$+x$		$+2x$		
Equilibrium			$1.00 - 2x$		x		$2x$		

The equilibrium-constant expression can now be used. Simply substitute all the exact equilibrium concentrations into the equilibrium-constant expression.

$$K_c = \frac{[Mg^{2+}][NH_3]^2}{[NH_4^+]^2} = \frac{x(2x)^2}{(1.00 - 2x)^2} = 0.556$$

The result is a cubic equation which can be approximately solved as follows. If x equals 0, the left hand side would be 0, or much less than 0.556; if x approaches its maximum value of 0.50, the left hand side becomes infinitely much larger than 0.556. In between these two extremes there is a value of x where both sides will agree closely with one another. Starting with an initial guess of x = 0.35, the following table of calculations, comparisons, and decisions are provided.

value of x	value of $\dfrac{x(2x)^2}{(1.00 - 2x)^2}$	Comparison to 0.5$\underline{5}$6	Decision for next x value
0.35	1.90	1.90 > 0.556	$x < 0.35$
0.30	0.675	0.675 > 0.556	$x < 0.30$
0.28	0.453	0.453 < 0.556	$x > 0.28$
0.29	0.553	0.553 < 0.556 (but not by much)	$x > 0.29$ (but not by much)
0.291	0.564	0.564 > 0.556	$x < 0.291$

The above tabulations show that x is very close to 0.29. Thus, the concentration of Mg^{2+} in the equilibrium solution is 0.29 M.

■ SOLUTIONS TO CUMULATIVE-SKILLS PROBLEMS

17.129. Using the K_{sp} of 1.1×10^{-21} for ZnS, calculate the $[S^{2-}]$ needed to maintain a saturated solution (without precipitation):

$$[S^{2-}] = \frac{1.1 \times 10^{-21}}{1.5 \times 10^{-4} \ M \ Zn^{2+}} = 7.\underline{3}3 \times 10^{-18} \ M$$

Next, use the overall H_2S ionization expression to calculate the $[H_3O^+]$ needed to achieve this $[S^{2-}]$ level:

$$[H_3O^+] = \sqrt{\frac{1.1 \times 10^{-20} \ (0.10 \ M)}{7.33 \times 10^{-18} \ M}} = 1.\underline{2}25 \times 10^{-2} \ M$$

Finally, calculate the buffer ratio of $[SO_4^{2-}]/[HSO_4^-]$ from the H_2SO_4 K_{a_2} expression where K_{a_2} has the value 1.1×10^{-2}:

$$\frac{[SO_4^{2-}]}{[HSO_4^-]} = \frac{K_{a_2}}{[H_3O^+]} = \frac{1.1 \times 10^{-2}}{1.225 \times 10^{-2}} = \frac{0.8981}{1.000}$$

If $[HSO_4^-] = 0.20 \ M$, then

$$[SO_4^{2-}] = 0.8981 \times 0.20 \ M = 0.1\underline{7}95 = 0.18 \ M$$

Because each mole of Na_2SO_4 provides one mole of sulfate ion, this is also the minimum molarity of Na_2SO_4 required to prevent ZnS precipitation.

17.131. Begin by solving for $[H_3O^+]$ in the buffer. Ignoring changes in $[HCHO_2]$ as a result of ionization in the buffer, you obtain

$$[H_3O^+] \cong 1.7 \times 10^{-4} \times \frac{0.45 \text{ M}}{0.20 \text{ M}} = 3.\underline{8}25 \times 10^{-4} \text{ M}$$

You should verify that this approximation is valid (you obtain the same result from the Henderson-Hasselbalch equation). The equilibrium for the dissolution of CaF_2 in acidic solution is obtained by subtracting twice the acid ionization of HF from the solubility equilibrium of CaF_2.

$CaF_2(s)$			$\rightleftharpoons$	$Ca^{2+}(aq) + 2F^-(aq)$	K_{sp}
$2H_3O^+(aq)$	$+$	$2F^-(aq)$	$\rightleftharpoons$	$2HF(aq) + 2 H_2O(l)$	$1/(K_a)^2$
$2H_3O^+(aq)$	$+$	$CaF_2(s)$	$\rightleftharpoons$	$Ca^{2+}(aq) + 2HF(aq) + 2 H_2O(l)$	$K_c = K_{sp}/(K_a)^2$

Therefore, $K_c = (3.4 \times 10^{-11}) \div (6.8 \times 10^{-4})^2 = 7.\underline{3}5 \times 10^{-5}$. In order to solve the equilibrium-constant equation, you require the concentration of HF, which you obtain from the acid-ionization constant for HF.

$$K_a = \frac{[H_3O^+][F^-]}{[HF]}$$

$$6.8 \times 10^{-4} = 3.825 \times 10^{-4} \times \frac{[F^-]}{[HF]}$$

$$\frac{[F^-]}{[HF]} = 1.778, \text{ or } [F^-] = 1.\underline{7}78 \, [HF]$$

Let x be the solubility of CaF_2 in the buffer. Then $[Ca^{2+}] = x$ and $[F^-] + [HF] = 2x$. Substituting from the previous equation, you obtain

$$2x = 1.778[HF] + [HF] = 2.778[HF], \text{ or } [HF] = 2x/2.\underline{7}78$$

You can now substitute for $[H_3O^+]$ and $[HF]$ into the equation for K_c.

$$K_c = \frac{[Ca^{2+}][HF]^2}{[H_3O^+]^2} = \frac{(x)(2x/2.778)^2}{(3.825 \times 10^{-4})^2} = 7.35 \times 10^{-5}$$

$$7.35 \times 10^{-5} = (3.543 \times 10^6)x^3$$

$$x^3 = 2.075 \times 10^{-11}$$

$$x = 2.\underline{7}48 \times 10^{-4} = 2.7 \times 10^{-4} \text{ M}$$

17.133. The net ionic equation is

$$Ba^{2+}(aq) + 2OH^-(aq) + Mg^{2+}(aq) + SO_4^{2-}(aq) \rightleftharpoons BaSO_4(s) + Mg(OH)_2(s)$$

Start by calculating the moles per liter of each ion after mixing and before precipitation. Use a total volume of $0.0450 + 0.0670 \text{ L} = 0.112 \text{ L}$.

M of SO_4^{2-} and $Mg^{2+} = (0.350 \text{ mol/L} \times 0.0670 \text{ L}) \div 0.112 \text{ L} = 0.209\underline{4} \text{ M}$

M of $Ba^{2+} = (0.250 \text{ mol/L} \times 0.0450 \text{ L}) \div 0.112 \text{ L} = 0.100\underline{4} \text{ M}$

M of $OH^- = (2 \times 0.250 \text{ mol/L} \times 0.0450 \text{ L}) \div 0.112 \text{ L} = 0.200\underline{89} \text{ M}$

Assemble a table showing the precipitation of $BaSO_4$ and $Mg(OH)_2$.

Conc. (M)	Ba^{2+}	+	SO_4^{2-}	+	$Mg^{2+} + 2OH^- \rightleftharpoons BaSO_4(s) + Mg(OH)_2(s)$	
Starting	0.1004		0.2094		0.2094	0.20089
Change	−0.1004		−0.1004		−0.1004	−0.20089
Equilibrium	0.0000		0.1090		0.1090	0.0000

In the case of $Mg(OH)_2$, because the $[OH^-]$ is limiting and happens to be $-0.20089\ M$, the change for Mg^{2+} is $(-0.20089\ M/2) = -0.1004\ M$.

To calculate $[Ba^{2+}]$, use the K_{sp} expression for $BaSO_4$.

$$[Ba^{2+}] = \frac{1.1 \times 10^{-10}}{0.1090\ M\ SO_4^{2-}} = 1.\underline{0}09 \times 10^{-9} = 1.0 \times 10^{-9}\ M$$

$$[SO_4^{2-}] = 0.10\underline{9}0 = 0.109\ M$$

Calculate the $[OH^-]$ using the K_{sp} expression for $Mg(OH)_2$:

$$[OH^-] = \sqrt{\frac{1.8 \times 10^{-11}}{0.1090\ M\ \ Mg^{2+}}} = 1.\underline{2}8 \times 10^{-5} = 1.3 \times 10^{-5}\ M$$

$$[Mg^{2+}] = 0.10\underline{9}0 = 0.109\ M$$

CHAPTER 18

Thermodynamics and Equilibrium

■ SOLUTIONS TO EXERCISES

Note on units and significant figures: The mole unit is omitted from all thermodynamic parameters such as $S°$, $\Delta S°$, etc. If the final answer to a solution needs to be rounded off, it is given first with one nonsignificant figure, and the last significant figure is underlined. The final answer is then rounded to the correct number of significant figures. In multistep problems, intermediate answers are given with at least one nonsignificant figure; however, only the final answer has been rounded off.

18.1.   When the liquid evaporates, it absorbs heat: ΔH_{vap} = 42.6 kJ/mol (42.6 × 10³ J/mol) at 25°C, or 298 K. The entropy change, ΔS, is

$$\Delta S = \frac{\Delta H_{vap}}{T} = \frac{42.6 \times 10^3 \text{ J/mol}}{298 \text{ K}} = 14\underline{2}.9 \text{ J/(mol•K)}$$

The entropy of one mole of the vapor equals the entropy of one mole of liquid (161 J/K) plus 142.9 J/K.

$$S° = (161 + 142.9) \text{ J/(mol•K)} = 30\underline{3}.9 = 304 \text{ J/(mol•K)}$$

18.2.   a. $\Delta S°$ is positive because there is an increase in moles of gas (Δn_{gas} = +1) from a solid reactant forming a mole of gas. (Entropy increases.)

   b. $\Delta S°$ is positive because there is an increase in moles of gas (Δn_{gas} = +1) from a liquid reactant forming a mole of gas. (Entropy increases.)

   c. $\Delta S°$ is negative because there is a decrease in moles of gas (Δn_{gas} = −1) from liquid and gaseous reactants forming two moles of solid. (Entropy decreases.)

   d. $\Delta S°$ is positive because there is an increase in moles of gas (Δn_{gas} = +1) from solid and liquid reactants forming a mole of gas and four moles of an ionic compound. (Entropy increases.)

18.3.   The reaction and standard entropies are given below. Multiply the $S°$ values by their stoichiometric coefficients, and subtract the entropy of the reactant from the sum of the product entropies.

$$C_6H_{12}O_6 \quad \rightarrow \quad 2C_2H_5OH(l) \quad + \quad 2CO_2(g)$$

$S°$:   212   2 x 160.7   2 x 213.7 J/K

$\Delta S° = \Sigma n S°(\text{products}) - \Sigma m S°(\text{reactants}) = [(2 \times 160.7 + 2 \times 213.7) - 212] \text{ J/K} = 53\underline{6}.8 = 537 \text{ J/K}$

18.4.   The reaction, standard enthalpy changes, and standard entropies are as follows:

$$CH_4(g) \quad + \quad 2O_2(g) \quad \rightarrow \quad CO_2(g) \quad + \quad 2H_2O(g)$$

ΔH_f°:	-74.87	0	-393.5	$2 \times (-241.8)$ kJ
S°:	186.1	2×205.0	213.7	2×188.7 J/K

Calculate ΔH° and ΔS° for the reaction by taking the values for products and subtracting the values for reactants.

$$\Delta H^\circ = \Sigma n \Delta H_f^\circ (\text{products}) - \Sigma m \Delta H_f^\circ (\text{reactants}) =$$

$$[(-393.5 + 2 \times -241.8) - (-74.87)] \text{ kJ} = -802.\underline{2}3 \text{ kJ}$$

$$\Delta S^\circ = \Sigma n S^\circ (\text{products}) - \Sigma m S^\circ (\text{reactants}) =$$

$$[(213.7 + 2 \times 188.7) - (186.1 + 2 \times 205.0)] \text{ J/K} = -5.0 \text{ J/K}$$

Now, substitute into the equation for ΔG° in terms of ΔH° and ΔS° ($= -5.0 \times 10^{-3}$ kJ/K):

$$\Delta G^\circ = \Delta H^\circ - T\Delta S^\circ = -802.\underline{2}3 \text{ kJ} - (298 \text{ K})(-5.0 \times 10^{-3} \text{ kJ/K}) = -800.\underline{7}4 = -800.7 \text{ kJ}$$

18.5.   Write the values of ΔG_f° multiplied by their stoichiometric coefficients below each formula:

$$CaCO_3(s) \quad \rightarrow \quad CaO(s) \quad + \quad CO_2(g)$$

ΔG_f°:	-1128.8	-603.5	-394.4 kJ

The calculation is

$$\Delta G^\circ = \Sigma n G_f^\circ (\text{products}) - \Sigma m G_f^\circ (\text{reactants}) =$$

$$[(-603.5) + (-394.4) - (-1128.8)] \text{ kJ} = 130.\underline{9} \text{ kJ}$$

18.6.   a.

$$C(\text{graphite}) \quad + \quad 2H_2(g) \quad \rightarrow \quad CH_4(g)$$

ΔG_f°:	0	0	-50.80 kJ

$$\Delta G^\circ = [(-50.80) - (0)] \text{ kJ} = -50.80 \text{ kJ (spontaneous reaction)}$$

b.

$$2H_2(g) \quad + \quad O_2(g) \quad \rightarrow \quad 2H_2O(l)$$

ΔG_f°:	0	0	$2 \times (-237.1)$ kJ

$$\Delta G^\circ = [(2 \times -237.1) - (0)] \text{ kJ} = -474.\underline{2} \text{ kJ (spontaneous reaction)}$$

c.

$$4HCN(g) \quad + \quad 5O_2(g) \quad \rightarrow \quad 2H_2O(l) \quad + \quad 4CO_2(g) \quad + \quad 2N_2(g)$$

ΔG_f°:	4×124.7	0	$2 \times (-237.1)$	$4 \times (-394.4)$	0 kJ

$$\Delta G^\circ = [(2 \times -237.1) + 4 \times (-394.4) - (4 \times 124.7)] \text{ kJ} = -2550.\underline{6} \text{ kJ (spontaneous reaction)}$$

d.

$$Ag^+(aq) \quad + \quad I^-(aq) \quad \rightarrow \quad AgI(s)$$

$\Delta G_f°$:   77.12   -51.59   -66.19 kJ

$\Delta G° = [(-66.19) - (77.12 - 51.59)]$ kJ $= -91.72$ kJ (spontaneous reaction)

18.7.   a. $K = K_p = P_{CO_2}$

       b. $K = K_{sp} = [Pb^{2+}][I^-]^2$

       c. $K = \dfrac{P_{CO_2}}{[H^+][HCO_3^-]}$

18.8.   First, calculate $\Delta G°$ using the $\Delta G_f°$ values from Table 18.2.

$$CaCO_3(s) \rightleftharpoons CaO(s) \quad + \quad CO_2(g)$$

$\Delta G_f°$:   -1128.8   -603.5   -394.4 kJ

Subtract $\Delta G_f°$ of reactants from that of the products:

$$\Delta G_f° = \Sigma n \Delta G_f°(\text{products}) - \Sigma m \Delta G_f°(\text{reactants}) =$$

$$[(-603.5) + (-394.4) - (-1128.8)] \text{ kJ} = 130.9 \text{ kJ}$$

Use the rearranged form of the equation, $\Delta G° = -RT \ln K$, to solve for $\ln K$. To get compatible units, express $\Delta G°$ in joules, and set R equal to 8.31 J/(mol•K). Substituting the numerical values into the expression gives

$$\ln K = \frac{-\Delta G°}{RT} = \frac{130.9 \times 10^3}{-8.31 \times 298} = -52.859$$

$$K = K_p = e^{-52.859} = 1.10 \times 10^{-23} = 1 \times 10^{-23}$$

18.9.   First, calculate $\Delta G°$ using the $\Delta G_f°$ values in the exercise.

$$Mg(OH)_2(s) \rightarrow Mg^{2+}(aq) \quad + \quad 2OH^-(aq)$$

$\Delta G_f°$:   -833.7   -454.8   2 x (-157.3) kJ

Hence, $\Delta G°$ for the reaction is

$$\Delta G° = [2 \times (-157.3) + (-454.8) - (-833.7)] \text{ kJ} = 64.3 \text{ kJ}$$

Now, substitute numerical values into the equation relating $\ln K$ and $\Delta G°$.

$$\ln K = \frac{-\Delta G°}{RT} = \frac{64.3 \times 10^3}{-8.31 \times 298} = -25.965$$

$$K = K_{sp} = e^{-25.965} = 5.289 \times 10^{-12} = 5 \times 10^{-12}$$

18.10. From Appendix C, you have

$$H_2O(l) \rightleftharpoons H_2O(g)$$

$\Delta H_f°$:   -285.8   -241.8 kJ

$S°$:   69.95   188.7 J/K

Calculate $\Delta H°$ and $\Delta S°$ from these values.

$$\Delta H° = [-241.8 - (-285.8)] \text{ kJ} = 44.\underline{0} \text{ kJ}$$

$$\Delta S° = [188.7 - 69.95] \text{ J/K} = 118.\underline{7}5 \text{ J/K}$$

Substitute $\Delta H°$, $\Delta S°$ ($= 0.11875$ kJ/K), and T ($= 318$ K) into the equation for $\Delta G_T°$:

$$\Delta G_T° = \Delta H° - T\Delta S° = 44.0 \text{ kJ} - (318 \text{ K})(0.11875 \text{ kJ/K}) = 6.\underline{2}3 \text{ kJ}$$

Substitute the value of $\Delta G°$ (6.23×10^3 J) at 318 K into the equation relating $\ln K$ and $\Delta G°$.

$$\ln K = \frac{-\Delta G°}{RT} = \frac{6.23 \times 10^3}{-8.31 \times 318} = -2.\underline{3}60$$

$$K = K_p = e^{-2.360} = 0.0\underline{9}43 = 0.09$$

$K_p = P_{H_2O}$, so the vapor pressure of H_2O is 0.09 atm ($\underline{7}1.7 = 70.$ mmHg).

The value is 71.9 mmHg in Appendix B.

18.11. First, calculate $\Delta H°$ and $\Delta S°$ using the given $\Delta H_f°$ and $S°$ values.

$$MgCO_3(s) \rightleftharpoons MgO(s) + CO_2(g)$$

$\Delta H_f°$:   -1111.7   -601.2   -393.5 kJ

$\Delta S°$:   65.9   26.9   213.7 J/K

$$\Delta H° = [-601.2 + (-393.5) - (-1111.7)] \text{ kJ} = 117.\underline{0} \text{ kJ}$$

$$\Delta S° = [(26.9 + 213.7) - 65.9] \text{ J/K} = 174.\underline{7} \text{ J/K}$$

Substitute these values into the expression relating T, $\Delta H°$, and $\Delta S°$ ($= 0.1747$ kJ/K).

$$T = \frac{\Delta H°}{\Delta S°} = \frac{117.0 \text{ kJ}}{0.1747 \text{ kJ/K}} = 669.\underline{7}2 \text{ K (lower than that for } CaCO_3\text{)}$$

■ ANSWERS TO CONCEPT CHECKS

18.1. The process is $I_2(s) \rightarrow I_2(g)$. The iodine atoms have gone from a state of some order (crystalline iodine) to one that is more disordered (gas). The entropy will have increased.

18.2. The standard free energy of formation for $NO(g)$ is 86.60 kJ/mol. This rather large positive value means the equilibrium constant is small. At equilibrium, the NO concentration is low.

18.3. a.   The standard free-energy change, $\Delta G°$, is independent of concentration, so it will not change.

       b.   The relationship between ΔG and $\Delta G°$ is given by $\Delta G = \Delta G° + RT \ln Q$, where Q is the reaction quotient. If the concentration of C is increased, it will cause the value of Q to increase and, in turn, ΔG to increase.

18.4.   You must break a chemical bond when N_2O_4 goes to $2NO_2$. It will take energy to do that, so you expect ΔH to be positive (the reaction is endothermic). Also, when you break a molecule in two, you generally increase the entropy (ΔS is positive). According to Table 18.3, the reaction should be nonspontaneous at relatively low temperature, but spontaneous at some higher temperature. That is, the concentration of NO_2 increases with temperature.

■ ANSWERS TO SELF-ASSESSMENT AND REVIEW QUESTIONS

18.1.   A spontaneous process is a chemical and/or a physical change that occurs by itself without the continuing intervention of an outside agency. Three examples are (1) a rock on a hilltop rolls down, (2) heat flows from a hot object to a cold one, and (3) iron rusts in moist air. Three examples of nonspontaneous processes are (1) a rock rolls uphill by itself, (2) heat flows from a cold object to a hot one, and (3) rust is converted to iron and oxygen.

18.2.   Because the energy is more dispersed in liquids than in solids, liquid benzene contains more entropy than does the same quantity of frozen benzene.

18.3.   The second law of thermodynamics states that for a spontaneous process, the total entropy of a system and its surroundings always increases. As stated in Section 18.2, a spontaneous process actually creates energy dispersal, or entropy.

18.4.   The relationship between entropy and enthalpy can be expressed in terms of the following equation:

$$\Delta S = \frac{\Delta H - \Delta G}{T}$$

At equilibrium, ΔG equals 0, so the equation reduces to $\Delta H/T$, whereas, when not at equilibrium, $\Delta G \neq 0$, so this is not the case. In contrast to a phase change at equilibrium, the entropy change for a spontaneous chemical reaction (at constant pressure) does not equal $\Delta H/T$ because entropy is created by the spontaneous reaction. This can be an increase in the entropy of the surroundings or of the system. An example of the latter is the reaction $N_2O_4(g) \rightarrow 2NO_2(g)$, where one reactant molecule forms two product molecules, thus increasing the randomness.

18.5.   The standard entropy of hydrogen gas at 25°C can be obtained by starting near 0.0 K as a reference point, where the entropy of perfect crystals of hydrogen is almost zero. Then, warm to room temperature in small increments, and calculate $\Delta S°$ for each incremental temperature change (say, 2 K) by dividing the heat absorbed by the average temperature (1 K is used as the average for 0 K to 2 K), and also take into account the entropy increases that accompany a phase change.

18.6. To predict the sign of $\Delta S°$, look for a change, Δn_{gas}, in the number of moles of gas. If there is an increase in moles of gas in the products (Δn_{gas} is positive), then $\Delta S°$ should be positive. A decrease in moles of gas in the products suggests $\Delta S°$ should be negative.

18.7. Free energy, G, equals $H - TS$; that is, it is the difference between the enthalpy of a system and the product of temperature and entropy. The free-energy change, ΔG, equals $\Delta H - T\Delta S$.

18.8. The standard free-energy change, $\Delta G°$, equals $\Delta H° - T\Delta S°$; that is, it is the difference between the standard enthalpy change of a system and the product of temperature and the standard entropy change of a system. The standard free-energy change of formation is the free-energy change when 1 mole of a substance is formed from its elements in their stable states at 1 atm and at a standard temperature, usually 25°C.

18.9. If $\Delta G°$ for a reaction is negative, the equation for the reaction is spontaneous in the direction written; that is, the reactants form the products as written. If it is positive, then the equation as written is nonspontaneous.

18.10. In principle, if a reaction is carried out so that no entropy is produced, the useful work obtained is the maximum useful work, w_{max}, and is equal to ΔG of the reaction.

18.11. When gasoline burns in an automobile engine, the change in free energy shows up as useful work. Gasoline, a mixture of hydrocarbons such as C_8H_{18} or octane, burns to yield energy, gaseous CO_2, and gaseous H_2O.

18.12. A nonspontaneous reaction can be made to occur by coupling it with a spontaneous reaction having a sufficiently negative $\Delta G°$ to furnish the required energy. (The net $\Delta G°$ of the coupled reactions must be negative.)

18.13. As a spontaneous reaction proceeds, the free energy (G) decreases until equilibrium is reached at a minimum G. See the diagram below.

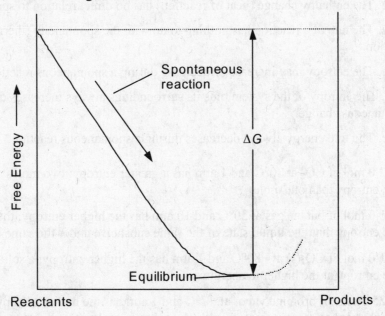

18.14. Because the equilibrium constant is related to $\Delta H°$ and $\Delta S°$ by $-RT \ln K = \Delta H° - T\Delta S°$, heat measurements alone can be used to obtain it. The standard enthalpy, $\Delta H°$, is the heat of reaction measured at constant pressure. The standard entropy change, $\Delta S°$, can be calculated from standard entropies, which are obtained from heat-capacity data.

18.15. The four combinations are as follows: (1) A negative $\Delta H°$ and a positive $\Delta S°$ always give a negative $\Delta G°$ and a spontaneous reaction. (2) A positive $\Delta H°$ and a negative $\Delta S°$ always give a positive $\Delta G°$ and a nonspontaneous reaction. (3) A negative $\Delta H°$ and a negative $\Delta S°$ may give a negative or a positive $\Delta G°$. At low temperatures, $\Delta G°$ will usually be negative and the reaction is spontaneous; at high temperatures, $\Delta G°$ will usually be positive and the reaction is nonspontaneous. (4) A positive $\Delta H°$ and a positive $\Delta S°$ may give a negative or a positive $\Delta G°$. At low temperatures, $\Delta G°$ will usually be positive and the reaction is nonspontaneous; at high temperatures, $\Delta G°$ will usually be negative and the reaction is spontaneous.

18.16. You can estimate the temperature at which a nonspontaneous reaction becomes spontaneous by substituting zero for $\Delta G°$ into the equation $\Delta G° = \Delta H° - T\Delta S°$ and then solving for T using the form $T = \Delta H°/\Delta S°$.

18.17. The answer is e, $\Delta G < 0$, $\Delta H > 0$, and $\Delta S > 0$.

18.18. The answer is c, III only.

18.19. The answer is d, 5.49 K

18.20. The answer is a, -956 kJ.

■ ANSWERS TO CONCEPTUAL PROBLEMS

18.23. a.   False. The enthalpy change (heat of reaction) has no direct relation to spontaneity.

   b.   False. The rate of a reaction has nothing to do with the spontaneity (thermodynamics) of a reaction.

   c.   False. The entropy may increase or decrease during a spontaneous reaction.

   d.   True. The entropy of the system plus its surroundings always increases during a spontaneous change.

   e.   False. The free energy always decreases during a spontaneous reaction.

18.25. a.   The 2.0 mol of CO_2 at 20°C and 1 atm has a greater entropy; two moles of substance have more entropy than one mole.

   b.   The 1.0 mol of butane gas at 20°C and 10 atm has the higher entropy; the gaseous state has more entropy than the liquid state of the same substance under the same conditions.

   c.   The 1.0 mol of $CO_2(s)$ at −80°C and 1 atm has the higher entropy; a solid substance has more entropy at the higher temperature.

   d.   The 25 grams of bromine vapor at −7°C and 1 atm has the higher entropy; the gaseous (vapor) state has more entropy than the liquid state of the same substance under the same conditions.

18.27. a. Since this is a gas-phase reaction, calculate the change in the number of moles of gas molecules, $\Delta n = 1 - 3 = -2$. This corresponds to a decrease in entropy, so ΔS is negative.

b. Since this is an equilibrium state, $\Delta G = 0$, so $\Delta H - T\Delta S = 0$ also. This gives $\Delta H = T\Delta S$, and since ΔS is negative, so is ΔH.

c. The reaction spontaneously re-establishes equilibrium, so ΔG is negative prior to equilibrium.

d. At equilibrium, $\Delta G = 0$.

18.29. a. Changes in volume will affect the position of the equilibrium but will not change the value of the equilibrium constant for a reaction.

b. The increase in volume of the container corresponds to a decrease in the pressure. According to Le Châtelier's principle, the reaction will shift toward the side with more gas molecules to re-establish the pressure. This means the reaction will shift toward the left side, $X(g) + Y(g)$. A reaction that shifts to the left has a Q value larger than the equilibrium constant.

c. Immediately after the volume change, the value of ΔS for the forward reaction will still be the same, negative. Since the reaction is now spontaneous in the reverse reaction, ΔG for the forward reaction must be positive.

■ SOLUTIONS TO PRACTICE PROBLEMS

Note on significant figures: The mole unit is omitted from all thermodynamic parameters such as $S°$, $\Delta S°$, etc. If the final answer to a solution needs to be rounded off, it is given first with one nonsignificant figure, and the last significant figure is underlined. The final answer is then rounded to the correct number of significant figures. In multistep problems, intermediate answers are given with at least one nonsignificant figure; however, only the final answer has been rounded off.

18.31. First, determine the enthalpy change for the reaction of 1.20 mol of $CHCl_3$.

$$\Delta H = 1.20 \text{ mol} \times \frac{29.6 \text{ kJ}}{1 \text{ mol}} = 35.5\underline{2} \text{ kJ} = 3.5\underline{5}2 \times 10^4 \text{ J}$$

Use the equilibrium relation between ΔS and ΔH_{vap} at the boiling point (61.2°C = 334.4 K):

$$\Delta S = \frac{\Delta H}{T} = \frac{3.552 \times 10^4 \text{J}}{334.4 \text{ K}} = 10\underline{6}.2 = 106 \text{ J/K}$$

18.33. First, determine the enthalpy change for the condensation of 1.00 mol of $CH_3OH(l)$. $\Delta H_{cond} = -\Delta H_{vap} = -38.0$ kJ/mol.

The entropy change for this condensation at 25°C (298 K) is

$$\Delta S = \frac{\Delta H_{cond}}{T} = \frac{-3.80 \times 10^4 \text{J}}{298 \text{ K}} = -12\underline{7}.51 \text{ J/K}$$

The entropy of one mole of liquid is calculated using the entropy of one mole of vapor, 255 J/(mol•K).

$$S_{liq} = S_{vap} + \Delta S_{cond} = 255 \text{ J/K} + (-127.51 \text{ J/K}) = 12\underline{7}.48 = 127 \text{ J/K}$$

18.35. a. $\Delta S°$ is negative because there is a decrease in moles of gas ($\Delta n_{gas} = -2$) from three moles of gaseous reactants forming one mole of gaseous product. (Entropy decreases.)

        b. $\Delta S°$ is not predictable from the rules given. The molecules N_2, O_2 and NO are of similar size and present in equal numbers. There is no change in moles of gas ($\Delta n_{gas} = 0$), since two moles of gaseous reactants form two moles of gaseous products. Also, there is no phase change occurring.

        c. $\Delta S°$ is positive because there is an increase in moles of gas ($\Delta n_{gas} = +1$) from five moles of gaseous reactants forming six moles of gaseous products. (Entropy increases.)

        d. $\Delta S°$ is positive because there is an increase in moles of gas ($\Delta n_{gas} = +1$) from a solid reactant and one mole of gaseous reactant forming two moles of gaseous products. (Entropy increases.)

18.37. The reaction and standard entropies are given below. Multiply the $S°$ values by their stoichiometric coefficients, and subtract the entropy of the reactant from the sum of the product entropies.

$$2Na(s) \quad + \quad Cl_2(g) \quad \rightarrow \quad 2NaCl(s)$$

        a. $S°$:   2 x 51.46   223.0   2 x 72.12 J/K

        $\Delta S° = \Sigma n S°(products) - \Sigma m S°(reactants) =$

                $[(2 \times 72.12) - (2 \times 51.46 + 223.0)]$ J/K $= -181.\underline{68} = -181.7$ J/K

$$Ag(s) \quad + \quad 1/2\ Cl_2(g) \quad \rightarrow \quad AgCl(s)$$

        b. $S°$:   42.55   1/2 x 223.0   96.2 J/K

        $\Delta S° = \Sigma n S°(products) - \Sigma m S°(reactants) =$

        $[(96.2) - (42.55 + 1/2 \times 223.0)]$ J/K $= -57.\underline{85} = -57.9$ J/K

$$CS_2(l) \quad + \quad 3O_2(g) \quad \rightarrow \quad CO_2(g) \quad + \quad 2SO_2(g)$$

        c. $S°$:   151.3   3 x 205.0   213.7   2 x 248.1 J/K

        $\Delta S° = \Sigma n S°(products) - \Sigma m S°(reactants) =$

        $[(213.7 + 2 \times 248.1) - (151.3 + 3 \times 205.0)]$ J/K $= -56.4$ J/K

$$2CH_3OH(l) \quad + \quad 3O_2(g) \quad \rightarrow \quad 2CO_2(g) \quad + \quad 4H_2O(g)$$

        d. $S°$:   2 x 126.8   3 x 205.0   2 x 213.7   4 x 188.7 J/K

        $\Delta S° = \Sigma n S°(products) - \Sigma m S°(reactants) =$

        $[(2 \times 213.7 + 4 \times 188.7) - (2 \times 126.8 + 3 \times 205.0)]$ J/K $= 313.\underline{6} = 314$ J/K

$$C_2H_4(g) \quad + \quad 3O_2(g) \quad \rightarrow \quad 2CO_2(g) \quad + \quad 2H_2O(l)$$

18.39. $S°$: 219.2 $\qquad$ 3 x 205.0 $\qquad$ 2 x 213.7 $\qquad$ 2 x 69.95 J/K

$\Delta S° = \Sigma nS°(\text{products}) - \Sigma mS°(\text{reactants}) =$

$[(2 \times 213.7 + 2 \times 69.95) - (219.2 + 3 \times 205.0)]$ J/K = $-266.\underline{9}0$ J/K

S decreases, as expected from the decrease in moles of gas.

18.41. The reaction, with standard enthalpies of formation and standard entropies written underneath, is

$$2CH_3OH(l) \quad + \quad 3O_2(g) \quad \rightarrow \quad 2CO_2(g) \quad + \quad 4H_2O(l)$$

$\Delta H_f°$: 2 x (-238.7) $\qquad$ 0 $\qquad$ 2 x (-393.5) $\quad$ 4 x (-285.8) kJ

$S°$: 2 x 126.8 $\qquad$ 3 x 205.0 $\qquad$ 2 x 213.7 $\quad$ 4 x 69.95 J/K

Calculate $\Delta H°$ and $\Delta S°$ for the reaction.

$\Delta H° = \Sigma n\Delta H_f°(\text{products}) - \Sigma m\Delta H_f°(\text{reactants}) =$

$[2 \times (-393.5) + 4 \times (-285.8) - 2 \times (-238.7)]$ kJ = -1452.8 kJ

$\Delta S° = \Sigma nS°(\text{products}) - \Sigma mS°(\text{reactants}) =$

$[(2 \times 213.7 + 4 \times 69.95) - (2 \times 126.8 + 3 \times 205.0)]$ J/K = $-161.\underline{4}0 = -161.4$ J/K

Now, substitute into the equation for $\Delta G°$ in terms of $\Delta H°$ and $\Delta S°$ ($= -0.16\underline{1}40$ kJ/K).

$\Delta G° = \Delta H° - T\Delta S° = -1452.8$ kJ $- (298$ K$) \times (-0.16140$ kJ/K$) = -1404.\underline{7}0 = -1404.7$ kJ

18.43. a. $K(s) + 1/2Br_2(l) \rightarrow KBr(s)$

b. $3/2H_2(g) + C(\text{graphite}) + 1/2Cl_2(g) \rightarrow CH_3Cl(l)$

c. $1/8S_8(\text{rhombic}) + H_2(g) \rightarrow H_2S(g)$

d. $As(s) + 3/2H_2(g) \rightarrow AsH_3(g)$

18.45. Write the values of $\Delta G_f°$ multiplied by their stoichiometric coefficients below each formula; then subtract $\Delta G_f°$ of the reactants from that of the products.

$$C_2H_4(g) \quad + \quad 3O_2(g) \quad \rightarrow \quad 2CO_2(g) \quad + \quad 2H_2O(l)$$

a. $\Delta G_f°$: 68.39 $\qquad$ 0 $\qquad$ -394.4 $\qquad$ 2 x (-237.1) kJ

$\Delta G° = \Sigma n\Delta G_f°(\text{products}) - \Sigma m\Delta G_f°(\text{reactants}) =$

$[2(-394.4) + 2(-237.1) - (68.39)]$ kJ = $-1331.\underline{3}9 = -1331.4$ kJ

$$CaCO_3(s) \quad + \quad 2H^+(aq) \quad \rightarrow \quad Ca^{2+}(aq) \quad + \quad H_2O(l) \quad + \quad CO_2(g)$$

b. $\Delta G_f°$: -1128.8 $\qquad$ 0 $\qquad$ -553.5 $\qquad$ -237.1 $\qquad$ -394.4 kJ

$\Delta G° = \Sigma n\Delta G_f°(\text{products}) - \Sigma m\Delta G_f°(\text{reactants}) =$

$[(-553.5) + (-237.1) + (-394.4) - (-1128.8)]$ kJ = -56.2 kJ

18.47. a.   Spontaneous reaction   b.   Spontaneous reaction

c.   Nonspontaneous reaction   d.   Equilibrium mixture; significant amounts of both

e.   Nonspontaneous reaction

18.49. Calculate $\Delta H°$ and $\Delta G°$ using the given $\Delta H_f°$ and $\Delta G_f°$ values.

$$Al_2O_3(s) + 2Fe(s) \rightarrow Fe_2O_3(s) + 2Al(s)$$

$\Delta H_f°$:	-1675.7	0	-825.5	0 kJ
$\Delta G_f°$:	-1582.3	0	-743.5	0 kJ

a.

$$\Delta H° = [(-825.5) - (-1675.7)] \text{ kJ} = 850.2 \text{ kJ}$$

$$\Delta G° = [(-743.5) - (-1582.3)] \text{ kJ} = 838.8 \text{ kJ}$$

The reaction is endothermic, absorbing 850.2 kJ of heat. The large positive value for $\Delta G°$ indicates that the equilibrium composition is mainly reactants.

$$COCl_2(g) + H_2O(l) \rightarrow CO_2(g) + 2HCl(g)$$

$\Delta H_f°$:	-220.1	-285.8	-393.5	2 x (-92.31) kJ
$\Delta G_f°$:	-205.9	-237.1	-394.4	2 x (-95.30) kJ

b.

$$\Delta H° = [-393.5 + (2)(-92.31) - (-220.1) - (-285.8)] \text{ kJ} = -72.\underline{2}2 = -72.2 \text{ kJ}$$

$$\Delta G° = [-394.4 + (2)(-95.30) - (-205.9) - (-237.1)] \text{ kJ} = -142.\underline{0}0 = -142.0 \text{ kJ}$$

The reaction is exothermic; the $\Delta G°$ value indicates mainly products at equilibrium.

18.51. Calculate $\Delta G°$ using the given $\Delta G_f°$ values.

$$2H_2(g) + O_2(g) \rightarrow 2H_2O(l)$$

$\Delta G_f°$:	0	0	2 x (-237.1) kJ

$$\Delta G° = [2(-237.1) - 0] \text{ kJ} = -474.2 \text{ kJ}$$

Maximum work equals $\Delta G°$ which equals −474.2 kJ. Because maximum work is stipulated, no entropy is produced.

18.53. Calculate $\Delta G°$ per 1 mol Zn(s) using the given $\Delta G_f°$ values.

$$Zn(s) + Cu^{2+}(aq) \rightarrow Zn^{2+}(aq) + Cu(s)$$

$\Delta G_f°$:	0	65.52	-147.0	0 kJ

$$\Delta G° = [(-147.0) - (65.52)] \text{ kJ} = -212.\underline{5}2 \text{ kJ/mol Zn}$$

$$-212.52 \text{ kJ/mol Zn} \times (4.85 \text{ g} \div 65.38 \text{ g/mol Zn}) = -15.\underline{7}6 = -15.8 \text{ kJ}$$

Maximum work equals $\Delta G°$ which equals −15.8 kJ. Because maximum work is stipulated, no entropy is produced.

18.55. a. $K = K_p = \dfrac{P_{CO_2} P_{H_2}}{P_{CO} P_{H_2O}}$ b. $K = K_{sp} = [Mg^{2+}][OH^-]^2$ c. $K = [Li^+]^2[OH^-]^2\, P_{H_2}$

18.57. First, calculate $\Delta G°$ using the $\Delta G_f°$ values from Appendix C.

$$H_2(g) \qquad Br_2(l) \qquad \rightarrow \qquad 2HBr(g)$$

$\Delta G_f°$:   0   0   2 x (-53.50) kJ

$\Delta G° = [2(-53.50) - 0]\, kJ = -107.00\, kJ$

Use the rearranged form of the equation, $\Delta G° = -RT \ln K$, to solve for $\ln K$. To get compatible units, express $\Delta G°$ in joules, and set R equal to 8.31 J/(mol•K). Substituting the numerical values into the expression gives

$$\ln K = \frac{-\Delta G°}{RT} = \frac{-107.00 \times 10^3}{-8.31 \times 298} = 43.\underline{2}08$$

$$K = e^{43.208} = \underline{5}.82 \times 10^{18} = 6 \times 10^{18}$$

18.59. First, calculate $\Delta G°$ using the $\Delta G_f°$ values from Appendix C.

$$CO(g) + 3H_2(g) \rightleftharpoons CH_4(g) + H_2O(g)$$

$\Delta G_f°$:   -137.2   0   -50.80   -228.6 kJ

Subtract $\Delta G_f°$ of the reactants from that of the products:

$\Delta G° = [(-50.80) + (-228.6) - (-137.2)]\, kJ = -142.20\, kJ$

Use the rearranged form of the equation, $\Delta G° = -RT \ln K$, to solve for $\ln K$. To get compatible units, express $\Delta G°$ in joules, and set R equal to 8.31 J/(mol•K). Substituting the numerical values into the expression gives

$$\ln K = \frac{-\Delta G°}{RT} = \frac{-142.20 \times 10^3}{-8.31 \times 298} = 57.\underline{4}22$$

$$K = K_p = e^{57.422} = \underline{8}.67 \times 10^{24} = 9 \times 10^{24}$$

18.61. First, calculate $\Delta G°$ using the $\Delta G_f°$ values from Appendix C.

$$Fe(s) + Cu^{2+}(aq) \rightleftharpoons Fe^{2+}(aq) + Cu(s)$$

$\Delta G_f°$:   0   65.52   -78.87   0 kJ

Hence

$\Delta G° = [(-78.87) - 65.52]\, kJ = -144.39\, kJ$

Now, substitute numerical values into the equation relating $\ln K$ and $\Delta G°$.

$$\ln K = \frac{-\Delta G°}{RT} = \frac{-144.39 \times 10^3}{-8.31 \times 298} = 58.\underline{3}06$$

Therefore,

$$K = K_c = e^{58.306} = \underline{2}.10 \times 10^{25} = 2 \times 10^{25}$$

18.63. From Appendix C, you have

$$C(graphite) + CO_2(g) \rightleftharpoons 2CO(g)$$

$\Delta H_f°$:	0	-393.5	2 x (-110.5) kJ
$S°$:	5.740	213.7	2 x (197.5) J/K

Calculate $\Delta H°$ and $\Delta S°$ from these values.

$$\Delta H° = [2(-110.5) - (-393.5)] \text{ kJ} = 172.\underline{5} \text{ kJ}$$

$$\Delta S° = [2(197.5) - (5.740 + 213.7)] \text{ J/K} = 175.\underline{56} \text{ J/K}$$

Substitute $\Delta H°$, $\Delta S°$ (= 0.17556 kJ/K), and T (= 1273 K) into the equation for $\Delta G_T°$.

$$\Delta G_T° = \Delta H° - T\Delta S° = 172.5 \text{ kJ} - (1273 \text{ K})(0.17556 \text{ kJ/K}) = -50.\underline{9}87 \text{ kJ}$$

Substitute the value of $\Delta G°$ (= -50.987×10^3 J) into the equation relating $\ln K$ and $\Delta G°$.

$$\ln K = \frac{-\Delta G°}{RT} = \frac{-50.987 \times 10^3}{-8.31 \times 1273} = 4.8\underline{1}98$$

$$K = K_p = e^{4.8198} = 1\underline{2}3.9 = 1.2 \times 10^2$$

Because K_p is greater than 1, the data predict that combustion of carbon should form significant amounts of CO product at equilibrium.

18.65. First, calculate $\Delta H°$ and $\Delta S°$ using the given $\Delta H_f°$ and $S°$ values.

$$2NaHCO_3(s) \rightarrow Na_2CO_3(s) + H_2O(g) + CO_2(g)$$

$\Delta H_f°$:	2 x (-950.8)	-1130.8	-241.8	-393.5 kJ
$\Delta S°$:	2 x 101.7	138.8	188.7	213.7 J/K

$$\Delta H° = [(-1130.8) + (-241.8) + (-393.5) - 2(-950.8)] \text{ kJ} = 135.5 \text{ kJ}$$

$$\Delta S° = [(138.8 + 188.7 + 213.7) - 2(101.7)] \text{ J/K} = 337.8 \text{ J/K } (0.3378 \text{ kJ/K})$$

Substitute these values into $\Delta G° = \Delta H° - T\Delta S°$; let $\Delta G° = 0$, and rearrange to solve for T.

$$T = \frac{\Delta H°}{\Delta S°} = \frac{135.5 \text{ kJ}}{0.3378 \text{ kJ/K}} = 40\underline{1}.1 = 401 \text{ K}$$

■ SOLUTIONS TO GENERAL PROBLEMS

18.67. The sign of $\Delta S°$ should be positive because there is an increase in moles of gas (Δn_{gas} = +5) as the solid reactant forms five moles of gas. The reaction is endothermic, denoting a positive $\Delta H°$. The fact that the reaction is spontaneous implies that the product, $T\Delta S°$, is larger than $\Delta H°$, so $\Delta G°$ is negative, as required for a spontaneous reaction.

18.69. The ΔH value $\cong$ BE(H−H) + BE(Cl−Cl) − 2BE(H−Cl) $\cong$ [436 + 242 − 2(431)] kJ ~ −184 kJ, and thus the reaction is exothermic. $\Delta S°$ should be positive because there is a increase in energy dispersal with the formation of unsymmetrical molecules from symmetrical H_2 and Cl_2. The reaction should be spontaneous because the contributions of both the ΔH term and the $-T\Delta S$ term are negative.

18.71. When the liquid freezes, it releases heat: $\Delta H_{fus} = -69.0$ J/g at 16.6°C (289.8 K). The entropy change is

$$\Delta S = \frac{\Delta H_{fus}}{T} = \frac{-69.0 \text{ J/g}}{289.8 \text{ K}} \times \frac{60.05 \text{ g}}{1 \text{ mol}} = -14.\underline{3}0 = -14.3 \text{ J/(K•mol)}$$

18.73. a. $\Delta S°$ is negative because there is a decrease in moles of gas ($\Delta n_{gas} = -1$) from one mole of gaseous reactant forming aqueous and liquid products. (Entropy decreases.)

   b. $\Delta S°$ is positive because there is an increase in moles of gas ($\Delta n_{gas} = +5$) from a solid reactant forming five moles of gas. (Entropy increases.)

   c. $\Delta S°$ is positive because there is an increase in moles of gas ($\Delta n_{gas} = +3$) from two moles of gaseous reactant forming five moles of gaseous products. (Entropy increases.)

   d. $\Delta S°$ is negative because there is a decrease in moles of gas ($\Delta n_{gas} = -1$) from three moles of gaseous reactants forming two moles of gaseous products. (Entropy decreases.)

18.75. $\Delta S°$ is negative because there is a decrease in the moles of gas ($\Delta n_{gas} = -2$) from three moles of gaseous reactant forming one mole of gaseous product plus liquid product.

18.77. Calculate $\Delta S°$ from the individual $S°$ values:

$$C_2H_5OH(l) \quad + \quad O_2(g) \quad \rightarrow \quad CH_3COOH(l) \quad + \quad H_2O(l)$$

$S°$:   160.7   205.0   159.8   69.95 J/K

$\Delta S° = \Sigma n S°(\text{products}) - \Sigma m S°(\text{reactants}) =$

$[(159.8 + 69.95) - (160.7 + 205.0)]$ J/K $= -135.\underline{9}5 = -136.0$ J/K

18.79. Calculate $\Delta G°$ using the $\Delta G_f°$ values from Appendix C.

$$H_2(g) \quad + \quad SO_2(g) \quad \rightarrow \quad H_2S(g) \quad + \quad O_2(g)$$

$\Delta G_f°$:   0   -300.1   -33.33   0 kJ

$\Delta G° = \Sigma n \Delta G_f°(\text{products}) - \Sigma m \Delta G_f°(\text{reactants}) =$

$[(-33.33) - (-300.1)]$ kJ $= 266.\underline{7}7 = 266.8$ kJ

Because $\Delta G°$ is positive, the reaction is nonspontaneous as written, at 25°C.

18.81. At low (room) temperature, $\Delta G°$ or ($\Delta H° - T\Delta S°$) must be positive, but at higher temperatures, $\Delta G°$ or ($\Delta H° - T\Delta S°$) must be negative. Thus, at the higher temperatures, the $-T\Delta S°$ term must become more negative than $\Delta H°$. Thus, $\Delta S°$ must be positive and so must $\Delta H°$.

18.83. First, calculate $\Delta G°$ using the values in Appendix C.

$$CaF_2(s) \rightleftharpoons Ca^{2+}(aq) \quad + \quad 2F^-(aq)$$

$\Delta G_f°$:   -1173.5   -553.5   2 x (-278.8) kJ

Hence, $\Delta G°$ for the reaction is

$\Delta G_f° = [-553.5 + 2(-278.8) - (-1173.5)]$ kJ $= 62.4$ kJ

Now, substitute numerical values into the equation relating $\ln K$ and $\Delta G°$.

$$\ln K = \frac{-\Delta G°}{RT} = \frac{62.4 \times 10^3}{-8.31 \times 298} = -25.\underline{1}98$$

$$K = K_{sp} = e^{-25.198} = \underline{1}.13 \times 10^{-11} = 1 \times 10^{-11}$$

18.85. From Appendix C, you have

$$COCl_2(g) \quad \rightarrow \quad CO(g) \quad + \quad Cl_2(g)$$

$\Delta H_f°$:	-220.1	-110.5	0 kJ
$S°$:	283.9	197.5	223.0 J/K

Calculate $\Delta H°$ and $\Delta S°$ from these values.

$\Delta H° = [(-110.5) - (-220.1)] \text{ kJ} = 109.6 \text{ kJ}$

$\Delta S° = [197.5 + 223.0 - 283.9] \text{ J/K} = 136.6 \text{ J/K} \ (0.1366 \text{ kJ/K})$

At 25°C: $\Delta G° = \Delta H° - T\Delta S° = 109.6 \text{ kJ} - (298 \text{ K})(0.1366 \text{ kJ/K}) = 68.\underline{8}9 = 68.9 \text{ kJ}$

At 800°C: $\Delta G_T° = \Delta H° - T\Delta S° = \underline{1}09.6 \text{ kJ} - (1073 \text{ K})(0.1366 \text{ kJ/K}) = -36.\underline{9}7 = -37.0 \text{ kJ}$

Thus, $\Delta G°$ changes from a positive value and a nonspontaneous reaction at 25°C to a negative value and a spontaneous reaction at 800°C.

18.87. a.

			$\underline{\Delta H°, \text{ kJ}}$
$CO_2(g) + 2H_2(g)$	$\rightarrow$	$HCHO(g) + H_2O(g)$	35
$HCHO(g) + 2H_2(g)$	$\rightarrow$	$CH_4(g) + H_2O(g)$	−201
$C(s) + O_2(g)$	$\rightarrow$	$CO_2(g)$	−393
$2H_2O(g)$	$\rightarrow$	$2H_2(g) + O_2(g)$	484
$C(s) + 2H_2(g)$	$\rightarrow$	$CH_4(g)$	−75 kJ

b.

$$C(s) \quad + \quad 2H_2(g) \quad \rightarrow \quad CH_4(g)$$

$S°$:	5.740	2 x 130.6	186.1 J/K

$\Delta S° = \Sigma nS°(\text{products}) - \Sigma mS°(\text{reactants}) =$

$[186.1 - 5.740 - 2(130.6)] \text{ J/K} = -80.\underline{8}4 \text{ J/K} \ (-0.08084 \text{ kJ/K})$

c. $\Delta G°$ for the reaction, which involves 1 mole of methane, is equal to $\Delta G_f°$ for methane and is obtained as follows:

$\Delta G_f° = \Delta G° = \Delta H° - T\Delta S°$

$= -75 \text{ kJ} - (298 \text{ K})(-0.08084 \text{ kJ/K})$

$= -50.\underline{9}0 = -51 \text{ kJ/mol}$

18.89. $\Delta H° = [-393.5 + 2(-285.8) - (-238.7)]$ kJ $= -726.4$ kJ

$\Delta G° = \Delta H° - T\Delta S°$

-702.2 kJ $= -726.4$ kJ $- (298$ K$)(\Delta S°)$

$\Delta S° = -\dfrac{(-702.2 \text{ kJ}) - (-726.4 \text{ kJ})}{298 \text{ K}} = -0.08120$ kJ/K $= -81.20$ J/K

$\Delta S° = -81.20$ J/K $= [2(70.0) + 213.7 - (126.8) - (3/2 \text{ mol}) \times S°(O_2)]$ J/K

$S°(O_2) = 205.40 = 205.4$ J/mol•K

18.91.   a.   The first reaction is

	$SnO_2(s)$	+	$2H_2(g)$	$\rightarrow$	$Sn(s)$	+	$2H_2O(g)$
$\Delta H_f°$:	-580.7		0		0		-241.8 kJ
$S°$:	52.3		130.6		51.55		188.7 J/K

$\Delta H° = [2(-241.8) - (-580.7)]$ kJ $= 97.1$ kJ $= 97.1 \times 10^3$ J

$\Delta S° = [2(188.7) + 51.55 - 2(130.6) - 52.3]$ J/K $= 115.45$ J/K

The second reaction is

	$SnO_2(s)$	+	$C(s)$	$\rightarrow$	$Sn(s)$	+	$CO_2(g)$
$\Delta H_f°$:	-580.7		0		0		-393.5 kJ
$S°$:	52.3		5.740		51.55		213.7 J/K

$\Delta H° = [-393.5 - (-580.7)]$ kJ $= 187.2$ kJ $= 187.2 \times 10^3$ J

$\Delta S° = [213.7 + 51.55 - 5.740 - 52.3]$ J/K $= 207.21$ J/K

b.   For H_2, at what temperature does $\Delta G = 0$?

$0 = \Delta H° - T\Delta S°$

$T = \dfrac{\Delta H}{\Delta S} = \dfrac{97.1 \times 10^3 \text{ J}}{115.45 \text{ J/K}} = 841.0 = 841$ K

At temperatures greater than 841 K, the reaction will be spontaneous.

For C, at what temperature does $\Delta G = 0$?

$T = \dfrac{\Delta H}{\Delta S} = \dfrac{187.2 \times 10^3 \text{ J}}{207.21 \text{ J/K}} = 903.4 = 903$ K

At temperatures greater than 904 K, the reaction will be spontaneous.

c.   From a consideration of temperature, the process with hydrogen would be preferred. But hydrogen is very expensive and carbon is cheap. On this basis, carbon would be preferred. Tin is produced commercially using carbon as the reducing agent.

18.93. a.   Formic acid is favored because it is of lower energy than CO and H_2O.

b.   The change in entropy for the decomposition of formic acid is positive as a mole of gas is produced. Thus, the change in entropy would be the driving force for this reaction, favoring the formation of products.

18.95. a.   If $\Delta G°$ is negative, then K must be greater than 1. Consequently, the products will predominate.

b.   The molecules must have enough energy to react when they collide with each other. Thus, it depends upon the activation energy for the reaction. Usually it is necessary to heat solids for a reaction to occur, because it is difficult to have effective collisions.

18.97. a. $C_4H_{10}(g) + 13/2O_2(g) \rightarrow 4CO_2(g) + 5H_2O(l)$

$$\Delta H° = \frac{-49.50 \text{ kJ}}{1.000 \text{ g}} \times \frac{58.12 \text{ g}}{1 \text{ mol}} = -287\underline{6}.94 \text{ kJ/mol}$$

$\Delta H° = \Sigma n\Delta H_f°(\text{products}) - \Sigma m\Delta H_f°(\text{reactants})$

$-2876.94 \text{ kJ} = [4(-393.5) + 5(-285.8) - (1 \text{ mol}) \times \Delta H_f°(C_4H_{10})] \text{ kJ}$

$\Delta H_f°(C_4H_{10}) = -12\underline{6}.06 = -126 \text{ kJ/mol}$

b. $\Delta G° = [4(-394.4) + 5(-237.1) - (-17.2)] \text{ kJ} = -2745.\underline{9} \text{ kJ}$

c. $\Delta G° = \Delta H° - T\Delta S°$

$-2745.9 \text{ kJ} = -2876.94 \text{ kJ} - (298 \text{ K}) \Delta S°$

$$\Delta S° = -\frac{(-2745.9 \text{ kJ}) - (-2876.94 \text{ kJ})}{298 \text{ K}} = -0.43\underline{9}7 \text{ kJ/K} = -440. \text{ J/K (for one mole)}$$

18.99. a. $\Delta H° = [-1285 - (-1288.3)] \text{ kJ} = \underline{3}.3 \text{ kJ} = 3.3 \times 10^3 \text{ J}$

$\Delta S° = [89 - 158.2] \text{ J/K} = -6\underline{9}.2 \text{ J/K}$

$\Delta G° = \Delta H° - T\Delta S°$

$\Delta G° = \underline{3}.3 \times 10^3 \text{ J} - (298 \text{ K})(-69.2 \text{ J/K}) = 2\underline{3}.921 \times 10^3 \text{ J}$

Now, substitute numerical values into the equation relating $\ln K$ and $\Delta G°$.

$$\ln K = \frac{-\Delta G°}{RT} = \frac{23.921 \times 10^3}{-8.31 \times 298} = -9.\underline{6}599$$

$K = e^{-9.6599} = \underline{6}.37 \times 10^{-5} = 6 \times 10^{-5}$

b.   The change in entropy is negative, greater order, so this causes H_3PO_4 to be a weak acid. Although the endothermic enthalpy change reduces the acid strength of H_3PO_4, the entropy term is more important at 25°C.

18.101. You must find a way to couple this nonspontaneous reaction to one that is sufficiently spontaneous; that is, you must couple this reaction to one having a more negative $\Delta G°$. Consider the spontaneous reaction of carbon monoxide with oxygen (the burning of CO):

$2CO(g) + O_2(g) \rightarrow 2CO_2(g); \Delta G° = -514.4 \text{ kJ}$

For 3 mol O_2, $\Delta G°$ is −1543 kJ, which is more negative than for the direct decomposition of 2 mol Fe_2O_3 to its elements (1487 kJ). The net result is to reduce iron(III) oxide to the metal by reacting the oxide with carbon monoxide

$$2Fe_2O_3(s) + 6CO(g) \rightarrow 4Fe(s) + 6CO_2(g); \quad \Delta G° = -56 \text{ kJ}$$

This is the reaction that occurs in a blast furnace, where iron ore is commercially reduced to iron.

■ SOLUTIONS TO STRATEGY PROBLEMS

18.103. The standard enthalpies of formation and the standard entropies of formation are

	$N_2H_4(g)$	$\rightarrow$	$N_2(g)$	+	$2H_2(g)$
$\Delta H_f°$:	95.35		0		0 kJ
S°:	238.6		191.6		2 x (130.6) J/K

a. The standard enthalpy change is

$$\Delta H° = 0 - \Delta H_f°[N_2H_4(g)] = -95.35 \text{ kJ}$$

b. The standard entropy change is

$$\Delta S° = [(191.6) + 2(130.6) - (238.6)] \text{ J/K} = 214.2 \text{ J/K}$$

The sign of the entropy change is positive, which is what you would expect since there is an increase in the number of moles of gas.

c. Since the enthalpy change is negative and the entropy change is positive, this reaction is spontaneous at all temperatures.

d. ΔG is less negative at lower temperatures, so this reaction will give greater product at higher temperatures.

18.105. Write out the expression for $\Delta G°$ for the reaction and solve for the free energy of formation of acetone. The reaction and standard thermodynamic values are

	$CH_3COCH_3(l)$	+	$4O_2(g)$	$\rightarrow$	$3CO_2(g)$	+	$3H_2O(l)$
$\Delta G_f°$:	x		0		3 x (-394.4)		3 x (-237.1) kJ

$$\Delta G° = -1739 \text{ kJ} = 3(-394.4 \text{ kJ}) + 3(-237.1 \text{ kJ}) - (1 \text{ mol})(x)$$

$$x = \Delta G_f°[CH_3COCH_3(l)] = -155.5 \text{ kJ/mol}$$

18.107. a. First, calculate the value of the equilibrium constant at 458°C.

$$K = \frac{[HI]^2}{[H_2][I_2]} = \frac{(1.550)^2}{(0.225)(0.225)} = 47.\underline{4}56$$

The free-energy change can now be calculated.

$$\Delta G = -RT \ln K = -(8.31 \times 10^{-3} \text{ kJ/mol·K})(731 \text{ K}) \ln(47.456) = -23.\underline{4}4 = -23.4 \text{ kJ/mol}$$

b.   The enthalpy change for the reaction at 458°C is

$$H_2(g)   +   I_2(g)   \rightarrow   2HI(g)$$

$\Delta H_f°$:   0   62.42   2 x (26.36) kJ

$\Delta H = \Delta H° = [2(26.36) - (62.42)]$ kJ $= -9.70$ kJ

Now rearrange the equation $\Delta G = \Delta H - T\Delta S$ and solve for ΔS.

$$\Delta S = \frac{\Delta H - \Delta G}{T} = \frac{(-9.70 \text{ kJ}) - (-23.44 \text{ kJ})}{731 \text{ K}} = 0.01880 \text{ kJ/K} = 18.8 \text{ J/K}$$

18.109. First, calculate the value of the equilibrium constant and the free energy at 220°C.

$$K = P_{CO_2} = 1.37$$

$$\Delta G = -RT \ln K = -(8.31 \times 10^{-3} \text{ kJ/mol} \bullet \text{K})(493 \text{ K}) \ln(1.37) = -1.289 \text{ kJ}$$

Next, calculate the change in standard enthalpy for the reaction.

$$Ag_2CO_3(s)   \rightarrow   Ag_2O(s)   +   CO_2(g)$$

$\Delta H_f°$:   -505.9   -31.05   (-393.5) kJ

$\Delta H° = [(-31.05) + (-393.5) - (-505.9)]$ kJ $= 81.35$ kJ

A reasonable assumption is that ΔH at 220°C is approximately equal to $\Delta H°$. This is a valid assumption because ΔH does not vary much with temperature. Now calculate ΔS at 220°C.

$$\Delta S = \frac{\Delta H - \Delta G}{T} = \frac{(81.35 \text{ kJ}) - (-1.289 \text{ kJ})}{493 \text{ K}} = 0.1676 \text{ kJ/K}$$

Next, assume that $\Delta S°$ is approximately equal to ΔS at 220°C. This is a valid assumption because ΔS does not vary much with temperature. Now calculate $\Delta G°$.

$$\Delta G° = \Delta H° - T\Delta S° = 81.35 \text{ kJ} - (298 \text{ K})(0.1676 \text{ kJ/K}) = 31.39 \text{ kJ}$$

Finally, calculate the equilibrium constant and pressure of CO_2 at 25°C.

$$\ln K = \frac{-\Delta G°}{RT} = \frac{-31.397 \times 10^3 \text{ J/mol}}{(8.31 \text{ J/mol} \cdot \text{K}) \times (298 \text{ K})} = -12.678$$

$$K = P_{CO_2} = e^{-12.678} = = 3.11 \times 10^{-6} = 3 \times 10^{-6} \text{ atm}$$

18.111. a.   The ratio of [B] to [A] is

$$\ln K = \frac{-\Delta G°}{RT} = \frac{-15.0 \times 10^3 \text{ J/mol}}{(8.31 \text{ J/mol} \cdot \text{K}) \times (298 \text{ K})} = -6.057$$

$$K = \frac{[B]}{[A]} = e^{-6.057} = 2.34 \times 10^{-3} = 2.3 \times 10^{-3}$$

b.   Combine the two equations and add the $\Delta G°$ values to get the overall reaction.

$$A(aq) + ATP(aq) + H_2O(l) \rightarrow B(aq) + ADP(aq) + H_2PO_4^-(aq)$$

$$\Delta G° = (-30.5 \text{ kJ/mol}) + (15.0 \text{ kJ/mol}) = -15.5 \text{ kJ/mol}$$

Now calculate the equilibrium constant.

$$\ln K = \frac{-\Delta G°}{RT} = \frac{-(-15.5 \times 10^3 \text{ J/mol})}{(8.31 \text{ J/mol·K}) \times (298 \text{ K})} = 6.2\underline{5}9$$

$$K = e^{6.259} = 5\underline{2}2.8$$

Write out the equilibrium constant for the reaction.

$$K = \frac{[B][ADP][H_2PO_4^-]}{[A][ATP]}$$

Rearrange this expression to get the ratio of [B] over [A].

$$\frac{[B]}{[A]} = \frac{K[ATP]}{[ADP][H_2PO_4^-]} = (5\underline{2}2.8)(500) = 2.\underline{6}1 \times 10^5$$

Finally, the ratio of coupled to uncoupled is

$$\frac{\text{Ratio(coupled)}}{\text{Ratio(uncoupled)}} = \frac{2.61 \times 10^5}{2.34 \times 10^{-3}} = 1.\underline{1}0 \times 10^8 = 1.1 \times 10^8$$

18.113. The equilibrium of interest and the available free energies of formation are

$$H_2O(l) \rightleftharpoons H^+(aq) + OH^-(aq)$$

$\Delta G_f°$:   -237.1   0   x kJ/mol

The standard free energy change for this reaction is

$$\Delta G° = \Sigma n \Delta G_f°(\text{products}) - \Sigma m \Delta G_f°(\text{reactants}) = [0 + \Delta G_f°(OH^-(aq)] - (-237.1) \text{ kJ}$$

First, use the equilibrium constant expression with the given pH and the relationship between $\Delta G°$ and K, i.e., $\Delta G° = -RT \ln K$, to calculate $\Delta G°$ at 25 °C for the reaction. The equilibrium constant expression for this reaction is $K_w = [H^+][OH^-]$. Because the pH = 7.00, $[H^+] = 1.00 \times 10^{-7}$ M, which is also the concentration of hydroxide ion, $[OH^-]$. Thus,

$$K_w = [H^+][OH^-] = (1.00 \times 10^{-7})^2 \text{ at } 25 °C$$

Calculate $\Delta G°$ using $\Delta G° = -RT \ln K$:

25.0°C: $\Delta G° = -(0.008314 \text{ kJ/K})(298 \text{ K})(\ln 1.00 \times 10^{-14}) = 79.\underline{8}7 \text{ kJ}$

Finally solve for the free energy of formation of $OH^-(aq)$, x.

$$\Delta G_f°(OH^-(aq)) = 79.\underline{8}7 \text{ kJ} - 237.1 \text{ kJ} = -157.\underline{2}3 = -157.2 \text{ kJ/mol}$$

A value of −157.2 kJ/mol is given in Table 18.2.

18.115. The process $Na^+(aq) + C_2H_3O_2(aq) \rightarrow NaC_2H_3O_2(s)$ occurs spontaneously without any outside intervention. Therefore the change in free energy, ΔG, is negative. The ions have gone from a more disordered state (freely moving ions) to a state of more order (crystalline). The entropy will have decreased so ΔS is negative. Since $\Delta G = \Delta H - T\Delta S$ and both ΔG and ΔS are negative, ΔH must also be negative. A negative enthalpy change corresponds to an exothermic process.

18.117. First, apply the assumption that both enthalpy and entropy changes change very little over the temperature range of 25 °C to 76.7°C. Next, use the relationship between ΔS_{vap} and ΔH_{vap} at the boiling point (76.7°C = 349.9 K):

$$\Delta S_{vap} = \frac{\Delta H_{vap}}{T} = \frac{29.82 \times 10^3\,\text{J/mol}}{349.9\,\text{K}} = 85.2\underline{2}4 = 85.22\,\text{J/K per mole}$$

Thus a good estimate for the standard entropy of vaporization, ΔS^o_{vap}, is 85.22 J/K for each mole of CCl_4 vaporized. To estimate the standard free energy of vaporization per mole of CCl_4 vaporized at 25 °C, use the relationship $\Delta G^o = \Delta H^o - T\Delta S^o$ at $T = 298$ K:

$$\Delta G^o = \Delta H^o - T\Delta S^o = 29.8\underline{2}\,\text{kJ} - (298\,\text{K})(85.22\,\text{J/K})(1\,\text{kJ}/1000\,\text{J}) = +4.4\underline{2}3 = +4.42\,\text{kJ}$$

18.119. Calculate ΔG^o for the reaction.

	$CH_4(g)$	+	$2O_2(g)$	$\rightarrow$	$CO_2(g)$	+	$2H_2O(g)$
ΔG_f^o:	-50.80		0		-394.4		2 x (-228.6) kJ

$$\Delta G^o = [(-394.4) + 2(-228.6) - (-50.80)]\,\text{kJ} = -800.\underline{8}0 = -800.8\,\text{kJ}$$

The maximum work that can be obtained from burning 1.00 mole of $CH_4(g)$ at 25°C is the absolute value of the standard free energy change, or 800.8 kJ.

The maximum work that can be obtained from the 1.00 m³ of liquid methane is

$$w_{max} = 1.00\,\text{m}^3 \times \frac{416\,\text{kg}}{1\,\text{m}^3} \times \frac{10^3\,\text{g}}{1\,\text{kg}} \times \frac{1\,\text{mol CH}_4}{16.04\,\text{g CH}_4} \times \frac{800.8\,\text{kJ}}{1.00\,\text{mol CH}_4} = 2.0\underline{7}6 \times 10^7\,\text{kJ}$$

The maximum height the 1700 kg truck can go up a hill is

$$h = \frac{w_{max}}{mg} = \frac{(2.076 \times 10^7\,\text{kJ})(1000\,\text{J/kJ})}{(1700\,\text{kg})(9.81\,\text{m/s}^2)} \times \frac{1\,\text{mi}}{1609\,\text{m}} = 773.\underline{9}9 = 774\,\text{mi}$$

In theory, with no energy losses, the given amount of fuel could jettison the truck beyond the typical orbit height of the *International Space Station* which ranges from ~200 miles to ~250 miles.

18.121. Considering the decomposition of water to produce hydrogen and oxygen,

	$2H_2O(g)$	$\rightarrow$	$2H_2(g)$	+	$O_2(g)$
ΔG_f^o:	2 x (-228.6) kJ		0		0

The standard free energy change for this reaction is

$$\Delta G^o = \Sigma n\Delta G_f^o(\text{products}) - \Sigma m\Delta G_f^o(\text{reactants})$$

$$\Delta G^o = [(0 + 0) - (2 \times -228.6)]\,\text{kJ} = +457.2\,\text{kJ}$$

Because $\Delta G°$ is positive, the decomposition of water is not spontaneous.

Next calculate the free energy change for the partial oxidation of carbon,

$$2C(s) \quad + \quad O_2(g) \quad \rightarrow \quad 2CO(g)$$

$\Delta G_f°:$ 0   0   2 x -137.2 kJ

$\Delta G° = [(2 \times -137.2) - (0 + 0)] \text{ kJ} = -274.4 \text{ kJ}$

Because $\Delta G°$ is negative, the partial oxidation of carbon is spontaneous.

As a useful means of manufacturing hydrogen gas, the spontaneous partial oxidation of carbon can be coupled to the nonspontaneous decomposition of water to produce an overall spontaneous process in the following manner.

			$\Delta G°$, kJ
$2H_2O(g)$	$\rightarrow$	$2H_2(g) + O_2(g)$	+457.2
$4C(s) + 2O_2(g)$	$\rightarrow$	$4CO(g)$	2×-274.4
$2H_2O(g) + 4C(s) + O_2(g)$	$\rightarrow$	$2H_2(g) + 4CO(g)$	-91.6 kJ

There are more ways of generating a spontaneous result. Had three times the partial oxidation of C reaction been used, the result would have been:

$$2H_2O(g) + 6C(s) + 2O_2(g) \rightarrow 2H_2(g) + 6CO(g), \Delta G° = -366.0 \text{ kJ}$$

Note that as the participation of the spontaneous reaction is increased in this case more and more $O_2(g)$ reactant would be required. Eventually this requirement would not be met by the atmosphere and costs for supplying it would increase.

■ SOLUTIONS TO CUMULATIVE-SKILLS PROBLEMS

18.123. For the dissociation of HBr, assume ΔH and ΔS are constant over the temperature range from 25°C to 375°C, and calculate the value of each to use to calculate K at 375°C. Start by calculating $\Delta H°$ and $\Delta S°$ at 25°C, using $\Delta H_f°$ and $S°$ values.

$$2HBr(g) \quad \rightarrow \quad H_2(g) \quad + \quad Br_2(g)$$

$\Delta H_f°:$ 2 x (-36.44)   0   30.91 kJ

$S°:$ 2 x 198.6   130.6   245.3 J/K

Calculate $\Delta H°$ and $\Delta S°$ from these values.

$\Delta H° = [30.91 - 2(-36.44)] \text{ kJ} = 103.79 \text{ kJ}$

$\Delta S° = [245.3 + 130.6 - 2(198.6)] \text{ J/K} = -21.3 \text{ J/K}$

Substitute $\Delta H°$, $\Delta S°$ ($= -0.02130$ kJ/K), and T (648 K) into the equation for $\Delta G_T°$.

$\Delta G_T° = \Delta H° - T\Delta S° = 103.79 \text{ kJ} - (648 \text{ K})(-0.02130 \text{ kJ/K}) = 117.\underline{59} \text{ kJ} = 117.\underline{59} \times 10^3 \text{ J}$

Now, substitute numerical values into the equation relating $\ln K$ and ΔG° ($= \Delta G_T^\circ$).

$$\ln K = \frac{-\Delta G^\circ}{RT} = \frac{117.59 \times 10^3}{-8.31 \times 648} = -21.\underline{8}37$$

$$K = e^{-21.837} = \underline{3}.28 \times 10^{-10}$$

Assuming x equals $[H_2]$ and $[Br_2]$, and assuming $[HBr] = (1.00 - 2x) \cong 1.00$ atm, substitute into the equilibrium expression:

$$K = \frac{[H_2][Br_2]}{[HBr]^2} = \frac{(x)(x)}{(1.00)^2} = \underline{3}.28 \times 10^{-10}$$

Solve for the approximate pressure of x:

$$x = \sqrt{(3.28 \times 10^{-10})(1.00)^2} = \underline{1}.81 \times 10^{-5} \text{ atm}$$

The percent dissociation at 1.00 atm is

$$\text{Percent dissociation} = \frac{2(1.81 \times 10^{-5} \text{ atm})}{1.00 \text{ atm}} \times 100\% = 0.00\underline{3}6\%$$

Based on Le Châtelier's principle, pressure has no effect on equilibrium. Therefore, the percent dissociation is 0.004% at 1.00 atm and at 10.0 atm.

18.125. For the dissociation of NH_3, assume ΔH and ΔS are constant over the temperature range from 25°C to 345°C, and calculate values of each to calculate K at 345°C.

$$2NH_3(g) \quad \rightarrow \quad 3H_2(g) \quad + \quad N_2(g)$$

ΔH_f°:   2 x (-45.90)   0   0 kJ

S°:   2 x 192.7   3 x 130.6   191.6 J/K

Calculate ΔH° and ΔS° from these values.

$$\Delta H^\circ = [0 - 2(-45.90)] \text{ kJ} = 91.80 \text{ kJ}$$

$$\Delta S^\circ = [3(130.6) + 191.6 - 2(192.7)] \text{ J/K} = 198.0 \text{ J/K}$$

Substitute ΔH°, ΔS° ($= 0.1980$ kJ/K), and T (618 K) into the equation for ΔG_T°.

$$\Delta G_T^\circ = \Delta H^\circ - T\Delta S^\circ = 91.8 \text{ kJ} - (618 \text{ K})(0.1980 \text{ kJ/K}) = -30.\underline{5}64 \text{ kJ} = -30.564 \times 10^3 \text{ J}$$

Now, substitute numerical values into the equation relating $\ln K$ and ΔG° ($= \Delta G_T^\circ$).

$$\ln K = \frac{-\Delta G^\circ}{RT} = \frac{-30.564 \times 10^3}{-8.31 \times 618} = 5.9\underline{5}1$$

$$K = K_p = e^{5.951} = 3\underline{8}4.2$$

Now obtain K_c.

$$K_c = K_p(RT)^{-2} = (384.2)(0.0821 \times 618)^{-2} = 0.1\underline{4}92$$

The starting concentration of NH_3 is 1.00 mol/20.0L = 0.0500 M. You obtain the following table:

	$2NH_3(g)$	$\rightarrow$	$3H_2(g)$	+	$N_2(g)$
Starting	0.0500		0		0
Change	-2x		+3x		+x
Equilibrium	0.0500 - 2x		3x		x

The equilibrium equation is

$$K_c = \frac{[H_2]^3[N_2]}{[NH_3]^2}$$

or

$$\frac{(3x)^3 x}{(0.0500 - 2x)^2} = 0.1492$$

$$\frac{x^4}{(0.0500 - 2x)^2} = \frac{0.1492}{27} = 5.528 \times 10^{-3}$$

Taking the square root of both sides of this equation gives

$$\frac{x^2}{(0.0500 - 2x)} = 0.07435$$

This can be rearranged into the following quadratic equation.

$$x^2 + (0.1487)x - (3.717 \times 10^{-3}) = 0$$

From the quadratic formula, you obtain

$$x = \frac{-0.1487 \pm \sqrt{(0.1487)^2 + 4(3.717 \times 10^{-3})}}{2}$$

The positive root is

$$x = 0.02180 \ M$$

Hence,

$$[NH_3] = 0.0500 - 2(0.02180) = 0.0064 \ M$$

Percent NH_3 dissociated $= \left(1 - \dfrac{0.0064 \ M}{0.0500 \ M}\right) \times 100\% = 87.2 = 87\%$

18.127. First, calculate $\Delta G°$ at each temperature, using $\Delta G° = -RT \ln K$:

25.0°C: $\Delta G° = -(0.008314 \text{ kJ/K})(298.2 \text{ K})(\ln 1.754 \times 10^{-5}) = 27.1501 \text{ kJ}$

50.0°C: $\Delta G_T° = -(0.008314 \text{ kJ/K})(323.2 \text{ K})(\ln 1.633 \times 10^{-5}) = 29.6184 \text{ kJ}$

Next, solve two equations in two unknowns assuming $\Delta H°$ and $\Delta S°$ are constant over the range of 25.0°C to 50.0°C. Use 0.2982 K(kJ/J) and 0.3232 K(kJ/J) to convert $\Delta S°$ in J to $T\Delta S°$ in kJ.

(1) 27.1501 kJ = $\Delta H° - [0.2982 \text{ K(kJ/J) } \Delta S°]$

(2) 29.6184 kJ = $\Delta H° - [0.3232 \text{ K(kJ/J) } \Delta S°]$

Then, rearrange Equation 2, and substitute for $\Delta H°$ into Equation 2:

(3)a. $\Delta H° = 0.3232 \text{ K(kJ/J) } \Delta S° + 29.6184 \text{ kJ}$

(3)b. 27.1501 kJ = $[0.3232 \text{ K(kJ/J) } \Delta S° + 29.6184 \text{ kJ}] - [0.2982 \text{ K(kJ/J) } \Delta S°]$

Solve for $\Delta S°$:

$$\Delta S° = \frac{(29.6184 - 27.1501) \text{ kJ}}{(0.2982 - 0.3232) \text{ K/(kJ/J)}} = -98.\underline{7}3 = -98.7 \text{ J/K}$$

Substitute this value into Equation 3a and solve for $\Delta H°$:

$\Delta H° = [(0.3232 \text{) K(kJ/J)} \times (-98.73 \text{ J/K})] + 29.6184 \text{ kJ} = -2.\underline{2}9 = -2.3 \text{ kJ}$

CHAPTER 19

Electrochemistry

■ SOLUTIONS TO EXERCISES

Note on significant figures: If the final answer to a solution needs to be rounded off, it is given first with one nonsignificant figure, and the last significant figure is underlined. The final answer is then rounded to the correct number of significant figures. In multistep problems, intermediate answers are given with at least one nonsignificant figure; however, only the final answer has been rounded off.

19.1.   Assign oxidation numbers to the skeleton equation (Step 1).

$$0 \quad\quad +5 \quad\quad\quad\quad +5 \quad\quad\quad +4$$
$$I_2 + NO_3^- \;\rightarrow\; IO_3^- + NO_2$$

Separate into two incomplete half-reactions (Step 2). Note that iodine is oxidized (increases in oxidation number), and nitrogen is reduced (decreases in oxidation number).

$$I_2 \;\rightarrow\; IO_3^-$$

$$NO_3^- \;\rightarrow\; NO_2$$

Balance each half-reaction separately. The oxidation half-reaction is not balanced in I, so place a two in front of IO_3^- (Step 3a). Then add six H_2O's to the left side to balance O atoms (Step 3b), and add twelve H^+ ions to the right side to balance H atoms (Step 3c). Finally, add ten electrons to the right side to balance the charge (Step 3d). The balanced oxidation half-reaction is

$$I_2 + 6H_2O \;\rightarrow\; 2IO_3^- + 12H^+ + 10e^-$$

The reduction half-reaction is balanced in N (Step 3a). Add one H_2O to the right side to balance O atoms (Step 3b), and add two H^+ ion to the left side to balance H atoms. Finally, add one electron to the left side to balance the charge (Step 3d).

The balanced reduction half-reaction is

$$NO_3^- + 2H^+ + e^- \;\rightarrow\; NO_2 + H_2O$$

Multiply the reduction half-reaction by 5 so that, when added, the electrons cancel (Step 4a).

$$I_2 + 6H_2O \;\rightarrow\; 2IO_3^- + 12H^+ + 10e^-$$
$$\underline{10NO_3^- + 20H^+ + 10e^- \;\rightarrow\; 10NO_2 + 10H_2O}$$
$$I_2 + 10NO_3^- + 20H^+ + 6H_2O + \cancel{10e^-} \;\rightarrow\;$$

$$2IO_3^- + 10NO_2 + 12H^+ + 10H_2O + \cancel{10e^-}$$

Simplify the equation by canceling the twelve H^+ and six H_2O that appear on both sides. The coefficients do not need to be reduced (Step 4b). The net ionic equation is

$$I_2(s) + 10NO_3^-(aq) + 8H^+(aq) \rightarrow 2IO_3^-(aq) + 10NO_2(g) + 4H_2O(l)$$

19.2. After balancing the equation as though it were in acid solution, you obtain

$$H_2O_2 + 2ClO_2 \rightarrow 2ClO_2^- + O_2 + 2H^+$$

Add two OH^- to both sides of the equation (Step 5), and replace the two H^+ and two OH^- on the right side with two H_2O. No further cancellation is required. The balanced equation for the reaction in basic solution is

$$H_2O_2 + 2ClO_2 + 2OH^- \rightarrow 2ClO_2^- + O_2 + 2H_2O$$

19.3. Silver ion is reduced at the silver electrode (cathode). The half-reaction is

$$Ag^+(aq) + e^- \rightarrow Ag(s)$$

The nickel electrode (anode) is where oxidation occurs. The half-reaction is

$$Ni(s) \rightarrow Ni^{2+}(aq) + 2e^-$$

Electron flow in the external circuit is from the nickel electrode (anode) to the silver electrode (cathode). Positive ions will flow in the solution portion of the circuit opposite to the direction of the electrons. A sketch of the cell is given below:

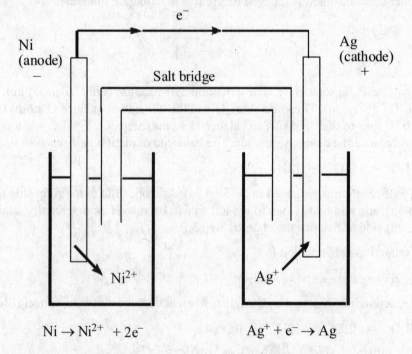

19.4. The notation for the cell is $Zn(s)|Zn^{2+}(aq)||H^+(aq)|H_2(g)|Pt(s)$.

19.5. The half-cell reactions are

$$Cd(s) \rightarrow Cd^{2+}(aq) + 2e^-$$

$$2H^+(aq) + 2e^- \rightarrow H_2(g)$$

Summing the half-cell reactions gives the overall cell reaction.

$$Cd(s) + 2H^+(aq) \rightarrow Cd^{2+}(aq) + H_2(g)$$

19.6. The half-reactions are

$$Zn(s) \rightarrow Zn^{2+}(aq) + 2e^-$$

$$Cu^{2+}(aq) + 2e^- \rightarrow Cu(s)$$

n equals 2, and the maximum work for the reaction as written is

$$w_{max} = -nFE_{cell} = -2 \times 9.6485 \times 10^4 \text{ C} \times 1.10 \text{ V} = -2.122 \times 10^5 \text{ V} \bullet \text{C} = -2.12 \times 10^5 \text{ J}$$

For 6.54 g of zinc metal, the maximum work is

$$6.54 \text{ g Zn} \times \frac{1 \text{ mol Zn}}{65.39 \text{ g Zn}} \times \frac{-2.123 \times 10^5 \text{ J}}{1 \text{ mol Zn}} = -2.123 \times 10^4 = -2.12 \times 10^4 \text{ J}$$

19.7. The half-reactions and corresponding electrode potentials are

$$Ag^-(aq) + e^- \rightarrow Ag(s) \qquad\qquad 0.80 \text{ V}$$

$$NO_3^-(aq) + 4H^-(aq) + 4e^- \rightarrow NO(g) + 2H_2O(l) \quad 0.96 \text{ V}$$

The stronger oxidizing agent is the one involved in the half-reaction with the more positive standard electrode potential, so NO_3^- is the stronger oxidizing agent.

19.8. In this reaction, Cu^{2+} is the oxidizing agent on the left side; I_2 is the oxidizing reagent on the right side. The corresponding standard electrode potentials are

$$Cu^{2+}(aq) + 2e^- \rightarrow Cu(s); \qquad E° = 0.34 \text{ V}$$

$$I_2(s) + 2e^- \rightarrow 2I^-(aq); E° = 0.54 \text{ V}$$

The stronger oxidizing agent is the one involved in the half-reaction with the more positive standard electrode potential, so I_2 is the stronger oxidizing agent. The reaction is nonspontaneous as written.

19.9. The reduction half-reactions and standard electrode potentials are

$$Zn^{2+}(aq) + 2e^- \rightarrow Zn(s); \qquad E°_{Zn} = -0.76 \text{ V}$$

$$Cu^{2+}(aq) + 2e^- \rightarrow Cu(s); \qquad E°_{Cu} = 0.34 \text{ V}$$

Reverse the first half-reaction and its half-cell potential to obtain

$$Zn(s) \rightarrow Zn^{2+}(aq) + 2e^-; \qquad -E°_{Zn} = 0.76 \text{ V}$$

$$Cu^{2+}(aq) + 2e^- \rightarrow Cu(s); \qquad E°_{Cu} = 0.34 \text{ V}$$

Obtain the cell potential by adding the half-cell potentials.

$$E°_{cell} = E°_{Cu} - E°_{Zn} = 0.34 \text{ V} + 0.76 \text{ V} = 1.10 \text{ V}$$

19.10. The half-cell reactions, the corresponding half-cell potentials, and their sums are displayed below:

$$Sn^{2+}(aq) \rightarrow Sn^{4+}(aq) + 2e^- \quad -E° = -0.15 \text{ V}$$

$$\underline{2Hg^{2+}(aq) + 2e^- \rightarrow Hg_2^{2+}(aq) \quad\quad E° = 0.90 \text{ V}}$$

$$Sn^{2+}(aq) + 2Hg^{2+}(aq) \rightarrow Sn^{4+}(aq) + Hg_2^{2+}(aq) \quad E°_{cell} = 0.75 \text{ V}$$

Note that each half-reaction involves two electrons; hence n equals 2. Also, $E°_{cell}$ equals 0.75 V, and the faraday constant, F, is 9.6485×10^4 C. Therefore,

$$\Delta G° = -nFE°_{cell} = -2 \times 9.6485 \times 10^4 \text{ C} \times 0.75 \text{ V} = -1.\underline{4}472 \times 10^5 \text{ J} = -1.4 \times 10^5 \text{ J}$$

Thus, the standard free-energy change is -1.4×10^2 kJ.

19.11. Write the equation with $\Delta G_f°$'s beneath each substance.

$$Mg(s) + Cu^{2+}(aq) \rightarrow Mg^{2+}(aq) + Cu(s)$$

$$\Delta G_f°: \quad 0 \quad\quad 65.52 \quad\quad -454.8 \quad\quad 0 \text{ kJ}$$

Hence,

$$\Delta G° = \Sigma n\Delta G_f°(\text{products}) - \Sigma m\Delta G_f°(\text{reactants})$$

$$= [(-454.8) - 65.52] \text{ kJ} = -520.\underline{32} \text{ kJ} = -5.20\underline{32} \times 10^5 \text{ J}$$

Obtain n by splitting the reaction into half-reactions.

$$Mg(s) \rightarrow Mg^{2+}(aq) + 2e^-$$

$$Cu^{2+}(aq) + 2e^- \rightarrow Cu(s)$$

Each half-reaction involves two electrons, so n equals 2. Therefore,

$$\Delta G° = -nFE°_{cell}$$

$$-5.2032 \times 10^5 \text{ J} = -2 \times 9.6485 \times 10^4 \text{ C} \times E°_{cell}$$

Rearrange and solve for $E°_{cell}$. Recall that J = C•V.

$$E°_{cell} = \frac{-5.2032 \times 10^5 \text{ J}}{-2 \times 9.6485 \times 10^4 \text{ C}} = 2.69\underline{63} = 2.696 \text{ V}$$

19.12. The half-reactions and standard electrode potentials are

$$Fe(s) \rightarrow Fe^{2+}(aq) + 2e^-; \quad -E°_{Fe} = 0.41 \text{ V}$$

$$Sn^{4+}(aq) + 2e^- \rightarrow Sn^{2+}(s); \quad E°_{Sn^{2+}} = 0.15 \text{ V}$$

The standard cell potential for the cell is

$$E°_{cell} = E°_{Fe} - E°_{Sn^{2+}} = 0.41 \text{ V} + 0.15 \text{ V} = 0.56 \text{ V}$$

Note that n equals 2. Substitute into the equation relating $E°$ and K. Also, $K = K_c$.

$$0.56 \text{ V} = \frac{0.0592}{2} \log K_c$$

Solving for K_c, yields

$$\log K_c = 1\underline{8}.91$$

Take the antilog of both sides, you get

$$K_c = \text{antilog}\,(18.91) = 8.2 \times 10^{1\underline{8}} = 10^{19}$$

19.13. The half-cell reactions, the corresponding half-cell potentials, and their sums are displayed below:

$$\begin{array}{llll} Zn(s) \rightarrow & Zn^{2+}(aq) + 2e^- & & -E° = 0.76\text{ V} \\ \underline{2Ag^+(aq) + 2e^- \rightarrow} & \underline{2Ag(s)} & & \underline{E° = 0.80\text{ V}} \\ Zn(s) + 2Ag^+(aq) \rightarrow & Zn^{2+}(aq) + 2Ag(s) & & E°_{cell} = 1.56\text{ V} \end{array}$$

Note that n equals 2. The reaction quotient is

$$Q = \frac{[Zn^{2+}]}{[Ag^+]^2} = \frac{0.200}{(0.00200)^2} = 5.0\underline{0} \times 10^4$$

The standard cell potential is 1.56 V, so the Nernst equation becomes

$$E_{cell} = E°_{cell} - \frac{0.0592}{n}\log Q$$

$$= 1.56 - \frac{0.0592}{2}\log\,(5.00 \times 10^4)$$

$$= 1.56 - 0.13\underline{9}09 = 1.4\underline{2}09 = 1.42\text{ V}$$

19.14. The half-cell reactions, the corresponding half-cell potentials, and their sums are displayed below:

$$\begin{array}{llll} Zn(s) \rightarrow & Zn^{2+}(aq) + 2e^- & & -E° = 0.76\text{ V} \\ \underline{Ni^{2+}(aq) + 2e^- \rightarrow} & \underline{Ni(s)} & & \underline{E° = -0.23\text{ V}} \\ Zn(s) + Ni^{2+}(aq) \rightarrow & Zn^{2+}(aq) + Ni(s) & & E°_{cell} = 0.53\text{ V} \end{array}$$

Note that n equals 2. The standard cell potential is 0.53 V, and the cell potential is 0.34 V, so the Nernst equation becomes

$$E_{cell} = E°_{cell} - \frac{0.0592}{n}\log Q$$

$$0.34\text{ V} = 0.53\text{ V} - \frac{0.0592}{2}\log Q$$

Rearrange and solve for log Q.

$$\log Q = \frac{2}{0.0592} \times (0.53 - 0.34) = 6.\underline{4}18$$

Take the antilog of both sides.

$$Q = \frac{[Zn^{2+}]}{[Ni^{2+}]} = \text{antilog}\,(6.418) = \underline{2}.623 \times 10^6$$

Substitute in $[Zn^{2+}] = 1.00 \ M$ and solve for $[Ni^{2+}]$.

$$\frac{1.00 \ M}{[Ni^{2+}]} = 2.624 \times 10^6$$

$$[Ni^{2+}] = \underline{3}.81 \times 10^{-7} = 4 \times 10^{-7} \ M$$

19.15. a. The cathode reaction is $K^+(l) + e^- \rightarrow K(l)$.

   The anode reaction is $2Cl^-(l) \rightarrow Cl_2(g) + 2e^-$.

   b. The cathode reaction is $K^+(l) + e^- \rightarrow K(l)$.

   The anode reaction is $4OH^-(aq) \rightarrow O_2(g) + 2H_2O(g) + 4e^-$.

19.16. The species you should consider for half-reactions are Ag^+ and H_2O. Two possible cathode reactions are

$$Ag^+(aq) + e^- \rightarrow Ag(s); \ E° = 0.80 \ V$$

$$2H_2O(l) + 2e^- \rightarrow H_2(g) + 2OH^-(aq); \ E° = -0.83 \ V$$

Because the silver electrode potential is larger than the reduction potential of water, Ag^+ is reduced. The only possible anode reaction is the oxidation of H_2O. The expected ½-reactions are

$$Ag^+(aq) + e^- \rightarrow Ag(s)$$

$$2H_2O(l) \rightarrow O_2(g) + 4H^+(aq) + 4e^-$$

19.17. The conversion of grams of silver to coulombs required to deposit this amount of silver is

$$0.365 \ g \ Ag \times \frac{1 \ mol \ Ag}{107.9 \ g} \times \frac{1 \ mol \ e^-}{1 \ mol \ Ag} \times \frac{96,485 \ C}{1 \ mol \ e^-} = 32\underline{6}.3 \ C$$

The time lapse, 216 min, equals $1.2\underline{9}6 \times 10^4$ s. Thus,

$$Current = \frac{charge}{time} = \frac{326.3 \ C}{1.2\underline{9}6 \ x \ 10^4 \ s} = 2.5\underline{1}8 \times 10^{-2} = 2.52 \times 10^{-2} \ A$$

19.18. When the current flows for 1.85×10^4 s, the amount of charge is

$$0.0565 \ A \times 1.85 \times 10^4 \ s = 1.0\underline{4}5 \times 10^3 \ C$$

Note that 4 mol of electrons are equivalent to 1 mol of O_2. Hence,

$$1.0\underline{4}5 \times 10^3 \ C \times \frac{1 \ mol \ e^-}{96,485 \ C} \times \frac{1 \ mol \ O_2}{4 \ mol \ e^-} \times \frac{32.00 \ g \ O_2}{1 \ mol \ O_2} = 0.086\underline{6}6 = 0.0867 \ g \ O_2$$

■ ANSWERS TO CONCEPT CHECKS

19.1. No sustainable current would flow. The wire does not contain mobile positively and negatively charged species necessary to balance the accumulation of charges in each of the half cells.

19.2. a. Standard reduction potentials are measured against some arbitrarily chosen standard reference half-reaction. Only differences in potentials can be measured. A voltaic cell made from H_2 and I_2 and corresponding solutions will have the same voltage regardless of the choice of the reference cell. If the I_2/I^- half-reaction is assigned a value of $E° = 0.00$ V, the H_2/H^+ half-reaction must have a voltage of $E° = -0.54$ V to keep the overall voltage the same.

   b. The voltage of a voltaic cell made from Cu and Zn and corresponding solutions will have the same measured voltage regardless of the choice of the reference half-reaction.

   c. The calculated voltage is 1.10 V and is the same either way.

19.3. a. Using the standard reduction potentials in Table 19.1, you see the voltage for this cell is positive, which suggests $\Delta G°$ is negative. Note that the use of the terms "voltaic" or "galvanic" usually implies a spontaneous cell.

   b. In order to reduce E_{cell}, change the concentrations in a way that increases the value of Q, where $Q = [Fe^{2+}] / [Cu^{2+}]$. An example would be $Fe(s)|Fe^{2+}(1.10\ M)||Cu^{2+}(0.50\ M)|Cu(s)$

19.4. The dissolved ions make seawater a better conductor than fresh water, thus the seawater plays a role similar to a salt bridge.

■ ANSWERS TO SELF-ASSESSMENT AND REVIEW QUESTIONS

19.1. A voltaic cell is an electrochemical cell in which a spontaneous reaction generates an electric current (energy). An electrolytic cell is an electrochemical cell that requires electric current (energy) to drive a nonspontaneous reaction to the right.

19.2. In both the voltaic and electrolytic cells, the cathode is the electrode at which reduction occurs, and the anode is the electrode at which oxidation occurs.

19.3. The SI unit of electrical potential is the volt (V).

19.4. The faraday (F) is the magnitude of charge on 1 mol of electrons; it equals 96,485 C, or 96,485 J/V.

19.5. It is necessary to measure the voltage of a voltaic cell when no current is flowing because the cell voltage exhibits its maximum value only when no current flows. Even if the current flows just for the time of measurement, the voltage drops enough so that what is measured is significantly less than the maximum.

19.6. Standard electrode potentials are defined relative to a standard electrode potential of zero volts (0.00, 0.000 V, etc.) for the $H^+/H_2(g)$ electrode. Because the cell potential is measured using the hydrogen electrode at standard conditions and a second electrode at standard conditions, the cell potential equals the $E°$ of the half-reaction at the second electrode.

19.7. The SI unit of energy equals joules (J) equals coulombs times volts (CV).

19.8.   The mathematical relationships are as follows:

$$\Delta G° = -nFE°_{cell}$$

$$\Delta G° = -RT \ln K$$

Combining these two equations gives

$$\ln K = \frac{nFE°_{cell}}{RT}$$

19.9.   The first step in the corrosion of iron is

$$2Fe(s) + O_2(g) + 2H_2O(l) \rightarrow 4OH^- + 2Fe^{2+}$$

The Nernst equation for this reaction is

$$E_{cell} = E°_{cell} - \frac{0.0592}{4} \log \frac{[OH^-]^4[Fe^{2+}]^2}{P_{O_2}}$$

If the pH increases, the $[OH^-]$ increases, and thus E_{cell} becomes more negative (this predicts that the reaction becomes less spontaneous). If the pH decreases, the $[OH^-]$ decreases, and thus E_{cell} becomes more positive (this predicts that the reaction becomes more spontaneous).

19.10.   The zinc-carbon cell has a zinc can as the anode; the cathode is a graphite rod surrounded by a paste of manganese dioxide and carbon black. Around this is a second paste of ammonium and zinc chlorides. The electrode reactions involve oxidation of zinc metal to zinc(II) ion and reduction of $MnO_2(s)$ to $Mn_2O_3(s)$ at the cathode. The lead storage battery consists of a spongy lead anode and a lead dioxide cathode, both immersed in aqueous sulfuric acid. At the anode, the lead is oxidized to lead sulfate; at the cathode, lead dioxide is reduced to lead sulfate.

19.11.   A fuel cell is essentially a battery that does not use up its electrodes. Instead, it operates with a continuous supply of reactants (fuel). An example is the hydrogen-oxygen fuel cell in which oxygen is reduced at one electrode to the hydroxide ion, and hydrogen is oxidized at the other electrode to water (H in the +1 oxidation state). Such a cell produces electrical energy in a spacecraft for long periods of time.

19.12.   During the rusting of iron, one end of a drop of water exposed to air acts as one electrode of a voltaic cell; at this electrode, an oxygen molecule is reduced by four electrons to four hydroxide ions. Oxidation of metallic iron to iron(II) ion at the center of the drop of water supplies the electrons, and the center serves as the other electrode of the voltaic cell. Thus, electrons flow from the center of the drop through the iron to the end of the drop.

19.13.   When iron or steel is connected to an active metal such as zinc, a voltaic cell is formed with zinc as the anode and iron as the cathode. Any type of moisture facilitates the formation of an electrolyte solution, and the zinc metal is then oxidized to zinc(II) ion in preference to the oxidation of iron metal. Oxygen is reduced at the cathode to hydroxide ions. If iron or steel is exposed to oxygen while connected to a less active metal such as tin, a voltaic cell is formed with iron as the anode and tin as the cathode, and iron is oxidized to iron(II) ion rather than tin being oxidized to tin(II) ion. Thus, exposed iron corrodes rapidly in a tin can. Fortunately, as long as the iron is covered by the tin, it cannot corrode.

19.14.   The addition of an ionic species such as strongly ionized sulfuric acid facilitates the passage of current through the solution.

19.15. Sodium metal can be prepared by electrolysis of molten sodium chloride.

19.16. The anode reaction in the electrolysis of molten potassium hydroxide is

$$4OH^- \rightarrow O_2(g) + 2H_2O(g) + 4e^-$$

19.17. The reason why different products are obtained is that water instead of Na^+ is reduced at the cathode during the electrolysis of aqueous NaCl. This is because water has a more positive $E°$ (smaller decomposition voltage). At the anode, water instead of chloride ion is oxidized because water has a less positive $E°$ (smaller decomposition voltage).

19.18. The Nernst equation for the electrode reaction of $2Cl^-(aq) \rightarrow Cl_2(g) + 2e^-$ is

$$E = -1.36 \text{ V} - \frac{0.0592}{2} \log\frac{1 \text{ atm}}{[Cl^-]^2} = -1.36 \text{ V} + 0.0592 \log [Cl^-]$$

This equation implies that E increases as $[Cl^-]$ increases. For a sufficiently large $[Cl^-]$, Cl^- will be more readily oxidized than the water solvent.

19.19. The answer is c, 11.

19.20. The answer is c, $2H_2O(l) + 2e^- \rightarrow H_2(g) + 2OH^-(aq)$.

19.21. The answer is a, 123 A.

19.22. The answer is b, the copper electrode is the anode.

■ ANSWERS TO CONCEPTUAL PROBLEMS

19.25. a. Since there is no species present to donate or accept electrons other than zinc, you would expect no change.

b. Since there is no species present to donate or accept electrons other than copper, you would expect no change.

c. According to the table of standard reduction potentials, the Cu^{2+} would undergo reduction, and the Zn would undergo oxidation. You would expect the Zn strip to dissolve as it becomes Zn^{2+}, the blue color of the solution to fade as the Cu^{2+} becomes Cu, and solid copper precipitate to form.

d. According to the table of standard reduction potentials, since Zn^{2+} cannot oxidize Cu, you would expect no change.

19.27. The Zn is a sacrificial electrode that keeps the hull from undergoing oxidation by the dissolved ions in seawater. Zn works because it is more easily oxidized than Fe.

19.29. Since there is more zinc present, the oxidation-reduction reactions in the battery will run for a longer period of time. This assumes zinc is the limiting reactant.

19.31. Pick elements or compounds to be reduced and one to be oxidized so that when the half-reactions are added together, the $E°_{cell}$ is about 0.90 V. For example

$$Cd(s) \rightarrow Cd^{2+}(aq) + 2e^- \qquad E°_{ox} = 0.40 \text{ V}$$

$$I_2(s) + 2e^- \rightarrow 2I^-(aq) \qquad E°_{red} = 0.54 \text{ V}$$

The overall balanced reaction and cell potential are

$$I_2(s) + Cd(s) \rightarrow 2I^-(aq) + Cd^{2+}(aq) \quad E°_{cell} = 0.94 \text{ V}$$

19.33. The effect of the various changes on the intensity of the light can be determined using the Nernst equation,

$$E_{cell} = E°_{cell} - \frac{0.0592}{n} \log Q$$

For this reaction, $E° = 1.10$ V, $n = 2$, and Q is the reaction quotient.

$$Q = \frac{[Zn^{2+}]}{[Cu^{2+}]}$$

If $Q > 1$, log Q is positive, and the net result will be a decrease in cell potential and a decrease in the intensity of light. If $Q < 1$, log Q is negative, and the net result will be an increase in cell potential and an increase in the intensity of light. At the start, both $[Zn^{2+}]$ and $[Cu^{2+}]$ are 1.0 M, so $Q = 1$, and log $Q = 0$, so $E_{cell} = E°_{cell}$.

a. If more $CuSO_4(s)$ is dissolved in the $CuSO_4$ solution, $[Cu^{2+}]$ would be greater than 1, so $Q < 1$. The effect is to increase the intensity of light.

b. If more $Zn(NO_3)_2(s)$ is dissolved in the $Zn(NO_3)_2$ solution, $[Zn^{2+}]$ would be greater than 1, so $Q > 1$. The effect is to decrease the intensity of light.

c. If H_2O is added to the $CuSO_4$ solution, $[Cu^{2+}]$ would be less than 1, so $Q > 1$. The effect is to decrease the intensity of light.

d. If the salt bridge is removed, the circuit would not be complete, and the cell potential would be zero. No current would flow.

■ SOLUTIONS TO PRACTICE PROBLEMS

Note on significant figures: If the final answer to a solution needs to be rounded off, it is given first with one nonsignificant figure, and the last significant figure is underlined. The final answer is then rounded to the correct number of significant figures. In multistep problems, intermediate answers are given with at least one nonsignificant figure; however, only the final answer has been rounded off.

19.35. In balancing oxidation-reduction reactions in acid, the four steps in the text will be followed. For part a, each step is shown. For the other parts, only a summary is shown.

a. Assign oxidation numbers to the skeleton equation (Step 1).

$$\overset{+6}{Cr_2O_7^{2-}} + \overset{+3}{C_2O_4^{2-}} \rightarrow \overset{+3}{Cr^{3+}} + \overset{+4}{CO_2}$$

Separate into two incomplete half-reactions (Step 2). Note that carbon is oxidized (increases in oxidation number), and chromium is reduced (decreases in oxidation number).

$$C_2O_4^{2-} \rightarrow CO_2$$
$$Cr_2O_7^{2-} \rightarrow Cr^{3+}$$

Balance each half-reaction separately. The oxidation half-reaction is not balanced in C, so place a 2 in front of CO_2 (Step 3a). Finally, add two electrons to the right side to balance the charge (Step 3d). The balanced oxidation half-reaction is

$$C_2O_4^{2-} \rightarrow 2CO_2 + 2e^-$$

The reduction half-reaction is not balanced in Cr, so place a 2 in front of Cr^{3+} (Step 3a). Add seven H_2O to the right side to balance O atoms (Step 3b), and add fourteen H^+ ions to the left side to balance H atoms (step 3c). Finally, add six electrons to the left side to balance the charge (Step 3d). The balanced reduction half-reaction is

$$Cr_2O_7^{2-} + 14H^+ + 6e^- \rightarrow 2Cr^{3+} + 7H_2O$$

Multiply the oxidation half-reaction by 3 so that, when added, the electrons cancel (Step 4a).

$$3C_2O_4^{2-} \rightarrow 6CO_2 + 6e^-$$
$$\underline{Cr_2O_7^{2-} + 14H^+ + 6e^- \rightarrow 2Cr^{3+} + 7H_2O}$$
$$Cr_2O_7^{2-} + 3C_2O_4^{2-} + 14H^+ + \cancel{6e^-} \rightarrow 2Cr^{3+} + 6CO_2 + 7H_2O + \cancel{6e^-}$$

The equation does not need to be simplified any further (Step 4b). The net ionic equation is

$$Cr_2O_7^{2-} + 3C_2O_4^{2-} + 14H^+ \rightarrow 2Cr^{3+} + 6CO_2 + 7H_2O$$

b. The two balanced half-reactions are

$$Cu \rightarrow Cu^{2+} + 2e^- \quad \text{(oxidation)}$$
$$NO_3^- + 4H^+ + 3e^- \rightarrow NO + 2H_2O \quad \text{(reduction)}$$

Multiply the oxidation half-reaction by 3 and the reduction half-reaction by 2, and then add together. Cancel the six electrons from each side. No further simplification is needed. The balanced equation is

$$3Cu + 2NO_3^- + 8H^+ \rightarrow 3Cu^{2+} + 2NO + 4H_2O$$

c. The two balanced half-reactions are

$$HNO_2 + H_2O \rightarrow NO_3^- + 3H^+ + 2e^- \quad \text{(oxidation)}$$
$$MnO_2 + 4H^+ + 2e^- \rightarrow Mn^{2+} + 2H_2O \quad \text{(reduction)}$$

Add the two half-reactions together and cancel the two electrons from each side. Also, cancel three H^+ ions and one H_2O from each side. The balanced equation is

$$MnO_2 + HNO_2 + H^+ \rightarrow Mn^{2+} + NO_3^- + H_2O$$

d. The two balanced half-reactions are

$$Mn^{2+} + 4H_2O \rightarrow MnO_4^- + 8H^+ + 5e^- \quad \text{(oxidation)}$$
$$PbO_2 + SO_4^{2-} + 4H^+ + 2e^- \rightarrow PbSO_4 + 2H_2O \quad \text{(reduction)}$$

Multiply the oxidation half-reaction by 2 and the reduction half-reaction by 5, and then add together. Cancel the ten electrons from each side. Also, cancel sixteen H^+ and eight H_2O from each side. The balanced equation is

$$5PbO_2 + 2Mn^{2+} + 5SO_4^{2-} + 4H^+ \rightarrow 5PbSO_4 + 2MnO_4^- + 2H_2O$$

e. The two balanced half-reactions are

$$HNO_2 + H_2O \rightarrow NO_3^- + 3H^+ + 2e^- \qquad \text{(oxidation)}$$

$$Cr_2O_7^{2-} + 14H^+ + 6e^- \rightarrow 2Cr^{3+} + 7H_2O \qquad \text{(reduction)}$$

Multiply the oxidation half-reaction by 3, and then add together. Cancel the six electrons from each side. Also, cancel nine H^+ and three H_2O from each side. The balanced equation is

$$3HNO_2 + Cr_2O_7^{2-} + 5H^+ \rightarrow 2Cr^{3+} + 3NO_3^- + 4H_2O$$

19.37. In balancing oxidation-reduction reactions in basic solution, the equation will first be balanced as if the equation were in acidic solution; then the extra two steps in the text will be followed.

a. The two balanced half-reactions are

$$Mn^{2+} + 2H_2O \rightarrow MnO_2 + 4H^+ + 2e^- \qquad \text{(oxidation)}$$

$$H_2O_2 + 2H^+ + 2e^- \rightarrow 2H_2O \qquad \text{(reduction)}$$

Add the two half-reactions together, and cancel the two electrons from each side. Also, cancel two H^+ and two H_2O from each side. The balanced equation in acidic solution is

$$Mn^{2+} + H_2O_2 \rightarrow MnO_2 + 2H^+$$

Now add two OH^- to each side (Step 5). Simplify by combining the H^+ and OH^- to give H_2O. No further simplification is required (Step 6). The balanced equation in basic solution is

$$Mn^{2+} + H_2O_2 + 2OH^- \rightarrow MnO_2 + 2H_2O$$

b. The two balanced half-reactions are

$$NO_2^- + H_2O \rightarrow NO_3^- + 2H^+ + 2e^- \qquad \text{(oxidation)}$$

$$MnO_4^- + 4H^+ + 3e^- \rightarrow MnO_2 + 2H_2O \qquad \text{(reduction)}$$

Multiply the oxidation half-reaction by 3 and the reduction half-reaction by 2, and then add together. Cancel the six electrons from each side. Also, cancel six H^+ and three H_2O from each side. The balanced equation in acidic solution is

$$2MnO_4^- + 3NO_2^- + 2H^+ \rightarrow 2MnO_2 + 3NO_3^- + H_2O$$

Now add two OH^- to each side. Simplify by combining the H^+ and OH^- to give H_2O. Then cancel one H_2O from each side. The balanced equation in basic solution is

$$2MnO_4^- + 3NO_2^- + H_2O \rightarrow 2MnO_2 + 3NO_3^- + 2OH^-$$

c.   The two balanced half-reactions are

$$Mn^{2+} + 2H_2O \rightarrow MnO_2 + 4H^+ + 2e^- \quad \text{(oxidation)}$$

$$ClO_3^- + 2H^+ + e^- \rightarrow ClO_2 + H_2O \qquad \text{(reduction)}$$

Multiply the reduction half-reaction by 2 and then add together. Cancel the two electrons from each side. Also, cancel four H^+ and two H_2O from each side. The balanced equation in acidic solution is

$$Mn^{2+} + 2ClO_3^- \rightarrow MnO_2 + 2ClO_2$$

Since there are no H^+ ions on either side, no further simplification is needed. The balanced equation in basic solution is identical to the balanced equation in acidic solution.

d.   The two balanced half-reactions are

$$NO_2 + H_2O \rightarrow NO_3^- + 2H^+ + e^- \qquad \text{(oxidation)}$$

$$MnO_4^- + 4H^+ + 3e^- \rightarrow MnO_2 + 2H_2O \ \text{(reduction)}$$

Multiply the oxidation half-reaction by 3 and then add together. Cancel the three electrons from each side. Also, cancel four H^+ and two H_2O from each side. The balanced equation in acidic solution is

$$MnO_4^- + 3NO_2 + H_2O \rightarrow MnO_2 + 3NO_3^- + 2H^+$$

Now add two OH^- to each side. Simplify by combining the H^+ and OH^- to give H_2O. Then cancel one H_2O from each side. The balanced equation in basic solution is

$$MnO_4^- + 3NO_2 + 2OH^- \rightarrow MnO_2 + 3NO_3^- + H_2O$$

e.   The two balanced half-reactions are

$$Cl_2 + 6H_2O \rightarrow 2ClO_3^- + 12H^+ + 10e^- \quad \text{(oxidation)}$$

$$Cl_2 + 2e^- \rightarrow 2Cl^- \qquad\qquad\qquad \text{(reduction)}$$

Multiply the reduction half-reaction by 5 and then add together. Cancel the ten electrons from each side. Also, divide all the coefficients by 2. The balanced equation in acidic solution is

$$3Cl_2 + 3H_2O \rightarrow 5Cl^- + ClO_3^- + 6H^+$$

Now add six OH^- to each side. Simplify by combining the H^+ and OH^- to give H_2O. Then cancel three H_2O from each side. The balanced equation in basic solution is

$$3Cl_2 + 6OH^- \rightarrow 5Cl^- + ClO_3^- + 3H_2O$$

19.39. a.   The two balanced half-reactions are

$$8H_2S \rightarrow S_8 + 16H^+ + 16e^- \qquad \text{(oxidation)}$$

$$NO_3^- + 2H^+ + e^- \rightarrow NO_2 + H_2O \qquad \text{(reduction)}$$

Multiply the reduction half-reaction by 16, and then add together. Cancel the sixteen electrons and sixteen H^+ from each side. The balanced equation is

$$8H_2S + 16NO_3^- + 16H^+ \rightarrow S_8 + 16NO_2 + 16H_2O$$

b.   The two balanced half-reactions are

$$Cu \rightarrow Cu^{2+} + 2e^- \qquad \text{(oxidation)}$$

$$NO_3^- + 4H^+ + 3e^- \rightarrow NO + 2H_2O \qquad \text{(reduction)}$$

Multiply the oxidation half-reaction by 3 and the reduction half-reaction by 2, and then add together. Cancel the six electrons from each side. The balanced equation is

$$2NO_3^- + 3Cu + 8H^+ \rightarrow 2NO + 3Cu^{2+} + 4H_2O$$

c.   The two balanced half-reactions are

$$SO_2 + 2H_2O \rightarrow SO_4^{2-} + 4H^+ + 2e^- \qquad \text{(oxidation)}$$

$$MnO_4^- + 8H^+ + 5e^- \rightarrow Mn^{2+} + 4H_2O \qquad \text{(reduction)}$$

Multiply the oxidation half-reaction by 5 and the reduction half-reaction by 2, and then add together. Cancel the ten electrons from each side. Also, cancel sixteen H^+ and eight H_2O from each side. The balanced equation is

$$2MnO_4^- + 5SO_2 + 2H_2O \rightarrow 5SO_4^{2-} + 2Mn^{2+} + 4H^+$$

d.   The two balanced half-reactions are

$$Sn(OH)_3^- + 3H_2O \rightarrow Sn(OH)_6^{2-} + 3H^+ + 2e^- \qquad \text{(oxidation)}$$

$$Bi(OH)_3 + 3H^+ + 3e^- \rightarrow Bi + 3H_2O \qquad \text{(reduction)}$$

Multiply the oxidation half-reaction by 3 and the reduction half-reaction by 2, and then add together. Cancel the six electrons from each side. Also, cancel six H^+ and six H_2O from each side. The balanced equation in acidic solution is

$$2Bi(OH)_3 + 3Sn(OH)_3^- + 3H_2O \rightarrow 3Sn(OH)_6^{2-} + 2Bi + 3H^+$$

Now add three OH^- to each side. Simplify by combining the H^+ and OH^- to give H_2O. Then cancel three H_2O on each side. The balanced equation in basic solution is

$$2Bi(OH)_3 + 3Sn(OH)_3^- + 3OH^- \rightarrow 3Sn(OH)_6^{2-} + 2Bi$$

19.41.   a.   The two balanced half-reactions are

$$I^- + 3H_2O \rightarrow IO_3^- + 6H^+ + 6e^- \qquad \text{(oxidation)}$$

$$MnO_4^- + 4H^+ + 3e^- \rightarrow MnO_2 + 2H_2O \qquad \text{(reduction)}$$

Multiply the reduction half-reaction by 2, and then add together. Cancel the six electrons from each side. Also, cancel six H^+ and three H_2O from each side. The balanced equation in acidic solution is

$$2MnO_4^- + I^- + 2H^+ \rightarrow 2MnO_2 + IO_3^- + H_2O$$

Now add two OH^- to each side. Simplify by combining the H^+ and OH^- to give H_2O. Then cancel one H_2O on each side. The balanced equation in basic solution is

$$2MnO_4^- + I^- + H_2O \rightarrow 2MnO_2 + IO_3^- + 2OH^-$$

b.   The two balanced half-reactions are

$$2Cl^- \rightarrow Cl_2 + 2e^- \qquad \text{(oxidation)}$$

$$Cr_2O_4^{2-} + 14H^+ + 6e^- \rightarrow 2Cr^{3+} + 7H_2O \qquad \text{(reduction)}$$

Multiply the oxidation half-reaction by 3, and then add together. Cancel the six electrons from each side. The balanced equation is

$$Cr_2O_7^{2-} + 6Cl^- + 14H^+ \rightarrow 2Cr^{3+} + 3Cl_2 + 7H_2O$$

c. The two balanced half-reactions are

$$S_8 + 16H_2O \rightarrow 8SO_2 + 32H^+ + 32e^- \quad \text{(oxidation)}$$

$$NO_3^- + 4H^+ + 3e^- \rightarrow NO + 2H_2O \qquad \text{(reduction)}$$

Multiply the oxidation half-reaction by 3 and the reduction half-reaction by 32, and then add together. Cancel the ninety-six electrons from each side. Also, cancel ninety-six H^+ and forty-eight H_2O from each side. The balanced equation is

$$3S_8 + 32NO_3^- + 32H^+ \rightarrow 32NO + 24SO_2 + 16H_2O$$

d. The two balanced half-reactions are

$$H_2O_2 \rightarrow O_2 + 2H^+ + 2e^- \quad \text{(oxidation)}$$

$$MnO_4^- + 4H^+ + 3e^- \rightarrow MnO_2 + 2H_2O \quad \text{(reduction)}$$

Multiply the oxidation half-reaction by 3 and the reduction half-reaction by 2, and then add together. Cancel the six electrons from each side. Also, cancel six H^+ from each side. The balanced equation in acidic solution is

$$3H_2O_2 + 2MnO_4^- + 2H^+ \rightarrow 3O_2 + 2MnO_2 + 4H_2O$$

Now add two OH^- to each side. Simplify by combining the H^+ and OH^- to give H_2O. Then cancel two H_2O on each side. The balanced equation in basic solution is

$$3H_2O_2 + 2MnO_4^- \rightarrow 3O_2 + 2MnO_2 + 2H_2O + 2OH^-$$

e. The two balanced half-reactions are

$$Zn \rightarrow Zn^{2+} + 2e^- \quad \text{(oxidation)}$$

$$2NO_3^- + 12H^+ + 10e^- \rightarrow N_2 + 6H_2O \quad \text{(reduction)}$$

Multiply the oxidation half-reaction by 5, and then add together. Cancel the ten electrons from each side. The balanced equation is

$$5Zn + 2NO_3^- + 12H^+ \rightarrow N_2 + 5Zn^{2+} + 6H_2O$$

19.43. Sketch of the cell:

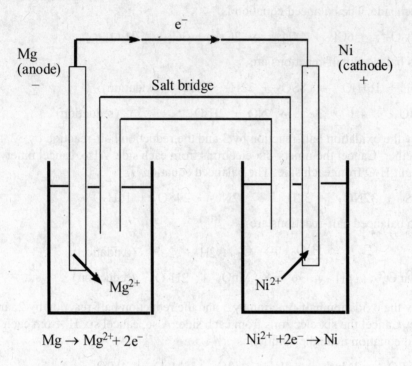

Mg (anode) − e^- Ni (cathode) +

Salt bridge

Mg^{2+} Ni^{2+}

$Mg \rightarrow Mg^{2+} + 2e^-$ $Ni^{2+} + 2e^- \rightarrow Ni$

19.45. Sketch of the cell:

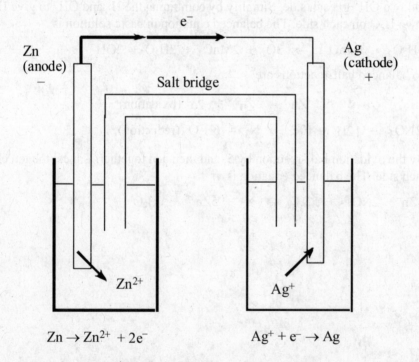

Zn (anode) − e^- Ag (cathode) +

Salt bridge

Zn^{2+} Ag^+

$Zn \rightarrow Zn^{2+} + 2e^-$ $Ag^+ + e^- \rightarrow Ag$

19.47. The electrode half-reactions and the overall cell reaction are

Anode: $Zn(s) + 2OH^-(aq) \rightarrow Zn(OH)_2(s) + 2e^-$

Cathode: $Ag_2O(s) + H_2O(l) + 2e^- \rightarrow 2Ag(s) + 2OH^-(aq)$

Overall: $Zn(s) + Ag_2O(s) + H_2O(l) \rightarrow Zn(OH)_2(s) + 2Ag(s)$

19.49. Because of its less negative $E°$, Pb^{2+} is reduced at the cathode and is written on the right; $Ni(s)$ is oxidized at the anode and is written first, at the left, in the cell notation. The notation is

$$Ni(s)|Ni^{2+}(aq)||Pb^{2+}(aq)|Pb(s).$$

19.51. Because of its less negative $E°$, H^+ is reduced at the cathode and is written on the right; $Ni(s)$ is oxidized at the anode and is written first, at the left, in the cell notation. The notation is

$$Ni(s)|Ni^{2+}(1\ M)||H^+(1\ M)|H_2(g)|Pt.$$

19.53. The $Fe(s)$, on the left, is the reducing agent. The Ag^+, on the right, is the oxidizing agent, gaining just one electron. Multiplying its half-reaction by 2 to equalize the numbers of electrons and writing both half-reactions give the overall cell reaction:

$$Fe(s) \rightarrow Fe^{2+}(aq) + 2e^-$$

$$\underline{2Ag^+(aq) + 2e^- \rightarrow 2Ag(s)}$$

$$Fe(s) + 2Ag^+(aq) \rightarrow Fe^{2+}(aq) + 2Ag(s)$$

19.55. The half-cell reactions, the overall cell reaction, and the sketch are

$$Cd(s) \rightarrow Cd^{2+}(aq) + 2e^-$$

$$\underline{Ni^{2+}(aq) + 2e^- \rightarrow Ni(s)}$$

$$Cd(s) + Ni^{2+}(aq) \rightarrow Cd^{2+}(aq) + Ni(s)$$

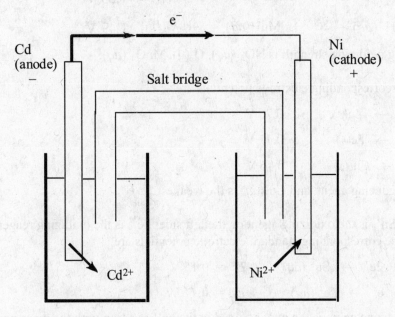

19.57. The half-cell reactions are

$$2Fe^{3+}(aq) + 2e^- \rightarrow 2Fe^{2+}(aq)$$

$$Zn(s) \rightarrow Zn^{2+}(aq) + 2e^-$$

n equals 2, and the maximum work for the reaction as written is

$$w_{max} = -nFE_{cell} = -2 \times 9.6485 \times 10^4 \text{ C} \times 0.72 \text{ V} = -1.\underline{3}89 \times 10^5 \text{ C} \bullet \text{V} = -1.\underline{3}89 \times 10^5 \text{ J}$$

Because this is the work obtained by reduction of 2 mol of Fe^{3+}, the work for 1 mol is

$$w_{max} = (-1.389 \times 10^5 \text{ J})/2 \text{ mol} = -6.\underline{9}45 \times 10^4 = -6.9 \times 10^4 \text{ J} = -69 \text{ kJ}$$

19.59. The half-cell reactions are

$$2Ag^+(aq) + 2e^- \rightarrow 2Ag(s)$$

$$Ni(s) \rightarrow Ni^{2+}(aq) + 2e^-$$

n equals 2, and the maximum work for the reaction as written is

$$w_{max} = -nFE_{cell} = -2 \times 9.6485 \times 10^4 \text{ C} \times 0.97 \text{ V} = -1.\underline{8}7 \times 10^5 \text{ C} \bullet \text{V} = -1.\underline{8}7 \times 10^5 \text{ J}$$

For 30.0 g of nickel, the maximum work is

$$30.0 \text{ g Ni} \times \frac{1 \text{ mol Ni}}{58.69 \text{ g Ni}} \times \frac{-1.87 \times 10^5 \text{ J}}{1 \text{ mol Ni}} = -9.\underline{5}6 \times 10^4 \text{ J} = -96 \text{ kJ}$$

19.61. The half-reactions and corresponding electrode potentials are

$$NO_3^-(aq) + 4H^+(aq) + 3e^- \rightarrow NO(g) + 2H_2O(l) \quad 0.96 \text{ V}$$

$$O_2(g) + 4H^+(aq) + 4e^- \rightarrow 2H_2O(l) \quad 1.23 \text{ V}$$

$$MnO_4^-(aq) + 8H^+(aq) + 5e^- \rightarrow Mn^{2+}(aq) + 4H_2O(l) \quad 1.49 \text{ V}$$

The order by increasing oxidizing strength is $NO_3^-(aq)$, $O_2(g)$, $MnO_4^-(aq)$.

19.63. The half-reactions and corresponding electrode potentials are

$$Zn^{2+}(aq) + 2e^- \rightarrow Zn(s) \quad -0.76 \text{ V}$$

$$Fe^{2+}(aq) + 2e^- \rightarrow Fe(s) \quad -0.41 \text{ V}$$

$$Cu^{2+}(aq) + e^- \rightarrow Cu^+(s) \quad 0.16 \text{ V}$$

$Zn(s)$ is the strongest reducing agent, and $Cu^+(aq)$ is the weakest.

19.65. a. In this reaction, Sn^{4+} is the oxidizing agent on the left side; Fe^{3+} is the oxidizing reagent on the right side. The corresponding standard electrode potentials are

$$Sn^{4+}(aq) + 2e^- \rightarrow Sn^{2+}(aq) \quad E° = 0.15 \text{ V}$$

$$Fe^{3+}(aq) + e^- \rightarrow Fe^{2+}(aq) \quad E° = 0.77 \text{ V}$$

The stronger oxidizing agent is the one involved in the half-reaction with the more positive standard electrode potential, so Fe^{3+} is the stronger oxidizing agent. The reaction is nonspontaneous as written.

b.   In this reaction, MnO_4^- is the oxidizing agent on the left side; O_2 is the oxidizing reagent on the right side. The corresponding standard electrode potentials are

$$O_2(g) + 4H^+(aq) + 4e^- \rightarrow 2H_2O(l) \qquad\qquad E° = 1.23 \text{ V}$$

$$MnO_4^-(aq) + 8H^+(aq) + 5e^- \rightarrow Mn^{2+}(aq) + 4H_2O(l) \qquad E° = 1.49 \text{ V}$$

The stronger oxidizing agent is the one involved in the half-reaction with the more positive standard electrode potential, so MnO_4^- is the stronger oxidizing agent. The reaction is spontaneous as written.

19.67.   The reduction half-reactions and standard electrode potentials are

$$Br_2(l) + 2e^- \rightarrow 2Br^-(aq) \qquad E° = 1.07 \text{ V}$$

$$Cl_2(g) + 2e^- \rightarrow 2Cl^-(aq) \qquad E° = 1.36 \text{ V}$$

$$F_2(g) + 2e^- \rightarrow 2F^-(aq) \quad E° = 2.87 \text{ V}$$

From these, you see that the order of increasing oxidizing strength is Br_2, Cl_2, F_2. Therefore, chlorine gas will oxidize Br^- but will not oxidize F^-. The balanced equation for the reaction is

$$Cl_2(g) + 2Br^-(aq) \rightarrow 2Cl^-(aq) + Br_2(l)$$

19.69.   The half-reactions and standard electrode potentials are

$$Cr(s) \rightarrow Cr^{3+}(aq) + 3e^- \qquad -E°_{Cr} = 0.74 \text{ V}$$

$$Hg_2^{2+}(aq) + 2e^- \rightarrow 2Hg(l) \qquad E°_{Hg} = 0.80 \text{ V}$$

Obtain the cell potential by adding the half-cell potentials.

$$E°_{cell} = E°_{Hg} - E°_{Cr} = 0.80 \text{ V} + 0.74 \text{ V} = 1.54 \text{ V}$$

19.71.   The half-reactions and standard electrode potentials are

$$Cr(s) \rightarrow Cr^{3+}(aq) + 3e^- \qquad -E°_{Cr} = 0.74 \text{ V}$$

$$I_2(s) + 2e^- \rightarrow 2I^-(aq) \quad E°_{I_2} = 0.54 \text{ V}$$

Obtain the cell potential by adding the half-cell potentials.

$$E°_{cell} = E°_{Cr} - E°_{I_2} = 0.54 \text{ V} + 0.74 \text{ V} = 1.28 \text{ V}$$

19.73.   The half-cell reactions, the corresponding half-cell potentials, and their sums are displayed below:

$$3Cu(s) \rightarrow 3Cu^{2+}(aq) + 6e^- \qquad E° = -0.34 \text{ V}$$

$$2NO_3^-(aq) + 8H^+(aq) + 6e^- \rightarrow 2NO(g) + 4H_2O(l) \qquad E° = 0.96 \text{ V}$$

$$\overline{}$$

$$3Cu(s) + 2NO_3^-(aq) + 8H^+(aq) \rightarrow$$
$$3Cu^{2+}(aq) + 2NO(g) + 4H_2O(l) \qquad E° = 0.62 \text{ V}$$

Note that each half-reaction involves six electrons, hence $n = 6$. Therefore,

$$\Delta G^\circ = -nFE^\circ_{cell} = -6 \text{ mol e}^- \times 9.6485 \times 10^4 \text{ C/mol e}^- \times 0.62 \text{ V} = -3.\underline{5}8 \times 10^5 \text{ J}$$

$$\Delta G^\circ = -3.6 \times 10^5 \text{ J}$$

Thus, the standard free-energy change is -3.6×10^2 kJ.

19.75. The half-cell reactions, the corresponding half-cell potentials, and their sums are displayed below:

$$
\begin{array}{ll}
2I^-(aq) \rightarrow I_2(s) + 2e^- & -E^\circ = -0.54 \text{ V} \\
\underline{Cl_2(g) + 2e^- \rightarrow 2Cl^-(aq)} & \underline{E^\circ = 1.36 \text{ V}} \\
2I^-(aq) + Cl_2(g) \rightarrow I_2(s) + 2Cl^-(aq) & E^\circ_{cell} = 0.82 \text{ V}
\end{array}
$$

Note that each half-reaction involves two electrons, hence $n = 2$. Therefore,

$$\Delta G^\circ = -nFE^\circ_{cell} = -2 \text{ mol e}^- \times 9.6485 \times 10^4 \text{ C/mol e}^- \times 0.82 \text{ V} = -1.\underline{5}8 \times 10^5 \text{ J}$$

$$\Delta G^\circ = -1.6 \times 10^5 \text{ J}$$

Thus, the standard free-energy change is -1.6×10^2 kJ.

19.77. Write the equation with the appropriate ΔG_f° beneath each substance.

$$
\begin{array}{lcccc}
 & Mg(s) + & 2Ag^+(aq) \rightarrow & Mg^{2+}(aq) + & 2Ag(s) \\
\Delta G_f^\circ: & 0 & 2 \times 77.12 & -454.8 & 0 \text{ KJ}
\end{array}
$$

Hence,

$$
\begin{aligned}
\Delta G^\circ &= \Sigma n \Delta G_f^\circ(\text{products}) - \Sigma m \Delta G_f^\circ(\text{reactants}) \\
&= [-454.8 - 2 \times 77.12] \text{ kJ} = -609.\underline{0}4 \text{ kJ} = -6.09\underline{0}4 \times 10^5 \text{ J}
\end{aligned}
$$

Obtain n by splitting the reaction into half-reactions.

$$Mg(s) \rightarrow Mg^{2+}(aq) + 2e^-$$

$$2Ag^+(aq) + 2e^- \rightarrow 2Ag(s)$$

Each half-reaction involves two electrons, so $n = 2$. Therefore,

$$\Delta G^\circ = -nFE^\circ_{cell}$$

$$-6.0904 \times 10^5 \text{ J} = -2 \text{ mol e}^- \times 9.6485 \times 10^4 \text{ C/mol e}^- \times E^\circ_{cell}$$

Rearrange and solve for E°_{cell}. Recall that $J = C \bullet V$.

$$E^\circ_{cell} = \frac{-6.0904 \times 10^5 \text{ J}}{-2 \times 9.6485 \times 10^4 \text{ C}} = 3.15\underline{6}1 = 3.156 \text{ V}$$

19.79. Write the equation with the appropriate ΔG_f° beneath each substance:

$$
\begin{array}{lcccccc}
 & PbO_2(s) + & 2HSO_4^-(aq) + & 2H^+(aq) + & Pb(s) \rightarrow & 2PbSO_4(s) + & 2H_2O(l) \\
\Delta G_f^\circ: & -215.4 & 2(-756.0) & 0 & 0 & 2(-813.2) & 2(-237.1) \text{ KJ}
\end{array}
$$

Hence,

$$\Delta G^\circ = [2 \times (-813.2) + 2 \times (-237.1) - (-215.4) - 2 \times (-756.0)] \text{ kJ}$$

$$= -373.\underline{2} \text{ kJ} = -3.73\underline{20} \times 10^5 \text{ J}$$

Obtain n by splitting the reaction into half-reactions.

$$\text{Pb}(s) + \text{HSO}_4^-(aq) \rightarrow \text{PbSO}_4(s) + \text{H}^+(aq) + 2e^-$$

$$\text{PbO}_2(s) + \text{HSO}_4^-(aq) + 3\text{H}^+(aq) + 2e^- \rightarrow \text{PbSO}_4(s) + 2\text{H}_2\text{O}(l)$$

Each half-reaction involves two electrons, so $n = 2$. Therefore,

$$\Delta G^\circ = -nFE^\circ_{cell}$$

$$-3.73\underline{200} \times 10^5 \text{ J} = -2 \text{ mol } e^- \times 9.6485 \times 10^4 \text{ C/mol } e^- \times E^\circ_{cell}$$

Rearrange and solve for E°_{cell}. Recall that $J = C \bullet V$.

$$E^\circ_{cell} = \frac{-3.73200 \times 10^5 \text{ J}}{-2 \times 9.6485 \times 10^4 \text{ C}} = 1.93\underline{39} = 1.934 \text{ V}$$

19.81. The half-reactions and standard electrode potentials are

$$\text{Cu}(s) \rightarrow \text{Cu}^{2+}(aq) + 2e^- \qquad -E^\circ_{Cu} = -0.34 \text{ V}$$

$$2\text{Fe}^{3+}(aq) + 2e^- \rightarrow 2\text{Fe}^{2+}(aq) \qquad E^\circ_{Fe^{3+}} = 0.77 \text{ V}$$

The standard cell potential for the cell is

$$E^\circ_{cell} = E^\circ_{Fe^{3+}} - E^\circ_{Cu} = 0.77 \text{ V} - 0.34 \text{ V} = 0.43 \text{ V}$$

Note that $n = 2$. Substitute into the equation relating E° and K. Note that $K = K_c$.

$$0.43 \text{ V} = \frac{0.0592}{2} \log K_c$$

Solving for K_c yields

$$\log K_c = 14.\underline{52}$$

Take the antilog of both sides:

$$K_c = \text{antilog} (14.52) = 3.4 \times 10^{\underline{14}} = 10^{14}$$

19.83. The half-reactions and standard electrode potentials are

$$\text{Cu}^+(aq) \rightarrow \text{Cu}^{2+}(aq) + e^- \qquad -E^\circ = -0.16 \text{ V}$$

$$\text{Cu}^+(aq) + e^- \rightarrow \text{Cu}(s) \quad E^\circ = 0.52 \text{ V}$$

The standard cell potential for the cell is

$$E^\circ_{cell} = 0.52 \text{ V} - 0.16 \text{ V} = 0.36 \text{ V}$$

Note that n equals 1. Substitute into the equation relating E° and K. Note that K equals K_c.

$$0.36 \text{ V} = \frac{0.0592}{1} \log K_c$$

Solving for K_c, you get

$$\log K_c = 6.\underline{0}81$$

Take the antilog of both sides:

$$K_c = \text{antilog}\,(6.081) = \underline{1}.2 \times 10^6 = 1 \times 10^6$$

19.85.   The half-cell reactions, the corresponding half-cell potentials, and their sums are displayed below:

$$
\begin{array}{ll}
2Cr(s) \rightarrow 2Cr^{3+}(aq) + 6e^- & -E° = 0.74 \text{ V} \\
\underline{3Ni^{2+}(aq) + 6e^- \rightarrow 3Ni(s)} & \underline{E° = -0.23 \text{ V}} \\
2Cr(s) + 3Ni^{2+}(aq) \rightarrow 2Cr^{3+}(aq) + 3Ni(s) & E°_{cell} = 0.51 \text{ V}
\end{array}
$$

Note that n equals 6. The reaction quotient is

$$Q = \frac{[Cr^{3+}]^2}{[Ni^{2+}]^3} = \frac{(1.0 \times 10^{-3})^2}{(1.5)^3} = 2.\underline{9}62 \times 10^{-7}$$

The standard cell potential is 0.51 V, so the Nernst equation becomes

$$E_{cell} = E°_{cell} - \frac{0.0592}{n} \log Q$$

$$= 0.51 - \frac{0.0592}{6} \log\,(2.962 \times 10^{-7})$$

$$= 0.51 - (-0.064\underline{4}1) = 0.5\underline{7}4 = 0.57 \text{ V}$$

19.87.   The half-cell reactions, the corresponding half-cell potentials, and their sums are displayed below:

$$
\begin{array}{ll}
10Br^-(aq) \rightarrow 5Br_2(l) + 10e^- & -E° = -1.07 \text{ V} \\
\underline{2MnO_4^-(aq) + 16H^+(aq) + 10e^- \rightarrow 2Mn^{2+}(aq) + 8H_2O(l)} & \underline{E° = 1.49 \text{ V}} \\
2MnO_4^-(aq) + 10Br^-(aq) + 16H^+(aq) \rightarrow & \\
\quad 2Mn^{2+}(aq) + 5Br_2(l) + 8H_2O(l) & E°_{cell} = 0.42 \text{ V}
\end{array}
$$

Note that n equals 10. The reaction quotient is

$$Q = \frac{[Mn^{2+}]^2}{[MnO_4^{2-}]^2[Br^-]^{10}[H^+]^{16}} = \frac{(0.15)^2}{(0.010)^2(0.010)^{10}(1.0)^{16}} = 2.2\underline{5} \times 10^{22}$$

The standard cell potential is 0.42 V, so the Nernst equation becomes

$$E_{cell} = E°_{cell} - \frac{0.0592}{n} \log Q = 0.42 - \frac{0.0592}{10} \log\,(2.25 \times 10^{22})$$

$$= 0.42 - (0.1\underline{3}23) = 0.2\underline{8}76 = 0.29 \text{ V}$$

19.89.   The overall reaction is

$$Cd(s) + Ni^{2+}(aq) \rightarrow Cd^{2+}(aq) + Ni(s)$$

Note that n equals 2. The reaction quotient is

$$Q = \frac{[Cd^{2+}]}{[Ni^{2+}]} = \frac{[Cd^{2+}]}{1.0} = [Cd^+]$$

The standard cell potential is 0.170 V, and the cell potential is 0.240 V, so the Nernst equation becomes

$$E_{cell} = E°_{cell} - \frac{0.0592}{n} \log Q$$

$$0.240 = 0.170 - \frac{0.0592}{2} \log Q$$

Rearrange and solve for $\log Q$.

$$\log Q = \frac{-2}{0.0592} \times (0.240 - 0.170) = -2.\underline{3}648$$

Take the antilog of both sides.

$$Q = [Cd^{2+}]/1.0 = \text{antilog} (-2.3648) = \underline{4}.31 \times 10^{-3} = 0.004 \ M$$

The Cd^{2+} concentration is 0.004 M.

19.91. a.   The cathode reaction is $Ca^{2+}(l) + 2e^- \rightarrow Ca(l)$.

The anode reaction is $S^{2-}(l) \rightarrow S(l) + 2e^-$.

b.   The cathode reaction is $Cs^+(l) + e^- \rightarrow Cs(l)$.

The anode reaction is $4OH^-(l) \rightarrow O_2(g) + 2H_2O(g) + 4e^-$.

19.93. a.   The species you should consider for half-reactions are Na^+, SO_4^{2-}, and H_2O. The possible cathode reactions are

$$Na^+(aq) + e^- \rightarrow Na(s) \qquad E° = -2.71 \ V$$

$$2H_2O(l) + 2e^- \rightarrow H_2(g) + 2OH^-(aq) \qquad E° = -0.83 \ V$$

Because the electrode potential for H_2O is larger (less negative), it is easier to reduce.

The possible anode reactions are

$$2H_2O(l) \rightarrow O_2(g) + 4H^+(aq) + 4e^- \qquad E° = -1.23 \ V$$

$$2SO_4^{2-}(aq) \rightarrow S_2O_8^{2-}(aq) + 2e^- \qquad E° = -2.01 \ V$$

Because the electrode potential for H_2O is less negative, it is easier to oxidize.

The expected half-reactions are

$$2H_2O(l) \rightarrow O_2(g) + 4H^+(aq) + 4e^- \qquad E° = -1.23 \ V$$

$$4H_2O(l) + 4e^- \rightarrow 2H_2(g) + 4OH^-(aq) \qquad E° = -0.83 \ V$$

The overall reaction is

$$2H_2O(l) \rightarrow 2H_2(g) + O_2(g)$$

b.   The species you should consider for half-reactions are K^+, Br^-, and H_2O. The possible cathode reactions are

$$K^+(aq) + e^- \rightarrow K(s) \qquad E° = -2.92 \ V$$

$$2H_2O(l) + 2e^- \rightarrow H_2(g) + 2OH^-(aq) \qquad E° = -0.83 \ V$$

Because the electrode potential for H_2O is larger (less negative), it is easier to reduce. The possible anode reactions are

$$2H_2O(l) \rightarrow O_2(g) + 4H^+(aq) + 4e^- \qquad E° = -1.23 \text{ V}$$

$$2Br^-(aq) \rightarrow Br_2(l) + 2e^- \qquad E° = -1.07 \text{ V}$$

Because the electrode potential for Br^- is less negative, it is easier to oxidize.

The expected half-reactions are

$$2Br^-(aq) \rightarrow Br_2(l) + 2e^- \qquad E° = -1.07 \text{ V}$$

$$2H_2O(l) + 2e^- \rightarrow H_2(g) + 2OH^-(aq) \qquad E° = -0.83 \text{ V}$$

The overall reaction is

$$2Br^-(aq) + 2H_2O(l) \rightarrow Br_2(l) + H_2(g) + 2OH^-(aq)$$

19.95. The conversion of grams of aluminum ($3.61 \text{ kg} = 3.61 \times 10^3$ g) to coulombs required to give this amount of aluminum is

$$3.61 \times 10^3 \text{ g} \times \frac{1 \text{ mol Al}}{26.98 \text{ g}} \times \frac{3 \text{ mol e}^-}{1 \text{ mol Al}} \times \frac{9.6485 \times 10^4 \text{ C}}{1 \text{ mol e}^-} = 3.8\underline{7}2 \times 10^7 = 3.87 \times 10^7 \text{ C}$$

19.97. The conversion of coulombs to grams of lithium is

$$5.00 \times 10^3 \text{ C} \times \frac{1 \text{ mol e}^-}{9.6485 \times 10^4 \text{ C}} \times \frac{1 \text{ mol Li}}{1 \text{ mol e}^-} \times \frac{6.941 \text{ g Li}}{1 \text{ mol Li}} = 0.359\underline{6} = 0.360 \text{ g Li}$$

■ SOLUTIONS TO GENERAL PROBLEMS

19.99.   a.   The half-reactions and net ionic equation are

$$3Fe(s) \rightarrow 3Fe^{2+}(aq) + 6e^-$$
$$2NO_3^-(aq) + 8H^+(aq) + 6e^- \rightarrow 2NO(g) + 4H_2O(l)$$
$$\overline{3Fe(s) + 2NO_3^-(aq) + 8H^+(aq) \rightarrow 3Fe^{2+}(aq) + 2NO(g) + 4H_2O(l)}$$

b.   The half-reactions and net ionic equation are

$$3Fe^{2+}(aq) \rightarrow 3Fe^{3+}(aq) + 3e^-$$
$$NO_3^-(aq) + 4H^+(aq) + 3e^- \rightarrow NO(g) + 2H_2O(l)$$
$$\overline{3Fe^{2+}(aq) + NO_3^-(aq) + 4H^+(aq) \rightarrow 3Fe^{3+}(aq) + NO(g) + 2H_2O(l)}$$

c.   Add the results from parts a and b, and divide all coefficients by a factor of 3.

$$3Fe(s) + 2NO_3^-(aq) + 8H^+(aq) \rightarrow 3Fe^{2+}(aq) + 2NO(g) + 4H_2O(l)$$
$$3Fe^{2+}(aq) + NO_3^-(aq) + 4H^+(aq) \rightarrow 3Fe^{3+}(aq) + NO(g) + 2H_2O(l)$$
$$\overline{Fe(s) + NO_3^-(aq) + 4H^+(aq) \rightarrow Fe^{3+}(aq) + NO(g) + 2H_2O(l)}$$

19.101. a. The two balanced half-reactions are

$$8S^{2-}(aq) \rightarrow S_8 + 16e^- \qquad \text{(oxidation)}$$

$$MnO_4(aq) + 4H^+ + 3e^- \rightarrow MnO_2 + 2H_2O \qquad \text{(reduction)}$$

Multiply the oxidation half-reaction by 3 and the reduction half-reaction by 16, and then add together. Cancel the forty-eight electrons from each side. The balanced equation in acidic solution is

$$16MnO_4^- + 24S^{2-} + 64H^+ \rightarrow 16MnO_2 + 3S_8 + 32H_2O$$

Now add sixty-four OH$^-$ to each side. Simplify by combining the H$^+$ and OH$^-$ to give H$_2$O. Then cancel thirty-two H$_2$O on each side. The balanced equation in basic solution is

$$16MnO_4^-(aq) + 24S^{2-}(aq) + 32H_2O(l) \rightarrow 16MnO_2(s) + 3S_8(s) + 64OH^-(aq)$$

b. The two balanced half-reactions are

$$HSO_3^- + H_2O \rightarrow SO_4^{2-} + 3H^+ + 2e^- \qquad \text{(oxidation)}$$

$$IO_3^- + 6H^+ + 6e^- \rightarrow I^- + 3H_2O \qquad \text{(reduction)}$$

Multiply the oxidation half-reaction by 3, and then add together. Cancel the six electrons from each side. Also, cancel six H$^+$ and three H$_2$O from each side. The balanced equation is

$$IO_3^-(aq) + 3HSO_3^-(aq) \rightarrow I^- + 3SO_4^{2-}(aq) + 3H^+(aq)$$

c. The two balanced half-reactions are

$$Fe(OH)_2 + H_2O \rightarrow Fe(OH)_3 + H^+ + e^- \qquad \text{(oxidation)}$$

$$CrO_4^{2-} + 4H^+ + 3e^- \rightarrow Cr(OH)_4^- \qquad \text{(reduction)}$$

Multiply the oxidation half-reaction by 3, and then add together. Cancel the three electrons and cancel three H$^+$ from each side. The balanced equation in acidic solution is

$$CrO_4^{2-}(aq) + 3Fe(OH)_2(s) + H^+(aq) + 3H_2O(l) \rightarrow Cr(OH)_4^-(aq) + 3Fe(OH)_3(s)$$

Now add one OH$^-$ to each side. Simplify by combining the H$^+$ and OH$^-$ to give H$_2$O. Then, combine the H$_2$O's on the left side into a single term. The balanced equation in basic solution is

$$CrO_4^{2-}(aq) + 3Fe(OH)_2(aq) + 4H_2O(l) \rightarrow Cr(OH)_4^-(aq) + 3Fe(OH)_3(s) + OH^-(aq)$$

d. The two balanced half-reactions are

$$Cl_2 + 2H_2O \rightarrow 2ClO^- + 4H^+ + 2e^- \qquad \text{(oxidation)}$$

$$Cl_2 + 2e^- \rightarrow 2Cl^- \qquad \text{(reduction)}$$

Add the two half-reactions together. Cancel the two electrons from each side. Divide all the coefficients by a factor of 2. The balanced equation in acidic solution is

$$Cl_2 + H_2O \rightarrow Cl^- + ClO^- + 2H^+$$

Now add two OH$^-$ to each side. Simplify by combining the H$^+$ and OH$^-$ to give H$_2$O. Then cancel one H$_2$O on each side. The balanced equation in basic solution is

$$Cl_2(aq) + 2OH^-(aq) \rightarrow Cl^-(aq) + ClO^-(aq) + H_2O(l)$$

19.103. This reaction takes place in basic solution. The skeleton equation is

$$Fe(OH)_2(s) + O_2(g) \rightarrow Fe(OH)_3(s)$$

The two balanced half-reactions are

$$Fe(OH)_2 + H_2O \rightarrow Fe(OH)_3 + H^+ + e^- \quad \text{(oxidation)}$$
$$O_2 + 4H^+ + 4e^- \rightarrow 2H_2O \quad \text{(reduction)}$$

Multiply the oxidation half-reaction by 4, and then add together. Cancel the four electrons from each side. Also, cancel four H^+ and two H_2O from each side. The balanced equation in acidic or in basic solution is

$$4Fe(OH)_2(s) + O_2(g) + 2H_2O(l) \rightarrow 4Fe(OH)_3(s)$$

19.105. The cell notation is $Ca(s)|Ca^{2+}(aq)||Cl_2(g)|Cl^-(aq)|Pt(s)$. The reactions are

$$\text{Anode: } Ca(s) \rightarrow Ca^{2+}(aq) + 2e^- \qquad\qquad -E° = 2.76 \text{ V}$$

$$\text{Cathode: } Cl_2(g) + 2e^- \rightarrow 2Cl^-(aq) \qquad\qquad E° = 1.36 \text{ V}$$

$$E°_{cell} = 1.36 \text{ V} + 2.76 \text{ V} = 4.12 \text{ V}$$

19.107. a. In this reaction, Fe^{3+} is the oxidizing agent on the left side; Ni^{2+} is the oxidizing reagent on the right side. The corresponding standard electrode potentials are

$$Ni^{2+}(aq) + 2e^- \rightarrow Ni(s) \qquad\qquad E° = -0.23 \text{ V}$$
$$Fe^{3+}(aq) + e^- \rightarrow Fe^{2+}(aq) \qquad\qquad E° = 0.77 \text{ V}$$

The stronger oxidizing agent is the one involved in the half-reaction with the more positive standard electrode potential, so Fe^{3+} is the stronger oxidizing agent. The oxidation of nickel by iron(III) is a spontaneous reaction.

b. In this reaction, Fe^{3+} is the oxidizing agent on the left side; Sn^{4+} is the oxidizing reagent on the right side. The corresponding standard electrode potentials are

$$Sn^{4+}(aq) + 2e^- \rightarrow Sn^{2+}(aq) \qquad\qquad E° = 0.15 \text{ V}$$
$$Fe^{3+}(aq) + e^- \rightarrow Fe^{2+}(aq) \qquad\qquad E° = 0.77 \text{ V}$$

The stronger oxidizing agent is the one involved in the half-reaction with the more positive standard electrode potential, so Fe^{3+} is the stronger oxidizing agent. The oxidation of tin(II) by iron(III) is a spontaneous reaction.

19.109. The half-cell reactions, the corresponding half-cell potentials, and their sums are displayed below:

$$
\begin{array}{lll}
Pb(s) \rightarrow Pb^{2+}(aq) + 2e^- & -E° = 0.13 \text{ V} \\
\underline{2H^+(aq) + 2e^- \rightarrow H_2(g)} & \underline{E° = 0.00 \text{ V}} \\
Pb(s) + 2H^+(aq) \rightarrow Pb^{2+}(aq) + H_2(g) & E°_{cell} = 0.13 \text{ V}
\end{array}
$$

Note that n equals 2. Next, use K_{sp} to calculate $[Pb^{2+}]$.

$$[Pb^{2+}] = \frac{K_{sp}}{[SO_4^{2-}]} = \frac{1.7 \times 10^{-8}}{1.0} = 1.7 \times 10^{-8} \, M$$

The reaction quotient for the cell reaction is

$$Q = \frac{[Pb^{2+}] \times P_{H_2}}{[H^+]^2} = \frac{(1.7 \times 10^{-8})(1.0)}{(1.0)^2} = 1.7 \times 10^{-8}$$

The standard cell potential is 0.13 V , so the Nernst equation becomes

$$E_{cell} = E^{\circ}_{cell} - \frac{0.0592}{n} \log Q$$

$$E_{cell} = 0.13 \text{ V} - \frac{0.0592}{2} \log (1.7 \times 10^{-8}) = 0.13 \text{ V} - (-0.2299 \text{ V}) = 0.3599 = 0.36 \text{ V}$$

19.111. a.   Note that $E^{\circ} = 0.010$ V and n equals 2. Substitute into the equation relating E° and K.

$$E^{\circ} = \frac{0.0592}{n} \log K$$

$$0.010 \text{ V} = \frac{0.0592}{2} \log K$$

Solving for K, you get

$$\log K = 0.3378$$

Take the antilog of both sides:

$$K = K_c = \text{antilog } (0.3378) = 2.176 = 2.2$$

b.   Substitute into the equilibrium expression using $[Sn^{2+}] = x$, and $[Pb^{2+}] = 1.0 \, M - x$.

$$K_c = \frac{[Sn^{2+}]}{[Pb^{2+}]} = \frac{x}{1.0 - x} = 2.176$$

$$x = 0.6851 \, M$$

$$[Pb^{2+}] = 1.0 \, M - x = 0.3149 = 0.3 \, M$$

19.113. a.   The number of faradays is

$$1.0 \text{ mol Na}^+ \times \frac{1 \text{ mol e}^-}{1 \text{ mol Na}^+} \times \frac{1 \, F}{1 \text{ mol e}^-} = 1.0 \, F$$

The number of coulombs is

$$1.0 \, F \times \frac{96{,}485 \text{ C}}{1 \, F} = 9.64 \times 10^4 = 9.6 \times 10^4 \text{ C}$$

b.   The number of faradays is

$$1.0 \text{ mol Cu}^{2+} \times \frac{2 \text{ mol e}^-}{1 \text{ mol Cu}^{2+}} \times \frac{1 \, F}{1 \text{ mol e}^-} = 2.0 \, F$$

The number of coulombs is

$$2.0 \, F \times \frac{96{,}485 \text{ C}}{1 \, F} = 1.92 \times 10^5 = 1.9 \times 10^5 \text{ C}$$

c.   The number of faradays is

$$1.0 \text{ g } H_2O \times \frac{1 \text{ mol } H_2O}{18.01 \text{ g } H_2O} \times \frac{4 \text{ mol } e^-}{2 \text{ mol } H_2O} \times \frac{1 \text{ } F}{1 \text{ mol } e^-} = 0.1\underline{1}10 = 0.11 \text{ } F$$

The number of coulombs is

$$0.1\underline{1}10 \text{ } F \times \frac{96,485 \text{ C}}{1 \text{ } F} = 1.\underline{0}7 \times 10^4 = 1.1 \times 10^4 \text{ C}$$

d.   The number of faradays is

$$1.0 \text{ g } Cl^- \times \frac{1 \text{ mol } Cl^-}{35.45 \text{ g } Cl^-} \times \frac{2 \text{ mol } e^-}{2 \text{ mol } Cl^-} \times \frac{1 \text{ } F}{1 \text{ mol } e^-} = 0.02\underline{8}20 = 0.028 \text{ } F$$

The number of coulombs is

$$0.02\underline{8}20 \text{ } F \times \frac{96,485 \text{ C}}{1 \text{ } F} = 2.\underline{7}21 \times 10^3 = 2.7 \times 10^3 \text{ C}$$

19.115.   From the electrolysis information, calculate the total moles of I_2 formed

$$65.4 \text{ s} \times (10.5 \times 10^{-3} \text{ A}) \times \frac{1 \text{ C}}{1 \text{ A} \cdot \text{s}} \times \frac{1 \text{ mol } e^-}{96,485 \text{ C}} \times \frac{1 \text{ mol } I_2}{2 \text{ mol } e^-} = 3.5\underline{5}8 \times 10^{-6} \text{ mol } I_2$$

From the balanced equation,

$$3.5\underline{5}8 \times 10^{-6} \text{ mol } I_2 \times \frac{1 \text{ mol } H_3AsO_3}{1 \text{ mol } I_2} \times \frac{1 \text{ mol As}}{1 \text{ mol } H_3AsO_3} \times \frac{74.92 \text{ g As}}{1 \text{ mol As}}$$

$$= 2.6\underline{6}6 \times 10^{-4} = 2.67 \times 10^{-4} \text{ g As}$$

19.117. a.   The spontaneous chemical reaction and maximum cell potential are

$Cd(s)$	$\rightarrow$	$Cd^{2+}(aq) + 2e^-$	$-E° = 0.40 \text{ V}$
$2Ag^+(aq) + 2e^-$	$\rightarrow$	$2Ag(s)$	$E° = 0.80 \text{ V}$
$Cd(s) + 2Ag^+(aq)$	$\rightarrow$	$2Ag(s) + Cd^{2+}(aq)$	$E°_{cell} = 1.20 \text{ V}$

b.   Addition of S^{2-} would greatly decrease the $Cd^{2+}(aq)$ concentration and help shift the equilibrium to the right, thus forming more Ag. The cell potential would increase.

c.   No effect. The size of the electrode makes no difference in the potential.

19.119.   Anode: $2H_2O(l) \rightarrow O_2(g) + 4H^+(aq) + 4e^-$

Cathode: $Cu^{2+}(aq) + 2e^- \rightarrow Cu(s)$

19.121. a.   First, find the moles of silver.

$$2.48 \text{ g Ag} \times \frac{1 \text{ mol Ag}}{107.9 \text{ g Ag}} = 0.022\underline{9}8 \text{ mol Ag}$$

The number of coulombs is

$$0.02298 \text{ mol Ag} \times \frac{1 \text{ mol } e^-}{1 \text{ mol Ag}} \times \frac{9.6485 \times 10^4 \text{ C}}{1 \text{ mol } e^-} = 22\underline{1}8 \text{ C}$$

Since amp × sec = coul, the number of seconds is

$$\text{Time} = \frac{2218 \text{ C}}{1.50 \text{ amp}} = 1.4\underline{7}8 \times 10^3 = 1.48 \times 10^3 \text{ s}$$

b. For the same amount of current, the grams of Cr would be

$$2218 \text{ C} \times \frac{1 \text{ mol e}^-}{96,485 \text{ C}} \times \frac{1 \text{ mol Cr}}{3 \text{ mol e}^-} \times \frac{52.00 \text{ g Cr}}{1 \text{ mol Cr}} = 0.398\underline{3} = 0.398 \text{ g}$$

19.123. a. Note that 3.50 hours = 12600 s, and the efficiency is 90.0%.

$$2.75 \text{ amp} \times 12600 \text{ s} \times \frac{1 F}{96,485 \text{ C}} \times 0.900 = 0.323\underline{2} = 0.323 \text{ } F$$

b. The moles of Au that were deposited is

$$\text{mol Au} = 21.221 \text{ g Au} \times \frac{1 \text{ mol Au}}{197.0 \text{ g}} = 0.107720 \text{ mol}$$

Since $1 F = 1$ mol e$^-$, the ratio of moles of e$^-$ to moles of Au is

$$\frac{\text{mol e}^-}{\text{mol Au}} = \frac{0.3232}{0.10772} = \frac{3.00}{1}$$

Thus, the ion must be Au^{3+}. The reaction is

$$\text{Au}^{3+}(aq) + 3\text{e}^- \rightarrow \text{Au}$$

19.125. a. The half-cell reactions, the corresponding half-cell potentials, and their sums are displayed below:

Zn(s)	$\rightarrow$	Zn^{2+}(aq) + 2e$^-$	$-E° = 0.76$ V
Cu^{2+}(aq) + 2e$^-$	$\rightarrow$	Cu(s)	$E° = 0.34$ V
Cu^{2+}(aq) + Zn(s)	$\rightarrow$	Zn^{2+}(aq) + Cu(s)	$E° = 1.10$ V

Use the Nernst equation to calculate the voltage of the cell.

$$E = E° - \frac{0.0592}{n} \log Q = E° - \frac{0.0592}{n} \log \frac{[\text{Zn}^{2+}]}{[\text{Cu}^{2+}]}$$

Note that n equals 2, [Zn^{2+}] = 0.200 M, and [Cu^{2+}] = 0.0100 M.

$$E° = 1.10 \text{ V} - \frac{0.0592}{2} \log \frac{[0.200]}{[0.0100]} = 1.10 \text{ V} - 0.038\underline{5}1 \text{ V} = 1.0\underline{6}1 = 1.06 \text{ V}$$

b. First, calculate the moles of electrons passing through the cell.

$$1.00 \text{ amp} \times 225 \text{ s} \times \frac{1 \text{ mol e}^-}{96,485 \text{ C}} = 0.00233\underline{2} \text{ mol e}^-$$

The moles of Cu deposited are

$$0.00233\underline{2} \text{ mol e}^- \times \frac{1 \text{ mol Cu}}{2 \text{ mol e}^-} = 0.00116\underline{6} \text{ mol Cu}$$

The moles of Cu remaining in the 1.00 L of solution are

$$0.0100 - 0.001166 = 0.008\underline{8}34 = 0.0088 \text{ mol}$$

Since the volume of the solution is 1.00 L, the molarity of Cu^{2+} is 0.0088 M.

19.127. a. Write the cell reaction with the $\Delta G_f°$'s beneath.

$$Cd(s) + Co^{2+}(aq) \rightarrow Cd^{2+}(aq) + Co(s)$$

$\Delta G_f°$:   0   -54.4   -77.6   0 kJ

Hence,

$$\Delta G° = \Sigma n \Delta G_f°(\text{products}) - \Sigma m \Delta G_f°(\text{reactants})$$

$$= [-77.6 + 54.4]\text{ kJ} = -23.\underline{2}\text{ kJ} = -2.32 \times 10^4 \text{ J}$$

b. Next, determine the standard cell potential for the cell. Note that n equals 2.

$$\Delta G° = -nFE°$$

$$-2.32 \times 10^4 \text{ J} = -2(9.6485 \times 10^4 \text{ C}) \times E°$$

Solve for $E°$ to get

$$E° = \frac{-2.32 \times 10^4 \text{ J}}{-2(9.6485 \times 10^4 \text{ C})} = 0.12\underline{02} = 0.120 \text{ V}$$

The half-reactions and voltages are

$Cd(s)$	$\rightarrow$ $Cd^{2+}(aq) + 2e^-$	$-E°_{ox} = 0.40$ V
$Co^{2+}(aq) + 2e^-$	$\rightarrow$ $Co(s)$	$E°_{red} = ?$
$Cd(s) + Co^{2+}(aq)$	$\rightarrow$ $Cd^{2+}(aq) + Co(s)$	$E° = 0.12\underline{02}$ V

The cell potential is

$$E° = E°_{red} + (-E°_{ox})$$

$$0.12\underline{02} \text{ V} = E°_{red} + 0.40 \text{ V}$$

$$E°_{red} = 0.12\underline{02} \text{ V} - 0.40 \text{ V} = -0.2\underline{7}97 = -0.28 \text{ V}$$

■ SOLUTIONS TO STRATEGY PROBLEMS

19.129. Since chromium metal is oxidized, and since reduction occurs at the cathode, the reaction at the cathode is

$$Pb^{2+}(aq) + 2e^- \rightarrow Pb(s)$$

19.131. The maximum work that can be obtained is

$$w_{max} = \Delta G = -nFE_{cell} = -(6 \text{ mol})(96{,}485 \text{ C/mol})(1.14 \text{ V}) = -659\underline{9}57 \text{ J} = -659.\underline{9} \text{ kJ}$$

This is the maximum amount of work for 2 moles of chromium. For 6.61 g Cr, the maximum work is

$$6.61 \text{ g Cr} \times \frac{1 \text{ mol Cr}}{52.00 \text{ g}} \times \frac{-659.9 \text{ kJ}}{2 \text{ mol Cr}} = -41.\underline{9}45 = -41.9 \text{ kJ}$$

19.133. The half-reactions and voltages are

$Cr(s)$	$\rightarrow$	$Cr^{3+}(aq) + 3e^-$	$E°_{ox} = 0.74 \text{ V}$
$3Ag^+(aq) + 3e^-$	$\rightarrow$	$3Ag(s)$	$E°_{red} = 0.80 \text{ V}$
$Cr(s) + 3Ag^+(aq)$	$\rightarrow$	$Cr^{3+}(aq) + 3Ag(s)$	$E° = 1.54 \text{ V}$

Now use the Nernst equation to calculate the cell potential.

$$E = E° - \frac{0.0592}{n} \log Q = E° - \frac{0.0592}{n} \log \frac{[Cr^{3+}]}{[Ag^+]^3}$$

Note that n equals 3, $[Cr^{3+}] = 0.10 \text{ M}$, and $[Ag^+] = 1.0 \times 10^{-4} \text{ M}$.

$$E° = 1.54 \text{ V} - \frac{0.0592}{3} \log \frac{[0.10]}{[1.0 \times 10^{-4}]^3} = 1.3\underline{2}2 = 1.32 \text{ V}$$

19.135. The answer is b, $Li + NaCl \rightarrow LiCl + Na$.

19.137. For a spontaneous reaction, the following reactions would occur.

Anode: $Ni(s) \rightarrow Ni^{2+}(aq) + 2e^-$ $E°_{ox} = 0.23 \text{ V}$

Cathode: $2Ag^+(aq) + 2e^- \rightarrow 2Ag(s)$ $E°_{red} = 0.80 \text{ V}$

As the reaction proceeds, $Ag(s)$ is produced at the cathode, and $Ni^{2+}(aq)$ is produced at the anode.

19.139. Some half-reactions of interest to this problem and standard reduction potentials include

$Mg^{2+}(aq) + 2e^-$	$\rightarrow$	$Mg(s)$	$E° = -2.38 \text{ V}$
$Al^{3+}(aq) + 3e^-$	$\rightarrow$	$Al(s)$	$E° = -1.66 \text{ V}$
$Cu^{2+}(aq) + 2e^-$	$\rightarrow$	$Cu(s)$	$E° = 0.34 \text{ V}$
$I_2(s) + 2e^-$	$\rightarrow$	$2I^-(aq)$	$E° = 0.54 \text{ V}$
$Ag^+(aq) + e^-$	$\rightarrow$	$Ag(s)$	$E° = 0.80 \text{ V}$

a. Initially there is not a strong enough reducing agent present to cause the reduction of Mg^{2+} or Cu^{2+}, so these metals will stay in solution. Iodide ions and silver solid, being reduced forms of the elements, are each stable since there are no strong oxidizing agents present.

b. Aluminum metal is a fairly strong reducing agent but not strong enough to reduce Mg^{2+}. When placed into the aqueous mixture Cu^{2+} ions will begin plating out onto the aluminum as the aluminum dissolves. The solution's blue tint due to dissolved copper(II) ion will also fade. Iodide ion and solid silver, being reduced forms of the elements, will remain unchanged.

c. The half-reaction for the reduction of Cu(II) ion with aluminum is

$$Cu^{2+}(aq) + 2e^- \rightarrow Cu(s)$$

d. For a reaction to occur upon the addition of $Al^{3+}(aq)$, the presence of a reducing agent stronger than $Al(s)$ would be required. Since there are no such reagents present, nothing happens when $Al^{3+}(aq)$ is added to the mixture.

19.141. As written, the half-cell reactions, the corresponding half-cell potentials, and their sums are displayed below:

$$
\begin{array}{lll}
3Fe(s) & \rightarrow 3Fe^{2+}(aq) + 6e^- & -E° = 0.41\ V \\
2Al^{3+}(aq) + 6e^- & \rightarrow 2Al(s) & E° = -1.66\ V \\
\hline
3Fe(s) + 2Al^{3+}(aq) & \rightarrow 3Fe^{2+}(aq) + 2Al(s) & E° = -1.25\ V
\end{array}
$$

a. Because $E_{cell}° < 0$, the reaction is nonspontaneous and requires energy input to occur. The cell is therefore an electrolytic cell. To be voltaic (or galvanic), $E_{cell}°$ must be greater than zero.

b. $Al^{3+}(aq)$ is being reduced.

c. The oxidizing agent is the species which is reduced, or $Al^{3+}(aq)$.

d. As the reaction proceeds, the concentration of $Fe^{2+}(aq)$ increases.

e. As Al^{3+} is reduced, it deposits on to the Al electrode. Hence, the mass of the $Al(s)$ increases as the reaction proceeds.

19.143. We are told that an unknown metal, either Ni or Zn, dissolves in a solution containing $Fe^{2+}(aq)$. For this to occur, the unknown metal needs to have a standard reduction potential more negative than the standard reduction potential for $Fe^{2+}(aq)$, or more negative than -0.41 V. The standard reduction potential for $Ni^{2+}(aq)$ is -0.23 and the standard reduction potential for $Zn^{2+}(aq)$ is -0.76 V. Thus, zinc metal is expected to react and is the likely unknown.

The half-cell reactions, the corresponding half-cell potentials, and their sums are displayed below:

$$
\begin{array}{lll}
Zn(s) & \rightarrow Zn^{2+}(aq) + 2e^- & -E° = 0.76\ V \\
Fe^{2+}(aq) + 2e^- & \rightarrow Fe(s) & E° = -0.41\ V \\
\hline
Fe^{2+}(aq) + Zn(s) & \rightarrow Zn^{2+}(aq) + Fe(s) & E° = 0.35\ V
\end{array}
$$

Thus the cell potential under standard contions for $Zn(s)$ reacting with $Fe^{2+}(aq)$ is 0.35 V.

■ SOLUTIONS TO CUMULATIVE-SKILLS PROBLEMS

19.145. The half-cell reactions, the corresponding half-cell potentials, and their sums are displayed below:

$$
\begin{array}{lll}
3Zn(s) & \rightarrow 3Zn^{2+}(aq) + 6e^- & -E° = 0.76\ V \\
2Cr^{3+}(aq) + 6e^- & \rightarrow 2Cr(s) & E° = -0.74\ V \\
\hline
2Cr^{3+}(aq) + 3Zn(s) & \rightarrow 3Zn^{2+}(aq) + 2Cr(s) & E° = 0.02\ V
\end{array}
$$

Note that n equals 6. Therefore,

$$\Delta G° = -nFE° = -6(9.6485 \times 10^4\ C)(0.02\ V) = -1.158 \times 10^4\ J = -11.58\ kJ$$

Write the cell reaction with the $\Delta H_f°$'s beneath.

$$
\begin{array}{lcccc}
2Cr^{3+}(aq) & + 3Zn(s) & \rightarrow 3Zn^{2+}(aq) & + 2Cr(s) \\
\Delta H_f°: \quad 2(-143.5) & 0 & 3(-153.9) & 0\ kJ
\end{array}
$$

Hence,

$$\Delta H° = \Sigma n \Delta H_f°(\text{products}) - \Sigma m \Delta H_f°(\text{reactants})$$

$$= [3(-153.9) - 2(-143.5)]\text{ kJ} = -174.7\text{ kJ}$$

Now calculate $\Delta S°$.

$$\Delta G° = \Delta H° - T\Delta S°$$

$$-11.58\text{ kJ} = -174.7\text{ kJ} - 298\text{ K} \times \Delta S°$$

Solving for $\Delta S°$ gives

$$\Delta S° = \frac{-174.7\text{ kJ} + 11.58\text{ kJ}}{298\text{ K}} = -0.5473\text{ kJ/K} = -5.5 \times 10^2\text{ J/K}$$

19.147. The half-cell reactions, the corresponding half-cell potentials, and their sums are displayed below:

$$
\begin{array}{llll}
4Br^-(aq) & \rightarrow & 2Br_2(l) + 4e^- & -E° = -1.07\text{ V} \\
O_2(g) + 4H^+(aq) + 4e^- & \rightarrow & 2H_2O(l) & E° = 1.23\text{ V} \\
\hline
O_2(g) + 4H^+(aq) + 4Br^-(aq) & \rightarrow & 2H_2O(l) + 2Br_2(l) & E° = 0.16\text{ V}
\end{array}
$$

Now, convert the pH to $[H^+]$.

$$[H^+] = \text{antilog}(-3.60) = 2.51 \times 10^{-4}\ M$$

Under standard conditions, $[Br^-] = 1\ M$, and the pressure of O_2 is 1 atm. Thus, substitute into the Nernst equation, where n equals 4.

$$E = E° - \frac{0.0592}{n}\log Q = E° - \frac{0.0592}{n}\log\frac{1}{[H^+]^4[Br^-]^4 \ \text{x} \ P_{O_2}}$$

$$= 0.16\text{ V} - \frac{0.0592}{4}\log\frac{1}{(2.51 \times 10^{-4})^4}$$

$$= 0.16\text{ V} - 0.2131\text{ V} = -0.0531 = -0.05\text{ V}$$

Thus, the reaction is nonspontaneous at this $[H^+]$.

19.149. Use the K_a to calculate $[H^+]$ for the buffer.

$$K_a = \frac{[H^+][OCN^-]}{[HOCN]} = 3.5 \times 10^{-4}$$

Rearrange, and solve for $[H^+]$, assuming $[HOCN]$ and $[OCN^-]$ remain constant in the buffer. Thus, $[H^+] = K_a = 3.5 \times 10^{-4}\ M$.

In Problem 19.147, $E°$ for this cell reaction was found to be 0.16 V. Under standard conditions, $[Br^-] = 1\ M$, and the pressure of O_2 is 1 atm. Thus, substitute into the Nernst equation, where n equals 4.

$$E = E^\circ - \frac{0.0592}{n} \log Q = E^\circ - \frac{0.0592}{n} \log \frac{1}{[H^+]^4[Br^-]^4 \times P_{O_2}}$$

$$= 0.16 \text{ V} - \frac{0.0592}{4} \log \frac{1}{(3.5 \times 10^{-4})^4}$$

$$= 0.16 \text{ V} - 0.20\underline{4}59 \text{ V} = -0.0\underline{4}455 = -0.04 \text{ V}$$

Thus, the reaction is nonspontaneous at this [H$^+$].

19.151. The half-cell reactions, the corresponding half-cell potentials, and their sums are displayed below:

$H_2(g)$	$\rightarrow$	$2H^+(aq) + 2e^-$	$-E^\circ = -0.00$ V
$2Ag^+(aq) + 2e^-$	$\rightarrow$	$2Ag(s)$	$E^\circ = 0.80$ V
$H_2(g) + 2Ag^+(aq)$	$\rightarrow$	$2H^+(aq) + 2Ag(s)$	$E^\circ = 0.80$ V

The standard hydrogen electrode has [H$^+$] = 1.0 M and the pressure of H$_2$ equals 1 atm. Substitute into the Nernst equation, where E = 0.45 V and n equals 2.

$$E = E^\circ - \frac{0.0592}{n} \log Q = E^\circ - \frac{0.0592}{n} \log \frac{[H^+]^2}{[Ag^+]^2 \times P_{H_2}}$$

$$0.45 \text{ V} = 0.80 \text{ V} - \frac{0.0592}{2} \log \frac{1}{[Ag^+]^2}$$

Using the properties of logs, rearrange to get

$$0.45 \text{ V} = 0.80 \text{ V} + 0.0592 \log[Ag^+]$$

Solve for [Ag$^+$].

$$\log[Ag^+] = \frac{0.45 - 0.80}{0.0592} = -5.\underline{9}12$$

$$[Ag^+] = 10^{-5.912} = \underline{1}.224 \times 10^{-6} \ M$$

Finally, determine the solubility product, using [SCN$^-$] = 0.10 M.

$$K_{sp} = [Ag^+][SCN^-] = (1.224 \times 10^{-6})(0.10) = \underline{1}.224 \times 10^{-7} = 1 \times 10^{-7}$$

CHAPTER 20

Nuclear Chemistry

■ SOLUTIONS TO EXERCISES

Note on significant figures: If the final answer to a solution needs to be rounded off, it is given first with one nonsignificant figure, and the last significant figure is underlined. The final answer is then rounded to the correct number of significant figures. In multistep problems, intermediate answers are given with at least one nonsignificant figure; however, only the final answer has been rounded off.

20.1. The nuclide symbol for potassium-40 is $^{40}_{19}\text{K}$. Similarly, the nuclide symbol for calcium-40 is $^{40}_{20}\text{Ca}$. The equation for beta emission is

$$^{40}_{19}\text{K} \rightarrow \, ^{40}_{20}\text{Ca} + \, ^{0}_{-1}\text{e}$$

20.2. Plutonium-239 has the nuclide symbol is $^{239}_{94}\text{Pu}$. An alpha particle has the symbol $^{4}_{2}\text{He}$. The nuclear equation is

$$^{239}_{94}\text{Pu} \rightarrow \, ^{A}_{Z}\text{X} + \, ^{4}_{2}\text{He}$$

From the superscripts you can write

239 = A + 4, or A = 235

Similarly, from the subscripts you can write

94 = Z + 2, or Z = 92

Hence, A = 235 and Z = 92, so the product is $^{235}_{92}\text{X}$. Because element 92 is uranium, symbol U, you write the product nucleus as $^{235}_{92}\text{U}$.

20.3. a. $^{118}_{50}\text{Sn}$ has atomic number 50. It has 50 protons and 68 neutrons. Because its atomic number is less than 83 and it has an even number of protons and neutrons, it is expected to be stable.

b. $^{76}_{33}\text{As}$ has atomic number 33. It has 33 protons and 43 neutrons. Because stable odd-odd nuclei are rare, you would expect $^{76}_{33}\text{As}$ to be one of the radioactive isotopes.

c. $^{227}_{89}\text{Ac}$ has atomic number 89. Because its atomic number is greater than 83, $^{227}_{89}\text{Ac}$ is radioactive.

20.4. a. $^{13}_{7}\text{N}$ has seven protons and six neutrons (fewer neutrons than protons). Its N/Z ratio is smaller than that in the stable ^{14}N nucleus, so it is expected to decay by electron capture or positron emission (more likely, because this is a light isotope).

b. $^{26}_{11}\text{Na}$ has 11 protons and 15 neutrons. It is expected to decay by beta emission.

20.5.   a.   The abbreviated notation is $^{40}_{20}\text{Ca}\,(\text{d},\text{p})\,^{41}_{20}\text{Ca}$.

   b.   The nuclear equation is $^{12}_{6}\text{C} + ^{2}_{1}\text{H} \rightarrow ^{13}_{6}\text{C} + ^{1}_{1}\text{H}$.

20.6.   You can write the nuclear equation as follows:

$$^{A}_{Z}\text{X} + ^{1}_{0}\text{n} \rightarrow ^{14}_{6}\text{C} + ^{1}_{1}\text{H}$$

To balance this equation in charge (subscripts) and mass number (superscripts), write the equations

$A + 1 = 14 + 1$ (from superscripts)

$Z + 0 = 6 + 1$ (from subscripts)

Hence, $A = 14$ and $Z = 7$. Therefore, the nucleus that produces carbon-14 by this reaction is $^{14}_{7}\text{N}$.

20.7.   Because an activity of 1.0 Ci is 3.7×10^{10} nuclei/s, the rate of decay in this sample is

$$\text{Rate} = 13 \text{ Ci} \times \frac{3.7 \times 10^{10} \text{ nuclei/s}}{1.0 \text{ Ci}} = 4.\underline{8}1 \times 10^{11} \text{ nuclei/s}$$

The number of nuclei in this 2.5-μg (2.5×10^{-6}-g) sample of $^{99m}_{43}\text{Tc}$ is

$$2.5 \times 10^{-6} \text{ g Tc-99m} \times \frac{1 \text{ mol Tc-99m}}{99 \text{ g Tc-99m}} \times \frac{6.02 \times 10^{23} \text{ Tc-99m nuclei}}{1 \text{ mol Tc-99m}}$$

$$= 1.\underline{5}2 \times 10^{16} \text{ Tc-99m nuclei}$$

The decay constant is

$$k = \frac{\text{rate}}{N_t} = \frac{4.81 \times 10^{11} \text{ nuclei/s}}{1.52 \times 10^{16} \text{ nuclei}} = 3.\underline{1}6 \times 10^{-5} = 3.2 \times 10^{-5}/\text{s}$$

20.8.   First, substitute the value of k into the equation relating half-life to the decay constant:

$$t_{\frac{1}{2}} = \frac{0.693}{k} = \frac{0.693}{4.18 \times 10^{-9}\,/\text{s}} = 1.6\underline{5}8 \times 10^{8} \text{ s}$$

Convert the half-life from seconds to years:

$$1.6\underline{5}8 \times 10^{8} \text{ s} \times \frac{1 \text{ min}}{60 \text{ s}} \times \frac{1 \text{ h}}{60 \text{ min}} \times \frac{1 \text{ d}}{24 \text{ h}} \times \frac{1 \text{ y}}{365 \text{ d}} = 5.2\underline{5}7 = 5.26 \text{ y}$$

20.9.   The conversion of the half-life to seconds gives

$$28.1 \text{ y} \times \frac{365 \text{ d}}{1 \text{ y}} \times \frac{24 \text{ h}}{1 \text{ d}} \times \frac{60 \text{ min}}{1 \text{ h}} \times \frac{60 \text{ s}}{1 \text{ min}} = 8.8\underline{6}1 \times 10^{8} \text{ s}$$

Because $t_{1/2} = 0.693/k$, solve this for k, and substitute the half-life in seconds.

$$k = \frac{0.693}{t_{1/2}} = \frac{0.693}{8.861 \times 10^{8} \text{ s}} = 7.8\underline{2}08 \times 10^{-10}\,/\text{s}$$

Before substituting into the rate equation, you need to know the number of nuclei in a sample containing 5.2×10^{-9} g of strontium-90.

$$5.2 \times 10^{-9} \text{ g Sr-90} \times \frac{1 \text{ mol Sr-90}}{90 \text{ g Sr-90}} \times \frac{6.02 \times 10^{23} \text{ Sr-90 nuclei}}{1 \text{ mol Sr-90}} = 3.\underline{4}78 \times 10^{13} \text{ Sr-90 nuclei}$$

Now, substitute into the rate equation:

Rate $= kN_t = (7.8208 \times 10^{-10}/\text{s}) \times (3.478 \times 10^{13} \text{ nuclei}) = 2.\underline{7}2 \times 10^{4}$ nuclei/s

Calculate the activity by dividing the rate (disintegrations of nuclei per second) by 3.70×10^{10} disintegrations of nuclei per second per curie.

$$\text{Activity} = 2.72 \times 10^{4} \text{ nuclei/s} \times \frac{1.0 \text{ Ci}}{3.7 \times 10^{10} \text{ nuclei/s}} = 7.\underline{3}51 \times 10^{-7} = 7.4 \times 10^{-7} \text{ Ci}$$

20.10. The decay constant, k, is $0.693/t_{1/2}$. If you substitute this into the equation

$$\ln \frac{N_t}{N_o} = -kt = -\frac{0.693\, t}{t_{1/2}}$$

Substitute the values $t = 25.0$ y and $t_{1/2} = 10.76$ y to get

$$\ln \frac{N_t}{N_o} = \frac{-0.693 \times 25.0 \text{ y}}{10.76 \text{ y}} = -1.6\underline{1}01$$

The fraction of krypton-85 remaining after 25.0 y is N_t/N_o.

$$\frac{N_t}{N_o} = e^{-1.6101} = 0.1\underline{9}99 = 0.20$$

20.11. The equation applied in this problem is

$$\ln \frac{N_t}{N_o} = -kt$$

The ratio of rates of disintegration is

$$\frac{N_o}{N_t} = \frac{15.3}{4.5} = 3.\underline{4}00$$

Therefore, substituting this value of N_o/N_t and $t_{1/2} = 5730$ y into the previous equation gives

$$t = \frac{t_{1/2}}{0.693} \ln \frac{N_o}{N_t} = \frac{5730 \text{ y}}{0.693} \ln (3.400) = 1.\underline{0}1 \times 10^{4} = 1.0 \times 10^{4} \text{ y}$$

20.12. a. First, determine the nuclear masses.

Nuclear mass of $^{234}_{90}\text{Th} = 234.03660$ amu $- (90 \times 0.000549$ amu$) = 233.9871\underline{9}0$ amu

Nuclear mass of $^{234}_{91}\text{Pa} = 234.04330$ amu $- (91 \times 0.000549$ amu$) = 233.9933\underline{4}1$ amu

Write the appropriate nuclear mass below each nuclide symbol. Then calculate Δm.

$$^{234}_{90}\text{Th} \quad \rightarrow \quad ^{234}_{91}\text{Pa} \quad + \quad ^{0}_{-1}\text{e}$$

$$233.987190 \quad\quad 233.993341 \quad\quad 0.000549 \text{ amu}$$

Hence,

$$\Delta m = (233.993341 + 0.000549 - 233.987190) \text{ amu} = 0.006700 \text{ amu}$$

The mass change for molar amounts in this reaction is 0.006700 g, or 6.700×10^{-6} kg. The energy change is

$$\Delta E = (\Delta m)c^2 = (6.700 \times 10^{-6} \text{ kg})(3.00 \times 10^8 \text{ m/s})^2 = 6.030 \times 10^{11} \text{ J/mol}$$

For 1.00 g Th-234, the energy change is

$$1.00 \text{ g Th-234} \times \frac{1 \text{ mol Th-234}}{234 \text{ g Th-234}} \times \frac{6.030 \times 10^{11} \text{ J}}{1 \text{ mol Th-234}} = 2.576 \times 10^9 = 2.58 \times 10^9 \text{ J}$$

b.   Convert the mass change for the reaction from amu to grams.

$$\Delta m = 0.006700 \text{ amu} \times \frac{1 \text{ g}}{1 \text{ amu} \times 6.02 \times 10^{23}} = 1.112 \times 10^{-26} \text{ g} = 1.112 \times 10^{-29} \text{ kg}$$

$$\Delta E = (\Delta m)c^2 = (1.112 \times 10^{-29} \text{ kg})(3.00 \times 10^8 \text{ m/s})^2 = 1.001 \times 10^{-12} \text{ J}$$

Convert this to MeV:

$$\Delta E = 1.001 \times 10^{-12} \text{ J} \times \frac{1 \text{ MeV}}{1.602 \times 10^{-13} \text{ J}} = 6.252 = 6.25 \text{ MeV}$$

■ ANSWERS TO CONCEPT CHECKS

20.1.   a.   Yes. Isotopes have similar chemical properties.

       b.   No, since the $^{3}_{1}\text{H}_2\text{O}$ molecule is more massive than $^{1}_{1}\text{H}_2\text{O}$.

       c. $^{3}_{1}\text{H}_2\text{O}$ should be radioactive.

20.2.   For the same radiation dosage (10 rads), the form of radiation with the highest RBE will cause the greatest biological damage. Therefore, the α particle will cause the most damage since it has the highest RBE (10).

20.3.   After 50,000 years, enough half-lives have passed (about 10) so there would be almost no carbon-14 present to detect and measure (about 0.1% would be left).

■ ANSWERS TO SELF-ASSESSMENT AND REVIEW QUESTIONS

20.1.   The two types of nuclear reactions and their equations are

Radioactive decay: $^{238}_{92}U \rightarrow\; ^{234}_{90}Th \;+\; ^4_2He$

Nuclear bombardment reactions: $^{27}_{13}Al \;+\; ^4_2He \rightarrow\; ^{30}_{15}P \;+\; ^1_0n$

20.2.   Magic numbers are the numbers of nuclear particles in completed shells of protons or neutrons. Examples of nuclei with magic numbers of protons are ^4_2He, $^{16}_8O$, and $^{40}_{20}Ca$.

20.3.   To predict whether a nucleus will be stable, look for nuclei that have one of the magic numbers of protons and neutrons. Also look for nuclei that have an even number of protons and an even number of neutrons. Nuclei that fall in the band of stability are also very stable. There are no stable nuclei above atomic number 83.

20.4.   The six common types of radioactive decay and the usual condition that leads to each type are listed below (see Table 20.2).

Alpha emission: $Z > 83$.

Beta emission: N/Z is too large.

Positron emission: N/Z is too small.

Electron capture: N/Z is too small.

Gamma emission: The nucleus is in an excited state.

Spontaneous fission: Mass number > 89.

20.5.   The isotopes that begin each of the natural radioactive decay series are uranium-238, uranium-235, and thorium-232.

20.6.   The equations are as follows:

a. $^{14}_7N \;+\; ^4_2He \rightarrow\; ^{17}_8O \;+\; ^1_1H$ (a N nucleus has been changed to an O nucleus)

b. $^{27}_{13}Al \;+\; ^4_2He \rightarrow\; ^{30}_{15}P \;+\; ^1_0n$ (the P-30 nucleus decays by positron emission)

20.7.   Particle accelerators are devices used to accelerate electrons, protons, alpha particles, and ions to very high speeds. They operate by accelerating the charged particle toward a plate with a charge opposite to that of the particle. Particle accelerators are required to accelerate alpha particles to speeds high enough to penetrate nuclei of large positive charge that normally scatter alpha particles.

20.8.   Before the discovery of transuranium elements, it was thought that americium ($Z = 95$) and curium ($Z = 96$) should be placed after actinium ($Z = 89$) in the periodic table as d-block transition elements. However, Seaborg and others discovered these elements had properties similar to the lanthanides and placed them in a second series under the lanthanides.

20.9.   The Geiger counter measures alpha particles by means of a tube filled with gas. When particles pass through the tube, they ionize the gas, freeing electrons, which creates a pulse of current that is detected by electronic equipment and is counted. A scintillation counter consists of phosphor, a substance that emits photons when struck by radiation; zinc sulfide is used for the detection of alpha particles; and sodium iodide containing thallium(I) iodide is used for gamma rays. The photons travel from the phosphor to a photoelectric detector, such as a photomultiplier, which magnifies the effect and gives a pulse of electric current that is measured.

20.10. A curie (Ci) equals 3.700×10^{10} nuclear disintegrations per second. A rad is the dosage of radiation that deposits 1×10^{-2} J of energy per kilogram of tissue. A rem is a unit of radiation dosage for biological destruction; it equals the rad multiplied by the relative biological effectiveness (RBE).

20.11. It will take cesium-137 three times its half-life of 30.2 y, or 90.6 y, to decay to 1/8 its original mass: 1 to 1/2 to 1/4 to 1/8 = 3 half-lives.

20.12. Because the $^{40}_{18}Ar$ was produced by radioactive decay of $^{40}_{19}K$, half the initial amount of $^{40}_{19}K$ has decomposed. The age equals the half-life of 1.28×10^9 y.

20.13. A radioactive tracer is a radioactive isotope added to a chemical, biological, or physical system to study it. For instance, $^{131}I^-$ is used as a tracer in the study of the dissolving of lead(II) iodide and its equilibrium in a saturated solution.

20.14. Isotope dilution is a technique designed to determine the quantity of a substance in a mixture or to determine the total volume of a solution by adding a known amount of an isotope to it. After removing a portion of the mixture, the fraction by which the isotope has been diluted provides a way of determining the quantity of substance or the total volume of solution.

20.15. Neutron activation analysis is an analysis based on the conversion of stable isotopes to radioactive isotopes by bombarding a sample with neutrons. An unstable nucleus results that then emits gamma rays or radioactive particles (such as beta particles). The amount of stable isotope is proportional to the measured emission.

20.16. The reason why the deuteron, ^2_1H, has a mass smaller than the sum of the masses of its constituents is that when nucleons come together to form a nucleus, energy is released. There must be an equivalent decrease in mass, because mass and energy are equivalent.

20.17. Iron-56 has a binding energy per nucleon near the maximum value. Two light nuclei, such as two C-12 nuclei, will undergo fusion (with the release of energy) as long as the product nuclei are lighter than iron-56 (which is the case with Na-23 and H-1).

20.18. The nuclear fission reactor operates by means of a chain reaction of nuclear fissions controlled to produce energy without explosion.

20.19. The answer is b, $^{216}_{84}Po \rightarrow {}^{212}_{82}Pb + {}^4_2He$.

20.20. The answer is e, 8.6×10^3 y.

20.21. The answer is d, 4.1×10^{-3}.

20.22. The answer is c, 19.7 min.

■ ANSWERS TO CONCEPTUAL PROBLEMS

20.23. a. After 10 half-lives have passed, the percentage of the original material that is left is

$$\left(\frac{1}{2}\right)^{10} \times 100\% = 0.0976 \cong 0.1\%$$

b. If you had a large quantity of material, 0.1% still would be a significant quantity. Also, if the material were particularly toxic in addition to being radioactive, the amount would be a significant quantity.

20.25. An atom of sodium-23 has 11 protons, 12 neutrons, and 11 electrons. Using the values in Table 20.3, the atomic mass of sodium-23 would be

(11)(1.00728 amu) + (12)(1.008665 amu) + (11)(0.000549 amu) = 23.190099 amu

Since the observed atomic weight is 22.98976 amu, it is not the same as the sum of the masses of the protons, neutrons, and electrons. Some of the expected mass is in the form of energy, the mass defect.

20.27. a. The container in the middle is depicted after 20 minutes have passed. This is equivalent to two half-lives ($t_{1/2}$ = 10 min). At this time, one-quarter of the original material remains present. Since there are four nuclides after 20 minutes, the original sample (t = 0) must have consisted of 16 nuclides. After 30 minutes have passed (three half-lives), one-eighth of the original material, or 2 nuclides, would be present. The pictures are

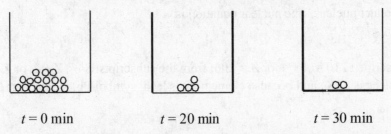

t = 0 min $\qquad$ t = 20 min $\qquad$ t = 30 min

b. The middle picture is not correct. The pile on the right (t = 10 min) containing 500 nuclides is one-half the original 1000 nuclides, so the half-life of the material is 10 minutes. The pile in the middle (t = 5 min) contains 750 nuclides, which represents one-quarter of the original material reacted. This is 1/2 × 1/2, which is not the correct way to determine the number of remaining nuclides. Instead, it is $(1/2)^{1/2}$, or 0.707. Thus, there should be 707 nuclides remaining after 5 min.

20.29. The large, positively charged He nucleus that makes up alpha (α) radiation is unable to pass through the atoms that make up solid materials such as wood without coming into contact or being deflected by the nuclei. Gamma (γ) radiation, however, with its small wavelength and high energy, can pass through large amounts of material without interaction, just as x rays can pass through skin and other soft tissue.

20.31.   Irradiation of food atoms with gamma radiation does not result in the creation of radioactive elements; therefore, the food cannot become radioactive. The addition of a radioactive element directly to the meat would make the meat radioactive. Under the right conditions, nuclear bombardment could also lead to the production of radioactive elements.

■ SOLUTIONS TO PRACTICE PROBLEMS

Note on significant figures: If the final answer to a solution needs to be rounded off, it is given first with one nonsignificant figure, and the last significant figure is underlined. The final answer is then rounded to the correct number of significant figures. In multistep problems, intermediate answers are given with at least one nonsignificant figure; however, only the final answer has been rounded off.

20.33. $^{87}_{37}Rb \rightarrow ^{87}_{38}Sr + ^{0}_{-1}e$

20.35. $^{232}_{90}Th \rightarrow ^{228}_{88}Ra + ^{4}_{2}He$

20.37.   Let X be the product nucleus. The nuclear equation is

$$^{18}_{9}F \rightarrow ^{A}_{Z}X + ^{0}_{1}e$$

From the superscripts: $18 = A + 0$, or $A = 18$; from the subscripts: $9 = Z + 1$, or $Z = 8$. Thus, the product of the reaction is $^{18}_{8}X$, and because element 8 is oxygen, symbol O, the nuclear equation is

$$^{18}_{9}F \rightarrow ^{18}_{8}O + ^{0}_{1}e$$

20.39.   Let X be the product nucleus. The nuclear equation is

$$^{210}_{84}Po \rightarrow ^{A}_{Z}X + ^{4}_{2}He$$

From the superscripts: $210 = A + 4$, or $A = 206$; from the subscripts: $84 = Z + 2$, or $Z = 82$. Thus, the product nucleus is $^{206}_{82}X$, and because element 82 is lead, symbol Pb, the nuclear equation is

$$^{210}_{84}Po \rightarrow ^{206}_{82}Pb + ^{4}_{2}He$$

20.41.   a.   Neither nucleus has an atomic number that is a magic number of protons. Find how many neutrons are in each nucleus.

Sb: No. of neutrons = $A - Z = 122 - 51 = 71$

Xe: No. of neutrons = $A - Z = 136 - 54 = 82$

Because 82 is a magic number for neutrons (implying stability of nucleus), you predict that $^{136}_{54}Xe$ is stable and $^{122}_{51}Sb$ is radioactive.

b. $^{204}_{82}Pb$ has a magic number of protons (82), so it is expected to be the stable nucleus, and $^{204}_{85}At$ is expected to be radioactive (atomic number greater than 83).

c. Rb does not have an atomic number that is a magic number of protons. Find the numbers of neutrons in the two isotopes.

$$^{87}_{37}\text{Rb : No. of neutrons} = 87 - 37 = 50$$

$$^{80}_{37}\text{Rb : No. of neutrons} = 80 - 37 = 43$$

Because 50 is a magic number for neutrons, you predict that $^{87}_{37}\text{Rb}$ is stable and $^{80}_{37}\text{Rb}$ is radioactive.

20.43. a. α-emission is most likely for nuclei with $Z > 83$.

b. positron emission (more likely; $Z < 20$) or electron capture because the mass number is less than twice the atomic number, or it has a relatively low N/Z ratio of 3/5.

c. β-emission because it has a relatively large N/Z ratio of 1.3)

20.45. α-emission decreases the mass number by 4; β-emission does not affect the mass number. $^{219}_{86}\text{Rn}$ belongs to the $^{235}_{92}\text{U}$ decay series because the difference in mass numbers is 16, which is divisible by 4. $^{220}_{86}\text{Rn}$ belongs to the $^{232}_{90}\text{Th}$ decay series because the difference in mass numbers is 12, which is divisible by 4.

20.47. a. $^{26}_{12}\text{Mg} \, (d, \alpha) \, ^{24}_{11}\text{Na}$

b. $^{16}_{8}\text{O} \, (n, p) \, ^{16}_{7}\text{N}$

20.49. a. $^{27}_{13}\text{Al} + ^{2}_{1}\text{H} \rightarrow ^{25}_{12}\text{Mg} + ^{4}_{2}\text{He}$

b. $^{10}_{5}\text{B} + ^{4}_{2}\text{He} \rightarrow ^{13}_{6}\text{C} + ^{1}_{1}\text{H}$

20.51. $\dfrac{12.6 \text{ MeV}}{1 \text{ proton}} = \dfrac{12.6 \times 10^6 \text{ eV}}{1 \text{ proton}} \times \dfrac{1.602 \times 10^{-19} \text{ J}}{1 \text{ eV}} \times \dfrac{1 \text{ kJ}}{10^3 \text{ J}} \times \dfrac{6.02 \times 10^{23} \text{ protons}}{1 \text{ mol}}$

$$= 1.2\underline{1}5 \times 10^9 = 1.22 \times 10^9 \text{ kJ/mol}$$

20.53. a. $^{6}_{3}\text{Li} + ^{1}_{0}\text{n} \rightarrow ^{A}_{Z}\text{X} + ^{3}_{1}\text{H}$

From the superscripts: $6 + 1 = A + 3$, or $A = 6 + 1 - 3 = 4$; from the subscripts: $3 + 0 = Z + 1$, or $Z = 3 - 1 = 2$. The product nucleus is $^{4}_{2}\text{X}$. The element with $Z = 2$ is helium (He), so the missing nuclide is $^{4}_{2}\text{He}$.

b. The reaction may be written

$$^{232}_{90}\text{Th} + ^{A}_{Z}\text{X} \rightarrow ^{235}_{92}\text{U} + ^{1}_{0}\text{n}$$

From the superscripts: $232 + A = 235 + 1$, or $A = 235 + 1 - 232 = 4$; from the subscripts: $90 + Z = 92 + 0$, or $Z = 92 - 90 = 2$. The projectile nucleus is $^{4}_{2}\text{X}$. The element with $Z = 2$ is helium, so the missing nuclide is $^{4}_{2}\text{He}$, or α. The reaction is then written

$$^{232}_{90}\text{Th} \, (\alpha, n) \, ^{235}_{92}\text{U}$$

20.55. The reaction may be written

$$\,_{Z}^{A}X + \,_{2}^{4}He \rightarrow \,_{96}^{242}Cm + \,_{0}^{1}n$$

From the superscripts: $A + 4 = 242 + 1$, or $A = 242 + 1 - 4 = 239$; from the subscripts: $Z + 2 = 96 + 0$, or $Z = 96 - 2 = 94$. The element with $Z = 94$ is plutonium (the target nucleus was $\,_{94}^{239}Pu$).

20.57. The rate of decay is 8.94×10^{10} nuclei/s. The number of nuclei in the sample is

$$0.250 \times 10^{-3} \text{ g H-3} \times \frac{1 \text{ mol H-3}}{3.02 \text{ g H-3}} \times \frac{6.02 \times 10^{23} \text{ nuclei}}{1 \text{ mol H-3}} = 4.9\underline{8}3 \times 10^{19} \text{ nuclei}$$

The rate equation is rate $= kN_t$. Solve for k.

$$k = \frac{\text{rate}}{N_t} = \frac{8.94 \times 10^{10} \text{ nuclei/s}}{4.98 \times 10^{19} \text{ nuclei}} = 1.7\underline{9}4 \times 10^{-9} = 1.79 \times 10^{-9} \text{ s}^{-1}$$

20.59. Find the rate of decay from the activity.

$$\text{Rate} = 20.4 \text{ Ci} \times \frac{3.700 \times 10^{10} \text{ nuclei/s}}{1 \text{ Ci}} = 7.5\underline{4}8 \times 10^{11} \text{ nuclei/s}$$

Convert the mass of S-35 to the number of nuclei. The molar mass in grams is approximately equal to the mass number.

$$0.48 \times 10^{-3} \text{ g S-35} \times \frac{1 \text{ mol S-35}}{35 \text{ g S-35}} \times \frac{6.02 \times 10^{23} \text{ nuclei}}{1 \text{ mol S-35}} = 8.\underline{2}56 \times 10^{18} \text{ nuclei}$$

Solve the rate equation for k and substitute.

$$k = \frac{\text{rate}}{N_t} = \frac{7.548 \times 10^{11} \text{ nuclei/s}}{8.256 \times 10^{18} \text{ nuclei}} = 9.\underline{1}4 \times 10^{-8} = 9.1 \times 10^{-8} \text{ s}^{-1}$$

20.61. $t_{1/2} = \dfrac{0.693}{k} = \dfrac{0.693}{1.7 \times 10^{-21} \text{ /s}} \times \dfrac{1 \text{ h}}{3600 \text{ s}} \times \dfrac{1 \text{ d}}{24 \text{ h}} \times \dfrac{1 \text{ y}}{365 \text{ d}} = 1.\underline{2}92 \times 10^{13} = 1.3 \times 10^{13} \text{ y}$

20.63. $k = \dfrac{0.693}{t_{1/2}} = \dfrac{0.693}{5.73 \times 10^{3} \text{ y}} \times \dfrac{1 \text{ y}}{365 \text{ d}} \times \dfrac{1 \text{ d}}{24 \text{ h}} \times \dfrac{1 \text{ h}}{3600 \text{ s}} = 3.8\underline{3}505 \times 10^{-12} = 3.84 \times 10^{-12}\text{/s}$

20.65. Find k from the half-life.

$$k = \frac{0.693}{t_{1/2}} = \frac{0.693}{2.69 \text{ d}} \times \frac{1 \text{ d}}{24 \text{ h}} \times \frac{1 \text{ h}}{3600 \text{ s}} = 2.9\underline{8}2 \times 10^{-6}\text{/s}$$

Before substituting into the rate equation, find the number of gold nuclei from the mass.

$$0.86 \times 10^{-3} \text{ g Au-198} \times \frac{1 \text{ mol Au-198}}{198 \text{ g Au-198}} \times \frac{6.02 \times 10^{23} \text{ Au-198 nuclei}}{1 \text{ mol Au-198}}$$

$$= 2.\underline{6}1 \times 10^{18} \text{ Au-198 nuclei}$$

Now find the rate.

$$\text{Rate} = kN_t = (2.982 \times 10^{-6}/\text{s})(2.61 \times 10^{18} \text{ nuclei}) = 7.\underline{7}9 \times 10^{12} \text{ nuclei/s}$$

$$\text{Activity} = 7.79 \times 10^{12} \text{ nuclei/s} \times \frac{1 \text{ Ci}}{3.700 \times 10^{10} \text{ nuclei/s}} = 2\underline{1}0.7 = 2.1 \times 10^2 \text{ Ci}$$

20.67. Find k from the half-life.

$$k = \frac{0.693}{t_{1/2}} = \frac{0.693}{14.3 \text{ d}} \times \frac{1 \text{ d}}{24 \text{ h}} \times \frac{1 \text{ h}}{3600 \text{ s}} = 5.6\underline{0}9 \times 10^{-7}/\text{s}$$

Solve the rate equation for N_t.

$$N_t = \frac{\text{rate}}{k} = \frac{6.3 \times 10^{12} \text{ nuclei/s}}{5.609 \times 10^{-7}/\text{s}} = 1.\underline{1}2 \times 10^{19} \text{ nuclei}$$

Convert N_t to the mass of P-32.

$$1.12 \times 10^{19} \text{ P-32 nuclei} \times \frac{1 \text{ mol P-32}}{6.02 \times 10^{23} \text{ P-32 nuclei}} \times \frac{32 \text{ g P-32}}{1 \text{ mol P-32}}$$

$$= 5.\underline{9}7 \times 10^{-4} = 6.0 \times 10^{-4} \text{ g P-32}$$

20.69. Substituting for $k = 0.693/t_{1/2}$ gives

$$\ln \frac{N_t}{N_o} = -kt = \frac{-0.693 \, t}{t_{1/2}} = \frac{-0.693 (12.0 \text{ h})}{15.0 \text{ h}} = -0.55\underline{4}4$$

Taking the antilog of both sides of this equation gives

$$\frac{N_t}{N_o} = e^{-0.5544} = 0.57\underline{4}41$$

After 12.0 h, 57.4% of the Na-24 remains.

$$6.0 \text{ μg} \times 0.57441 = 3.\underline{4}46 \text{ μg} = 3.4 \text{ μg}$$

20.71. After 1.97 s, the amount of nitrogen-17 remaining is 100% − 28.0% = 72.0%, so $N_t/N_o = 0.720$.

$$\ln \frac{N_t}{N_o} = -kt = \frac{-0.693 \, t}{t_{1/2}}$$

$$\ln (0.720) = \frac{-0.693(1.97 \text{ s})}{t_{1/2}}$$

Solve for $t_{1/2}$.

$$t_{1/2} = \frac{-0.693(1.97 \text{ s})}{\ln(0.720)} = 4.1\underline{5}58 = 4.16 \text{ s}$$

20.73. At $t = 0$, the rate is 125 nuclei/s, and at time $t = 10.0$ d, the rate is 107 nuclei/s. Thus,

$$\ln \frac{N_t}{N_o} = -kt = = \frac{-0.693\,t}{t_{1/2}}$$

Substituting yields

$$\ln \left(\frac{107 \text{ nuclei/s}}{125 \text{ nuclei/s}} \right) = \frac{-0.693\,(10.0 \text{ d})}{t_{1/2}}$$

Solve for the half-life.

$$t_{1/2} = \frac{-0.693\,(10.0 \text{ d})}{\ln \left(\dfrac{107}{125} \right)} = 44.\underline{5}7 = 44.6 \text{ d}$$

20.75. Use the equation for the number of nuclei in a sample after a time, t.

$$\ln \frac{N_t}{N_o} = -kt = \frac{-0.693\,t}{t_{1/2}}$$

Rearrange this to give an expression for t.

$$t = \frac{t_{1/2}}{0.693} \ln \frac{N_o}{N_t}$$

At $t = 0$, the rate is 15.3 nuclei/s, and at a later time t, the rate is 8.1 nuclei/s. Since the half-life for carbon-14 is 5730 y,

$$t = \frac{5730 \text{ y}}{0.693} \ln \left(\frac{15.3}{8.1} \right) = 5.\underline{2}58 \times 10^3 = 5.3 \times 10^3 \text{ y}$$

20.77. The half-life of carbon-14 is 5730 y, and the age of the sandals is 9.0×10^3 y. Substitute into the equation

$$\ln \frac{N_t}{N_o} = \frac{-0.693\,t}{t_{1/2}} = \frac{-0.693\,(9.0 \times 10^3 \text{ y})}{5730 \text{ y}} = -1.\underline{0}88$$

Taking the antilog of both sides, you obtain

$$\frac{N_t}{N_o} = \frac{(\text{activity})_t}{(\text{activity})_o} = e^{-1.088} = 0.3\underline{3}67$$

Therefore, the activity for a gram sample is

$$(\text{activity})_t = 15.3 \text{ disintegrations/(min} \bullet \text{g)} \times 0.3\underline{3}67 = 5.\underline{1}519 \text{ disintegrations/(min} \bullet \text{g)}$$

$$= 5.2 \text{ disintegrations/(min} \bullet \text{g)}$$

20.79. $\Delta m = \dfrac{\Delta E}{c^2} = \dfrac{-393.5 \times 10^3 \text{ J}}{(3.00 \times 10^8 \text{ m/s})^2} = \dfrac{-3.935 \times 10^5 \text{ kg} \bullet \text{m}^2 / \text{s}^2}{(3.00 \times 10^8 \text{ m/s})^2}$

$$= -4.3\underline{7}2 \times 10^{-12} = -4.37 \times 10^{-12} \text{ kg} = -4.37 \times 10^{-9} \text{ g}$$

20.81. First, determine the nuclear masses.

Nuclear mass of $_1^2H$ = 2.01400 amu − 0.000549 amu = 2.013451 amu

Nuclear mass of $_1^3H$ = 3.01605 amu − 0.000549 amu = 3.015501 amu

Nuclear mass of $_2^4He$ = 4.00260 amu − (2 × 0.000549 amu) = 4.001502 amu

Write the appropriate nuclear mass below each nuclide symbol, and calculate Δm.

$$_1^2H + _1^3H \rightarrow \quad _2^4He + _0^1n$$

Masses: 2.013451   3.015501   4.001502   1.008665 amu

Δm = (4.001502 + 1.008665 − 2.013451 − 3.015501) amu = −0.018785 amu

The energy change for 1 mol is

$$\Delta E = (\Delta m)c^2 = (-0.018785 \times 10^{-3} \text{ kg})(2.998 \times 10^8 \text{ m/s})^2$$

$$= -1.68839 \times 10^{12} \text{ kg} \bullet \text{m}^2/\text{s}^2 = -1.688 \times 10^{12} \text{ J}$$

Finally, calculate the energy change in MeV for one $_1^2H$ nucleus.

$$\frac{-1.68839 \times 10^{12} \text{ J}}{1 \text{ mol}} \times \frac{1 \text{ mol}}{6.022 \times 10^{23} \text{ nuclei}} \times \frac{1 \text{ MeV}}{1.602 \times 10^{-13} \text{ J}} = -17.501 = -17.50 \text{ MeV}$$

20.83. Mass of three protons = 3 × 1.00728 amu = 3.02184 amu

Mass of three neutrons = 3 × 1.008665 amu = 3.025995 amu

Total mass of nucleons = (3.02184 + 3.025995) amu = 6.047835 amu

Nuclear mass of $_3^6Li$ = 6.01512 amu − (3 × 0.000549 amu) = 6.013473 amu

Mass defect = total nucleon mass − nuclear mass = (6.047835 − 6.013473) amu

$$= 0.034362 = 0.03436 \text{ amu}$$

$$\Delta E = (\Delta m)c^2 = 0.034362 \text{ amu} \times \frac{1 \text{ g}}{6.022 \times 10^{23} \times 1 \text{ amu}} \times \frac{1 \text{ kg}}{10^3 \text{ g}}$$

$$\times (2.998 \times 10^8 \text{ m/s})^2 \times \frac{1 \text{ MeV}}{1.602 \times 10^{-13} \text{ J}} = 32.013 \text{ MeV}$$

Binding energy per nucleon = $\frac{32.013 \text{ MeV}}{6 \text{ nucleons}}$ = 5.3356 = 5.336 MeV/nucleon

■ SOLUTIONS TO GENERAL PROBLEMS

20.85. Na-20, having fewer neutrons than the stable Na-23, is expected to decay to a nucleus with a lower atomic number (and hence a higher N/Z ratio) by electron capture or positron emission. Na-26, having more neutrons than the stable isotope, is expected to decay by beta emission to give a nucleus with a higher atomic number (and hence a lower N/Z ratio).

20.87. The overall reaction may be written

$$_{92}^{235}U \rightarrow \; _{82}^{207}Pb \; + n \; _{2}^{4}He \; + m \; _{-1}^{0}e$$

From the superscripts:

$$235 = 207 + (n \times 4) + (m \times 0)$$

$$n = \frac{235 - 207}{4} = 7$$

From the subscripts, and with n equal to 7, you get

$$92 = 82 + (n \times 2) + m \times (-1)$$

$$m = 82 - 92 + (7 \times 2) = 4$$

Therefore, there are seven α emissions and four β emissions.

20.89. $_{83}^{209}Bi \; + \; _{2}^{4}He \; \rightarrow \; _{85}^{A}At \; + 2 \; _{0}^{1}n$

From the superscripts: $209 + 4 = A + (2 \times 1)$, or $A = 213 - 2 = 211$.

The reaction is

$$_{83}^{209}Bi \; + \; _{2}^{4}He \; \rightarrow \; _{85}^{211}At \; + 2 \; _{0}^{1}n$$

20.91. $_{92}^{238}U \; + \; _{6}^{12}C \; \rightarrow \; _{Z}^{A}X \; + 4 \; _{0}^{1}n$

From the superscripts: $238 + 12 = A + (4 \times 1)$, or $A = 250 - 4 = 246$; from the subscripts: $92 + 6 = Z + (4 \times 0)$, or $Z = 98$.

The element with $Z = 98$ is californium (Cf), so the equation is

$$_{92}^{238}U \; + \; _{6}^{12}C \; \rightarrow \; _{98}^{246}Cf \; + 4 \; _{0}^{1}n$$

20.93. Use the equation for the number of nuclei in a sample after a time, t.

$$\frac{N_t}{N_o} = \frac{-0.693 \; t}{t_{1/2}}$$

Rearrange this to give an expression for t.

$$t = \frac{t_{1/2}}{0.693} \ln \frac{N_o}{N_t}$$

Substituting yields

$$t = \frac{(12.3 \text{ y})}{0.693} \ln \frac{N_o}{0.70 \; N_o} = 6.\underline{3}2 = 6.3 \text{ y}$$

20.95. In the annihilation, the final mass is zero; that is, all mass is converted to energy. Therefore,

$$\Delta m = 0 - \text{mass of positron} - \text{mass of electron}$$

$$= -2(0.000549 \text{ amu}) \times \frac{1 \text{ g}}{6.022 \times 10^{23} \text{ amu}} \times \frac{1 \text{ kg}}{10^3 \text{ g}} = -1.8\underline{2}33 \times 10^{-30} \text{ kg}$$

The energy of each photon is $-\Delta E/2$.

$$E_{photon} = \frac{-\Delta E}{2} = \frac{-(\Delta m)c^2}{2} = \frac{-(-1.8233 \times 10^{-30}\ kg)(2.998 \times 10^8\ m/s)^2}{2} = 8.1939 \times 10^{-14}\ J$$

The energy of a photon is related to its wavelength by the equation

$$E = \frac{hc}{\lambda}$$

where h is Planck's constant. Therefore,

$$\lambda = \frac{hc}{E} = \frac{(6.626 \times 10^{-34}\ J \cdot s)(2.998 \times 10^8\ m/s)}{(8.1939 \times 10^{-14}\ J)} = 2.4243 \times 10^{-12} = 2.42 \times 10^{-12}\ m$$

The wavelength of the photons is 2.42 pm.

20.97. First, determine the nuclear masses of each of the nuclei:

Nuclear mass of $^{235}_{92}U$ = 235.04392 amu − (92 × 0.000549 amu) = 234.993412 amu

Nuclear mass of $^{136}_{53}I$ = 135.8401 amu − (53 × 0.000549 amu) = 135.811003 amu

Nuclear mass of $^{96}_{39}Y$ = 95.8629 amu − (39 × 0.000549 amu) = 95.841489 amu

Write the appropriate nuclear mass below each nuclide symbol, and calculate Δm.

$$^1_0n \quad + \quad ^{235}_{92}U \quad \rightarrow \quad ^{136}_{53}I \quad + \quad ^{96}_{39}Y \quad + \quad 4\,^1_0n$$

Masses: 1.008665   234.993412   135.811003   95.841489   1.008665 amu

$$\Delta m = [135.811003 + 95.841489 + 4 \times 1.008665 - (1.008665 + 234.993412)]\ amu$$

$$= -0.314925\ amu$$

When 1 mol of U-235 undergoes fission, the change in mass is −0.314925 g. Therefore, for 5.00 kg of U-235, the change in mass is

$$5.00 \times 10^3\ g\ U\text{-}235 \times \frac{1\ mol\ U\text{-}235}{235.04392\ g\ U\text{-}235} \times \frac{-0.314925\ g}{1\ mol\ U\text{-}235} = -6.699\ g$$

Converting mass to energy gives

$$E = (\Delta m)c^2 = (-6.699 \times 10^{-3}\ kg)(2.998 \times 10^8\ m/s)^2 = -6.021 \times 10^{14}\ J$$

For the combustion of carbon:

$$C(graphite) \quad + \quad O_2(g) \quad \rightarrow \quad CO_2(g)$$

ΔH_f^o 0   0   -394 kJ/mol

For the reaction, $\Delta H = \Delta E = -394$ kJ/mol.

$$5.00 \times 10^3\ g \times \frac{1\ mol\ C}{12.01\ g\ C} \times \frac{-394\ kJ}{1\ mol\ C} = -1.64029 \times 10^5 = -1.64 \times 10^5\ kJ$$

The energy released in the fission of 5.00 kg of U-235 (6.02×10^{11} kJ) is more than 3 million times larger than the energy released by burning 5.00 kg of C (1.64×10^5 kJ).

20.99. a. The balanced equation is

$$^{47}_{20}\text{Ca} \rightarrow\ ^{47}_{21}\text{Sc} +\ ^{0}_{-1}\beta$$

b. Use the rate law to find the initial amount. The time is 48 h (2.0 d), and the half-life is 4.536 d. Substituting

$$\ln\frac{N_t}{N_o} = -kt = \frac{-0.693\ t}{t_{1/2}} = \frac{-0.693\ (2.0\ \text{d})}{4.536\ \text{d}} = -0.3055$$

Taking the antilog of each side gives

$$\frac{N_t}{N_o} = \frac{A_t}{A_o} = e^{-0.3055} = 0.7367$$

Since A_t is 10.0 μg, you can solve for A_o.

$$A_o = \frac{10.0\ \mu\text{g}}{0.7367} = 13.57 = 14\ \mu\text{g Ca-47}$$

Convert this to mass of $^{47}\text{CaSO}_4$.

$$13.57\ \mu\text{g Ca-47} \times \frac{143.07\ \text{g CaSO}_4}{47\ \text{g Ca}} = 41.31 = 41\ \mu\text{g}\ (4.1 \times 10^{-5}\ \text{g})$$

20.101. a. The balanced equations are

$$^{82}_{35}\text{Br} \rightarrow\ ^{82}_{36}\text{Kr} +\ ^{0}_{-1}\beta$$

$$2\text{H}\,^{82}_{35}\text{Br}\,(g) \rightarrow \text{H}_2 + 2\,^{82}_{36}\text{Kr} + 2\,^{0}_{-1}\beta$$

b. Use the rate law to find the fraction remaining. The time is 10.0 h (0.4167 d), and the half-life is 1.471 d. Substituting yields

$$\ln\frac{N_t}{N_o} = -kt = \frac{-0.693\ t}{t_{1/2}} = \frac{-0.693\ (0.4167\ \text{d})}{1.471\ \text{d}} = -0.1963$$

Taking the antilog of each side gives

$$\frac{N_t}{N_o} = \frac{A_t}{A_o} = e^{-0.1963} = 0.8218$$

Therefore, the number of moles of $\text{H}\,^{82}_{35}\text{Br}$ remaining after 10.0 h is

$$A_t = 0.0150\ \text{mol} \times 0.8218 = 0.01233 = 0.0123\ \text{mol}$$

The reaction can be summarized as follows:

$$\begin{array}{ccccc} 2\text{HBr} & \rightarrow & \text{H}_2 & + & 2\text{Kr} \\ 0.0150 - 2y & & y & & 2y \end{array}$$

From this, you can determine y.

$$0.0150\ \text{mol} - 2y = 0.01233\ \text{mol, or } y = 0.00134\ \text{mol}$$

To calculate the pressure in the flask, you need the total moles of gas. This is

$$\text{Total moles} = \text{mol H}\,^{82}_{35}\text{Br} + \text{mol H}_2 + \text{mol Kr} = (0.0150 - 2y) + y + 2y$$

$$= 0.0150 + y = 0.0150 + 0.001\underline{3}4 = 0.016\underline{3}4 \text{ mol}$$

Therefore, the pressure in the flask is

$$P = \frac{nRT}{V} = \frac{0.016\underline{3}4 \text{ mol} \times 0.0821 \text{ L} \cdot \text{atm/K} \cdot \text{mol} \times 295 \text{ K}}{1.00 \text{ L}} = 0.39\underline{5}7 = 0.396 \text{ atm}$$

20.103. An alpha particle is a helium-4 nuclide, with two protons and two neutrons. In terms of the shell model, helium has two protons in a $1s$ level and two neutrons in a $1s$ level, both of which are equal to the magic number 2. Thus, it is especially stable.

20.105. Positron emission tomography (PET) is a technique for following biochemical processes within the organs of the human body. Like magnetic resonance imaging, a PET scan produces an image of a two-dimensional slice through a body organ of a patient. The image shows the distribution of some positron-emitting isotope present in a compound that was administered earlier by injection. By comparing the PET scan of the patient with that of a healthy subject, a physician can diagnose the presence or absence of disease. Some isotopes used in PET scans are carbon-11, nitrogen-13, oxygen-15, and flurine-18. All have short half-lives, so the radiation dosage to the patient is minimal.

■ SOLUTIONS TO STRATEGY PROBLEMS

20.107. a. $^{31}_{14}\text{Si} \rightarrow {}^{31}_{15}\text{P} + {}^{A}_{Z}\text{X}$

From the superscripts: $31 = 31 + A$, or $A = 0$; from the subscripts: $14 = 15 + Z$, or $Z = -1$. The missing particle is $^{0}_{-1}\text{X}$, which represents an electron. The reaction is then written

$$^{31}_{14}\text{Si} \rightarrow {}^{31}_{15}\text{P} + {}^{0}_{-1}\text{e}$$

b. $^{44}_{22}\text{Ti} + {}^{A}_{Z}\text{X} \rightarrow {}^{44}_{21}\text{Sc}$

From the superscripts: $44 + A = 44$, or $A = 0$; from the subscripts: $22 + Z = 21$, or $Z = -1$. The missing particle is $^{0}_{-1}\text{X}$, which represents an electron. The reaction is then written

$$^{44}_{22}\text{Ti} + {}^{0}_{-1}\text{e} \rightarrow {}^{44}_{21}\text{Sc}$$

c. $^{252}_{98}\text{Cf} \rightarrow {}^{142}_{56}\text{Ba} + {}^{A}_{Z}\text{X} + 4\,{}^{1}_{0}\text{n}$

From the superscripts: $252 = 142 + A + 4(1)$, or $A = 106$; from the subscripts: $98 = 56 + Z$, or $Z = 42$. The missing particle is $^{106}_{42}\text{X}$. The element with atomic number 42 is molybdenum. The reaction is then written

$$^{252}_{98}\text{Cf} \rightarrow {}^{142}_{56}\text{Ba} + {}^{106}_{42}\text{Mo} + 4\,{}^{1}_{0}\text{n}$$

20.109. a. $^{238}_{94}\text{Pu} \rightarrow {}^{234}_{92}\text{U} + {}^{4}_{2}\text{He}$

b.   Use the first-order rate equation to determine the fraction remaining after 45 y.

$$\ln \frac{N_t}{N_o} = -kt = \frac{-0.693\,t}{t_{1/2}} = \frac{-0.693\,(45 \text{ y})}{87.7 \text{ y}} = -0.3\underline{5}56$$

Taking the antilog of each side gives

$$\frac{N_t}{N_o} = \frac{A_t}{A_o} = e^{-0.3556} = 0.7\underline{00}$$

Therefore, the mass remaining after 45 y is

$$A_t = 250.0 \text{ g} \times 0.7\underline{00} = 1\underline{7}5.2 = 1.8 \times 10^2 \text{ g}$$

20.111. a.   Rn-222 has an atomic number of 86. Nuclides with atomic numbers above 83 decay by alpha emission.

b.   The equation for the decay is

$$^{222}_{86}\text{Rn} \rightarrow {}^{218}_{84}\text{Po} + {}^4_2\text{He}$$

c.   Use the first-order rate equation to determine the fraction remaining after 15.0 d.

$$\ln\frac{N_t}{N_o} = -kt = \frac{-0.693\,t}{t_{1/2}} = \frac{-0.693\,(15.0 \text{ d})}{3.82 \text{ d}} = -2.7\underline{2}12$$

Taking the antilog of each side gives

$$\frac{N_t}{N_o} = \frac{A_t}{A_o} = e^{-2.7212} = 0.065\underline{7}95$$

Therefore, the mass remaining after 15.0 d is

$$A_t = 150.0 \text{ g} \times 0.065795 = 9.8\underline{6}9 = 9.87 \text{ g}$$

20.113. Use the equation for the number of nuclei in a sample after a time, t.

$$\ln\frac{N_t}{N_o} = -kt = \frac{-0.693\,t}{t_{1/2}}$$

Rearrange this to give an expression for t.

$$t = \frac{t_{1/2}}{0.693}\ln\frac{N_o}{N_t} = \frac{57 \text{ h}}{0.693}\ln\frac{N_o}{0.25N_o} \times \frac{1 \text{ d}}{24 \text{ h}} = 4.\underline{7}5 = 4.8 \text{ days}$$

20.115. The rate of a radioactive decay process is given by

$$\text{Rate} = kN_t = \frac{0.693\,N_t}{t_{1/2}} = \frac{0.693\,m_t}{M_m t_{1/2}}$$

Because the isotopes are different and have different molar masses (M_m), the appropriate ratio for the comparison of the different masses is $m_t/M_m t_{1/2}$. Since pile A has twice the mass of pile B, if the half-life multiplied by the atomic mass of radioactive substance A is twice the half-life multiplied by the atomic mass of radioactive substance B, the rates of decay will be the same for both piles.

20.117. a.   Converting any 1.0-g mass directly to energy gives

$$\Delta E = (\Delta m)c^2 = (-1.0 \times 10^{-3} \text{ kg})(2.998 \times 10^8 \text{ m/s})^2$$
$$= -8.\underline{9}8 \times 10^{13} = -9.0 \times 10^{13} \text{ J} = -9.0 \times 10^{10} \text{ kJ}$$

b. For the combustion of a 1.0-g sample of graphite:

$$C(graphite) \quad + \quad O_2(g) \quad \rightarrow \quad CO_2(g)$$

$$\Delta H_f° \qquad 0 \qquad\qquad\quad 0 \qquad\qquad\qquad\qquad -394 \text{ kJ/mol}$$

For the reaction, $\Delta H = \Delta E = -394$ kJ/mol.

$$1.0 \text{ g C} \times \frac{1 \text{ mol C}}{12.01 \text{ g C}} \times \frac{-394 \text{ kJ}}{1 \text{ mol C}} = -3\underline{2}.8 = -3.3 \times 10^1 \text{ kJ}$$

c. $-8.9\underline{8} \times 10^{10} \text{ kJ} \times \dfrac{1 \text{ g C}}{-32.8 \text{kJ}} \times \dfrac{1 \text{ g coal}}{1 \text{ g C}} = 2.7\underline{4} \times 10^9 = 2.7 \times 10^9 \text{ g coal} = 2.7 \times 10^6 \text{ kg coal}$

20.119. a. Rn-222 has an atomic number of 86. Nuclides with atomic numbers above 83 decay by alpha emission. The equation for the decay is

$$^{222}_{86}\text{Rn} \rightarrow {}^{218}_{84}\text{Po} + {}^{4}_{2}\text{He}$$

a. $k = \dfrac{0.693}{t_{1/2}} = \dfrac{0.693}{3.82 \text{ d}} \times \dfrac{1 \text{ d}}{24 \text{ h}} \times \dfrac{1 \text{ h}}{3600 \text{ s}} = 2.0\underline{9}97 \times 10^{-6} = 2.10 \times 10^{-6}/\text{s}$

c. Because an activity of 1.0 Ci is 3.7×10^{10} nuclei/s, the rate of decay in this 1-L sample is

$$\text{Rate} = 4 \times 10^{-12} \text{ Ci} \times \frac{3.7 \times 10^{10} \text{ nuclei/s}}{1.0 \text{ Ci}} = 0.\underline{1}48 \text{ nuclei/s}$$

Since the rate, R, equals kN_t, we can calculate the number of nuclei in the 1-L sample using the rate constant found in part b.

$$N_t = \frac{R}{k} = \frac{0.\underline{1}48 \text{ nuclei/s}}{2.0\underline{9}97 \times 10^{-6}/\text{s}} = \underline{7}.04 \times 10^4 \text{ nuclei}$$

Finally the mass of $^{222}_{86}\text{Rn}$ in the 1-L sample is determined.

$$\underline{7}.04 \times 10^4 \text{ nuclei} \times \frac{1 \text{ mol Rn-222}}{6.022 \times 10^{23} \text{ nuclei}} \times \frac{222 \text{ g Rn-222}}{1 \text{ mol Rn-222}} = \underline{2}.6 \times 10^{-17} = 3 \times 10^{-17} \text{ g Rn-222}$$

20.121. Cf-251 has an atomic number of 98. Nuclides with atomic numbers above 83 decay by alpha emission. The equation for the decay is

$$^{251}_{98}\text{Cf} \rightarrow {}^{247}_{96}\text{Cm} + {}^{4}_{2}\text{He}$$

■ SOLUTIONS TO CUMULATIVE-SKILLS PROBLEMS

20.123. Calculate the number of P-32 nuclei in the sample (N_t). For this, you need the formula mass of Na_3PO_4 containing 15.6% of P-32 and $(100.0 - 15.6)\% = 84.4\%$ naturally occurring P. The formula mass of Na_3PO_4 containing naturally occurring P is 163.9 amu; the formula mass of Na_3PO_4 with 100% P-32 is 165.0. The formula mass of Na_3PO_4 containing 15.6% P-32 is obtained from the weighted average of the formula masses:

$$(163.9 \text{ amu} \times 0.844) + (165.0 \text{ amu} \times 0.156) = 16\underline{4}.1 \text{ amu}$$

The moles of P in the sample equal

$$0.0545 \text{ g Na}_3\text{PO}_4 \times \frac{1 \text{ mol Na}_3\text{PO}_4}{164.1 \text{ g Na}_3\text{PO}_4} \times \frac{1 \text{ mol P}}{1 \text{ mol Na}_3\text{PO}_4} = 3.3\underline{2}1 \times 10^{-4} \text{ mol P}$$

and the moles of P-32 equal

$$(3.321 \times 10^{-4} \text{ mol P}) \times 0.156 = 5.1\underline{8}1 \times 10^{-5} \text{ mol P-32}$$

Then, the number of P-32 nuclei is

$$(5.181 \times 10^{-5} \text{ mol P-32}) \times \frac{6.022 \times 10^{23} \text{ P-32 nuclei}}{1 \text{ mol P-32}} = 3.1\underline{2}0 \times 10^{19} \text{ P-32 nuclei}$$

Now, calculate the rate of disintegrations. Because the rate $= kN_t$, first find the value of k in reciprocal seconds:

$$k = \frac{0.693}{t_{1/2}} = \frac{0.693}{14.3 \text{ d}} \times \frac{1 \text{ d}}{24 \text{ h}} \times \frac{1 \text{ h}}{3600 \text{ s}} = 5.6\underline{0}9 \times 10^{-7} \text{ /s}$$

Therefore, the rate of disintegrations is

$$\text{Rate} = kN_t = (5.609 \times 10^{-7}/\text{s}) \times (3.120 \times 10^{19} \text{ P-32 nuclei}) = 1.7\underline{5}0 \times 10^{13}$$

$$= 1.75 \times 10^{13} \text{ P-32 nuclei/s}$$

20.125. First, determine the mass of polonium-210 nuclei in 1.0000 g of PoO_2.

$$1.0000 \text{ g PoO}_2 \times \frac{210 \text{ g Po}}{242 \text{ g PoO}_2} = 0.86\underline{7}768 \text{ g Po-210}$$

Use the rate law to find the fraction of polonium-210 that decayed. The time is 48.0 h (2.00 d), and the half-life is 138.4 d. Substituting

$$\ln \frac{N_t}{N_o} = -kt = \frac{-0.693 \, t}{t_{1/2}} = \frac{-0.693 \, (2.00 \text{ d})}{138.4 \text{ d}} = -0.0100\underline{1}4$$

Take the antilog of each side to get the fraction of polonium-210 remaining.

$$\frac{N_t}{N_o} = e^{-0.010014} = 0.99\underline{0}035$$

Thus, the fraction of polonium-210 that decayed is $1 - 0.99\underline{0}035 = 0.00\underline{9}964$. This can now be converted to moles of helium formed.

$$0.86\underline{7}768 \text{ g Po} \times 0.00\underline{9}964 \times \frac{1 \text{ mol Po}}{210 \text{ g Po}} \times \frac{1 \text{ mol He}}{1 \text{ mol Po}} = \underline{4}.117 \times 10^{-5} \text{ mol He}$$

Now, calculate the volume of He at 25°C and 735 mmHg.

$$V = \frac{nRT}{P} = \frac{(4.117 \times 10^{-5} \text{ mol})(0.0821 \text{ L} \cdot \text{atm}/(\text{K} \cdot \text{mol})(298 \text{ K})}{(735/760) \text{ atm}} = 0.00\underline{1}04 = 0.001 \text{ L} = 1 \text{ mL}$$

20.127. $2p + 2n \rightarrow {}^{4}_{2}He$

Nuclear mass of ${}^{4}_{2}He = 4.00260$ amu $- (2 \times 0.000549$ amu$) = 4.001502$ amu

On a mole basis, the mass difference, Δm, is

$\Delta m = [4.001502 - 2(1.00728) - 2(1.00867)]$ g/mol $= -0.030398$ g/mol

$\qquad = -3.0398 \times 10^{-5}$ kg/mol

The energy evolved per mole is

$\Delta E = (\Delta m)c^2 = -3.0398 \times 10^{-5}$ kg/mol $\times (2.998 \times 10^8$ m/s$)^2$

$\qquad = -2.7321 \times 10^{12}$ kg•m^2/s^2 /mol $= -2.7321 \times 10^{12}$ J/mol

$\qquad = 2.732 \times 10^{12}$ J evolved per mole

Next calculate $\Delta H°$ for burning of ethane:

$C_2H_6(g) + 7/2O_2(g) \rightarrow \qquad 2CO_2(g) + \qquad 3H_2O(g)$

$\Delta H_f° = -84.68 \qquad\qquad 0 \qquad\quad 2(-393.5) \qquad 3(-241.8)$ kJ

$\Delta H° = [2(-393.5) + 3(-241.8) - (-84.68)]$ kJ $\qquad = (-1427.72)$ kJ/mol ethane

Now calculate the moles of ethane needed to obtain 2.7321×10^{12} J, or 2.7321×10^9 kJ heat:

-2.7321×10^9 kJ $\times \dfrac{1 \text{ mol ethane}}{-1427.72 \text{ kJ}} = 1.9136 \times 10^6$ mol ethane

Finally, convert moles to liters at 25°C and 725 mmHg.

$V = \dfrac{nRT}{P} = \dfrac{(1.9136 \times 10^6 \text{ mol}) [0.0821 \text{ L•atm}/(\text{K•mol})] (298 \text{ K})}{(725/760) \text{ atm}} = 4.907 \times 10^7 = 4.91 \times 10^7$ L

CHAPTER 21

Chemistry of the Main-Group Elements

■ ANSWERS TO CONCEPT CHECKS

21.1.   Given the high energy needs of animals to move and maintain body temperature, breaking the very strong triple bond of N_2 requires too much energy compared to the lower-energy double bond of O_2.

21.2.   The only intermolecular forces in these materials are very weak van der Waals forces.

■ ANSWERS TO SELF-ASSESSMENT AND REVIEW QUESTIONS

21.1.   An alloy is a material with metallic properties that is either a compound or a mixture. If the alloy is a mixture, it may be homogeneous (a solution) or heterogeneous. Gold jewelry is made from an alloy that is a solid solution of gold containing some silver.

21.2.   A metal is a material that is lustrous (shiny), has high electrical and heat conductivities, and is malleable and ductile.

21.3.   A rock is a naturally occurring solid material composed of one or more minerals. A mineral is a naturally occurring inorganic solid substance or solid solution with a definite crystalline structure. An ore is a rock or mineral from which a metal or nonmetal can be economically produced. Bauxite, the principal ore of aluminum, is a rock.

21.4.   The basic steps in the production of a pure metal from a natural source follow. (1) Preliminary treatment: separating the metal-containing mineral from the less desirable parts of the ore. The mineral may also be transformed by chemical reaction to a metal compound that is more easily reduced to the free metal. (2) Reduction: The metal compound is reduced to the free metal by electrolysis or chemical reduction. (3) Refining: The free metal is purified.

(1) Preliminary treatment: Aluminum oxide is obtained from bauxite by the Bayer process. Bauxite contains aluminum hydroxide, aluminum oxide hydroxide, and other worthless constituents. It is mixed with hot, aqueous sodium hydroxide solution, which dissolves the amphoteric aluminum minerals along with some silicates. When the solution is cooled, $Al(OH)_3$ precipitates, leaving the silicates behind. The aluminum hydroxide is finally calcined (heated strongly in a furnace) to produce purified aluminum oxide, Al_2O_3. (2) Reduction: Aluminum is then obtained by reduction using the Hall-Héroult process, which is the electrolysis of a molten mixture of aluminum oxide in cryolyte (Na_3AlF_6). (3) Refining: The aluminum can be further refined and purified.

21.5.   Lead is obtained from its sulfide ore by roasting, which forms lead(II) oxide. It is then heated with coke in a blast furnace, where it is reduced to lead metal.

21.6.   (1) Iron oxide is reduced to iron using coke and limestone. The molten iron flows to the bottom of the blast furnace while carbon dioxide gas escapes. Impurities in the iron react with the calcium oxide from the limestone and produce slag, which floats to the top. (2) The Mond process is a chemical procedure that depends on the formation, and later decomposition, of a volatile compound of the metal (nickel tetracarbonyl). The compound decomposes over pellets of pure nickel heated to 230°C. (3) Copper is purified by electrolysis using a pure copper negative electrode. Electrons from the impure copper positive electrode flow to the positive pole of the battery, leaving copper(II) ions behind in the solution. These electrons replace the ones that plate out on the pure copper electrode, enlarging it.

21.7.   The Dow process use seashells ($CaCO_3$) as a source of the base. When heated, calcium carbonate decomposes to calcium oxide (CaO) and carbon dioxide (CO_2).

$$CaCO_3(s) \xrightarrow{\Delta} CaO(s) + CO_2(g)$$

The calcium oxide reacts with water to produce calcium hydroxide, the base.

$$CaO(s) + H_2O(l) \longrightarrow Ca(OH)_2(aq)$$

The calcium hydroxide reacts with the magnesium ion in seawater to form a magnesium hydroxide precipitate.

$$Ca(OH)_2(aq) + Mg^{2+}(aq) \longrightarrow Mg(OH)_2(s) + Ca^{2+}(aq)$$

The magnesium hydroxide is then treated with hydrochloric acid (HCl) to yield magnesium chloride.

$$Mg(OH)_2(s) + 2HCl(aq) \longrightarrow MgCl_2(aq) + 2H_2O(l)$$

The dry magnesium chloride is melted and electrolyzed at 700°C to yield the metal.

$$MgCl_2(l) \rightarrow Mg(l) + Cl_2(g)$$

21.8.   The flowchart for the preparation of aluminum from its ore (bauxite) follows.

(1)   Preliminary treatment (the Bayer process): Mix the ore with hot $NaOH(aq)$. Cool and filter the $Al(OH)_3$ precipitate. Heat the precipitate in a furnace to convert to Al_2O_3.

(2)   Reduction (the Hall-Héroult process): Melt a mixture of Al_2O_3 with cryolyte produced from $Al(OH)_3$ by the reaction

$$Al(OH)_3(s) + 3NaOH(aq) + 6HF(aq) \longrightarrow Na_3AlF_6(aq) + 6H_2O(l)$$

The electrolytic cell has carbon electrodes and a molten cryolyte electrolyte, at about 1000°C, into which some aluminum oxide is dissolved. The reaction is

$$2Al_2O_3(s) + 3C(sq) \xrightarrow{electrolysis} 4Al(l) + 3CO_2(g)$$

21.9.   In a metal, the outer orbits of an enormous number of metal atoms overlap to form an enormous number of molecular orbitals that are delocalized over the metal. As a result, a large number of energy levels are crowded together into bands. These bands are half-filled with electrons. When a voltage is applied to the metal crystal, electrons are excited to the unoccupied orbitals and move toward the positive pole of the voltage source. This is electrical conductivity.

21.10. The mineral source is given after the name of the metal: lithium–lithium aluminum silicate; sodium–sodium chloride; magnesium–seawater (Dow process) and dolomite or magnesite; calcium–calcium oxide; aluminum–bauxite; tin–cassiterite; and lead–galena.

21.11. The reactions are

$$2Li(s) + 2H_2O(l) \rightarrow 2LiOH(aq) + H_2(g)$$

$$4Li(s) + O_2(g) \rightarrow 2Li_2O(s)$$

$$2Na(s) + 2H_2O(l) \rightarrow 2NaOH(aq) + H_2(g)$$

$$2Na(s) + O_2(g) \rightarrow Na_2O_2(s)$$

21.12. The reaction is similar to that of lithium carbonate with calcium hydroxide:

$$Li_2CO_3(aq) + Ba(OH)_2(aq) \rightarrow 2LiOH(aq) + BaCO_3(s)$$

21.13. Potassium is expected to be more reactive than lithium because metals become more reactive going down Group IA. This is partly because potassium is much larger, so its $4s$ electron is lost more readily than the $2s$ electron of lithium.

21.14. The reaction is $2Na(s) + 2C_2H_5OH(l) \rightarrow H_2(g) + 2NaOC_2H_5(aq)$.

21.15. a.   Cathode reaction: $Na^+(l) + e^- \rightarrow Na(l)$

Anode reaction: $2Cl^-(l) \rightarrow Cl_2(g) + 2e^-$

b.   Cathode reaction: $Na^+(l) + e^- \rightarrow Na(l)$

Anode reaction: $4OH^-(aq) \rightarrow O_2(g) + 2H_2O(g) + 4e^-$

21.16. Sodium hydroxide is manufactured by the electrolysis of aqueous sodium chloride, which also produces chlorine gas as a major product.

21.17. The uses are given after each compound: sodium chloride–used for making sodium hydroxide and in seasoning; sodium hydroxide–used in aluminum production and in producing sodium compounds such as soap; and sodium carbonate–used to make glass and as washing soda with many detergent preparations.

21.18. The main step in the Solvay process involves the reaction of carbon dioxide with ammonia and sodium chloride to form sodium bicarbonate:

$$NH_3(g) + H_2O(l) + CO_2(g) + NaCl(aq) \rightarrow NaHCO_3(s) + NH_4Cl(aq)$$

21.19. $2Mg(s) + O_2(g) \rightarrow 2MgO(s)$

$Mg(s) + H_2O(g) \rightarrow MgO(s) + H_2(g)$

$2Mg(s) + CO_2(g) \rightarrow 2MgO(s) + C(s)$

21.20. a.   Calcium oxide is prepared industrially from calcium carbonate:

$$CaCO_3(s) \rightarrow CaO(s) + CO_2(g)$$

b.   Calcium hydroxide is prepared from the reaction of calcium oxide and water:

$$CaO(s) + H_2O(l) \rightarrow Ca(OH)_2(aq)$$

21.21. $CaCO_3(s) + 2HCl(aq) \rightarrow CO_2(g) + CaCl_2(aq) + H_2O(l)$

21.22. $Ca(OH)_2 + CO_2(g) \rightarrow CaCO_3(s) + H_2O(l)$

$Ca(OH)_2 + Na_2CO_3(aq) \rightarrow CaCO_3(s) + 2NaOH(aq)$

21.23. $Fe_2O_3(s) + 2Al(s) \rightarrow 2Fe(l) + Al_2O_3(s)$

21.24. Some major uses of aluminum oxide: making abrasives for grinding tools, fusing with small amounts of other metal oxides to make synthetic sapphires and rubies, and making industrial ceramics.

21.25. To purify municipal water, aluminum sulfate and calcium hydroxide are added to waste water, forming a gelatinous precipitate of aluminum hydroxide. Colloidal particles of clay (usually present in the waste water) and other substances adhere to the aluminum hydroxide, whose particles are large enough to be filtered from the water to purify it.

21.1. Lead(IV) oxide, PbO_2, is formed by first packing a paste of PbO into the lead metal grids of the storage battery. When the battery is charged at the factory, the PbO is oxidized by electrolysis to PbO_2. This gives the proper cathode for a new battery.

21.27. Lead pigments are no longer used for house paints because of the possibility of lead poisoning. If chips of lead paint are eaten by children, or if the dust from lead paint that has been removed is breathed by adults or children, lead(II) ion can enter the bloodstream. The lead(II) ion can ultimately inhibit the production of red blood cells, causing anemia. (The Pb^{2+} ion can also be absorbed in the brains of children and cause irreversible brain damage.)

21.28. $Pb(NO_3)_2(aq) + CrO_4^{2-}(aq) \rightarrow PbCrO_4(s) + 2NO_3^-(aq)$

21.29. In the steam-reforming process, steam and hydrocarbons from natural gas or petroleum react at high temperature and pressure in the presence of a catalyst to form carbon monoxide and hydrogen. A typical reaction involving propane (C_3H_8) is

$$C_3H_8(g) + 3H_2O(g) \xrightarrow[\Delta]{Ni} 3CO(g) + 7H_2(g)$$

The carbon monoxide is removed from the mixture by reacting with steam in the presence of a catalyst to give carbon dioxide and more hydrogen.

$$CO(g) + H_2O(g) \xrightarrow[\Delta]{catalyst} CO_2(g) + H_2(g)$$

Finally, the carbon dioxide is removed by dissolving it in a basic aqueous solution.

21.30. The three isotopes of hydrogen and their symbols are as follows: protium, ^1_1H, or H, which is most abundant; deuterium, ^2_1H, or D; and tritium, ^3_1H, or T. Tritium is radioactive, with a half-life of 12.3 years.

21.31. The combustion of hydrogen produces more heat per gram than that of any other fuel (120 kJ/g). Unlike hydrocarbons, it is a clean fuel since the product is environmentally benign water. These features, in the face of a dwindling supply of hydrocarbons, indicate that hydrogen gas may become the favorite fuel of the twenty-first century.

21.32. A binary hydride is a compound that contains hydrogen and one other element. There are three categories of binary hydrides. The first type is an ionic hydride, which contains the hydride ion, H^-, and is formed via reaction with an alkali metal or larger Group IIA metal. An example is LiH. A second type is a covalent hydride, which is a molecular compound in which hydrogen is covalently bonded to another element. An example is NH_3. The third type is a metallic hydride formed from a transition metal and hydrogen. These compounds contain hydrogen spread throughout a metal crystal and occupying the holes in the crystal lattice, sometimes in nonstoichiometric amounts. Thus, the composition is variable. An example is $TiH_{1.7}$.

21.33. Catenation is the ability of an atom to bond covalently to like atoms, as in ethylene, $H_2C=CH_2$.

21.34. Carbon monoxide attaches to the iron in the hemoglobin of red blood cells and blocks the combination of hemoglobin with oxygen molecules normally carried by the hemoglobin.

21.35. $CO_2(g) + H_2O(l) \rightleftharpoons H_2CO_3(aq)$

$H_2CO_3(aq) \rightleftharpoons H^+(aq) + HCO_3^-(aq)$

$HCO_3^-(aq) \rightleftharpoons H^+(aq) + CO_3^{2-}(aq)$

21.36. Elementary silicon is obtained by reducing quartz sand (SiO_2) with coke (C) in an electric furnace at 3000°C. The reaction is

$$SiO_2(l) + 2C(s) \longrightarrow Si(l) + 2CO(g)$$

The impure silicon is converted into silicon tetrachloride ($SiCl_4$), which is purified by distillation (b.p. 58°C).

$$Si(s) + 2Cl_2(g) \longrightarrow SiCl_4(g)$$

The purified $SiCl_4$ is reduced by passing the vapor with hydrogen through a hot tube, where pure silicon crystallizes on the tube. In the final step, this polycrystalline silicon is fashioned into a rod that consists of a single crystal from which wafers are cut.

21.37. The condensation reaction between two silicic acid molecules is represented by

21.38. Certain bacteria in the soil and in the roots of plants convert N_2 to ammonium and nitrate compounds. The plants then use these nitrogen compounds to make proteins and other complex nitrogen compounds. Animals eat the plants. Ultimately, the animals die, and bacteria in the decaying organic matter convert the nitrogen compounds back to N_2.

21.39. Rutherford removed oxygen from the air by burning a substance that would combine with the oxygen. He also removed any carbon dioxide formed by the burning by reacting it with KOH. The gas left contained primarily nitrogen, as well as small amounts (< 1%) of noble gases.

21.40.   These oxides are nitrous oxide, N_2O; nitrogen monoxide, NO; N_2O_3; nitrogen dioxide, NO_2; dinitrogen tetroxide, N_2O_4; and N_2O_5. The oxidation numbers in each are +1, +2, +3, +4, +4, and +5, respectively.

21.41.   Natural gas, or CH_4, and steam react to form CO and H_2. The CO is reacted with steam to form CO_2 plus additional H_2. The CO_2 is removed from the H_2 by dissolving it in basic aqueous solution; the H_2 is then reacted with N_2 in the Haber process to form NH_3.

21.42.   Ammonia is burned in the presence of a platinum catalyst to form NO, which is then reacted with O_2 to form NO_2. The NO_2 is dissolved in water to form HNO_3 and NO. The NO is recycled back to the second step to react with more O_2 to form more NO_2.

21.43.   White phosphorus is a molecular solid with the formula P_4. The phosphorus atoms are arranged at the corners of a regular tetrahedron with a 60° P–P–P bond angle, an angle considerably smaller than the normal tetrahedral bond angle. This accounts for the weakness of the P–P bonds and their high reactivity, as stronger bonds such as P–O can replace them.

21.44. $P_4(s) + 5O_2(g) \rightarrow P_4O_{10}(s)$

   $P_4O_{10}(s) + 6H_2O(l) \rightarrow 4H_3PO_4(aq)$

21.45.   The first method is the treatment of $Ca_3(PO_4)_2$ with sulfuric acid, giving phosphoric acid and insoluble calcium sulfate. The second method is the treatment of $Ca_3(PO_4)_2$ with HF, giving phosphoric acid and insoluble calcium fluoride.

21.46.

21.47.   Polyphosphates are added to detergents to form complexes with metal ions and thus prevent their precipitation onto clothes.

21.48.   Priestley prepared oxygen by heating mercury(II) oxide:

   $2HgO(s) \xrightarrow{\Delta} 2Hg(l) + O_2(g)$

21.49.   The most important commercial means of producing oxygen is by distillation of liquid air. Air is filtered to remove dust particles, cooled to freeze out water and carbon dioxide, liquefied, and finally warmed until nitrogen and argon distill, leaving liquid oxygen behind.

21.50.   Oxides are binary oxygen compounds in which oxygen is in the −2 oxidation state, whereas in peroxides, the oxidation number of oxygen is −1 and the anion is O_2^{2-}. In the superoxides, the oxidation number of oxygen is −1/2 and the anion is O_2^-. Examples: H_2O (oxide), H_2O_2 (peroxide), and KO_2 (superoxide).

21.51. CrO_3 is an example of an acidic oxide; Cr_2O_3, MgO, and Fe_3O_4 are basic oxides.

21.52. Three natural sources of sulfur or sulfur compounds are sulfate minerals, sulfide minerals, and coal or petroleum products.

21.53. Rhombic sulfur is a yellow crystalline solid with a lattice consisting of crown-shaped S_8 molecules; that is, eight sulfur atoms are arranged in a crown-shaped ring.

21.54. The monoclinic sulfur allotrope can be prepared from rhombic sulfur by first melting the rhombic sulfur and then cooling it to crystals of monoclinic sulfur. A liquid sulfur allotrope of long spiral chains of sulfur atoms can be prepared by heating rhombic sulfur above 160°C but keeping it below 200°C. Plastic sulfur allotrope can be prepared by pouring this liquid sulfur allotrope into water. Finally, gaseous allotropes of S_8, S_6, S_4, and S_2 molecules can be formed by boiling sulfur at 445°C.

21.55. The Frasch process involves melting sulfur deposits with superheated water, using air to force the melted sulfur upward to the surface, and cooling it to form solid sulfur.

21.56. The initial burning of hydrogen sulfide produces some sulfur as well as sulfur dioxide:

$$8H_2S(g) + 4O_2(g) \rightarrow S_8(s) + 8H_2O(g)$$

$$2H_2S(g) + 3O_2(g) \rightarrow 2SO_2(g) + 2H_2O(g)$$

The sulfur dioxide reacts with hydrogen sulfide to form more sulfur:

$$16H_2S(g) + 8SO_2(g) \rightarrow 3S_8(s) + 16H_2O(g)$$

21.57. a. $2HCl(aq) + ZnS(s) \rightarrow ZnCl_2(aq) + H_2S(g)$

   b. $S_8(s) + 8O_2(g) \rightarrow 8SO_2(g)$

21.58. First step: $S_8(s) + 8O_2(g) \rightarrow 8SO_2(g)$

   Second step: $2SO_2(g) + O_2(g) \rightarrow 2SO_3(g)$

   Third step: $SO_3(g) + H_2O(l) \rightarrow H_2SO_4(aq)$

21.59. a. $16H_2S(g) + 8SO_2(g) \rightarrow 3S_8(s) + 16H_2O(g)$

   b. $Cr_2O_7^{2-}(aq) + 3SO_2(g) + 2H^+(aq) \rightarrow 2Cr^{3+}(aq) + 3SO_4^{2-}(aq) + H_2O(l)$

   c. $Cu(s) + 2H_2SO_4(l) \rightarrow CuSO_4(aq) + 2H_2O(l) + SO_2(g)$

   d. $8Na_2SO_3(aq) + S_8(s) \rightarrow 8Na_2S_2O_3(aq)$

21.60. $4HCl + MnO_2(s) \rightarrow MnCl_2(aq) + Cl_2(g) + 2H_2O(l)$

21.61. a. $I_2(aq) + Cl^-(aq) \rightarrow NR$

   b. $Cl_2(aq) + 2Br^-(aq) \rightarrow Br_2(aq) + 2Cl^-(aq)$

   c. $Br_2(aq) + 2I^-(aq) \rightarrow I_2(s) + 2Br^-(aq)$

   d. $Br_2(aq) + Cl^-(aq) \rightarrow NR$

21.62. Add chlorine water and methylene chloride. For NaCl, there will be no reaction; for NaBr, the lower organic layer will turn orange; and for NaI, the lower organic layer will turn violet.

21.63. Chlorine is used in preparing chlorinated hydrocarbons, as a bleaching agent, and as a disinfectant.

21.64. Sodium hypochlorite is prepared by reacting chlorine with NaOH:

$$Cl_2(g) + 2NaOH(aq) \rightarrow NaClO(aq) + NaCl(aq) + H_2O(l)$$

21.65. Industrially, sodium chloride is electrolyzed to form chlorine gas. The chlorine gas is then heated with sodium hydroxide solution, forming $NaClO_3$ (and NaCl). The ClO_3^- is electrolyzed at the anode to form the ClO_4^- anion. This is mixed with sulfuric acid, and the $HClO_4$ is distilled at reduced pressure (below 92°C) to isolate $HClO_4$.

21.66. Bartlett found that PtF_6 reacted with molecular oxygen. Because the first ionization energy of xenon was slightly less than that of molecular oxygen, he reasoned that PtF_6 ought to react with xenon also.

21.67. The answer is d, I and II only.

21.68. The answer is e, jet fuel.

21.69. The answer is d, phosphoric acid.

21.70. the answer is b, NaClO.

■ ANSWERS TO CONCEPTUAL PROBLEMS

21.71. If air were present, the oxygen in the air would react with the coal (undergo oxidation) by the following equation:

$$C(s) + O_2(g) \rightarrow CO_2(g)$$

21.73. The metallic character decreases from left to right and increases going down a column.

21.75. This means aluminum hydroxide reacts with both acids and bases. For example,

$$Al(OH)_3(s) + 3HCl(aq) \rightarrow 3H_2O(l) + AlCl_3(aq)$$

and

$$Al(OH)_3(s) + NaOH(aq) \rightarrow Na^+(aq) + Al(OH)_4^-(aq)$$

21.77. Oxygen is a very electronegative element, and its bonding involves only the s and p orbitals, in contrast to bonding using the d orbitals in sulfur, etc. Molecular oxygen is a reactive gas, but it forms mainly compounds in which its oxidation state is −2, compared with compounds of sulfur, etc., which exhibit positive oxidation states as well as the −2 state.

21.79. Consulting the table of standard reduction potentials (Appendix I), you find that HBr cannot be prepared by adding sulfuric acid to NaBr because the hot, concentrated acid will oxidize the bromide ion to bromine.

■ SOLUTIONS TO PRACTICE PROBLEMS

Note on significant figures: If the final answer to a solution needs to be rounded off, it is given first with one nonsignificant figure, and the last significant figure is underlined. The final answer is then rounded to the correct number of significant figures. In multistep problems, intermediate answers are given with at least one nonsignificant figure; however, only the final answer has been rounded off.

21.81. $Fe_2O_3(s) + 3H_2(g) \rightarrow 2Fe(s) + 3H_2O(g)$

21.83 In the reaction (Problem 21.81), 3 mol of H_2 are used to form 2 mol of iron. Using the respective atomic masses of 55.85 g/mol for Fe and 2.016 g/mol for H_2, you can calculate the mass of Fe as follows:

$$2.00 \times 10^3 \text{ g } H_2 \times \frac{1 \text{ mol } H_2}{2.016 \text{ g } H_2} \times \frac{2 \text{ mol Fe}}{3 \text{ mol } H_2} \times \frac{55.85 \text{ g Fe}}{1 \text{ mol Fe}}$$

$$= 3.6\underline{9}3 \times 10^4 = 3.69 \times 10^4 \text{ g} = 36.9 \text{ kg Fe}$$

21.85. The equation, with $\Delta H_f°$'s recorded beneath each substance, is

$$PbS(s) + 3/2O_2(g) \rightarrow PbO(s) + SO_2(g)$$

$$\begin{array}{cccc} -98.3 & 0 & -219.4 & -296.8 \text{ (kJ)} \end{array}$$

$$\Delta H° = [(-219.4 + (-296.8) - (-98.3)] \text{ kJ} = -417.9 \text{ kJ (exothermic)}$$

21.87. The energy levels in potassium metal are

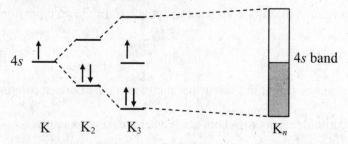

21.89. The number of sodium atoms in a 1.00-mg crystal of sodium is

$$1.00 \times 10^{-3} \text{ g Na} \times \frac{1 \text{ mol Na}}{22.99 \text{ g Na}} \times \frac{6.02 \times 10^{23} \text{ Na atoms}}{1 \text{ mol Na}} = 2.6\underline{1}8 \times 10^{19} \text{ Na atoms}$$

Each sodium atom contributes an energy level for the 3s orbital to the valence band, so the number of energy levels in the valence band is 2.62×10^{19}.

21.91. $CO_2(g) + NH_3(g) + NaCl(aq) + H_2O(l) \xrightarrow{\Delta} NaHCO_3(s) + NH_4Cl(aq)$

$2NaHCO_3(s) \rightarrow Na_2CO_3(s) + CO_2(g) + H_2O(g)$

$Na_2CO_3(aq) + Ca(OH)_2(aq) \rightarrow 2NaOH(aq) + CaCO_3(s)$

21.93.   a. $2K(s) + Br_2(l) \rightarrow 2KBr(s)$

      b. $2K(s) + 2H_2O(l) \rightarrow 2KOH(aq) + H_2(g)$

      c. $2NaOH(s) + CO_2(g) \rightarrow Na_2CO_3(s) + H_2O(l)$

      d. $Li_2CO_3(aq) + 2HNO_3(aq) \rightarrow H_2O(l) + 2LiNO_3(aq) + CO_2(g)$

      e. $K_2SO_4(aq) + Pb(NO_3)_2(aq) \rightarrow PbSO_4(s) + 2KNO_3(aq)$

21.95. $^{227}_{89}Ac \rightarrow \, ^{223}_{87}Fr + \, ^{4}_{2}He$

21.97. $Ca(OH)_2$ can be identified directly by adding an anion that will precipitate the Ca^{2+} (and not the Na^+). For example, adding CO_3^{2-} will precipitate $CaCO_3$ but will not precipitate Na^+ ion.

21.99. $BaCl_2$ can be separated by adding SO_4^{2-} ion, precipitating $BaSO_4$ and leaving $MgCl_2$ in solution because it is soluble (see Table 4.1). Filtering the solution will separate the $BaSO_4$. The filtrate contains soluble $MgCl_2$.

21.101. $^{230}_{90}Th \rightarrow \, ^{226}_{88}Ra + \, ^{4}_{2}He$

21.103.   a. $BaCO_3(s) \xrightarrow{\Delta} BaO(s) + CO_2(g)$

      b. $Ba(s) + 2H_2O(l) \rightarrow Ba(OH)_2(aq) + H_2(g)$

      c. $Mg(OH)_2(s) + 2HNO_3(aq) \rightarrow 2H_2O(l) + Mg(NO_3)_2(aq)$

      d. $Mg(s) + NiCl_2(aq) \rightarrow Ni(s) + MgCl_2(aq)$

      e. $2NaOH(aq) + MgSO_4(aq) \rightarrow Mg(OH)_2(s) + Na_2SO_4(aq)$

21.105.   The equation is $Ca(HCO_3)_2(aq) + Ca(OH)_2(aq) \rightarrow 2CaCO_3(s) + 2H_2O(l)$. Using a 1:1 ratio of $Ca(OH)_2$ to Ca^{2+} ion in the reaction, calculate the mass of $Ca(OH)_2$:

$$0.0250 \text{ L Ca}^{2+} \times \frac{0.12 \text{ mol Ca}^{2+}}{\text{L Ca}^{2+}} \times \frac{1 \text{ mol Ca(OH)}_2}{1 \text{ mol Ca}^{2+}} \times \frac{74.09 \text{ g Ca(OH)}_2}{1 \text{ mol Ca(OH)}_2}$$

$$= 0.2\underline{2}2 = 0.22 \text{ g Ca(OH)}_2$$

21.107. $Al(H_2O)_6^{3+}(aq) + HCO_3^-(aq) \rightarrow Al(H_2O)_5OH^{2+}(aq) + H_2O(l) + CO_2(g)$

21.109.   Test portions of solutions of each compound with each other; the results can differentiate the compounds. For example, if one solution is poured into one of the other solutions and gives no precipitate, then that means $BaCl_2$ was mixed with KOH, and the third solution is $Al_2(SO_4)_3$. Adding the third solution of $Al_2(SO_4)_3$ to both of the first two solutions will form a precipitate with only $BaCl_2$. [$Al_2(SO_4)_3$ and excess KOH form soluble $Al(OH)_4^-$.] If, instead, one solution is poured into one of the other solutions and a precipitate forms, that means $BaCl_2$ was mixed with $Al_2(SO_4)_3 \rightarrow BaSO_4$, and the third solution is KOH, etc. Thus, all three are identified.

21.111. $Sn(H_2O)_6^{2+}(aq) + H_2O(l) \rightarrow Sn(H_2O)_5(OH)^+(aq) + H_3O^+(aq)$

21.113. The half-reactions and their sum are as follows:

$$
\begin{array}{lll}
PbO_2 + 4H^+ + 2e^- & \rightarrow & Pb^{2+} + 2H_2O \\
\underline{2Cl^-} & \rightarrow & \underline{Cl_2 + 2e^-} \\
PbO_2 + 4H^+ + 2Cl^- & \rightarrow & Pb^{2+} + Cl_2 + 2H_2O
\end{array}
$$

Adding $2Cl^-$ to both sides gives

$$PbO_2 + 4HCl \rightarrow PbCl_2 + Cl_2 + 2H_2O$$

21.115. a. $Al_2O_3(s) + 3H_2SO_4(aq) \rightarrow Al_2(SO_4)_3(aq) + 3H_2O(l)$

  b. $Al(s) + 3AgNO_3(aq) \rightarrow 3Ag(s) + Al(NO_3)_3(aq)$

  c. $Pb(NO_3)_2(aq) + 2NaI(aq) \rightarrow PbI_2(s) + 2NaNO_3(aq)$

  d. $8Al(s) + 3Mn_3O_4(s) \rightarrow 9Mn(s) + 4Al_2O_3(s)$

  e. $2Ga(OH)_3(s) \rightarrow Ga_2O_3(s) + 3H_2O(g)$

21.117. For 3.5×10^4 kg $(3.5 \times 10^7$ g) of hydrogen, you get

$$3.5 \times 10^7 \text{ g } H_2 \times \frac{1 \text{ mol } H_2}{2.016 \text{ g } H_2} \times \frac{-484 \text{ kJ}}{2 \text{ mol } H_2} = -4.\underline{2}01 \times 10^9 = -4.2 \times 10^9 \text{ kJ}$$

Thus, 4.2×10^9 kJ of heat is evolved in the process.

21.119. a.   The oxidation state of H in CaH_2 is -1.

  b.   The oxidation state of H in H_2O is $+1$.

  c.   The oxidation state of C in CH_4 is -4.

  d.   The oxidation state of S in H_2SO_4 is $+6$.

21.121. a.   Carbon has four valence electrons. These are directed tetrahedrally, and the orbitals should be sp^3 hybrid orbitals. Each C–H bond is formed by the overlap of a $1s$ orbital of a hydrogen atom with one of the singly occupied sp^3 hybrid orbitals of the carbon atom.

  b.   Silicon has four valence electrons. (Two more electrons are added for the -2 charge.) These are directed octahedrally, and the orbitals should be sp^3d^2 hybrid orbitals. Each Si–F bond is formed by the overlap of a $2p$ orbital of a fluorine atom with one of the singly occupied sp^3d^2 hybrid orbitals of the silicon atom.

  c.   Carbon has four valence electrons. The single C–C bond is a sigma bond formed by the overlap of the sp^2 orbital of the middle carbon and the sp^3 orbital of the CH_3 carbon. The other three orbitals of the CH_3 carbon are used to form the C–H bonds by overlapping with the orbital of the hydrogen atom. The C=C double bond is a sigma bond formed by the overlap of the sp^2 hybrid orbitals of those carbon atoms, and a pi bond formed by the overlap of the unhybridized p orbitals. The C–H bonds on the middle carbon and the CH_2 carbon are formed by the overlap of the sp^2 orbital of carbon and the s orbital of hydrogen.

  d.   Silicon has four valence electrons. These are directed tetrahedrally, and the orbitals should be sp^3 hybrid orbitals. Each Si–H bond is formed by the overlap of a $1s$ orbital of a hydrogen atom with one of the singly occupied sp^3 hybrid orbitals of the silicon atom.

21.123. a.   The equation, with $\Delta H_f°$'s recorded beneath each substance, is

$$CH_4(g) \quad \rightarrow \quad C(graphite) \quad + \quad 2H_2(g)$$

$\Delta H_f°$:   -74.87   0   0 kJ

$$\Delta H° = [0 - (-74.87)] \text{ kJ} = 74.87 \text{ kJ}$$

b.   The equation, with $\Delta H_f°$'s recorded beneath each substance, is

$$C_2H_6(g) \quad \rightarrow \quad C_2H_4(g) \quad + \quad H_2(g)$$

$\Delta H_f°$:   -84.68   52.47   0 kJ

$$\Delta H° = [52.47 - (-84.68)] \text{ kJ} = 137.15 \text{ kJ}$$

21.125. a. $CO_2(g) + Ba(OH)_2(aq) \rightarrow BaCO_3(s) + H_2O(l)$

b. $MgCO_3(s) + 2HBr(aq) \rightarrow CO_2(g) + H_2O(l) + MgBr_2(aq)$

21.127. $C(s) + O_2(air) \rightarrow CO_2(g)$

$CO_2(g) + NaOH(aq) \rightarrow NaHCO_3(aq)$

$2NaHCO_3(aq) \xrightarrow{\Delta} Na_2CO_3(s) + H_2O(l) + CO_2(g)$

21.129. The diamond-like structure of silicon implies that each silicon atom is tetrahedrally bonded to four other silicon atoms. The hybridization is sp^3. Each bond is formed by the overlap of an sp^3 hybrid orbital on each silicon atom to make a sigma bond.

21.131. The molar mass of silicon dioxide ($SiO2$) is 60.09 g/mol. Thus,

$$5.00 \text{ kg Si} \times \frac{1 \text{ mol Si}}{28.09 \text{ g Si}} \times \frac{1 \text{ mol SiO}_2}{1 \text{ mol Si}} \times \frac{60.09 \text{ g SiO}_2}{1 \text{ mol SiO}_2} = 10.\underline{6}959 = 10.7 \text{ kg SiO}_2$$

21.133. Spodumene, $LiAl(SiO_3)_2$ has the following structure:

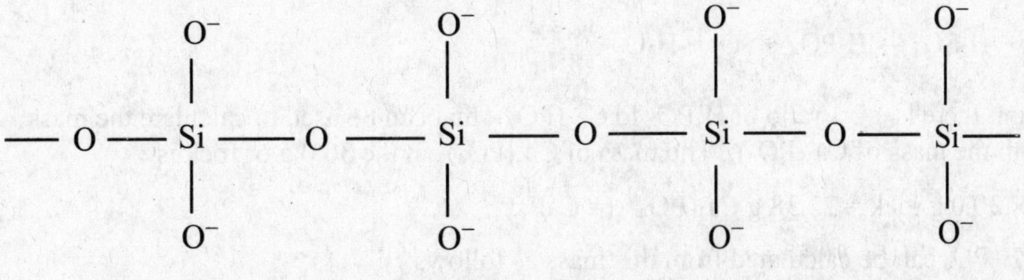

The drawing represents two of the sets of tetrahedra forming a portion of a long chain. There is a net −8 charge on the fragment, which includes two sets of two SiO_3 units. Thus, the $(SiO_3)_2$ unit has a −4 charge. This would have to be balanced by one Li^+ and one Al^{3+} for every two SiO_3. Thus, the empirical formula is $LiAl(SiO_3)_2$.

21.135. The equation is $Mg_3N_2(s) + 6H_2O(l) \rightarrow 3Mg(OH)_2(aq) + 2NH_3(g)$. Using a 1:2 ratio of Mg_3N_2 to NH_3, calculate the mass of NH_3 formed as follows:

$$7.50 \text{ g } Mg_3N_2 \times \frac{1 \text{ mol } Mg_3N_2}{100.915 \text{ g } Mg_3N_2} \times \frac{2 \text{ mol } NH_3}{1 \text{ mol } Mg_3N_2} \times \frac{17.03 \text{ g } NH_3}{1 \text{ mol } NH_3} = 2.5\underline{3}1 = 2.53 \text{ g}$$

21.137. Prepare HNO_3 from NH_3:

$$4NH_3(g) + 5O_2(g) \xrightarrow{Pt} 4NO(g) + 6H_2O(g)$$

$$2NO(g) + O_2(g) \rightarrow 2NO_2(g)$$

$$3NO_2(g) + H_2O(l) \rightarrow 2HNO_3(aq) + NO(g)$$

To prepare N_2O, use the HNO_3 just prepared:

$$NH_3(g) + HNO_3(aq) \rightarrow NH_4NO_3(aq)$$

$$NH_4NO_3(aq) \rightarrow NH_4NO_3(s)$$

$$NH_4NO_3(s) \xrightarrow{\Delta} N_2O(g) + 2H_2O(g)$$

21.139. The reduction of NO_3^- ion to NH_4^+ ion is an eight-electron reduction, and the oxidation of zinc to zinc(II) ion is a two-electron oxidation. Balancing the equation involves multiplying the zinc half-reaction by 4 to achieve an eight-electron oxidation. The final equation is

$$4Zn(s) + NO_3^-(aq) + 10H^+(aq) \rightarrow 4Zn^{2+}(aq) + NH_4^+(aq) + 3H_2O(l)$$

21.141. PBr_4^+ has four pairs of electrons around the P atom, arranged in a tetrahedral fashion. The hybridization of P is sp^3. Each bond is formed by the overlap of a $4p$ orbital from Br with an sp^3 hybrid orbital from P.

21.143. The balanced half-reactions are

Oxidation: $H_3PO_3 + H_2O \rightarrow H_3PO_4 + 2H^+ + 2e^-$

Reduction: $H_2SO_4 + 2H^+ + 2e^- \rightarrow SO_2 + 2H_2O$

The overall balanced equation is

$$H_3PO_3 + H_2SO_4 \rightarrow H_3PO_4 + SO_2 + H_2O$$

21.145. In the equation, there is a 2:1 ratio of H_3PO_4 to $Ca_3(PO_4)_2$ that can be used to calculate the mass of H_3PO_4 from the mass of $Ca_3(PO_4)_2$. The mass of $Ca_3(PO_4)_2$ in the 30.0 g of rock is

$$0.746 \times 30.0 \text{ g rock} = 22.\underline{3}8 \text{ g } Ca_3(PO_4)_2 \ (= CaP)$$

The mass of H_3PO_4 can be calculated from this mass as follows:

$$22.38 \text{ g } CaP \times \frac{1 \text{ mol } CaP}{310.2 \text{ g } CaP} \times \frac{2 \text{ mol } H_3PO_4}{1 \text{ mol } CaP} \times \frac{98.0 \text{ g } H_3PO_4}{1 \text{ mol } H_3PO_4} = 14.\underline{1}4 = 14.1 \text{ g } H_3PO_4$$

21.147. a. $4Li(s) + O_2(g) \rightarrow 2Li_2O(s)$

     b.   Organic materials burn in excess O_2 to give CO_2 and H_2O. The nitrogen becomes N_2:

$$4CH_3NH_2(g) + 9O_2(g) \rightarrow 4CO_2(g) + 2N_2(g) + 10H_2O(g)$$

     c. $2(C_2H_5)_2S + 15O_2 \rightarrow 8CO_2(g) + 10H_2O(g) + 2SO_2(g)$

21.149. a. $x_S + 6x_F = 0$

     The oxidation number of F in compounds is always -1.

$$x_S = -6x_F = -6(-1) = +6$$

     b. $x_S + 3x_O = 0$

     The oxidation number of O in most compounds is -2.

$$x_S = -3x_O = -3(-2) = +6$$

     c. $x_S + 2x_H = 0$

     The oxidation number of H in most compounds is $+1$.

$$x_S = -2x_H = -2(+1) = -2$$

     d. $x_{Ca} + x_S + 3x_O = 0$

     The oxidation number of Ca in compounds is $+2$; the oxidation number of O in most compounds is -2.

$$x_S = -x_{Ca} - 3x_O = -(+2) - 3(-2) = +4$$

21.151. The reduction of $8H_2SeO_3$ to Se_8 is a 32-electron reduction, and the oxidation of $8H_2S$ to S_8 is a 16-electron oxidation. Balancing the equation requires multiplying the H_2S half-reaction by 2 to achieve a 32-electron oxidation. The final equation is

$$8H_2SeO_3(aq) + 16H_2S(g) \rightarrow Se_8(s) + 2S_8(s) + 24H_2O(l)$$

21.153. In the equation, there is a 2:1 ratio of $NaHSO_3$ to Na_2CO_3 that can be used to calculate the mass of $NaHSO_3$ from 25.0 g of Na_2CO_3. The mass of $NaHSO_3$ is calculated as follows:

$$25.0 \text{ g } Na_2CO_3 \times \frac{1 \text{ mol } Na_2CO_3}{106.0 \text{ g } Na_2CO_3} \times \frac{2 \text{ mol } NaHSO_3}{1 \text{ mol } Na_2CO_3} \times \frac{104.0 \text{ g } NaHSO_3}{1 \text{ mol } NaHSO_3}$$

$$= 49.\underline{0}56 = 49.1 \text{ g } NaHSO_3$$

21.155. $Ba(ClO_3)_2(aq) + H_2SO_4(aq) \rightarrow 2HClO_3(aq) + BaSO_4(s)$

21.157. The balanced half-reactions are

     Oxidation: $2HCl \rightarrow Cl_2 + 2H^+ + 2e^-$

     Reduction: $K_2Cr_2O_7 + 14H^+ + 6e^- \rightarrow 2Cr^{3+} + 2K^+ + 7H_2O$

Multiply the oxidation half-reaction by 3. After adding and cancellation of the hydrogen ions and electrons, the resulting overall balanced equation is

$$K_2Cr_2O_7 + 6HCl + 8H^+ \rightarrow 2Cr^{3+} + 3Cl_2 + 2K^+ + 7H_2O$$

If eight Cl^- are added to each side, the equation can also be written as a molecular equation.

$$K_2Cr_2O_7 + 14HCl \rightarrow 2CrCl_3 + 3Cl_2 + 2KCl + 7H_2O$$

21.159. a.   The electron-dot formula of Cl_2O is

The VSEPR model predicts a bent (angular) molecular geometry. You can describe the four electron pairs on O using sp^3 hybrid orbitals. The diagramming for the bond formation follows:

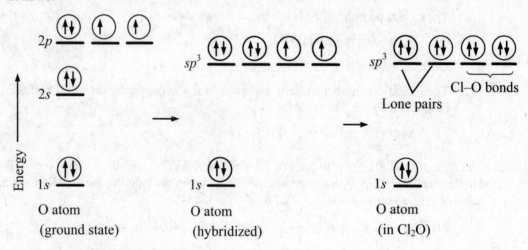

b.   An electron-dot formula of BrO_3^- is

$$
\begin{bmatrix}
\cdot\overset{\cdot\cdot}{O}\cdot \\
\cdot\overset{\cdot\cdot}{Br} \; \overset{\cdot\cdot}{O}\cdot \\
\cdot\overset{\cdot\cdot}{O}\cdot
\end{bmatrix}^{-}
$$

The VSEPR model predicts a trigonal pyramidal geometry. You can describe the four electron pairs on Br using sp^3 hybrid orbitals. The diagramming for the bond formation follows:

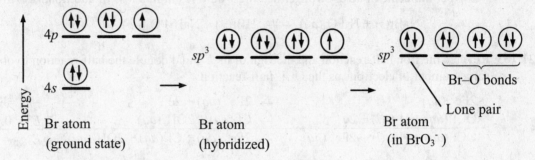

(Note: The additional electron accounts for the -1 charge of the ion; the bonds to O atoms are coordinate covalent.)

c. The electron-dot formula of BrF_3 is

F
Br F
F

The five electron pairs on Br have a trigonal bipyramidal arrangement. Putting the lone pairs in equatorial positions to reduce repulsions gives a T-shaped molecular geometry for BrF_3. You can describe the five electron pairs on Br in terms of sp^3d hybrid orbitals. The diagramming for the bond formation follows:

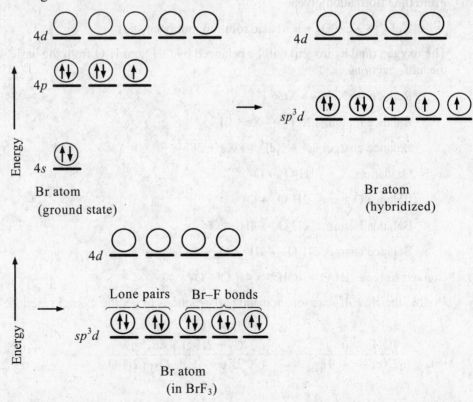

21.161. a. $Br_2(aq) + 2NaOH(aq) \rightarrow H_2O(l) + NaOBr(aq) + NaBr(aq)$

b.   Assume, by analogy with H_2SO_4 and NaCl, that the usual heating causes a loss of one H^+ per molecule of acid. Stronger heating would result in a loss of additional H^+ from $H_2PO_4^-$.

$$NaBr(s) + H_3PO_4(aq) \xrightarrow{\Delta} HBr(g) + NaH_2PO_4(aq)$$

21.163. Reverse the iron half-reaction and the sign of its $E°$, and double the half-reaction to obtain the same number of electrons as the OCl^- half-reaction:

$2Fe^{2+}(aq)$	$\rightarrow 2Fe^{3+}(aq) + 2e^-$	$-E° = -0.77$ V
$OCl^-(aq) + H_2O(l) + 2e^-$	$\rightarrow Cl^-(aq) + 2OH^-(aq)$	$E° = 0.90$ V
$OCl^-(aq) + H_2O(l) + 2Fe^{2+}(aq)$	$\rightarrow 2Fe^{3+}(aq) + Cl^-(aq) + 2OH^-(aq)$	$E°_{cell} = 0.13$ V

Because $E°_{cell}$ is positive, the reaction is spontaneous at standard conditions.

21.165. The total number of valence electrons is $8 + (4 \times 7) = 36$. These are distributed to give the following Lewis formula:

The six electron pairs on Xe would have an octahedral arrangement, suggesting sp^3d^2 hybridization. The lone pairs on Xe would be directed above and below the molecule, which has a square-planar geometry.

21.167. From the information given,

$$XeF_2 \rightarrow Xe + O_2 + F^- \text{ (basic solution; not balanced)}$$

The oxygen (and hydrogen) will be balanced by OH^- and H_2O from the basic solution. Balance the half-reactions.

Reduction: $XeF_2 \rightarrow Xe + F^-$

Balance F atoms: $XeF_2 \rightarrow Xe + 2F^-$

Balance charge: $2e^- + XeF_2 \rightarrow Xe + 2F^-$

Oxidation: $H_2O \rightarrow O_2$

Balance O atoms: $2H_2O \rightarrow O_2$

Balance H atoms: $2H_2O \rightarrow 4H^+ + O_2$

Balance charge: $2H_2O \rightarrow 4H^+ + O_2 + 4e^-$

Convert to base: $2H_2O + 4OH^- \rightarrow 4H_2O + O_2 + 4e^-$

Double the Xe half-reaction, and add half-reactions to get the overall reaction:

$4e^- + 2XeF_2$	$\rightarrow$	$2Xe + 4F^-$
$4OH^-$	$\rightarrow$	$O_2 + 2H_2O + 4e$
$2XeF_2 + 4OH^-$	$\rightarrow$	$2Xe + 4F^- + O_2 + 2H_2O$

■ SOLUTIONS TO GENERAL PROBLEMS

21.169. Sphalerite, ZnS, has the molar mass 97.48 g/mol. Thus

$$1.00 \text{ metric ton} \times 0.870 \text{ ZnS} \times \frac{1 \text{ mol ZnS}}{97.48 \text{ g ZnS}} \times \frac{1 \text{ mol Zn}}{1 \text{ mol ZnS}} \times \frac{65.41 \text{ g Zn}}{1 \text{ mol Zn}}$$

$$= 0.58\underline{3}77 = 0.584 \text{ metric ton Zn}$$

21.171. The equations are

$$2HCl + Mg(OH)_2(s) \rightarrow MgCl_2 + 2H_2O$$

$$HCl + NaOH \rightarrow NaCl + H_2O$$

Using a 1:1 ratio of HCl to NaOH, calculate the moles of HCl reacting with NaOH:

$$\left[\frac{0.4987 \text{ mol HCl}}{L} \times 0.05000 \text{ L} \right] - \left[\frac{0.2456 \text{ mol NaOH}}{L} \times 0.03942 \text{ L} \right] = 0.01525\underline{3} \text{ mol HCl}$$

The mass of $Mg(OH)_2$ is

$$0.015253 \text{ mol HCl} \times \frac{1 \text{ mol Mg(OH)}_2}{2 \text{ mol HCl}} \times \frac{58.33 \text{ g Mg(OH)}_2}{1 \text{ mol Mg(OH)}_2} = 0.444\underline{8}6 \text{ g Mg(OH)}_2$$

The mass percentage is

$$\frac{0.44486 \text{ g}}{5.436 \text{ g}} \times 100\% = 8.18\underline{3}7 = 8.184\%$$

21.173. The equation, with ΔH_f°'s recorded beneath each substance, is

$$Fe_2O_3(s) + \quad 2Al(s) \quad \rightarrow \quad 2Fe(s) \quad + \quad Al_2O_3(s)$$

$$\Delta H_f^\circ: \quad -825.5 \qquad\quad 0 \qquad\qquad\quad 0 \qquad\qquad -1675.7 \text{ kJ}$$

$$\Delta H^\circ = [-1675.7 - (-825.5)] \text{ kJ} = -850.2 \text{ kJ}$$

For 1 mol of iron,

$$\frac{-850.2 \text{ kJ}}{2 \text{ mol Fe}} = -425.1 \text{ kJ/mol Fe}$$

21.175. From the ideal gas law, the moles of CO_2 are

$$n = \frac{PV}{RT} = \frac{(745/760 \text{ atm})(0.03456 \text{ L})}{(0.0821 \text{ L} \cdot \text{atm/K} \cdot \text{mol})(294 \text{ K})} = 0.0014\underline{0}35 \text{ mol CO}_2$$

The equation is $CaCO_3(s) + 2HCl \rightarrow CO_2(g) + CaCl_2(aq) + H_2O(l)$. Using a 1:1 mole ratio of CO_2 to $CaCO_3$, the mass of $CaCO_3$ is

$$0.0014035 \text{ mol CO}_2 \times \frac{1 \text{ mol CaCO}_3}{1 \text{ mol CO}_2} \times \frac{100.1 \text{ g CaCO}_3}{1 \text{ mol CaCO}_3} = 0.140\underline{4}9 \text{ g CaCO}_3$$

The mass percentage of $CaCO_3$ is

$$\frac{0.14049 \text{ g}}{0.1662 \text{ g}} \times 100\% = 84.\underline{5}3 = 84.5\% \text{ } CaCO_3$$

21.177. The equation is $NaCl + NH_3 + H_2O + CO_2 \rightarrow NaHCO_3 + NH_4Cl$. Using a 1:1 mole ratio of NaCl to $NaHCO_3$, the mass of NaCl is

$$10.00 \text{ g } NaHCO_3 \times \frac{1 \text{ mol } NaHCO_3}{84.00 \text{ g } NaHCO_3} \times \frac{1 \text{ mol NaCl}}{1 \text{ mol } NaHCO_3} \times \frac{58.44 \text{ g NaCl}}{1 \text{ mol NaCl}}$$

$$= 6.95\underline{7}1 = 6.957 \text{ g NaCl}$$

21.179. Write the reaction with the $\Delta H_f°$'s and $S°$'s below:

$$SrCO_3 \text{ (s)} \quad \rightarrow \quad SrO(s) \quad + \quad CO_2(g)$$

$\Delta H_f°$:   -1220.1   -592.0   -393.5 kJ

$S°$:   97.1   55.52   213.7 J/K

$\Delta H° = [-592.0 - 393.5 - (-1220.1)] \text{ kJ} = 234.6 \text{ kJ}$

$\Delta S° = [55.52 + 213.7 - 97.1] \text{ J/K} = 172.\underline{1}2 \text{ J/K} = 0.17212 \text{ kJ/K}$

Finally, determine the temperature.

$\Delta G° = \Delta H° - T\Delta S°$

$0 = 234.6 \text{ kJ} - T(0.17212 \text{ kJ/K})$

$$T = \frac{234.6 \text{ kJ}}{0.17212 \text{ kJ/K}} = 136\underline{3}.0 = 1363 \text{ K}$$

21.181. The overall disproportionation reaction can be considered as the sum of the following reactions:

$2e^- + 2In^+(aq) \qquad \rightarrow \qquad 2In(s)$

$In^+(aq) \qquad \rightarrow \qquad In^{3+}(aq) + 2e^-$

$\overline{3In^+(aq) \qquad \rightarrow \qquad 2In(s) + In^{3+}}$

$E°_{cell} = E°_{cathode} - E°_{anode} = [(-0.21) - (-0.40)] \text{ V} = 0.19 \text{ V}$

$\Delta G° = -nFE°_{cell} = -(2)(9.65 \times 10^4 \text{ C})(0.19 \text{ J/C}) = -3.\underline{6}67 \times 10^4 \text{ J} = -37 \text{ kJ}$

$\Delta G°$ for the reaction as written is negative, so the disproportionation does occur spontaneously.

21.183. Using the ideal gas law, the amount of CO_2 is

$$n = \frac{PV}{RT} = \frac{(30.0/760 \text{ atm})(1.00 \text{ L})}{(0.0821 \text{ L} \cdot \text{atm/K} \cdot \text{mol})(298 \text{ K})} = 1.6\underline{1}4 \times 10^{-3} \text{ mol } CO_2$$

The balanced equation is $2LiOH(s) + CO_2(g) \rightarrow Li_2CO_3(s) + H_2O(g)$, so use the mole ratio 1 mol CO_2 to 2 mol LiOH. Therefore, the mass of LiOH is

$$1.614 \times 10^{-3} \text{ mol } CO_2 \times \frac{2 \text{ mol LiOH}}{1 \text{ mol } CO_2} \times \frac{23.95 \text{ g LiOH}}{1 \text{ mol LiOH}}$$

$$= 7.7\underline{3}1 \times 10^{-2} = 7.73 \times 10^{-2} \text{ g LiOH}$$

21.185. Assume a sample of 100.0 g fertilizer. This contains 17.1 g P. Convert this to the mass of $Ca(H_2PO_4)_2 \bullet H_2O$ in the 100.0 g of fertilizer.

$$17.1 \text{ g P} \times \frac{1 \text{ mol P}}{30.97 \text{ g P}} \times \frac{1 \text{ mol Ca(H}_2\text{PO}_4)_2 \bullet \text{H}_2\text{O}}{2 \text{ mol P}} \times \frac{252.1 \text{ g Ca(H}_2\text{PO}_4)_2 \bullet \text{H}_2\text{O}}{1 \text{ mol Ca(H}_2\text{PO}_4)_2 \bullet \text{H}_2\text{O}}$$

$$= 69.\underline{5}89 \text{ g Ca(H}_2\text{PO}_4)_2$$

The mass percent $Ca(H_2PO_4)_2 \bullet H_2O$ in the fertilizer is

$$\text{Mass percent Ca(H}_2\text{PO}_4)_2\bullet\text{H}_2\text{O} = \frac{69.589 \text{ g Ca(H}_2\text{PO}_4)_2 \bullet \text{H}_2\text{O}}{100 \text{ g fertilizer}} \; 100\% = 69.\underline{5}89 = 69.6\%$$

21.187. $2NaCl + 2H_2O \rightarrow 2NaOH + H_2 + Cl_2$ (electrolysis)

$2NaOH + Cl_2 \rightarrow NaClO + NaCl + H_2O$ (spontaneous)

One mole of NaClO is produced for every two moles of NaCl. Thus, the reaction requires two electrons per mole of NaClO produced.

Convert the 1.00×10^3 L of NaOCl to time:

$$1.00 \times 10^3 \text{ L} \times \frac{1000 \text{ mL}}{1 \text{ L}} \times \frac{1.00 \text{ g soln}}{1 \text{ mL}} \times \frac{5.25 \text{ g NaOCl}}{100 \text{ g soln}} \times \frac{1 \text{ mol NaOCl}}{74.44 \text{ g NaOCl}}$$

$$\text{x} \; \frac{2 \text{ mol e}^-}{1 \text{ mol NaOCl}} \times \frac{9.65 \times 10^4 \text{ C}}{1 \text{ mol e}^-} \times \frac{1 \text{ s}}{3.00 \times 10^3 \text{ C}} \times \frac{1 \text{ h}}{3600 \text{ s}} = 12.\underline{6}0 = 12.6 \text{ h}$$

21.189. The reactions are

$$H_2O + NaOCl + 2I^- \rightarrow I_2 + NaCl + 2OH^-$$

$$I_2 + 2Na_2S_2O_3 \rightarrow 2NaI + Na_2S_4O_6$$

The mass of NaOCl is

$$0.0346 \text{ L Na}_2\text{S}_2\text{O}_3 \times \frac{0.100 \text{ mol Na}_2\text{S}_2\text{O}_3}{1 \text{ L}} \times \frac{1 \text{ mol I}_2}{2 \text{ mol Na}_2\text{S}_2\text{O}_3} \times \frac{1 \text{ mol NaOCl}}{1 \text{ mol I}_2}$$

$$\times \frac{74.44 \text{ g NaOCl}}{1 \text{ mol NaOCl}} = 0.12\underline{8}8 \text{ g NaOCl}$$

If the density of bleach is taken as 1.00 g/mL, then 5.00 mL = 5.00 g. Thus, the mass percent is

$$\text{Mass percent NaOCl} = \frac{\text{mass NaOCl}}{\text{mass bleach}} \times 100\% = \frac{0.1288 \text{ g}}{5.00 \text{ g}} \times 100\% = 2.5\underline{7}5 = 2.58\%$$

21.191. A superconductor is a material that abruptly loses its resistance to an electric current when cooled to a definite characteristic temperature. This means that an electric current will flow in a superconductor without heat loss, unlike the current in a typical conductor. Once a current has been started in a superconducting circuit, it continues to flow indefinitely. Another intriguing property of a superconductor is its perfect diamagnetism. It became possible to construct superconducting magnets with high magnetic fields by starting an electric current in a superconducting circuit. Such magnets are being used in medical magnetic resonance imaging.

21.193. In 1985, Harold W. Kroto approached Richard E. Smalley and Robert F. Curl to do some experiments to simulate the conditions in certain stars to see what sorts of carbon-containing molecules might be produced. The research group had previously constructed an instrument in which they used an intense laser beam to vaporize solids. The hot vapor produced in this way could then be directed as a molecular beam into a mass spectrometer, where the molecular masses of the species in the vapor could be measured. The experiments on the vaporization of graphite produced surprising results. Molecular clusters of 2 to 30 carbon atoms were found, as expected; but in addition, the mass spectrum of the vapor consistently showed the presence of a particularly abundant molecule, C_{60}.

■ SOLUTIONS TO STRATEGY PROBLEMS

21.195. The product of the combustion of sulfur in excess oxygen is sulfur trioxide. The reaction is

$$2S(s) + 3O_2(g) \rightarrow 2SO_3(g)$$

When sulfur trioxide dissolves in water, sulfuric acid forms. The reaction is

$$SO_3(g) + H_2O(l) \rightarrow H_2SO_4(aq)$$

When aqueous $BaCl_2$ is added to a solution of sulfuric acid, a white precipitate forms, which is barium sulfate. The reaction is

$$BaCl_2(aq) + H_2SO_4(aq) \rightarrow BaSO_4(s) + 2HCl(aq)$$

To determine the mass of precipitate that forms, first determine the limiting reagent. Since the reactants are in a one-to-one mole ratio, calculate the moles of each reactant. For $BaCl_2$,

$$(0.1028 \ M)(75.6 \times 10^{-3} \ L) = 0.0077716 \ mol \ BaCl_2$$

For sulfuric acid, note that one mole of sulfur corresponds to one mole of sulfuric acid.

$$(0.325 \text{ g S}) \times \frac{1 \text{ mol S}}{32.07 \text{ g}} \times \frac{1 \text{ mol H}_2\text{SO}_4}{1 \text{ mol S}} = 0.01013 \text{ mol H}_2\text{SO}_4$$

Therefore, $BaCl_2$ is the limiting reactant. The mass of $BaSO_4$ that forms is

$$0.0077716 \text{ mol} \times \frac{233.40 \text{ g}}{1 \text{ mol BaSO}_4} = 1.813 = 1.81 \text{ g}$$

21.197. a.　$SO_2(g) + 2H_2S(g) \rightarrow 3S(s) + 2H_2O(g)$

　　b.　First, determine the limiting reagent by calculating the moles of each reactant.

$$\text{Moles of H}_2\text{S} = 15.1 \text{ g} \times \frac{1 \text{ mol H}_2\text{S}}{34.086 \text{ g}} = 0.4430 \text{ mol}$$

$$\text{Moles of SO}_2 = n = \frac{PV}{RT} = \frac{(748/760 \text{ atm})(5.00 \text{ L})}{(0.08206 \text{ L} \bullet \text{atm/K} \bullet \text{mol})(295 \text{ K})} = 0.2032 \text{ mol}$$

Since it takes two moles of H_2S for each mole of SO_2, there is sufficient H_2S to react completely with the SO_2, and SO_2 is the limiting reactant. The mass of sulfur produced is

$$(0.2032 \text{ mol SO}_2) \times \frac{3 \text{ mol S}}{1 \text{ mol SO}_2} \times \frac{32.07 \text{ g}}{1 \text{ mol S}} = 19.54 = 19.5 \text{ g S}$$

21.199. a. The difference in mass of the metal sulfide and metal oxide is due to replacement of S with O in the formula of the compound. Use this difference to determine the number of moles of sulfur and moles of oxygen in the compound.

$$\text{Moles} = \frac{\text{mass difference}}{\text{molar mass difference}} = \frac{6.125 \text{ g} - 5.714 \text{ g}}{32.07 \text{ g/mol} - 16.00 \text{ g/mol}} = 0.02557 \text{ mol}$$

Since sulfide, oxide, and sulfate ions all have a −2 charge, the number of moles of each ion is the same in the compound. Using the mass of the metal sulfide, the mass of the metal present is

Mass metal = 6.125 g − (0.02557 mol)(32.07 g/mol) = 5.304 g

Using the mass of SO_4^{2-} (96.07 g/mol), determine the mass of the metal sulfate.

Mass metal sulfate = 5.304 g + (0.02557 mol)(96.07 g/mol) = 7.761 g

The mass of the metal sulfate given in the problem is 7.763 g, so the data are consistent with the precipitate being a sulfate.

b. Assume the metal can have a +1, +2, +3, or +4 charge. The formulas of the corresponding sulfides are M_2S, MS, M_2S_3, and MS_2, respectively. Use this information to determine the molar mass of the metal in each case.

$$M_2S: \quad \frac{5.304 \text{ g M}}{0.02557 \text{ mol S}} \times \frac{1 \text{ mol S}}{2 \text{ mol M}} = 103.7 = 104 \text{ g/mol}$$

$$MS: \quad \frac{5.304 \text{ g M}}{0.02557 \text{ mol S}} \times \frac{1 \text{ mol S}}{1 \text{ mol M}} = 207.4 = 207 \text{ g/mol}$$

$$M_2S_3: \quad \frac{5.304 \text{ g M}}{0.02557 \text{ mol S}} \times \frac{3 \text{ mol S}}{2 \text{ mol M}} = 311.1 = 311 \text{ g/mol}$$

$$MS_2: \quad \frac{5.304 \text{ g M}}{0.02557 \text{ mol S}} \times \frac{2 \text{ mol S}}{1 \text{ mol M}} = 414.8 = 415 \text{ g/mol}$$

The last two are too high; however, 104 g/mol corresponds to rhodium (Rh), and 207 g/mol corresponds to lead (Pb). There is not enough information to decide about rhodium, but for lead, Pb^{2+} is common.

21.201. a. $P_4(s) + 5O_2(g) \rightarrow P_4O_{10}(s)$

b. When P_4O_{10} is dissolved in water, phosphoric acid forms, which dissociates and produces an acidic solution according to

$$H_3PO_4(aq) + H_2O(l) \rightleftharpoons H_3O^+(aq) + H_2PO_4^-(aq), \, K_a = 6.9 \times 10^{-3}$$

The equilibrium-constant expression is

$$K_a = \frac{[H_3O^+][H_2PO_4^-]}{[H_3PO_4]} = \frac{(x)^2}{[H_3PO_4]_o - x}$$

Use the pH to determine the value of x.

$$x = [H_3O^+] = 10^{-pH} = 10^{-2.091} = 8.109 \times 10^{-3} \, M$$

Rearrange the equilibrium-constant expression and solve for the initial phosphoric acid concentration.

$$[H_3PO_4]_0 = x + \frac{(x)^2}{K_a} = 8.109 \times 10^{-3}\,M + \frac{(8.109 \times 10^{-3})^2}{6.9 \times 10^{-3}} = 0.01\underline{7}64\,M$$

The mass of phosphorus can now be determined.

$$(0.01764\,M) \times (1.258\,L) \times \frac{1\text{ mol P}}{1\text{ mol H}_3\text{PO}_4} \times \frac{30.97\text{ g}}{1\text{ mol P}} = 0.6\underline{8}7 = 0.69\text{ g P}$$

c. $2H_3PO_4(aq) + 3Ca(NO_3)_2(aq) \rightarrow Ca_3(PO_4)_2(s) + 6HNO_3(aq)$

d. The mass of calcium phosphate formed is

$$(0.01764\,M) \times (1.258\,L) \times \frac{1\text{ mol Ca}_3(\text{PO}_4)_2}{2\text{ mol H}_3\text{PO}_4} \times \frac{310.18\text{ g}}{1\text{ mol Ca}_3(\text{PO}_4)_2} = 3.\underline{4}4 = 3.4\text{ g}$$

21.203. The reaction and corresponding thermodynamic data are summarized as follows.

$CO_2(g) + C(\text{graphite}) \rightarrow 2CO(g)$

$\Delta H_f^{\,\circ}$ -393.5   0   -110 kJ/mol

S° 213.7   5.740   197.5 J/mol·K

Calculate the standard enthalpy change and the standard entropy change for the reaction.

$\Delta H_{rxn}^{\circ} = [2(-110.5) - (-393.5)]\text{ kJ} = 172.5\text{ kJ}$

$\Delta S_{rxn}^{\circ} = [2(197.5) - (213.7) - (5.740)]\text{ J/K} = 175.\underline{5}6\text{ J/K} = 0.175\underline{5}6\text{ kJ/K}$

Assume that the enthalpy change and the entropy change do not vary appreciably with temperature, and use them to calculate ΔG at the higher temperature.

$\Delta G_{rxn} = \Delta H_{rxn} - T\Delta S_{rxn} = (172.5\text{ kJ}) - (2273\text{ K})(0.17556\text{ kJ/K}) = -226.\underline{5}4\text{ kJ}$

Write out the free-energy change in terms of the equilibrium constant.

$\Delta G_{rxn} = -RT\ln K = -226.54\text{ kJ/mol}$

Rearrange and solve for K.

$$\ln K = \frac{-\Delta G}{RT} = \frac{-(-226.54\text{ kJ/mol})}{(8.314 \times 10^{-3}\text{ kJ/mol·K})(2273\text{ K})} = 11.9\underline{8}8$$

$K = e^{11.988} = 1.\underline{6}0 \times 10^5 = 1.6 \times 10^5$

21.205. Since the potential is positive, the reaction is spontaneous, and copper metal dissolves in dilute nitric acid to form nitrogen monoxide gas and a solution of copper(II) nitrate.

CHAPTER 22

The Transition Elements and Coordination Compounds

■ SOLUTIONS TO EXERCISES

22.1. a. Pentaamminechlorocobalt(III) chloride

b. Potassium aquapentacyanocobaltate(III)

c. Pentaaquahydroxoiron(III) ion

22.2. a. $K_4[Fe(CN)_6]$

b. $[Co(NH_3)_4Cl_2]Cl$

c. $[PtCl_4]^{2-}$

22.3. a. No geometric isomers.

b.

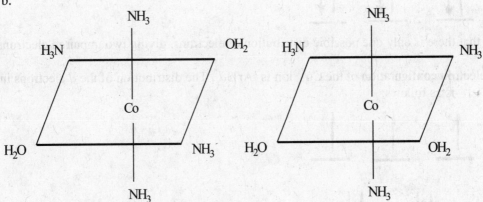

22.4.   a.   No optical isomers.

b.

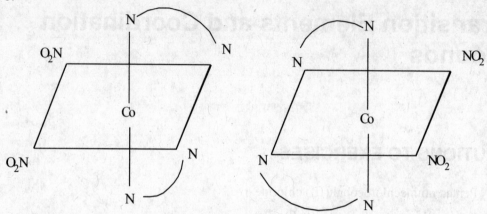

22.5.   The electron configuration of Ni^{2+} is $[Ar]3d^8$. The distribution of electrons among the d orbitals of Ni in $[Ni(H_2O)_6]^{2+}$ is as follows:

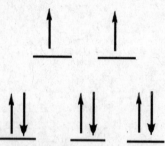

Note that there is only one possible distribution of electrons, giving two unpaired electrons.

22.6.   The electron configuration of the Co^{2+} ion is $[Ar]3d^7$. The distribution of the d electrons in $[CoCl_4]^{2-}$ is as follows:

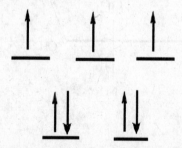

22.7.   The approximate wavelength of the maximum absorption for $[Fe(H_2O)_6]^{3+}$, which is pale purple, is 530 nm. The approximate wavelength of the maximum absorption for $[Fe(CN)_6]^{3-}$, which is red, is 500 nm. The shift is in the expected direction because CN^- is a more strongly bonding ligand than H_2O. As a result, Δ should increase, and the wavelength of the absorption should decrease, when H_2O is replaced by CN^-.

■ ANSWERS TO CONCEPT CHECKS

22.1.   Because silver nitrate does not precipitate AgCl from the complex, you conclude that chlorine is not present as free chloride ions; the Cl is presumably present as a complex. Potassium ion is likely present as K^+, which would account for two of the ions present in each formula unit. The other would be a complex ion of platinum with six chlorine atoms (a complex of Pt with six Cl^- ions). The charge on this complex ion must be 2– to counter the charges from the K^+ ions, so its formula is $[PtCl_6]^{2-}$. The formula of the complex, then, is $K_2[PtCl_6]$.

22.2.   The addition of silver nitrate to the complex precipitates AgCl equivalent to two Cl^- ions per formula unit. Since each formula unit consists of three ions, the complex appears to consist of two Cl^- ions plus a complex ion with a charge of 2+. The formula of the complex would then be $[Co(NH_3)_4(H_2O)Br]Cl_2$.

22.3.   a.   If you were to place a mirror to the right of complex X, complex A would directly represent what you would see in the mirror, so it is a mirror image. Note that complexes B and C are exactly the same, and A and E are the same; in both cases, they differ only by rotation (spin one of the complexes in each pair 180° to see this). Therefore, A and E are mirror images of X.

         b.   Optical isomers are nonsuperimposable mirror images of one another. The mirror images of molecule X, which are molecules A and E, are both nonsuperimposable mirror images, and are optical isomers of X.

         c.   To answer this part, you need to rotate each of the complexes to see if they have the same bonding arrangement in space with each of the ligands. Models A and E are the same complex, neither of which has the same bonding arrangement as complex X, so the complex they represent is a geometric isomer. Models B and C represent the same complex that also has a different bonding arrangement than complex X, so the complex they represent is also a geometric isomer. Complex D is the same complex as complex X, so it is not a geometric isomer.

■ ANSWERS TO SELF-ASSESSMENT AND REVIEW QUESTIONS

22.1.   Characteristics of the transition elements that set them apart from the main-group elements are the following: (1) The transition elements are metals with high melting points (only the IIB elements have low melting points). Most main-group elements have low melting points. (2) Each of the transition metals has several oxidation states (except for the Group IIIB and IIB elements). Most main-group metals have only one oxidation state in addition to zero. (3) Transition-metal compounds are often colored, and many are paramagnetic. Most main-group compounds are colorless and diamagnetic.

22.2.   Technetium has the electron configuration $[Kr] 4d^5 5s^2$.

22.3.   Molybdenum has the highest melting point of all elements in the fifth period because it has the maximum number of unpaired electrons, which contributes to the strength of the metal bonding.

22.4.   One reason why iron, cobalt, and nickel are similar in properties is that these elements have similar covalent radii.

22.5.   Nickel falls in the fourth period; accordingly, it has a much smaller covalent radius than the corresponding metals, palladium and platinum, in the fifth and sixth periods. However, palladium and platinum have very similar covalent radii.

22.6. $Cr(s) + 2HCl(aq) + 6H_2O(l) \rightarrow [Cr(H_2O)_6]^{2+} + 2Cl^-(aq) + H_2(g)$

$Cu(s) + HCl(aq) \rightarrow NR$

22.7. $Cr_2O_3(s) + 6HCl(aq) + 9H_2O(l) \rightarrow 2[Cr(H_2O)_6]^{3+} + 6Cl^-(aq)$

22.8.   Four of the water molecules are associated with the copper(II) ion, and the fifth is hydrogen-bonded to the sulfate ion as well as to water molecules on the copper(II) ion. Heating changes the blue color to a white color, the color of anhydrous $CuSO_4$. The blue color is associated with $[Cu(H_2O)_4]^{2+}$. When the water molecules leave the copper ion, the blue color is lost.

22.9.   Two Cu^{2+} ions gain a total of two electrons in forming one Cu_2O. The HCHO loses two electrons in forming $HCOO^-$ ion. Thus, the final equation is

$$2Cu^{2+}(aq) + HCHO(aq) + 5OH^-(aq) \rightarrow Cu_2O(s) + HCOO^-(aq) + 3H_2O(l)$$

22.10.   Werner showed that the electrical conductance of a solution of $[Pt(NH_3)_4Cl_2]Cl_2$ corresponded to that of three ions in solution and that two of the chloride ions could be precipitated as AgCl, whereas the other two could not.

22.11.   A complex ion is a metal atom or ion with Lewis bases attached to it through coordinate covalent bonds. A ligand is a Lewis base attached to a metal ion in a complex; it may be either a molecule or an anion, rarely a cation. The coordination number of a metal atom in a complex ion is the total number of bonds the metal forms with ligands. An example of a complex ion is $[Fe(CN)_6]^{4-}$; an example of a ligand is CN^-; and the coordination number of the preceding complex ion is 6.

22.12.   A bidentate ligand is a ligand that bonds to a metal ion through two atoms. Two examples are ethylenediamine, $H_2N-C_2H_4-NH_2$, and the oxalate ion, $^-O_2C-CO_2^-$.

22.13.

22.14. The three properties are isomerism, paramagnetism, and color (or absorption of visible and ultraviolet radiation).

22.15. a. Ionization isomerism involves isomers that are alike in that the same anions are present in the formula, but different anions are coordinated to the metal ion. For example, the sulfate ion is coordinated to cobalt in $[Co(NH_3)_5(SO_4)]Br$, but the bromide ion is coordinated to cobalt in $[Co(NH_3)_5Br]SO_4$.

b. Hydrate isomerism involves differences in the placement of water molecules in the complex ion. For example, $CrCl_3 \bullet 6H_2O$ exists as $[Cr(H_2O)_6]Cl_3$, $[Cr(H_2O)_4Cl_2]Cl \bullet 2H_2O$, and one other isomer.

c. Coordination isomers are those in which both the cation and the anion are complex, and the ligands are distributed between the two metal atoms in different ways. For example,

$$[Cu(NH_3)_4][PtCl_4] \text{ and } [Pt(NH_3)_4][CuCl_4]$$

d. Linkage isomers are those in which two different donor atoms on the ligand may bond to the metal ion. For example, SCN^- can bond to a metal ion through the sulfur atom or through the nitrogen atom.

22.16. Geometric isomers are isomers in which the atoms are joined to one another in the same way but differ because some atoms occupy different relative positions in space. In $[Pt(NH_3)_2Cl_2]$, the two NH_3's (or Cl's) can be arranged *trans* or *cis* to one another. Optical isomers are isomers that are nonsuperimposable mirror images of one another. See Figure 22.16 for an example of two cobalt optical isomers.

22.17. A *d* optical isomer rotates the plane of polarized light to the right (dextrorotatory), and an *l* optical isomer rotates the plane to the left (levorotatory).

22.18. A racemic mixture is a mixture of 50% of the *d* isomer and 50% of the *l* isomer. One method of resolving a racemic mixture is to prepare a salt with an optically active ion of the opposite charge and crystallize the salts. They will no longer be optical isomers and will have different solubilities, so one can be precipitated before the other.

22.19. According to valence bond theory, a ligand orbital containing two electrons overlaps an unoccupied orbital on the metal ion.

22.20. a. In the high-spin complex ion, all 3*d* orbitals of Fe^{2+} are occupied (four of the 3*d* orbitals each contain only one electron). Because they are occupied, those orbitals cannot be used for ligand bonding. Instead, d^2sp^3 hybrid orbitals form from the 4*s*, the three 4*p*, and two of the 4*d* orbitals. Each of six ligands donates a pair of electrons to one of these sp^3d^2 hybrid orbitals.

b. In the low-spin complex ion, the six electrons in the 3*d* orbitals are paired, so they occupy only three of the 3*d* orbitals. Then sp^3d^2 hybrid orbitals form from two of the 3*d*, the 4*s*, and the three 4*p* orbitals. Each of six ligands donates a pair of electrons to one of these d^2sp^3 hybrid orbitals.

22.21. The d orbitals of a transition-metal atom may have different energies in the octahedral field of six negative charges because the electron pairs of the ligands point directly at the d_{z^2} and $d_{x^2-y^2}$ orbitals. These orbitals are raised much more in energy than the other three d orbitals because they occupy space between the ligands. Thus, there is a crystal field splitting between the first two d orbitals mentioned and the d_{xy}, d_{xz}, and d_{yz} orbitals.

22.22. a.   A high-spin Fe(II) octahedral complex is

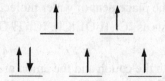

b.   A low-spin Fe(II) octahedral complex is

22.23. Crystal field splitting is the difference in energy between the two sets of d orbitals for a given structure (such as octahedral) in complex ions. It is determined experimentally by measuring the energy of light absorbed by complex ions.

22.24. The spectrochemical series is the arrangement of ligands in order of the relative size of the crystal field splittings (Δ) they induce in the d orbitals of a given oxidation state of a given metal ion. The order is the same, no matter what metal or oxidation state is involved. For Cl^-, H_2O, NH_3, and CN^-, the order of increasing crystal field splitting is

$$Cl^- < H_2O < NH_3 < CN^-$$

where CN^- always acts as a strong-bonding ligand.

22.25. Pairing energy, P, is the energy required to place two electrons in the same orbital. If the crystal field splitting (Δ) is small because of weak-bonding ligands, then the pairing energy will be larger, and the complex will be high-spin. If the crystal field splitting (Δ) is large because of strong-bonding ligands, then the pairing energy will be smaller, and the complex will be low-spin.

22.26. The complex absorbing red light would appear as a mixture of blue and green (approximately).

22.27. The answer is e, 6.

22.28. The answer is a, $[Zn(NH_3)_2Cl_2]$.

22.29. The answer is b, dicyanobis(ethylenediamine)chromium(III) chloride.

22.30. The answer is a, 0.

■ ANSWERS TO CONCEPTUAL PROBLEMS

22.31. Because one mole of chloride ion is precipitated per formula unit of the complex, the chlorine atoms must be present as chloride ion. All the other ligands are coordinated to the cobalt. An appropriate formula is $[Co(NH_3)_4(NO_2)_2]Cl$.

22.33. "Hexacyano" means that there are six CN^- ligands bonded to the iron cation. The Roman numeral II means the oxidation state of the iron cation is +2, so the overall charge of the complex ion is 4−. This requires four potassium ions to counterbalance the 4− charge.

22.35. The given compound must consist of a chloride ion (which can be precipitated with $AgNO_3$ solution) and a $[Co(NH_3)_4Br_2]^+$ ion, giving $[Co(NH_3)_4Br_2]Cl$. The structural formula of a possible constitutional isomer is $[Co(NH_3)_4BrCl]Br$.

■ SOLUTIONS TO PRACTICE PROBLEMS

Note on significant figures: If the final answer to a solution needs to be rounded off, it is given first with one nonsignificant figure, and the last significant figure is underlined. The final answer is then rounded to the correct number of significant figures. In multistep problems, intermediate answers are given with at least one nonsignificant figure; however, only the final answer has been rounded off.

22.37. a.   The charge on the carbonate ion is 2−. For $FeCO_3$ to be neutral, the oxidation number of iron must be +2.

b.   The oxidation number of oxygen is −2. For the sum of the oxidation numbers of all atoms to be zero, manganese must be in the +4 oxidation state.

c.   The oxidation number of the chlorine is −1, so the oxidation number of copper must be +2.

d.   The oxidation number of oxygen is −2. The oxidation number of chlorine is −1. For the sum of the oxidation numbers to be zero, the oxidation number of chromium must be +6.

$$+6 + 2(-2) + 2(-1) = 0$$

22.39. The half-reactions are

$$Fe^{2+} \rightarrow Fe^{3+} + e^-$$

$$4H^+ + NO_3^- + 3e^- \rightarrow NO + 2H_2O$$

The balanced equation is

$$3Fe^{2+} + NO_3^- + 4H^+ \rightarrow 3Fe^{3+} + NO + 2H_2O$$

22.41. a.   Four. There are four cyanide groups coordinated to the gold atom.

b.   Six. There are four ammonia molecules and two water molecules coordinated to the cobalt.

c.   Four. Each of the ethylenediamine molecules bonds to the gold atom through two nitrogen atoms.

d.   Six. Each ethylenediamine molecule bonds to the chromium atom through two nitrogen atoms, and the oxalate ion bonds to the chromium through two oxygen atoms.

22.43. **a.** The charge on the $[Ni(CN)_4]^{2-}$ ion is 2– to balance the charge from the two K^+ ions. Each cyanide ion has a charge of 1–. The sum of the oxidation number of nickel and the charge on the cyanide ions must equal the charge, so

$$-2 = [4 \times (-1)] + 1 \times [\text{ox. no. (Ni)}]$$

Ox. no. (Ni) = $-2 - (-4)$ = +2

b. The charge on ethylenediamine is zero, so the oxidation number of Mo is equal to the charge on the complex ion.

Ox. no. (Mo) = +3

c. Oxalate ion has a charge of 2–, so

Ox. no. of Cr = charge of complex ion $-3 \times$ (charge of oxalate ion)

$$= (-3) - [3 \times (-2)] = +3$$

d. Chloride ion has a charge of 1–, so the charge on the complex ion is 2+. The NH_3 ligands are neutral and contribute nothing to the charge of the complex ion.

Ox. no. of Co = charge of complex ion – charge of nitrite ligand = +2 – (–1) = +3

22.45. **a.** The charge on each chloride ligand is 1–; the charge on the oxalate ligand is 2–. The ammonia ligands are neutral.

Ox. no. of Cr = charge of complex ion – charge of oxalate – $2 \times$ (charge of chloride)

$$= -1 - (-2) - 2(-1) = +3$$

b.

Formula	Name
NH_3	Ammine
Cl^-	Chloro
$C_2O_4{}^{2-}$	Oxalato

c. Six. The chromium atom has one bond to each of the NH_3 ligands and Cl^- ligands and two bonds to the $C_2O_4{}^{2-}$ ligand.

d. If each NH_3 were replaced by one Cl^-, and the $C_2O_4{}^{2-}$ ligand were replaced by two Cl^- ligands, there would be a total of six Cl^- ligands bonded to a chromium atom in the +3 oxidation state.

Charge on complex ion = ox. no. of Cr + $6 \times$ (charge on chloride ligand)

$$= +3 + [6 \times (-1)] = -3 \dots \text{(or 3–)}$$

22.47. **a.** Potassium hexafluoroferrate(III)

b. Diamminediaquacopper(II) ion

c. Ammonium aquapentafluoroferrate(III)

d. Dicyanoargentate(I) ion

22.49. a.   Pentacarbonyliron(0)

b.   Dicyanobis(ethylenediamine)rhodium(III) ion

c.   Tetraamminesulfatochromium(III) chloride

d.   Tetraoxomanganate(VII) ion (Permanganate is the usual name.)

22.51. a.   The charge on the complex ion equals

Ox. no. of Mn + 6 × (charge on cyanide ion) = +3 + 6(−1) = −3

Hence, the formula is $K_3[Mn(CN)_6]$.

b.   The charge on the complex ion equals

Ox. no. of Zn + 4 × (charge on cyanide ion) = +2 + 4(−1) = −2

Hence, the formula is $Na_2[Zn(CN)_4]$.

c.   The charge on the complex ion equals

Ox. no. of Co + 2 × (charge on chloride ion)

Note that the ammine ligand (NH_3) is neutral. You get +3 + 2(−1) = +1. The formula is $[Co(NH_3)_4Cl_2]NO_3$.

d.   The charge on the cation equals the oxidation number of Cr (+3). The charge on the anion equals

Ox. no. of Cu + 4 × (charge on chloride ion) = +2 + 4(−1) = −2

The formula is $[Cr(NH_3)_6]_2[CuCl_4]_3$.

22.53. a.

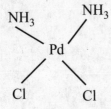   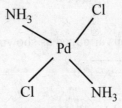

cis   *trans*

b.   No geometric isomerism.

c.   No geometric isomerism.

d.

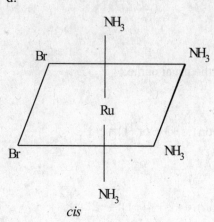

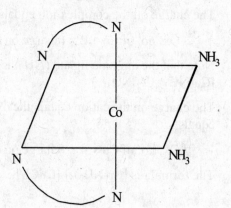

22.55. a.

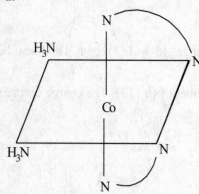

b.   No optical isomers.

22.57. a. V^{3+} has two *d* electrons arranged as shown:

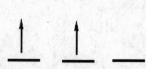

There are two unpaired electrons.

b. Co^{2+} has seven *d* electrons. In the high-spin case, they are arranged as follows:

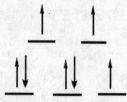

There are three unpaired e^-.

c. Mn^{3+} has four d electrons. In the low-spin case, they are arranged as follows:

There are two unpaired e^-.

22.59. a. Pt^{2+} has eight electrons in the $5d$ subshell. Because the complex is diamagnetic, the crystal field felt by the d orbitals is probably square planar (no low-spin tetrahedral complexes are known). The arrangement of the d electrons is

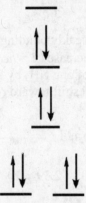

b. Co^{2+} has seven d electrons. One unpaired electron implies a low-spin complex. A square planar field will lead to low-spin complexes, so the geometry is probably square planar with the d electrons arranged as follows:

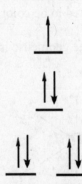

c. Fe^{3+} has five d electrons. If they are all unpaired (that is, a high-spin complex), the field felt by the metal ion is probably tetrahedral with the d electrons arranged as follows:

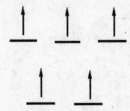

d. Co^{2+} has seven d electrons. Three unpaired electrons imply a high-spin complex. A tetrahedral field will lead to high-spin complexes, so the geometry is probably tetrahedral with the d electrons arranged as follows:

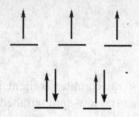

22.61. Purple (from Table 22.7)

22.63. Yes. According to the spectrochemical series, H_2O is a more weakly bonding ligand than NH_3, so Δ should decrease. The wavelength of the absorption should increase ($\lambda = hc/\Delta$). The light absorbed by $[Co(NH_3)_6]^{3+}$ is violet-blue, and the replacement of one NH_3 by H_2O shifts this toward blue. Thus, the observed (complementary) color should shift toward red, as is observed.

22.65. $\Delta = \dfrac{hc}{\lambda} = \dfrac{(6.626 \times 10^{-34} \text{ J} \cdot \text{s}) (2.998 \times 10^8 \text{ m/s})}{(500 \times 10^{-9} \text{ m})} \times 6.02 \times 10^{23} \text{ /mol}$

$$= 2.3917 \times 10^5 = 2.39 \times 10^5 \text{ J/mol (239 kJ/mol)}$$

■ SOLUTIONS TO GENERAL PROBLEMS

22.67. The color in transition-metal complexes is due to absorption of light when a d electron moves to a higher energy level. Because Sc^{3+} has no d electrons, it is expected to be colorless.

22.69. If $[Co(NH_3)_4Cl_2]^+$ had a regular planar hexagonal geometry, three geometric isomers would be expected.

The known existence of only two isomers of the complex rules out planar hexagonal geometry as a possibility.

22.71. The reaction and equilibrium-constant equation are

$$K_c = 2.1 \times 10^{-13} = \frac{[Cu^{2+}][NH_3]^4}{[Cu(NH_3)_4^{2+}]}$$

Concentration (M)	$Cu^{2+}(aq)$	$+$	$4NH_3(aq)$	$\rightleftharpoons$	$[Cu(NH_3)_4]^{2+}(aq)$
Start	0.10		0.40		0
Change	$-x$		$-4x$		$+x$
Equilibrium	$0.10 - x$		$0.40 - 4x$		x

Substituting into the equilibrium expression, you obtain

$$2.1 \times 10^{-13} = \frac{(0.10 - x)[4(0.10 - x)]^4}{x}$$

To simplify, let $y = 0.10 - x$. Then $x = 0.10 - y$. The above equation becomes

$$2.1 \times 10^{-13} = \frac{y(4y)^4}{(0.10 - y)}$$

Assume y is small compared to 0.10. Then $0.10 - y \cong 0.10$.

$$2.1 \times 10^{-13} = \frac{y(4y)^4}{(0.10)}$$

$$y^5 = \frac{(2.1 \times 10^{-13})(0.10)}{4^4} = 8.\underline{2}03 \times 10^{-17}$$

$$y = \sqrt[5]{8.203 \times 10^{-17}} = 6.\underline{0}64 \times 10^{-4}$$

Going back to the above assumption, you find that, to two significant figures, $0.10 - 0.00061 = 0.10$. The assumption was valid.

At equilibrium:

$$[Cu^{2+}] = (0.10 - x)\, M = y = 6.\underline{0}64 \times 10^{-4} = 6.1 \times 10^{-4}\, M$$

$$[NH_3] = 4(0.10 - x)\, M = 4y = 4 \times 6.\underline{0}64 \times 10^{-4} = 2.\underline{4}3 \times 10^{-3} = 2.4 \times 10^{-3}\, M$$

$$[Cu(NH_3)_4]^{2+} = x = (0.10 - y) = 0.10\, M$$

22.73. Commercial mayonnaise and salad dressing use EDTA to remove traces of metal ions. Metal ions can catalyze undesirable reactions or else provide nutrient for bacteria, resulting in off-flavors and spoilage of the product. EDTA is a polydentate ligand that forms particularly stable chelates with many metal ions, effectively removing those ions from the product. Many commercial products contain chelating agents such as EDTA.

22.75. Hemoglobin is an iron-containing substance in red blood cells responsible for the transport of O_2 from the lungs to various parts of the body. Myoglobin is a similar substance in muscle tissue, acting as a reservoir for storage of O_2 and as a transporter of O_2 within muscle cells. Hemoglobin is essentially a four-unit structure of myoglobinlike units, but it does not function simply as four independent units of myoglobin. For it to function efficiently as a transporter of O_2 from the lungs and then be able to release that O_2 easily to myoglobin, hemoglobin must be less strongly attached to O_2 in the vicinity of a muscle cell than is myoglobin.

■ SOLUTIONS TO STRATEGY PROBLEMS

22.77. a. Since CO_3^{2-} is bidentate, there are six ligands attached to the cobalt atom, and the complex ion is octahedral.

b. The cobalt must have an oxidation state of +3 since the carbonate ion has a charge of 2−, and the complex has a charge of 1+ overall.

22.79. a. The complex $[Ir(en)_3]^{3+}$ has a nonsuperimposable mirror image, so it has optical isomers.

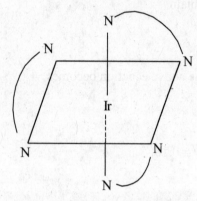 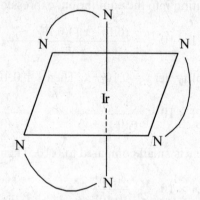

b. The complex $[Ir(H_2O)_3Cl_3]$ can exist in two different geometric forms. However, each form has a superimposable mirror image, so the complex does not have optical isomers.

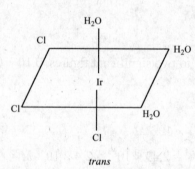 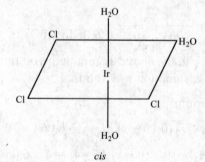

trans   *cis*

22.81. a. The complex $[Fe(en)_2Cl_2]Cl$ has an octahedral geometry. The en ligands are bidentate.

b. The oxidation state of the Fe is +3. The complex ion is $[Fe(en)_2Cl_2]^+$ and there are two chloride ions, each with a 1− charge.

c. There are two possible geometric isomers. The two chlorine atoms can be 90° apart (*cis*) or 180° apart (*trans*). In the case of the *trans* isomer, it has a superimposable mirror image and is not optically active. In the case of the *cis* isomer, it has a nonsuperimposable mirror image and is optically active.

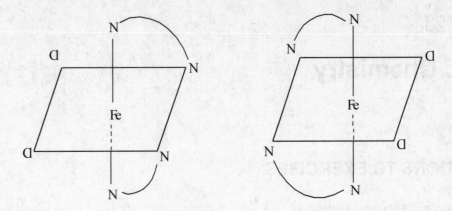

22.83. The name of $K_2[MoOCl_4]$ is potassium tetrachlorooxomolybdate(IV).

22.85. Absorption in the blue region of the spectrum suggests that the value of Δ is probably large, and thus the complex is expected to be low-spin. Low-spin complexes exist when the energy spacing (Δ) is large. It takes more energy to promote an electron to a higher energy level than to pair electrons. Blue light has a higher energy than red light, so absorption of blue light suggests a low-spin complex.

22.87. Compared to octahedral complexes, the crystal field splitting, Δ, is considerably smaller in tetrahedral complexes. As a result tetrahedral complexes are always high-spin. Thus a d^4-tetrahedral complex would be paramagnetic with the d electrons distributed as follows:

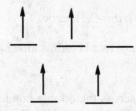

22.89. The complex $[Mn(NH_3)_6]^{2+}$ is a high-spin octahedral complex. The central Mn^{2+} ion has 5 d-electrons. If they are all unpaired, the pairing energy is greater than the splitting energy and the electrons are distributed into all 5 d orbitals. A low-spin complex would have only one unpaired electron.

22.91. a.   The name of $[Co(NH_3)_6]^{3+}$ is hexaamminecobalt(III) ion, and the name of $[Fe(H_2O)_6]^{2+}$ is hexaaquairon(II) ion.

    b.   With six ligands each, both of these complex ions have octahedral geometry.

    c.   The $[Co(NH_3)_6]^{3+}$ ion has a central d^6 Co^{2+} ion. The complex must be low-spin for it to be diamagnetic, i.e., all six d electrons are paired in the three lowest degenerate orbitals. The $[Fe(H_2O)_6]^{2+}$ ion also has a central d^6 Fe^{2+} ion. This complex must be high-spin for it to be paramagnetic, i.e., the six electrons are spread out among all five d orbitals before pairing occurs. Thus, the greatest crystal field splitting energy is associated with the $[Co(NH_3)_6]^{3+}$ ion. Its stronger-binding NH_3 ligands produce a higher energy gap (Δ) than the weaker-binding H_2O ligands.

CHAPTER 23

Organic Chemistry

■ SOLUTIONS TO EXERCISES

23.1.   The condensed structural formula is

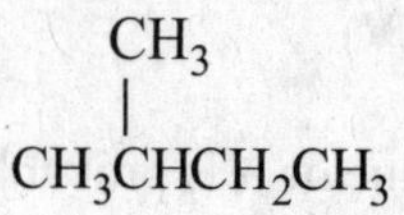

$$CH_3$$
$$|$$
$$CH_3CHCH_2CH_3$$

23.2.   a.   Geometric isomers are possible.

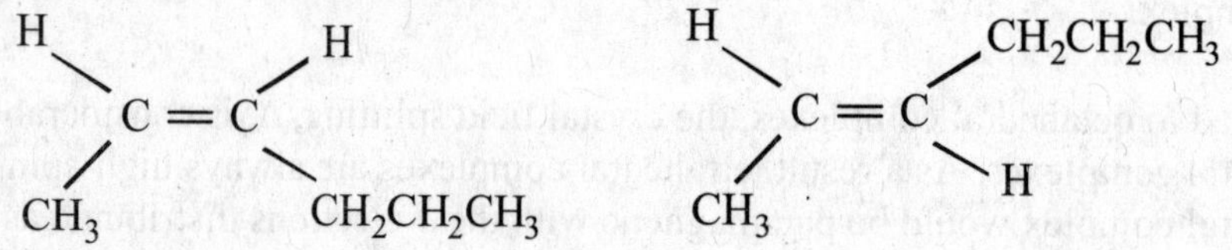

        cis-2-Hexene   *trans*-2-Hexene

        b.   No geometric isomers are possible because there are two H atoms attached to the second carbon of the double bond.

23.3.   According to Markownikoff's rule, when HBr is added across the double bond in 1-butene, the H will add to carbon 1 (the C atom with the most bonds to H atoms) and the Br will add to carbon 2.

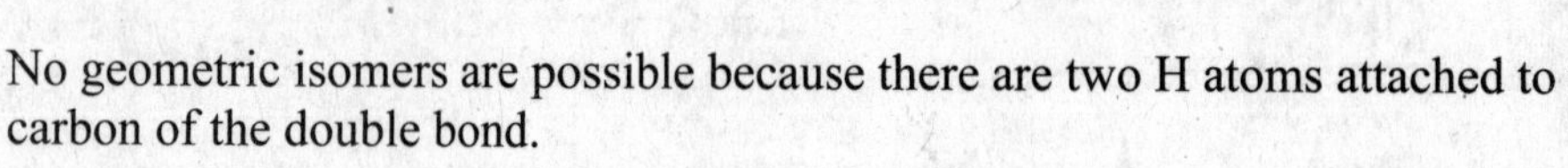

$$H_2C = CH - CH_2 - CH_3 \ + \ HBr \rightarrow H_3C - CH - CH_2 - CH_3$$
$$|$$
$$Br$$

The product is 2-bromobutane.

23.4.   a.   The longest continuous chain is numbered as follows:

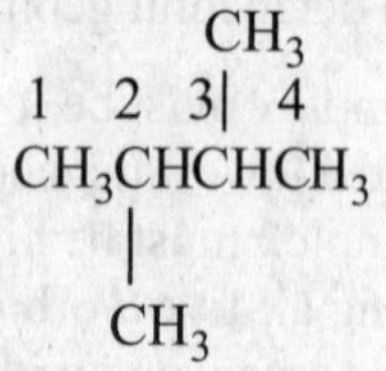

$$CH_3$$
$$1 \quad 2 \quad 3| \quad 4$$
$$CH_3CHCHCH_3$$
$$|$$
$$CH_3$$

The name of the compound is 2,3-dimethylbutane.

b.   To give the substituents the smaller numbers, the longest continuous chain is numbered as follows:

$$
\begin{array}{c}
\overset{4\quad5\quad6}{CH_2CH_2CH_3} \\
\overset{1\quad2\quad3|}{CH_3CHCHCH_2CH_3} \\
| \\
CH_3
\end{array}
$$

The name of the compound is 3-ethyl-2-methylhexane.

23.5.   First write out the carbon skeleton for octane.

$$
\begin{array}{c}
\overset{1|\;\;2|\;\;3|\;\;4|\;\;5|\;\;6|\;\;7|\;\;8|}{-C-C-C-C-C-C-C-C-} \\
|\;\;\;|\;\;\;|\;\;\;|\;\;\;|\;\;\;|\;\;\;|\;\;\;|
\end{array}
$$

Then attach the alkyl groups.

$$
\begin{array}{c}
CH_3 \\
\overset{1|\;\;2|\;\;3|\;\;4|\;\;5|\;\;6|\;\;7|\;\;8|}{-C-C-C-C-C-C-C-C-} \\
|\;\;\;|\;\;\;|\;\;\;|\;\;\;|\;\;\;|\;\;\;|\;\;\;| \\
CH_3
\end{array}
$$

Finally, fill out the structure with H atoms.

$$
\begin{array}{c}
CH_3 \\
| \\
CH_3CH_2CCH_2CH_2CH_2CH_2CH_3| \\
| \\
CH_3
\end{array}
$$

23.6.   a.   The numbering of the carbon chain is

$$
\begin{array}{c}
\overset{1\quad2\quad3\quad4}{CH_3C=CHCHCH_3} \\
\quad|\quad\;\;\overset{5}{|} \\
\;\;CH_3\;\;\;CH_2 \\
\quad\quad\quad\overset{6}{|} \\
\quad\quad\quad CH_3
\end{array}
$$

Because the longest chain containing a double bond has six carbons, this is a hexene. It is a 2-hexene because the double bond is between carbons 2 and 3. The name of the compound is 2,4-dimethyl-2-hexene.

b.   The numbering of the longest chain with a double bond is

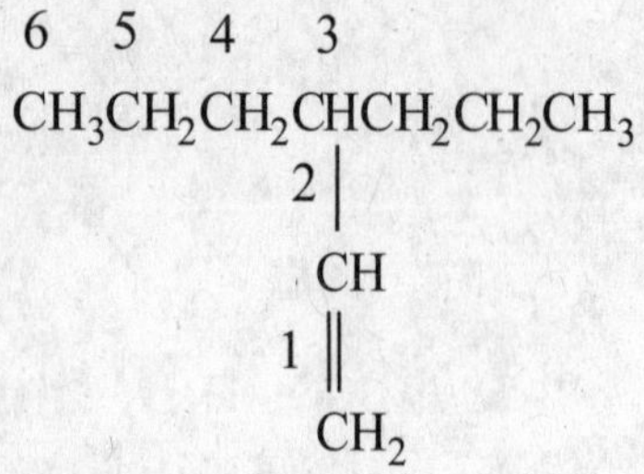

$$
\begin{array}{cccc}
6 & 5 & 4 & 3 \\
\end{array}
$$
$$CH_3CH_2CH_2CHCH_2CH_2CH_3$$
$$2\ |$$
$$CH$$
$$1\ \|$$
$$CH_2$$

The longest chain containing the double bond has six carbon atoms; therefore, this is a hexene. It is a 1-hexene because the double bond is between carbons 1 and 2. The name of the compound is 3-propyl-1-hexene.

23.7.   First write out the carbon skeleton for 2-heptene.

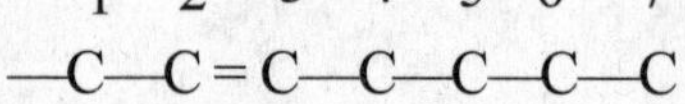

$$
\begin{array}{ccccccc}
1 & 2 & 3 & 4 & 5 & 6 & 7 \\
\end{array}
$$
$$—C—C = C—C—C—C—C$$

Then add the alkyl groups.

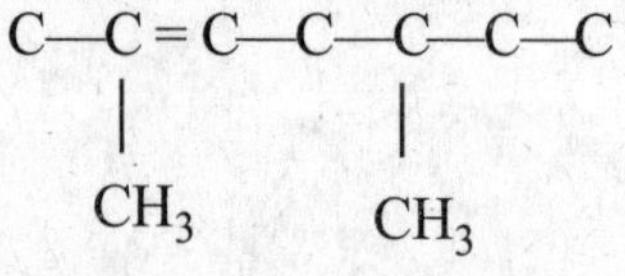

$$C—C = C—C—C—C—C$$
$$\quad |\qquad\qquad |$$
$$\quad CH_3\qquad\ CH_3$$

Finally, add the H atoms.

$$CH_3C = CHCH_2CHCH_2CH_3$$
$$\quad |\qquad\qquad |$$
$$\quad CH_3\qquad\ CH_3$$

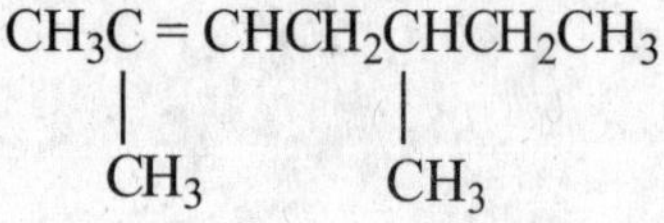

23.8.   The two isomers of $CH_3CH_2CH = CHCH_2CH_3$ are *cis*-3-hexene and *trans*-3-hexene.

23.9.   a.   There are only three carbons in the chain. The compound is propyne.

b.   The longest continuous chain containing the triple bond has five carbon atoms. The compound is 3-methyl-1-pentyne.

23.10.   a.   This compound has an ethyl group attached to a benzene ring.

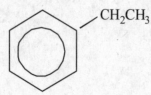

b.   This compound has one phenyl group attached to each carbon atom in the ethane molecule.

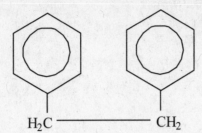

23.11. Because the compound has an –OH group, it is an alcohol. The longest carbon chain in the molecule has six carbons.

$$\overset{\displaystyle OH}{\underset{\displaystyle \underset{CH_2CH_3}{|}}{\overset{6\quad5\quad4\quad3|\ 2\quad1}{CH_3CH_2CH_2CCH_2CH_3}}}$$

The name of the compound is 3-ethyl-3-hexanol.

23.12. a.   Dimethyl ether

b.   Methyl ethyl ether

23.13. a.   There are two alkyl groups attached to the carbonyl; therefore, the compound is a ketone. There are five carbon atoms in the chain. The name of the compound is 2-pentanone.

b.   There is a hydrogen atom attached to the carbonyl, so the compound is an aldehyde. The numbering of the stem carbon chain is

$$\overset{\displaystyle O}{\underset{\displaystyle}{\overset{1\parallel\quad2\quad3\quad4}{H-C-CH_2CH_2CH_3}}}$$

The name of the compound is butanal.

■ ANSWERS TO CONCEPT CHECKS

23.1. a. C_7H_{16}

$$\underset{\displaystyle \underset{CH_3}{|}}{\overset{\displaystyle \overset{CH_3}{|}}{CH_3CHCHCH_2CH_3}}$$

b.

23.2. Since, by definition, heptane is zero octane and 2,2,4-trimethylpentane is 100 octane, a mixture of 10% heptane and 90% 2,2,4-trimethylpentane would produce a 90 octane mixture.

23.3. a. C_5H_{10}

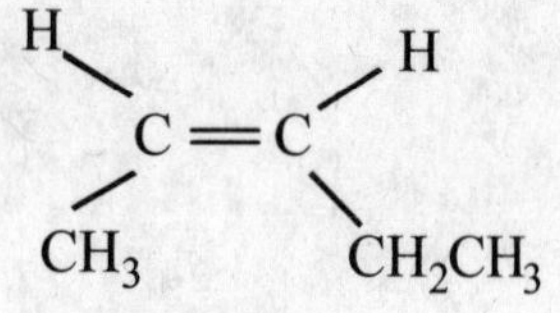

b.

c. *cis*-2-pentene

■ ANSWERS TO SELF-ASSESSMENT AND REVIEW QUESTIONS

23.1. The formula of an alkane with 30 carbon atoms is $C_{30}H_{62}$.

23.2.

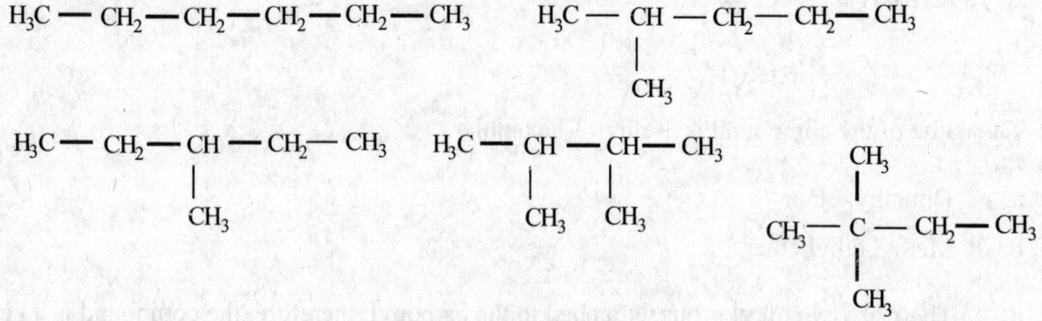

23.3. The structures of a seven-carbon alkane, cycloalkane, alkene, and aromatic hydrocarbon are

$CH_3-CH_2-CH_2-CH_2-CH_2-CH_2-CH_3$

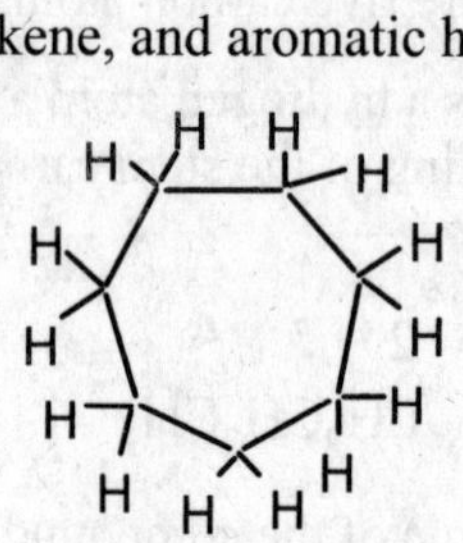

$CH_2=CH-CH_2-CH_2-CH_2-CH_2-CH_3$

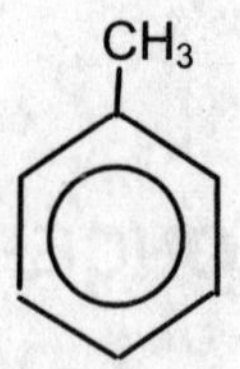

(toluene)

23.4. The two isomers of 2-butene are the *cis* and *trans* geometric isomers:

cis-2-Butene   *trans*-2-Butene

In the *cis*-2-butene, the two methyl groups are on the same side of the double bond; in the *trans* isomer, they are on opposite sides.

23.5. The structural formulas for the isomers of ethyl-methylbenzene are

23.6. Methane: source–natural gas; use–home fuel.

    Octane: source–petroleum; use–auto fuel.

   Ethylene: source–petroleum refining; use–chemical industry raw material.

  Acetylene: source–methane; use–acetylene torch.

23.7.

CH_3CH_2Cl CH_2ClCH_2Cl $CHCl_2CHCl_2$ CCl_3CCl_3

CH_3CHCl_2 $CH_2ClCHCl_2$ $CHCl_2CCl_3$

CH_3CCl_3 CH_2ClCCl_3

23.8. A substitution reaction is a reaction in which part of the reagent molecule is substituted for a hydrogen atom on a hydrocarbon or hydrocarbon group. For example,

$$CH_4 + Cl_2 \rightarrow CH_3Cl + HCl$$

An addition reaction is a reaction in which parts of the reagent are added to each carbon atom of a carbon-carbon multiple bond, which then becomes a C—C single bond. For example,

$$CH_2 = CH_2 + Br_2 \rightarrow CH_2Br–CH_2Br$$

23.9. The major product of HCl plus acetylene should be $Cl_2HC–CH_3$ because Markownikoff's rule predicts this.

23.10.   The structures are

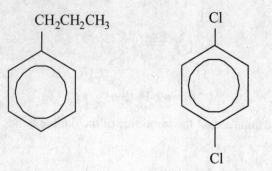

Propylbenzene   Paradichlorobenzene

23.11.   A functional group is a reactive portion of a molecule that undergoes predictable reactions no matter what the rest of the molecule is like. An example is a C=C bond, which always reacts with bromine or other addition reagents to add part of each reagent to each carbon atom.

23.12.   An aldehyde is different from a ketone, a carboxylic acid, and an ester in that a hydrogen atom is always attached to the carbonyl group in addition to a hydrocarbon group.

23.13.   Methanol: source–$CO + H_2$; use–solvent.

   Ethanol: source–fermentation of glucose; use–solvent.

   Ethylene glycol: source–ethylene; use–antifreeze.

   Glycerol: source–from soap making; use–foods.

   Formaldehyde: source–oxidation of methanol; use–plastics and resins.

23.14.   a.   CO is a carbonyl group (ketone).

   b. CH_3O—C is an ether group.

   c.   C=C is a double bond.

   d.   COOH is a carboxylic acid group.

   e.   CHO is an aldehyde (carbonyl).

   f. CH_2OH, or –OH, is a hydroxyl group (primary alcohol).

23.15.   The answer is e, 6.

23.16.   The answer is d, $CH_3CH=CHCH_3$.

23.17.   The answer is d, C_4H_{10}.

23.18.   The answer is c, 3-methyl-2-pentanol.

■ ANSWERS TO CONCEPTUAL PROBLEMS

23.19. a. The molecules with carbon chains in the $C_5 - C_{11}$ range will no longer be present because they have all boiled off. Additionally, some of the heavily branched C_{12} chains will boil off.

b. The molecules with carbon chains greater than C_{11} will be left in the barrel because they boil at temperatures above 200°C. (Keep in mind that the heavily branched C_{12} chains will have boiled off at or slightly below 200°C.)

c. Low-molecular-mass hydrocarbons have fewer polarizable electrons; therefore, they have weaker London forces than the longer chains and, as a result, boil at a lower temperature.

d. The more compact 2,3-dimethylbutane would boil at a lower temperature.

23.21. Since carbon would have more than four bonds in this case, CH_5 would be in violation of the octet rule.

23.23. a. The molecular formulas are trimethylamine, C_3H_9N; acetaldehyde, C_2H_4O; 2-propanol, C_3H_8O; and acetic acid, $C_2H_4O_2$.

b. The condensed structural formulas are

trimethylamine: $N(CH_3)_3$

acetaldehyde: $\overset{\overset{\displaystyle O}{\parallel}}{CH_3CH}$

2-propanol: $\overset{\overset{\displaystyle OH}{\parallel}}{CH_3CHCH_3}$

acetic acid: $\overset{\overset{\displaystyle O}{\parallel}}{CH_3COH}$

c. The functional groups in the molecules are trimethylamine, amine (tertiary); acetaldehyde, aldehyde; 2-propanol, alcohol; and acetic acid, carboxylic acid.

23.25. The molecules increase regularly in molecular mass. Therefore, you expect their intermolecular forces (dispersion forces) and thus their melting points to increase.

■ SOLUTIONS TO PRACTICE PROBLEMS

23.27. The condensed structural formula is $CH_3CH_2CH_2CH_3$.

23.29.

a.

cis-3-Hexene   *trans*-3-Hexene

b.

cis-3-Methyl-3-hexene   *trans*-3-Methyl-3-hexene

23.31. a. $C_2H_4 + 3O_2 \rightarrow 2CO_2 + 2H_2O$

      b.

$$CH_2{=}CH_2 \ + \ MnO_4^- \ + \ H_2O \ \rightarrow \ \overset{\overset{\displaystyle OH\ OH}{|\ \ |}}{CH_2CH_2} \ + \ MnO_2$$

Oxidation: $CH_2{=}CH_2 \rightarrow \overset{\overset{\displaystyle OH\ OH}{|\ \ |}}{CH_2CH_2}$

Balance O: $2OH^- \ + CH_2 = CH_2 \rightarrow \overset{\overset{\displaystyle OH\ OH}{|\ \ |}}{CH_2CH_2}$

Balance e⁻ $2OH^- \ + CH_2 = CH_2 \rightarrow \overset{\overset{\displaystyle OH\ OH}{|\ \ |}}{CH_2CH_2} \ + \ 2e^-$

Reduction: $MnO_4^- \rightarrow MnO_2$

Balance O: $MnO_4^- + 2H_2O \rightarrow MnO_2 + 4OH^-$

Balance e⁻: $MnO_4^- + 2H_2O + 3e^- \rightarrow MnO_2 + 4OH^-$

Add half-reactions:

$$3 \left(2OH^- + CH_2 = CH_2 \rightarrow \overset{\overset{\displaystyle OH\ OH}{|\ \ \ |}}{CH_2CH_2} + 2e^- \right)$$

$$2 \left(MnO_4^- + 2H_2O + 3e^- \rightarrow MnO_2 + 4OH^- \right)$$

$$\cancel{6}OH^- + 3CH_2 = CH_2 + 2MnO_4^- + 4H_2O \rightarrow 3\ \overset{\overset{\displaystyle OH\ OH}{|\ \ \ |}}{CH_2CH_2} + 2MnO_2 + \overset{2}{\cancel{8}}OH^-$$

$$3CH_2 = CH_2 + 2MnO_4^- + 4H_2O \rightarrow 3\ \overset{\overset{\displaystyle OH\ OH}{|\ \ \ |}}{CH_2CH_2} + 2MnO_2 + 2OH^-$$

b. $$CH_2 = CH_2 + Br_2 \rightarrow \overset{\overset{\displaystyle Br\ Br}{|\ \ \ |}}{CH_2CH_2}$$

c.

d.

23.33. $C_2H_6 + Br_2 \rightarrow C_2H_5Br + HBr$

23.35. According to Markownikoff's rule, the major product is the one obtained when the H atom adds to the carbon atom of the double bond that already has more hydrogen atoms attached to it. Therefore, 2-bromo-2-methylpropane is the major product.

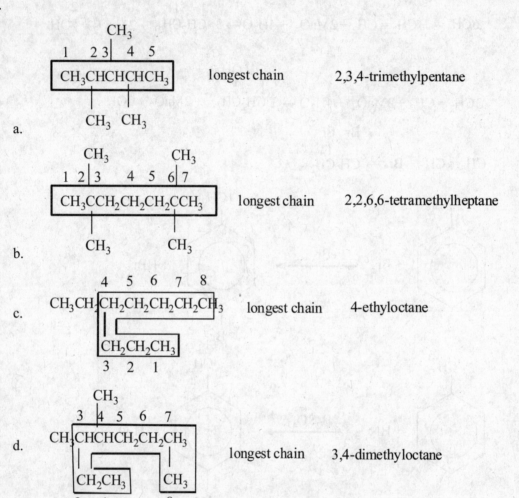

23.37.

a.   CH₃CHCHCHCH₃   longest chain   2,3,4-trimethylpentane

b.   CH₃CCH₂CH₂CH₂CCH₃   longest chain   2,2,6,6-tetramethylheptane

c.   CH₃CH₂CH₂CH₂CH₂CH₂CH₃   longest chain   4-ethyloctane

d.   CH₃CHCHCH₂CH₂CH₃   longest chain   3,4-dimethyloctane

23.39.

a.   CH₃CHCHCH₂CH₂CH₃

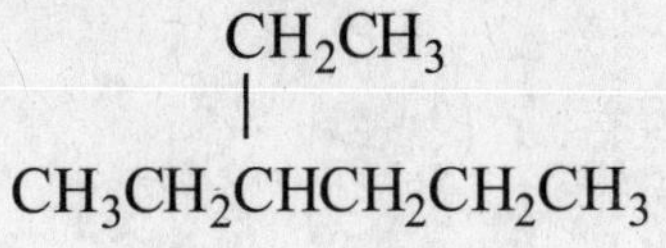

b.
$$\underset{\underset{CH_3CH_2CHCH_2CH_2CH_3}{|}}{CH_2CH_3}$$

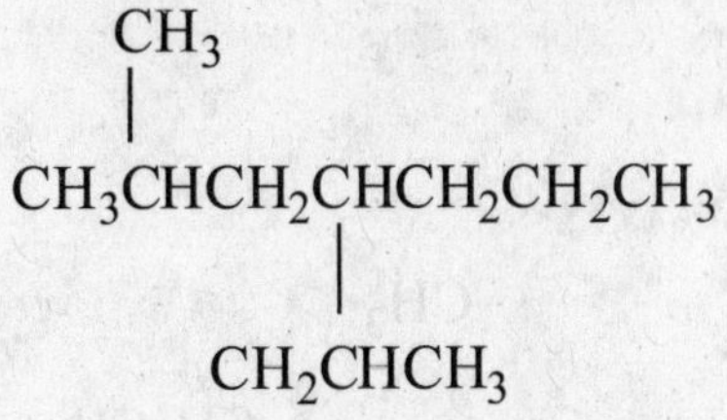

c.
$$\underset{\underset{CH_3CHCH_2CHCH_2CH_2CH_3}{|}}{CH_3}$$

$$\underset{\underset{CH_2CHCH_3}{|}}{}$$

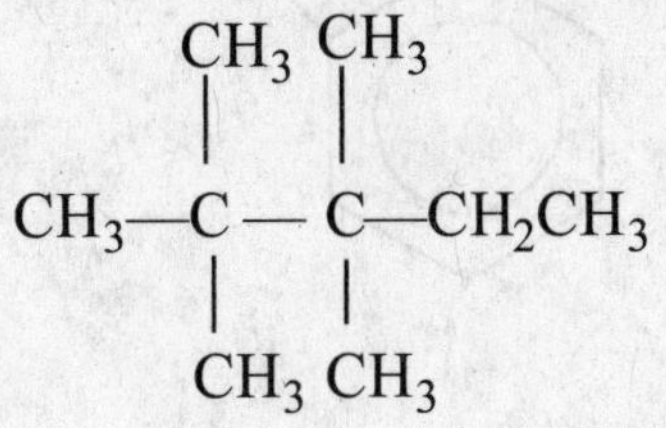

d.
$$\underset{\underset{CH_3 \quad CH_3}{|}}{\overset{\overset{CH_3 \quad CH_3}{|}}{CH_3-\underset{}{C}-\underset{}{C}-CH_2CH_3}}$$

23.41. a. 2-pentene

b. 2,5-dimethyl-2-hexene

23.43.

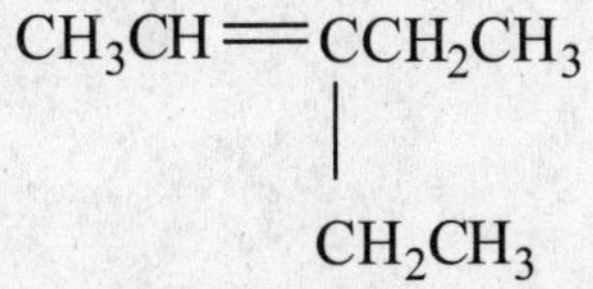

a.
$$\underset{\underset{CH_2CH_3}{|}}{CH_3CH=CCH_2CH_3}$$

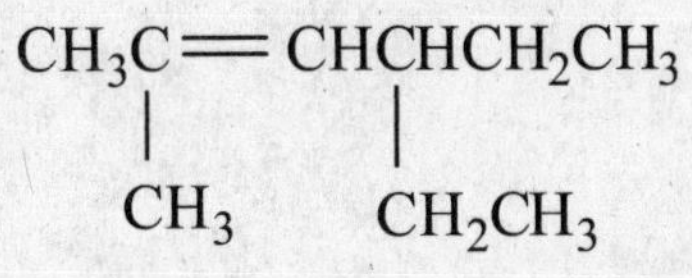

b.
$$\underset{\underset{CH_3 \qquad CH_2CH_3}{|}}{\overset{\overset{CH_2CH_3}{|}}{CH_3C=CHCHCH_2CH_3}}$$

23.45. The two isomers are *cis*-2-pentene and *trans*-2-pentene.

23.47. a. 2-butyne

b. 3-methyl-1-pentyne

23.49.

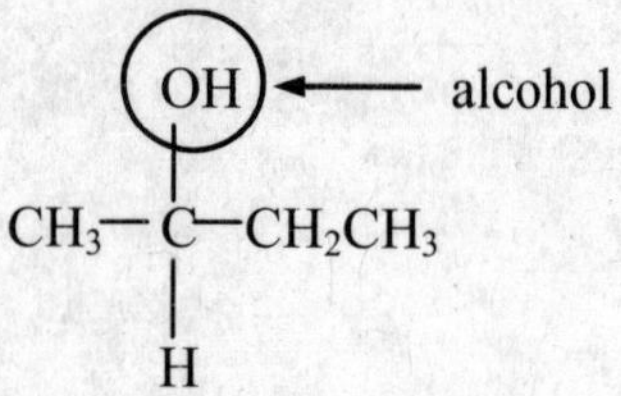

a.

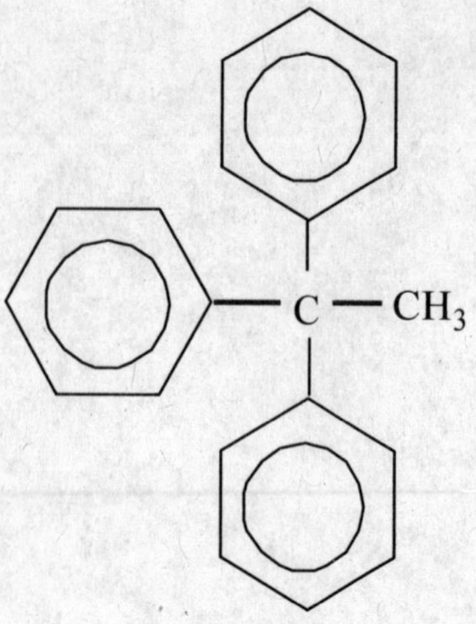

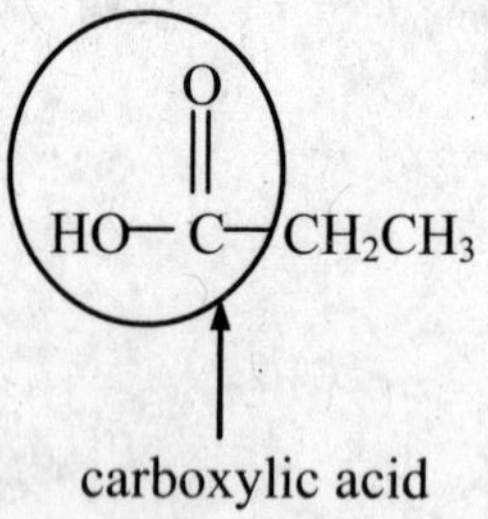

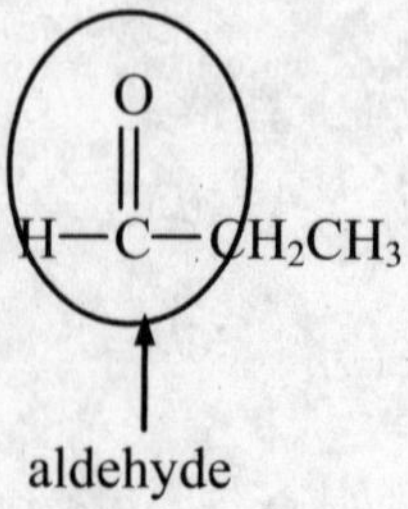

b.

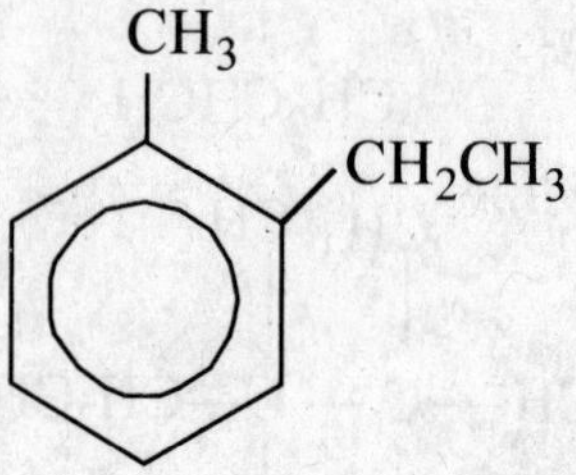

23.51.

a.

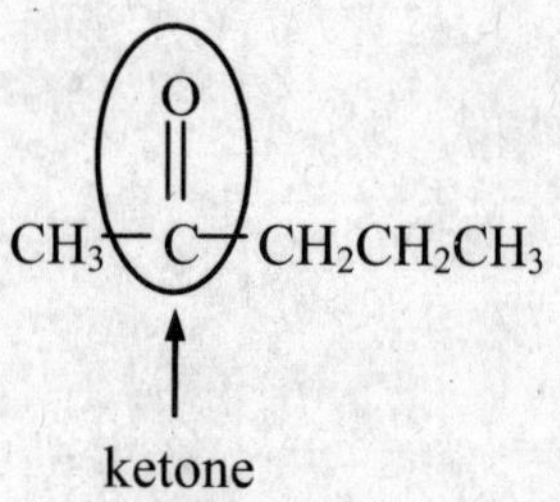

ketone

b.

c.

carboxylic acid

d.

aldehyde

23.53. a.   1-pentanol

b.   2-pentanol

c.   2-propyl-1-pentanol

d.   6-methyl-4-octanol

23.55. a.   secondary alcohol

b.   secondary alcohol

c.   primary alcohol

d.   primary alcohol

23.57. a.   ethyl propyl ether

b.   methyl isopropyl ether

23.59. a.   butanone

b.   butanal

c.   4,4-dimethylpentanal

d.   3-methyl-2-pentanone

23.61. a.   secondary amine (bond from phenyl ring was meant to be connected directly to N atom)

b.   secondary amine

■ SOLUTIONS TO GENERAL PROBLEMS

23.63. a.   3-methylbutanoic acid

b.   *trans*-5-methyl-2-hexene

c.   2,5-dimethyl-4-heptanone

d.   4-methyl-2-pentyne

23.65.

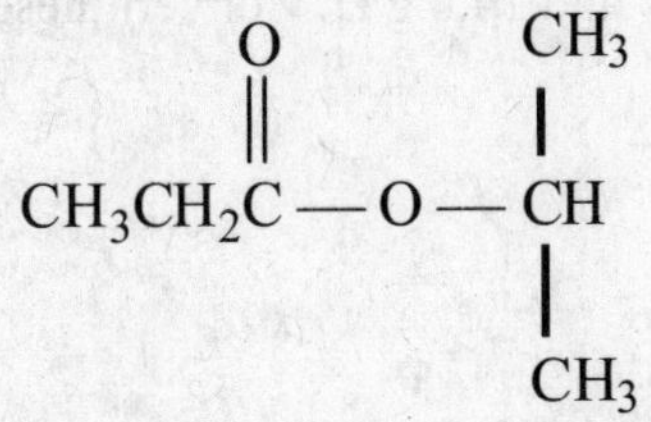

$$CH_3CH_2C \overset{\overset{\displaystyle O}{\|}}{} \!-\! O \!-\! \overset{\overset{\displaystyle CH_3}{|}}{\underset{\underset{\displaystyle CH_3}{|}}{CH}}$$

a.

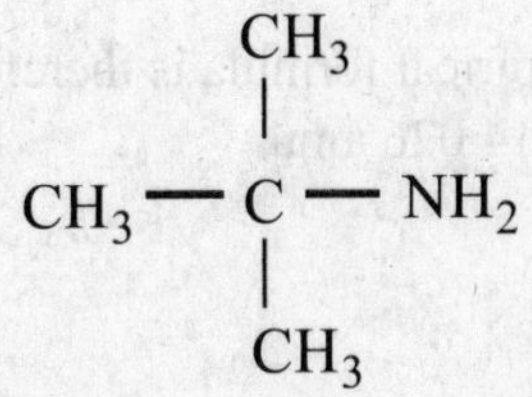

$$CH_3 \!-\! \overset{\overset{\displaystyle CH_3}{|}}{\underset{\underset{\displaystyle CH_3}{|}}{C}} \!-\! NH_2$$

b.

$$CH_3CH_2CH_2CH_2C \overset{\overset{\displaystyle CH_3}{|}}{\underset{\underset{\displaystyle CH_3}{|}}{\text{—}}} COOH$$

c.

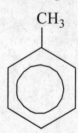

d.

23.67. a. Addition of dichromate ion in acidic solution to propionaldehyde will cause the reagent to change from orange to green as the aldehyde is oxidized. Under similar conditions, acetone (a ketone) would not react.

b. Addition of a solution of Br_2 in CCl_4 to $CH_2{=}CH{-}C{\equiv}C{-}CH{=}CH_2$ would cause the bromine color to disappear as the Br_2 was added to the multiple bonds. Addition of benzene to Br_2 in CCl_4 results in no reaction. Aromatic rings are not susceptible to attack by Br_2 in the absence of a catalyst.

23.69. a. ethylene, $CH_2 = CH_2$

b. There must be an aromatic ring in the compound or the double bonds would react with Br_2. The compound is toluene, and the correct formula is

CH₃

c. methylamine, CH_3NH_2

d. methanol, CH_3OH

23.71. Assume 100.0 g of the unknown. This contains 85.6 g C and 14.4 g H. Convert these amounts to moles.

$$85.6 \text{ g} \times \frac{1 \text{ mol C}}{12.01 \text{ g C}} = 7.1\underline{2}7 \text{ mol C}$$

$$14.4 \text{ g H} \times \frac{1 \text{ mol H}}{1.008 \text{ g H}} = 14.\underline{2}857 \text{ mol H}$$

The molar ratio of H to C is 14.2857:7.12, or 2.00:1. The empirical formula is therefore CH_2. This formula unit has a mass of $[12.01 + 2 \times (1.008)]$ amu = 14.026 amu.

$$\frac{56.1 \text{ amu}}{1 \text{ molecule}} \times \frac{1 \text{ formula unit}}{14.026 \text{ amu}} = \frac{4.00 \text{ formula units}}{1 \text{ molecule}}$$

The molecular formula is $(CH_2)_4$, or C_4H_8. The formula (C_nH_{2n}) indicates that the compound is either an alkene or a cycloalkane. Because it reacts with water and H_2SO_4, it must be an alkene. The product of the addition of H_2O to a double bond is an alcohol. Because the alcohol produced can be oxidized to a ketone, it must be a secondary alcohol. The only secondary alcohol with four carbon atoms is 2-butanol.

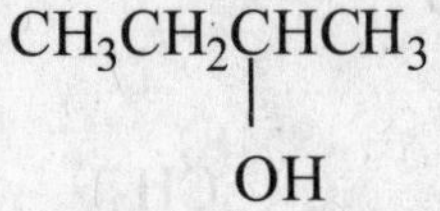

$$CH_3CH_2\overset{\displaystyle |}{\underset{\displaystyle OH}{CH}}CH_3$$

The original hydrocarbon from which it was produced is either 1-butene or 2-butene.

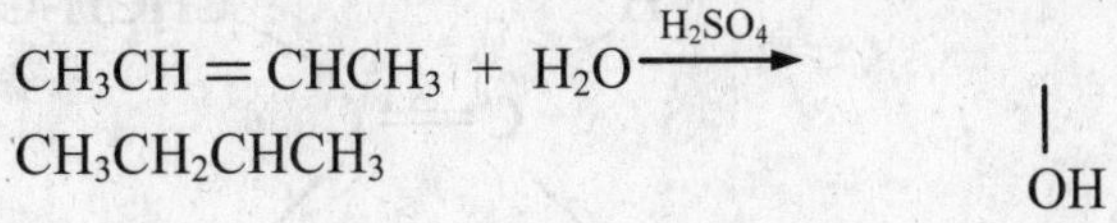

$$CH_3CH = CHCH_3 \ + \ H_2O \xrightarrow{\ H_2SO_4\ }$$
$$CH_3CH_2CHCH_3 \qquad\qquad\qquad \underset{\displaystyle OH}{\overset{\displaystyle |}{}}$$

or

$$CH_3CH_2CH = CH_2 \ + \ H_2O \xrightarrow{\ H_2SO_4\ } CH_3CH_2\underset{\displaystyle OH}{\overset{\displaystyle |}{CH}}CH_3$$

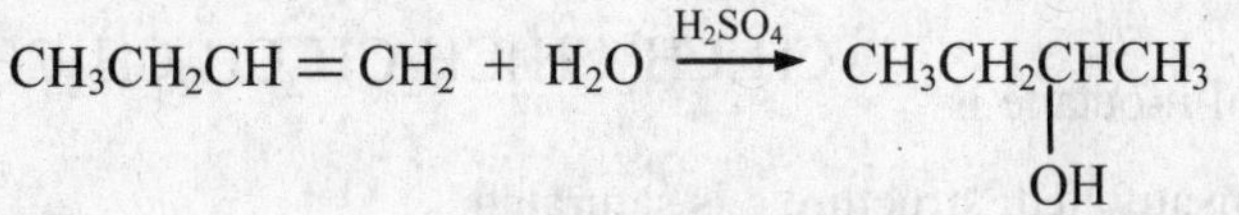

■ SOLUTIONS TO STRATEGY PROBLEMS

23.73. a. The functional group present is an alcohol.

  b. The IUPAC name is 2-methyl-3-hexanol.

23.75. The molecule has three functional groups: aldehyde, alcohol, and carboxylic acid.

23.77. a. The molecular formula of the compound is C_6H_{12}.

  b. The condensed structural formula is $CH_3CH=CHCH_2CH_2CH_3$.

  c. The IUPAC name of the compound is *trans*-2-hexene.

23.79. The structure implied by the given name is

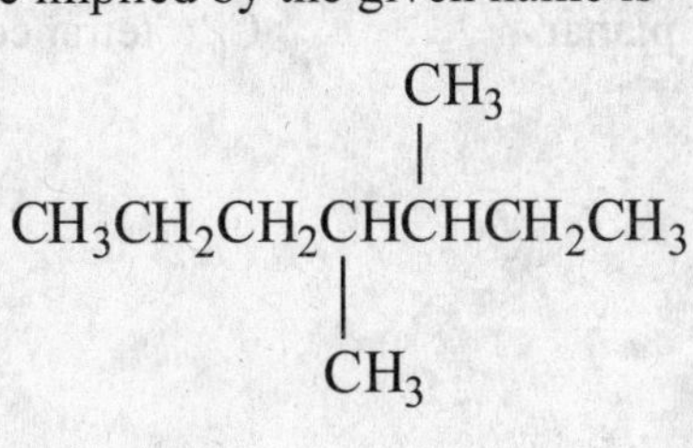

$$CH_3CH_2CH_2\overset{\displaystyle \overset{\displaystyle CH_3}{|}}{CH}\overset{\displaystyle \overset{\displaystyle }{}}{CH}\underset{\displaystyle \underset{\displaystyle CH_3}{|}}{}CH_2CH_3$$

The name given is incorrect. The correct IUPAC name for the compound is 3,4-dimethylheptane.

23.81. a. 3,4-dimethylpentanal

  b. 3-methylpentanoic acid

23.83.

a. The structural formula of chlorobenzene is

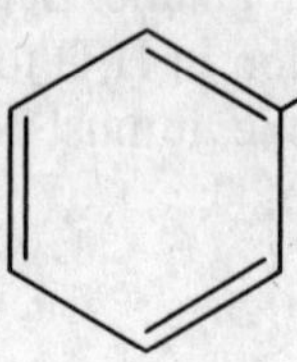

b. The structural formula of 4-methyl-2-hexene is

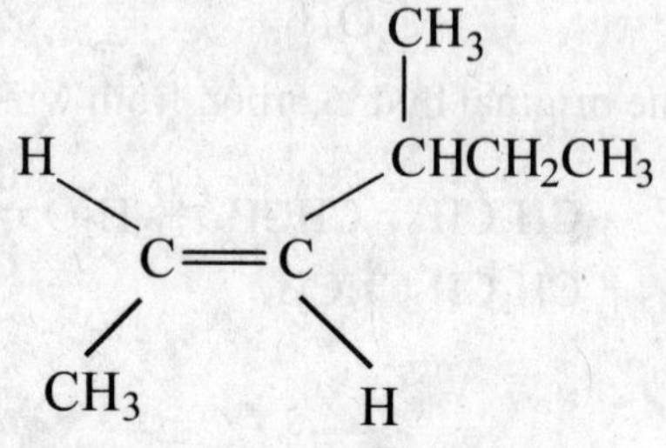

$$CH_3CH_2CH_2CH_2CH_2CH_2CH_2CH_3$$

c. The structural formula of *n*-octane is

d. Structures a and b are unsaturated; structure c is saturated.

23.85 All important amino acids found in living organisms have the following general structure:

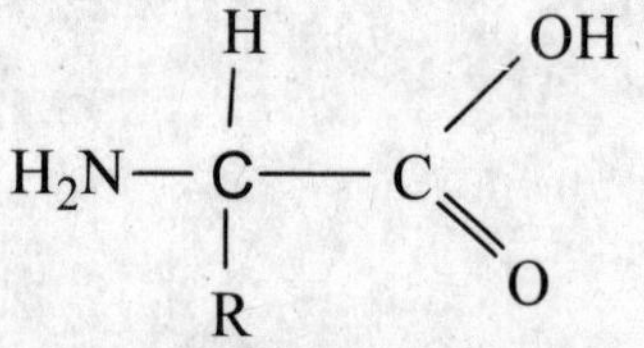

On the left is an amine functional group and on the right is a carboxylic acid group. Different amino acids have unique R attachments.

23.87 Numbering the seven carbon atoms from left to right, the molecular geometry around each carbon atom is as follows:

C_1 : tetrahedral C_2 : trigonal planar C_3 : trigonal planar

C_4 : tetrahedral C_5 : trigonal planar C_6 : tetrahedral

C_7 : trigonal planar

CHAPTER 24

Polymer Materials: Synthetic and Biological

■ SOLUTIONS TO EXERCISES

24.1.   This addition polymer is formed when vinylidene chloride adds to itself across the double bond.

$$\cdots + CH_2{=}CCl_2 + CH_2{=}CCl_2 + CH_2{=}CCl_2 + \cdots \rightarrow$$

$$-CH_2-CCl_2-CH_2-CCl_2-CH_2-CCl_2-$$

■ ANSWERS TO CONCEPT CHECKS

24.1.   The carboxyl group, –COOH, of either of the amino acids could be bonded through a peptide bond to the amino group, –NH$_2$, of the other. The structures of these two dipeptides are

24.2.   In RNA, the bases are adenine (A), guanine (G), cytosine (C), and uracil (U), but not thymine (T). The complimentary bases are A and T, A and U, and G and C. So, A in DNA would have U as a compliment in RNA; T in DNA would have A as a compliment in RNA; G in DNA would have C in RNA as a compliment; and C in DNA would have G in RNA as a compliment. Here, then, is the RNA sequence complimentary to the DNA sequence given in the problem statement:

UACGAUGCCUAAGUU.

■ ANSWERS TO SELF-ASSESSMENT AND REVIEW QUESTIONS

24.1.   An addition reaction is a polymer formed by linking together many molecules by addition reactions. The monomers have multiple bonds that will undergo addition reactions. An example is the formation of polypropylene from propene.

$$\cdots + \underset{\underset{CH_3}{|}}{CH}=CH_2 + \underset{\underset{CH_3}{|}}{CH}=CH_2 + \underset{\underset{CH_3}{|}}{CH}=CH_2 + \cdots \longrightarrow$$

$$-\underset{\underset{CH_3}{|}}{CH}-CH_2-\underset{\underset{CH_3}{|}}{CH}-CH_2-\underset{\underset{CH_3}{|}}{CH}-CH_2-$$

A condensation polymer is formed by linking together many molecules by condensation reactions. An example is the formation of nylon.

$$+ \cdots H-\underset{\underset{H}{|}}{N}(CH_2)_6\underset{\underset{H}{|}}{N}-H + HO-\underset{\underset{O}{\|}}{C}(CH_2)_4\underset{\underset{O}{\|}}{C}-OH$$

$$+H-\underset{\underset{H}{|}}{N}(CH_2)_6\underset{\underset{H}{|}}{N}-H + HO-\underset{\underset{O}{\|}}{C}(CH_2)_4\underset{\underset{O}{\|}}{C}-OH+ \cdots \xrightarrow{\Delta}$$

$$\sim\underset{\underset{H}{|}}{N}(CH_2)_6\underset{\underset{H}{|}}{N}-\underset{\underset{O}{\|}}{C}(CH_2)_4\underset{\underset{O}{\|}}{C}-\underset{\underset{H}{|}}{N}(CH_2)_6\underset{\underset{H}{|}}{N}-\underset{\underset{O}{\|}}{C}(CH_2)_4\underset{\underset{O}{\|}}{C}\sim+ nH_2O$$

24.2. The addition reaction for one isoprene molecule to another is

$$CH_2=\underset{\underset{CH_3}{|}}{C}-CH=CH_2+CH_2=\underset{\underset{CH_3}{|}}{C}-CH=CH_2 \longrightarrow CH_2=\underset{\underset{CH_3}{|}}{C}-CH-CH_2CH_2-\underset{\underset{CH_3}{|}}{C}CH=CH_2$$

24.3 . The chain polymer obtained by the reaction of ethylene glycol with malonic acid can be represented by

$$\sim OCH_2CH_2O-\underset{\underset{O}{\|}}{C}CH_2\underset{\underset{O}{\|}}{C}-OCH_2CH_2O-\underset{\underset{O}{\|}}{C}CH_2\underset{\underset{O}{\|}}{C}\sim$$

24.4. The pi electrons in polyacetylene would have to shift as follows.

24.5.   Experiments show that iodine inserts itself into the plastic between polyacetylene molecules, where it forms triiodide ion. Each ion carries a negative charge that was abstracted from a pi orbital of the polymer molecule. The polymer material is left with a positive charge, or hole. The triiodide ion can facilitate the movement of an electron from an uncharged polymer molecule to a positively charged molecule (a hole). In effect, the hole moves. The movement of holes through the material constitutes an electric current.

24.6.   The primary structure of a protein consists of the order, or sequence, of the amino-acid units in the protein polymer. What makes one protein different from another of the same size is the arrangement of the various possible amino acids in the sequence. For example, there are 120 different sequences possible for a polypeptide with just five different amino acids. The basis of the unique conformation of a protein is the folding and coiling into a three-dimensional conformation in aqueous solution due to the different side-chain amino-acid units. In stable conformations, the nonpolar side chains are buried within the structure away from water, and the polar groups are on the surface of the conformation, where they can hydrogen-bond with water.

24.7.   The secondary structure of a protein is the simpler coiled or parallel arrangement of the protein chain. The tertiary structure consists of the folded nature of the structure.

24.8.   An enzyme is a specific body catalyst, usually a globular protein, that possesses active sites. The specificity of an enzyme is explained by the active sites at which substrates will bind. Substrates fit into the active sites as a key fits into a lock.

24.9.   D-ribose and 2-deoxy-D-ribose have identical structures except that D-ribose has an –OH group on carbon two whereas 2-deoxy-D-ribose has an –H instead.

24.10.   It is possible for glucose to exist in three forms in any solution such as blood: the straight-chain form, the α-D-glucopyranose form, and the β-D-glucopyranose form.

24.11.   The complementary base pairs are the nucleotide bases that form strong hydrogen bonds with one another: adenine and thymine, adenine and uracil, and guanine and cytosine. A DNA molecule consists of two polynucleotide chains with base pairing along their entire lengths. The two chains are coiled about each other to form a double helix.

24.12.   The only difference between ribonucleotides and deoxyribonucleotides is the sugar: Ribonucleotides contain β-D-ribose, and deoxyribonucleotides contain 2-deoxy-β-D-ribose, with both sugars having furanose rings. Both form polymers by condensation (loss of H_2O).

24.13.   The genetic code is the relationship between the nucleotide sequence in DNA and the amino-acid sequence in proteins. Genetic information is coded into the linear sequence of nucleotides in the DNA molecule, and this coding then directs the synthesis of the specific proteins that make a cell unique.

24.14.   A codon is a code structure in messenger RNA; each such structure has a particular sequence of three nucleotides and is usually denoted simply by its bases. An anticodon is a triplet sequence in transfer RNA complementary to the codon in DNA; the transfer RNA uses the anticodon to carry an amino acid to a ribosome. The messenger RNA and transfer RNA bond to each other through the codon and anticodon, respectively.

24.15. There are four RNA bases, and three of these are arranged in a specific order in each codon. Since there are four different possibilities for each base in the codon, there are $4 \times 4 \times 4 = 64$ different triplet codons.

24.16. A polypeptide is produced as follows: Imagine you have a ribosome with messenger RNA attached in the proper way for translation, and the first codon is in position to be read. (The messenger RNA has been synthesized with a sequence of bases complementary to that of the gene before attachment.) Transfer RNAs bring up various amino acids to be bonded to each other until a termination codon appears to signal the end of the chain, which is then released from the ribosome.

24.17. The answer is d, amino and carboxyl.

24.18. The answer is c, rubber.

24.19. The answer is d, hydrogen.

24.20. The answer is d, adenine.

■ ANSWERS TO CONCEPTUAL PROBLEMS

24.21. a.   Since a homopolymer consists of the same monomer units linked together, examples are
        −A−A−, −B−B−, and −C−C−

        b.   Since a copolymer contains different monomer units linked together, an example is
        −A−B−.

        c.   A ratio of one C unit to every two A units would produce the desired copolymer:
        −A−C−A−.

24.23. The fully ionized form of ornithine is

$$^{+}H_3NCH_2CH_2CH_2 - \overset{\overset{\displaystyle H}{|}}{\underset{\underset{\displaystyle NH_3^{+}}{|}}{C}} - COO^{-}$$

24.25. Mark off the message into triplets beginning at the left. Then refer to Table 24.3 to determine which amino acid is represented by each triplet.

        AGA | GUC | CGA | GAC | UUG | ACG | UGA

        The corresponding amino-acid sequence is Arg−Val−Arg−Asp−Leu−Thr. The triplet UGA is the code to end the sequence.

■ SOLUTIONS TO PRACTICE PROBLEMS

24.27. $nCF_2=CF_2 \rightarrow -CF_2-CF_2-CF_2-CF_2-CF_2-CF_2-$

24.29. The two monomer units for this polymer are

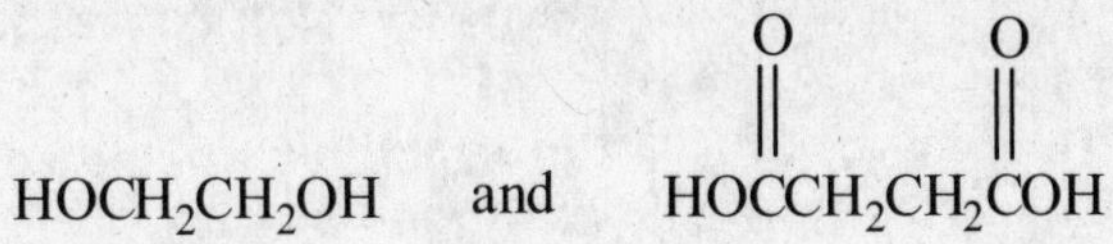

$$HOCH_2CH_2OH \quad \text{and} \quad HOCCH_2CH_2COH$$

(with two C=O groups shown above the second structure)

24.31. a. When this monomer undergoes an addition reaction, the triple bond is converted into a double bond, just as it is with acetylene. The resulting polymer contains alternating single and double bonds and, therefore, could produce a conducting polymer.

b. When this monomer (propylene) undergoes an addition reaction, the double bond is converted into a single bond. Since the polymer does not contain any double bonds, this monomer cannot produce a conducting polymer.

24.33. The zwitterion for alanine is

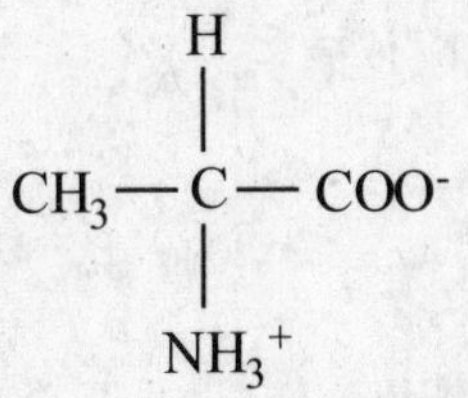

$$CH_3 - \overset{\overset{\displaystyle H}{|}}{\underset{\underset{\displaystyle NH_3^+}{|}}{C}} - COO^-$$

24.35. There are two possible dipeptides containing one molecule each of L-alanine and L-histidine, ala–his and his–ala.

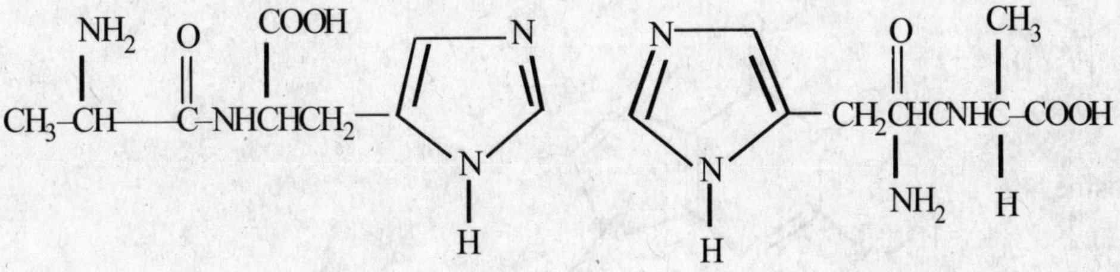

ala-his   his-ala

24.37. DNA consists of two strands of polynucleotides with the adenine units in one strand paired to the thymine units in the other. Similarly, guanine units are paired with cytosine units. Thus, the adenine-thymine molar ratio is 1:1, and the molar ratio of guanine to cytosine is 1:1.

24.39. Adenosine consists of ribose and adenine.

24.41. Three hydrogen bonds link a guanine-cytosine base pair.

Because only two hydrogen bonds link an adenine-uracil base pair, the bonding would be expected to be stronger in the guanine-cytosine pair.

24.43. If a codon consisted of two nucleotides, there would be 4×4, or 16, possible codons using the four nucleotides. Because there are 20 amino acids that must be represented uniquely by a codon for protein synthesis, the codon must be longer than two nucleotides. A two-nucleotide codon would not be workable as an amino-acid code.

24.45. When DNA is denatured, the hydrogen bonds between base pairs are broken. DNA with a greater percentage composition of guanine and cytosine would be denatured less readily than DNA with a greater percentage composition of adenine and thymine, because there are more hydrogen bonds between the former than between the latter.

24.47. Mark off the message into triplets beginning at the left.

GGA | UCC | CGC | UUU | GGG | CUG | AAA | UAG

Gly–Ser–Arg–Phe–Gly–Leu–Lys

Note that the UAG at the right codes for the end of the sequence.

■ SOLUTIONS TO GENERAL PROBLEMS

24.49. The codons have bases that are complementary to those in the anticodon.

Anticodons	GAC	UGA	GGG	ACC
Codons	CUG	ACU	CCC	UGG

24.51. Consult Table 24.3 to find which nucleotides correspond to the amino acids in the sequence.

leu–ala–val–glu–asp–cys–met–trp–lys

CUU GCU GUU GAA GAU UGU AUG UGG AAA

24.53. The addition polymer that forms from *cis* −1,2-dichloroethene is

—CHCH—CHCH—CHCH—CHCH—
   | | | | | | | |
   Cl Cl   Cl Cl   Cl Cl   Cl Cl

24.55. The monomer units that make up Kevlar are

24.57. The amino acid with the nonpolar side chain is

NH$_2$
|
CH$_3$SCH$_2$CH$_2$CHCOOH

The other amino acid has a polar SH group in the side chain.

24.59. The zwitterion for serine is

NH$_3^+$
|
HOCH$_2$CHCOO$^-$

24.61. The two possibilities are

24.63. The number of possible sequences is $6 \times 5 \times 4 \times 3 \times 2 \times 1$, or 720.

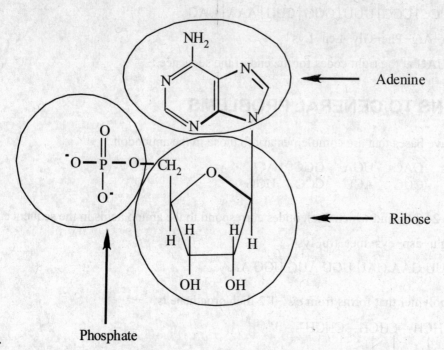

24.65.

24.67. Polymers are actually macromolecules consisting of long chains of similar groups of atoms. Carothers's idea is to consider two functional groups that chemically link together. This was represented as the linking of a hook and an eye. Carothers further suggested finding a molecule having two of the same functional groups at the ends of the molecule; this would be equivalent to a molecule with hooks at both ends. Then the reaction of several such molecules would result in a larger molecule. With many such molecules, the product would be a long-chain molecule: a macromolecule.

24.69. The atomic force microscope is a cousin of a scanning tunneling microscope. Both microscopes use a probe to scan a surface; but whereas the scanning tunneling microscope measures an electric current between the probe tip and the sample, the atomic microscope measures the attractive van der Waals force between the probe tip and the sample.

■ SOLUTIONS TO STRATEGY PROBLEMS

24.71. First, determine the number of moles of NaOH used in the titration.

$$(0.2183 \ M) \times (98.6 \times 10^{-3} \ L) = 0.02152 \ \text{mol NaOH}$$

Since the compound is a dicarboxylic acid, the moles of acid in the titration are

$$0.02152 \ \text{mol NaOH} \times \frac{1 \ \text{mol acid}}{2 \ \text{mol NaOH}} = 0.01076 \ \text{mol acid}$$

The molar mass of the compound is

$$\frac{1.273 \ g}{0.01076 \ \text{mol acid}} = 118.28 \ \text{g/mol}$$

A dicarboxylic acid has two COOH units, each of which weighs 45 g/mol. This accounts for $45 \times 2 = 90$ g/mol so far. The other 28 g/mol could be C_2H_4, giving a dicarboxylic acid with the following possible structural formula.

$$\underset{\displaystyle \text{HOCCH}_2\text{CH}_2\text{COH}}{\overset{\displaystyle \text{O} \qquad\quad \text{O}}{\underset{\parallel\qquad\quad\parallel}{}}}$$

The condensation reaction with ethylene glycol will produce the following polyester.

$$\text{HOCH}_2\text{CH}_2\text{OH} \;+\; \underset{\text{HOCCH}_2\text{CH}_2\text{COH}}{\overset{\text{O}\quad\;\;\text{O}}{}} \longrightarrow$$

$$\sim\text{OCH}_2\text{CH}_2\text{O}-\text{CCH}_2\text{CH}_2\text{C}-\text{OCH}_2\text{CH}_2\text{O}-\text{CCH}_2\text{CH}_2\text{C}\sim \;+\; n\text{H}_2\text{O}$$

24.73. The structure of rubber (poly-*cis*-isoprene) is

The monomer unit of isoprene has the formula C_5H_8 and contains one double bond that is available to react with Br_2. Each C_5H_8 unit weighs 68.11 g/mol. For each mole of monomer units that react, one mole of Br_2 also reacts. In the process, for one monomer unit, one carbon-carbon double bond is broken, one bromine-bromine bond is broken, one carbon-carbon single bond is formed, and two carbon-bromine bonds are formed. The enthalpy change for the reaction can be estimated using the bond energy values from Table 9.5. The monomer unit of isoprene has the formula C_5H_8 and contains one double bond that is available to react with Br_2. Each C_5H_8 unit weighs 68.11 g/mol. For each mole of monomer units that react, one mole of Br_2 also reacts. In the process, for one monomer unit, one carbon-carbon double bond is broken, one bromine-bromine bond is broken, one carbon-carbon single bond is formed, and two carbon-bromine bonds are formed. The enthalpy change for the reaction can be estimated using the bond energy values from Table 9.5.

$$\Delta H^\circ_{rxn} \cong \text{BE(C=C)} + \text{BE(Br--Br)} - \text{BE(C--C)} - 2\text{BE(C--Br)}$$

$$= (602 \text{ kJ}) + (190 \text{ kJ}) - (346 \text{ kJ}) - 2(285 \text{ kJ}) = -124 \text{ kJ}$$

This is the energy released per mole of monomer units. Thus, for 10.0 g of rubber, the heat released is

$$10.0 \text{ g} \times \frac{1 \text{ mol monomer units}}{68.11 \text{ g}} \times \frac{-124 \text{ kJ}}{1 \text{ mol monomer units}} = -18.\underline{2}0 = -18.2 \text{ kJ}$$

24.75. a. The number of tripeptides that are possible when four bases are used is $4 \times 4 \times 4 = 64$. The number of tripeptides that are possible when four bases are used is $4 \times 4 \times 4 = 64$.

b. Yes, this is enough to establish a code for all of the 20 amino acids.

c. The number of possible tetrapeptides when two bases are used is $2 \times 2 \times 2 \times 2 \times = 16$.

d.   No, this is not enough to establish the code for the 20 amino acids.

e.   If the bases are taken in groups of five, then 32 combinations are possible. Therefore, develop a hypothetical code using these combinations. For example, using the bases U and T, the 32 possible combinations are

UUUUU	UTUUU	TUUUU	TTUUU
UUUUT	UTUUT	TUUUT	TTUUT
UUUTU	UTUTU	TUUTU	TTUTU
UUTUU	UTTUU	TUTUU	TTTUU
UUUTT	UTUTT	TUUTT	TTUTT
UUTUT	UTTUT	TUTUT	TTTUT
UUTTU	UTTTU	TUTTU	TTTTU
UUTTT	UTTTU	TUTTT	TTTTT

Now, arbitrarily assign amino acids to 20 of these possible code sequences.

UUUUU (gly)	UTUUU (glu)	TUUUU (met)	TTUUU (leu)
UUUUT (ala)	UTUUT (his)	TUUUT (ser)	TTUUT (ile)
UUUTU (val)	UTUTU (lys)	TUUTU (cys)	TTUTU (pro)
UUTUU (leu)	UTTUU (arg)	TUTUU (thr)	TTTUU (phe)
UUUTT (ile)	UTUTT (end)	TUUTT (asp)	TTUTT (trp)
UUTUT (pro)	UTTUT (gly)	TUTUT (glu)	TTTUT (met)
UUTTU (phe)	UTTTU (ala)	TUTTU (tyr)	TTTTU (ser)
UUTTT (trp)	UTTTT (val)	TUTTT (asn)	TTTTT (cys)

The base sequence for the tripeptide leu–ala–val would be

$$UUTUU\ UTTTU\ UUUTU$$

24.77. Rearrange the boiling-point-depression formula and solve for the molality of the solution.

$$c_m = \frac{\Delta T_b}{K_b} = \frac{0.0556°C}{0.512\ °C/m} = 0.1085\ m$$

The molar mass of ribose ($C_5H_{10}O_5$) is 150.13 g/mol, and for deoxyribose ($C_5H_{10}O_4$) the molar mass is 134.13 g/mol. Let $\times$ be the mass of ribose; then 1.500 g $-\ \times$ is the mass of deoxyribose. In 100.0 g of water, the total moles of solute is

Moles solute $= c_m \times$ kg solvent $= 0.1085\ m \times 0.1000$ kg $= 0.01085$ mol

Also

$$\text{Moles solute} = \frac{x}{150.13\ \text{g/mol}} + \frac{1.500\ \text{g} - x}{134.13\ \text{g/mol}} = 0.01085\ \text{mol}$$

Solve in the normal way.

$(134.13\ x) + (150.13)(1.500\ \text{g} - x) = (0.01085\ \text{g})(150.13)(134.13)$

$134.13 \times + 225.195\ \text{g} - 150.13 \times = 218.48\ \text{g}$

$x = 0.419\ \text{g}$

The percentage of ribose in the mixture is

$$\frac{0.419\ \text{g}}{1.500\ \text{g}} \times 100\% = 27.9 = 28\%$$

24.79. From the description, it appears that the monomer units of the material must be a dicarboxylic acid and a dialcohol. When the dialcohol is oxidized, it produces another dicarboxylic acid, with a molecular mass of 90.0 amu. A carboxylic acid group (COOH) has a molecular mass of 45.02 amu, so the dicarboxylic acid obtained from the alcohol must be HOOCCOOH, which is oxalic acid ($H_2C_2O_4$). When oxalic acid reacts with NaOH, the following reaction occurs.

$$H_2C_2O_4(aq) + 2NaOH(aq) \rightarrow Na_2C_2O_4(aq) + 2H_2O(l)$$

The mass of oxalic acid that would react with 30.5 mL of 0.1056 M NaOH is

$$(0.1056\ M) \times (30.5 \times 10^{-3}\ L) \times \frac{1\ mol\ H_2C_2O_4}{2\ mol\ NaOH} \times \frac{90.0\ g}{1\ mol\ H_2C_2O_4} = 0.1449 = 0.145\ g$$

This agrees with the data given in the problem. When calcium chloride solution is added to the acid solution, a white precipitate forms, which is calcium oxalate, CaC_2O_4.